Preface

The British Catalogue of Music is a record of new music—with the exception of certain types of popular music—published in Great Britain. In addition, it records foreign music available in this country through a sole agent and books about music. It is based on the works deposited at the Copyright Receipt Office of the British Library where copies of all new publications must be sent by law and is the most complete list of current British music available. The Catalogue is presented in three sections:

    Classified Section
    Composer and Title Index
    Subject Index

Instruments, musical forms

While the Classified Section displays the works systematically according to the instrument or combination for which a work is written, the Subject Index lists the principle musical forms and musical character and it shows by means of the class symbol where works having such forms or musical character are to be found in the Classified Section. For example, in the Subject Index under the word Sonatas the following entries may be found:

Sonatas: Arrangements for 2 pianos	QNUK/AE
Sonatas: Organ	RE
Sonatas: Piano duets, 4 hands	QNVE
Sonatas: Violin solos, Unaccompanied	SPME

It will be seen that this group of entries enables you to assemble all the works in sonata form no matter for what instrument the music is, or was originally, written. Under the word Violin the following may be found:

Violin	S
Violin: Accompanying female voices: Choral works	FE/S
Violin: Books	AS
Violin & orchestra	MPS
Violin & string orchestra	RXMPS

This group directs you first to the place S in the Classified Section, where music for the violin is found, including works composed originally for other instruments and arranged for violin. It also directs you to works in which the violin figures in combination with other instruments. It thus provides at one and the same time the link between an instrument and its place in the Classified Section and an exhaustive guide to all the works in which that particular instrument figures. It should be borne in mind that class symbols which include () "brackets" or / "stroke" precede letters in the arrangement. Thus:

is followed by	A
which is followed by	A(....)
which is followed by	A/....
which is followed by	AA
which is followed by	AB
which is followed by	B. etc.

Music literature

Books about music which normally appear in the British National Bibliography are also included in this catalogue. They occur in the sequences lettered A and B of the Classified Section. They are indexed in exactly the same way as musical works in the Composer and Title Index and are designated by the qualification "Books" in the Subject Index. Thus, in the second group above, the entry Violin: Books, directing you to AS, indicates that books about the violin will be found at that place.

Composers

When the composer or author of a work is known, look under his name in the Composer and Title Index. The information given here, including the publisher and price, will be adequate for most purposes. If, on the other hand, the fullest information about a work is required, turn to the entry in the Classified Section. This may be found by means of the class symbol (group of letters) at the end of the entry in the Composer and Title Index.

Titles, series, editors and arrangers

Entries are made in the Composer and Title Index under the titles of all works, so that, if you do not know the composer or author, a work can be found by looking up its title in the Composer and Title Index. If you do not know either the composer or the title, it may still be possible to trace the work if the name of the editor or arranger is known and, in the case of vocal works, the author of the words.

Prices

Prices given are those current at the time of the first recording of an entry in this catalogue. In a few cases prices of parts are not given but can be obtained on application to the publishers.

Abbreviations

Most of the abbreviations used in describing musical works are self-explanatory. The size of a musical work is indicated by one of the following conventional symbols: *8vo* for works up to 10½ in in height, *4to* for works over 10½ in to 12 in. in height, and *fol.* for works over 12 in. in height. The abbreviation *obl.* (oblong) is added to show when a work is of unusual proportions, and a single sheet is designated by the abbreviations *s.sh.* The abbreviations used for the description of books in the sections A and B are those in use in the British National Bibliography.

Patrick Mills
Editor
British Catalogue of Music

Outline of the Classification

The following outline is given for general information only. Users are advised to consult the Subject Index to discover the exact location of required material in the Classified Section.

MUSICAL LITERATURE

A	General Works
	Common sub-divisions
A(B)	Periodical
A(C)	Encyclopaedias
A(D)	Composite works, symposia, essays by several writers
A(E)	Anecdotes, personal reminiscences
A(K)	Economics
A(M)	Persons in music
A(MM)	Musical profession
A(MN)	Music as a career
A(P)	Individuals
A(Q)	Organisations
A(QT)	Terminology
A(QU)	Notation
A(R)	Printing
A(S)	Publishing
A(T)	Bibliographies
A(U)	Libraries
A(V)	Musical education
A(X)	History of music
A(Y)	Music of particular localities
A/AM	Theory of music
A/CC	Aesthetics
A/CY	Technique of music
A/D	Composition
A/E	Performance
A/F	Recording
A/FY	Musical character
A/G	Folk music
A/GM	Music associated with particular occupations
A/H	Dance music
A/HM	Ballet music
A/J	Music accompanying drama
A/JR	Film music
A/KD	Music to accompany social customs
A/L	Religious music
A/LZ	Elements of music
A/R	Harmony
A/S	Forms of music
A/Y	Fugue
AB	Works on vocal music
AC	Works on opera
ACM	Works on musical plays
AD-AX	Works on music for particular vocal or instrumental performers, enumerated like D-X below
B	Works on individual composers (including libretti and other verbal texts of particular musical works)
BZ	Works on non-European music

MUSIC: SCORES AND PARTS

C/AY	Collections not limited to work of particular composer, executant, form or character
C/AZ	Collections of a particular composer not otherwise limited
C/G-C/Y	Collections illustrating music of particular form, character, etc., enumerated like A/G-A/Y above
CB	Vocal music
CC	Opera. Vocal scores with keyboard
CM	Musical plays. Vocal score with keyboard
D	Choral music
DC	Oratorios, Cantatas, Masses
DF	Liturgical, Service music
DH	Motets, Anthems, Hymns
DW	Songs, etc.
E	Choral music with instruments other than keyboard
EZ	Choral music unaccompanied
F	Choral music. Female voices
G	Choral music. Male voices
J	Unison vocal works
K	Vocal solos
L	Instrumental music
M	Orchestral music
N	Chamber music
PVV	Music for individual instruments and instrumental groups
PW	Keyboard instruments
Q	Piano
R	Organ
RW	String instruments
S	Violin
SQ	Viola
SR	Cello
SS	Double bass
TQ	Harp
TS	Guitar
U	Wind instruments
V	Woodwind
VR	Flute
VS	Recorder
VT	Oboe
VU	Saxophone
VV	Clarinet
VW	Bassoon
W	Brass
WS	Trumpet
WT	Horn
WU	Trombone
WX	Bass tuba
X	Percussion instruments
Z	Non-European music

British Catalogue of Music

1979

A record of music and books about music recently published in Great Britain, based upon the material deposited at the Copyright Receipt Office of the British Library, arranged according to a system of classification with a Composer and Title Index, a Subject Index, and a List of Music Publishers.

The British Library BIBLIOGRAPHIC SERVICES DIVISION

The British Catalogue of Music is compiled within

The British Library

BIBLIOGRAPHIC SERVICES DIVISION

Store Street London WC1E 7DG

Telephone: 01-636 1544

Telex: 21462

ISBN 0–900220–82–1

ISSN 0068–1407

British Library Cataloguing in Publication data

British Catalogue of Music
1979

1. Music–Bibliography
I British Library Bibliographic Services Division
016.78   ML118

ISBN 0–900220–82–1
ISSN 0068–1407

Produced by computer-controlled phototypesetting by Computaprint Ltd London
and additional phototypesetting by Bishopsgate Press Ltd London
Printed in Great Britain by Whitstable Litho Ltd, Whitstable, Kent

Classified section

This section contains entries under Subjects, Executants and Instruments according to a system of classification, a synopsis of which appears in the preliminary pages. The Composer and Title Index and the Subject Index which follow this section are the key to both the classification and to this section.

The following are used for sizes of musical works:

8vo. for works up to 10½ in. in height.
4to. for works between 10½in. and 12 in. in height.
fol. for works over 12 in. in height.
obl. indicates a work of unusual proportions.
s.sh. means a single sheet.

A — Music literature
Britten, Benjamin, *Baron Britten*
On receiving the first Aspen Award : a speech / by Benjamin Britten. — London : Faber, 1978. — 3-23p ; 20cm.
Originally published: 1964.
ISBN 0-571-10023-6 Sd : £0.80 : CIP rev.
1.Ti

(B78-09111)

Dinn, Freda
The observer's book of music / [by] Freda Dinn. — 4th ed. / illustrated by Colin Twinn. — London : F. Warne, 1979. — 180p, 8p of plates : ill(some col), music ; 15cm. — (The observer's pocket series ; 16)
Spine title: Music. — First ed. published: 1953. — Bibl.: p.176. — Index.
ISBN 0-7232-1581-2 : £1.25
1.Ti 2.Music 3.Sr

(B79-50001)

Falla, Manuel de
On music and musicians / [by] Manuel de Falla ; [selected] with an introduction and notes by Federico Sopeña ; translated [from the Spanish] by David Urman and J.M. Thomson. — London [etc.] : Boyars ; [London] : [Distributed by Calder and Boyars], 1979. — xiv,117p : facsim, port ; 23cm.
Facsims on lining papers. — Translation of: 'Escritos sobre música y músicos'. Buenos Aires : Espasa-Calpe Argentina, 1950.
ISBN 0-7145-2600-2 : £5.95
1.Ti 2.Sopeña, Federico

(B79-14910)

Hendrie, Gerald
Introduction to music / prepared by Gerald Hendrie and Trevor Bray ; for the [Open University] Course Team, with exercises for Unit 10 by John Rutter. — Milton Keynes : Open University Press, 1978 [i.e. 1979]. — 81p : ill, music, ports ; 30cm. — (An arts foundation course ; units 10 and 11-12) (A101 ; 10 and 11-12)
With answers. — List of sound discs : p.79-81.
ISBN 0-335-05414-5 Pbk : Unpriced
1.Ti 2.Bray, Trevor 3.Rutter, John 4.Open University 5.Sr

(B79-16836)

The **musical** companion / edited by A.L. Bacharach & J.R. Pearce ... — Revised ed. — London [etc.] : Pan Books, 1979. — 800p : ill, music ; 20cm.
This ed. originally published: London : Gollancz, 1977. — Index.
ISBN 0-330-25670-x Pbk : £2.95
1.Bacharach, Alfred Louis 2.Pearce, J R

(B79-50002)

Sessions, Roger Huntington
Roger Sessions on music : collected essays / edited by Edward T. Cone. — Princeton ; Guildford : Princeton University Press, 1979. — xi,388p : music ; 23cm.
ISBN 0-691-09126-9 : £14.10
1.Cone, Edward T

(B79-14909)

Shaw, Bernard
The great composers : reviews and bombardments / by Bernard Shaw ; edited with an introduction by Louis Crompton. — Berkeley [etc.] ; London : University of California Press, 1978. — xxvii,378p : 1 ill ; 24cm.
Index.
ISBN 0-520-03253-5 : £17.15
1.Ti 2.Crompton, Louis

(B79-00561)

Spence, Keith
Living music / author Keith Spence ; consultant Hugo Cole. — London : H. Hamilton, [1979]. — 143p : ill(some col), facsims(1 col), music, ports(some col) ; 30cm.
Bibl.: p.138. — Index.
ISBN 0-241-10116-6 : £6.95
1.Ti

(B79-20262)

A(BC) — Directories
International music guide. — London : Tantivy Press [etc.].
1979 / edited by Derek Elley. — 1978. — 304p : ill, facsim, ports ; 21cm.
Index.
ISBN 0-498-02242-0 Pbk : £3.50
ISSN 0140-7147
1.Elley, Derek

(B79-28897)

Schirmer pronouncing pocket manual of musical terms / edited by Theodore Baker. — 4th ed. / revised by Nicolas Slonimsky. — New York : Schirmer ; London : Collier Macmillan, 1978. — xxi, 297p : ill, music ; 14cm.
Previous ed. [i.e. newly rev. and augmented ed.] New York : Schirmer, 1947.
ISBN 0-02-870250-6 Pbk : £1.45
1.Baker, Theodore 2.Slonimsky, Nicolas 3.Pocket manual of musical terms

(B79-04535)

A(D/XM78) — Essays, 1900-1977
Dahlhaus, Carl
Schönberg und andere : gesammelte Aufsätze zur neuen Musik / [von] Carl Dahlhaus ; mit einer Einleitung von Hans Oesch. — Mainz ; London [etc.] : Schott, 1978. — 412p : music ; 24cm.
Bibl.: p.399-411.
Pbk : £14.00
1.Ti

(B79-08129)

A(D/YVVA) — Essays. Armenia
Essays on Armenian music / edited by V[e]rej Nersessian. — London : Kahn and Averill for the Institute of Armenian Music, 1978. — 222p : facsims, music ; 24cm.
Facsimile reprints of: 7 articles in German, French and English originally published between 1970 and 1977.
ISBN 0-900707-49-6 : £6.95
1.Nersessian, Verej 2.Institute of Armenian Music

(B79-33551)

A(DE) — Questions & answers
Race, Steve
My music. — London : Robson, Sept. 1979. — [224]p.
ISBN 0-86051-072-7 : £5.25 : CIP entry
1.Ti
(B79-22652)

A(M) — Musicians
Rosenberg, Deena
The music makers / [by] Deena Rosenberg, Bernard Rosenberg ;
foreword by Barry S. Brook. — New York ; Guildford : Columbia
University Press, 1979. — xvii,466p : ports ; 24cm.
'These documents are painstakingly assembled out of taped and transcribed,
three-way, open-ended interviews ...' - p.5. — Index.
ISBN 0-231-03953-0 : £10.30
1.Ti 2.Rosenberg, Bernard
(B79-10473)

A(M/C) — Musicians. Encyclopaedias
Baker, Theodore
Baker's biographical dictionary of musicians. — 6th ed. /
completely revised by Nicolas Slonimsky. — New York : Schirmer
Books ; London : Collier Macmillan, 1978. — xxvii,1955p ; 25cm.
Previous ed.: published as 'Biographical dictionary of musicians'. New
York : G. Schirmer, 1958.
ISBN 0-02-870240-9 : £55.00
1.Slonimsky, Nicolas 2.Biographical dictionary of musicians
(B79-17757)

**A(M/YLCO/XPC3) — Musicians. Poland. Oświęcin. Auschwitz
concentration camp, 1943-1945**
Fénelon, Fania
The musicians of Auschwitz / [by] Fania Fénelon ; with Marcelle
Routier ; translated from the French by Judith Landry. —
London : Sphere, 1979. — 253p ; 18cm.
This translation originally published: London : Joseph, 1977. — Translation
of 'Sursis pour l'orchestre'. Paris : Stock, 1976.
ISBN 0-7221-3466-5 Pbk : £0.95
1.Ti 2.Routier, Marcelle
(B79-19444)

A(QM/XDZK196) — Ornaments, 1590-1785
Neumann, Frederick, b.1907
Ornamentation in baroque and post-baroque music : with special
emphasis on J.S. Bach / [by] Frederick Neumann. — Princeton ;
Guildford : Princeton University Press, 1978. — xiv,631p : music ;
29cm.
Bibl.: ;.605-611. — Index.
ISBN 0-691-09123-4 : £33.40
1.Ti
(B79-07465)

A(QTF) — Polylingual terminology
Grigg, Carolyn Doub
Music translation dictionary / compiled by Carolyn Doub Grigg.
— Westport, Conn. ; London : Greenwood Press, 1978. — xvi,
336p ; 25cm.
Bibl.: p.xi-xvi. — Index.
ISBN 0-313-20559-0 : £16.95
1.Ti
(B79-36910)

A(QU) — Notation
Read, Gardner
Modern rhythmic notation / [by] Gardner Read. —
Bloomington ; London : Indiana University Press, 1978. — ix,
202p : ill, music ; 24cm.
Index.
ISBN 0-253-33867-0 : £15.75
1.Ti
(B79-21876)

A(T) — Bibliographies
Bibliographie des Musikschriftums / herausgegeben vom Staatlichen
Institut für Musikforschung Preussischer Kulturbesitz. — Mainz ;
London [etc.] : Schott.
1972 / [Bearbeitung und Redaktion, Elisabeth Wilker]. — 1978. — xv,
479p ; 25cm.
Index.
£30.00
ISBN 3-7957-1472-9
1.Wilker, Elisabeth 2.Staatlichen Institut für Musikforschung Preussischer
Kulturbesitz
(B79-30467)

A(U) — Librarianship
Jones, Malcolm, b.1943
Music librarianship / [by] Malcolm Jones. — London : Bingley
[etc.], 1979. — 3-130p ; 23cm. — (Outlines of modern
librarianship)
Bibl.: p.125-127. — Index.
ISBN 0-85157-274-x : £4.00 : CIP rev.
1.Ti 2.Sr
(B79-11403)

A(U/YDLJ/WM) — Euing Music Collection. Catalogues
University of Glasgow. *Library*
Musicke of sundrie kindes : handlist to the exhibition [held in the]
Glasgow University Library, Exhibition Room, 11th January-18th
February 1978. — [Glasgow] ([Glasgow G12 8QG]) : [The
Library], [1978]. — [5],15p ; 30cm.
ISBN 0-85261-148-x Sd : £0.50
1.Ti
(B79-14348)

A(V) — Education
Swanwick, Keith
A bass for music education / [by] Keith Swanwick. — [Windsor] :
NFER, [1979]. — [7],124p : ill, music ; 22cm.
Bibl.: p.119-121. — Index.
ISBN 0-85633-180-5 Pbk : £4.75
1.Ti
(B79-32714)

A(V/BC) — Education. Yearbooks
International Society for Music Education
ISME yearbook. — Mainz ; London [etc.] : Schott.
Vol.6 : 1979 : Music education - the person first : papers of the 13th
International Conference, London, Ontario, Canada, 1978 / Egon Kraus,
editor. — 1979. — 177p : ill ; 22cm.
At head of title: International music education. — Bibl.
Pbk : £9.60
ISBN 3-7957-0105-8
ISSN 0172-0597
1.Ti 2.Kraus, Egon 3.Music education - the person first 4.International
music education
(B79-32713)

A(VC) — Teaching
Phillips, Jill
Give your child music / [by] Jill Phillips. — London : Elek, 1979.
— 167p : ill, music ; 26cm.
Bibl.: p.165-166.
ISBN 0-236-40145-9 : £5.95
1.Ti
(B79-14614)

The **Tobin** colour music system. — Bishop's Stortford (Southmill
Rd, Bishop's Stortford, Herts. CM23 3DH) : Helicon Press.
Composition. Teacher's manual. — 1977. — [2],38p : ill, music ; 21x30cm.
ISBN 0-905684-16-8 Sd : £3.00
(B79-14905)

The **Tobin** music system. — Sawbridgeworth (Knight St.,
Sawbridgeworth, Herts. CM21 9AX) : Helicon Press.
Harmony. Teachers' manual. — [1978]. — [2],61p : ill, music ; 22x31cm.
ISBN 0-905684-19-2 Sp : £3.00
(B79-14906)
Rhythm and pitch. Teachers' manual. — [1977]. — [1],60p : ill, music ;
21x31cm.
ISBN 0-905684-05-2 Sp : £3.00
(B79-14907)
Scales and key signatures (the composer's palette). Teachers' manual. —
[1977]. — 61,[22]p : ill, forms, music ; 22x31cm.
ISBN 0-905684-18-4 Sp : £3.00
(B79-14908)

A(VC/YE) — Teaching. Germany
Abel-Struth, Sigrid
Ziele des Musik-Lernens / [von] Sigrid Abel-Struth. — Mainz ;
London [etc.] : Schott.
T.1 : Beitrag zur Entwicklung ihrer Theorie. — 1978. — 162p : ill ; 21cm.
— (Musikpädagogik ; Bd 12)
Bibl.: p.143-162.
Pbk : £8.00
ISBN 3-7957-1711-6
1.Ti 2.Sr
(B79-14009)

A(VC/YT) — Teaching. United States
Mark, Michael L
Contemporary music education / [by] Michael L. Mark. — New
York : Schirmer Books ; London : Collier Macmillan, 1978. —
xiv,338p : ill, form, music ; 25cm.
Bibl. — Index.
ISBN 0-02-871640-x : £11.25
1.Ti
(B79-19443)

A(VC/Z) — Teaching - related to composers
Lawrence, Ian
Composers and the nature of music education / [by] Ian
Lawrence. — London : Scolar Press, 1978. — 230p : music ;
23cm.
Bibl.: p.202-225. — Index.
ISBN 0-85967-401-0 : £10.00
1.Ti
(B79-00558)

A(VG) — Primary schools
Bergethon, Bjornar
Musical growth in the elementary school / [by] Bjornar
Bergethon, Eunice Boardman. — 3rd ed. — Sydney [etc.] ;
London : Holt, Rinehart and Winston, 1978. — vii,291p : ill,
music ; 28cm.
This ed. originally published: Sydney : Holt, Rinehart and Winston, 1976. —
Previous ed.: 1970. — Bibl.: p.276-278. — Index.
Pbk : £9.25
ISBN 0-03-900119-9
1.Ti 2.Boardman, Eunice
(B79-07190)

Wachhaus, Gustav
Fundamental classroom music skills : theory and performing
techniques / [by] Gustav Wachhaus, Terry Lee Kuhn. — New
York ; London [etc.]: Holt, Rinehart and Winston, 1979. — xi,
328p : ill, music ; 28cm.
Index.
ISBN 0-03-041775-9 Sp : £7.75
1.Ti 2.Kuhn, Terry Lee
(B79-12529)

A(VG/GR) — Primary schools. Activities
Thompson, Diana
Pompaleerie jig / [by] Diana Thompson, Kate Baxter ; graphics
by Mike Hall. — Leeds : E.J. Arnold, 1978. — 47p : ill(chiefly
col), music ; 19x26cm.
ISBN 0-560-00319-6 Sd : £1.30
1.Ti 2.Baxter, Kate
(B79-04968)

A(VK) — Secondary schools
Bergethon, Bjornar
Musical growth in the elementary school / [by] Bjornar
Bergethon, Eunice Boardman. — 4th ed. / prepared by Bjornar
Bergethon. — New York ; London [etc.] : Holt, Rinehart and
Winston, 1979. — xi,267p : ill, music ; 28cm.
Previous ed.: New York : Holt, Rinehart and Winston, 1975. — Bibl.:
p.250-251. — Index.
ISBN 0-03-020856-4 Sp : £8.50
1.Ti 2.Boardman, Eunice
(B79-10207)

A(VMX) — Handicapped children
Kennard, Daphne
Access to music for the physically handicapped schoolchild and
school leaver : report on 3-year project, 1973-1976 / by Daphne J.
Kennard. — London (346 Kensington High St., W14 8NS) :
Disabled Living Foundation, 1977. — leaf,ii,100p ; 30cm.
Bibl.: p.96-100.
ISBN 0-901908-31-2 Sp : £2.00
1.Ti 2.Disabled Living Foundation
(B79-33201)

Kennard, Daphne
Music to help disabled children to move / by Daphne Kennard
and Moyna Gilbertson. — Crawley (A.P.C.P. Publications, 25
Goff's Park Rd, Southgate, Crawley, W. Sussex RH11 8AX) :
Association of Paediatric Chartered Physiotherapists, [1979?]. —
[2],24p ; 21cm.
Bibl.: p.18-21.
Sd : £0.50
1.Ti 2.Gilbertson, Moyna 3.Association of Paediatric Chartered
Physiotherapists
(B79-13819)

A(X) — History
Pocket musical history : with biographical list of famous composers
and landmarks in the history of musical development. — [Revised
ed.] / revised by David Willison. — Croydon (421a Brighton Rd,
Croydon, Surrey CR2 6YR) : Alfred Lengnick and Co., 1977. —
16p ; 23x8cm.
Previous ed.: 1945.
Sd : £0.10
1.Willison, David 2.Alfred Lengnick & Company
(B79-07464)

Politoske, Daniel Theodore
Music / [by] Daniel T. Politoske. — 2nd ed. / art essays by
Martin Werner. — Englewood Cliffs ; London [etc.] :
Prentice-Hall, 1979. — xvi,479p,[24]p of plates : ill(some col),
facsims, maps, music, ports(some col) ; 25cm.
Text on lining papers. — Previous ed.: 1974. — Bibl.: p.460-463. — Lists of
sound discs. — Index.
ISBN 0-13-607556-8 : £9.05
1.Ti 2.Werner, Martin
(B79-34988)

Rowen, Ruth Halle
Music through sources and documents / [by] Ruth Halle Rowen.
— Englewood Cliffs ; London [etc.] : Prentice-Hall, 1979. — xiv,
386p : ill, music ; 23cm.
Bibl.: p.357-358. — Index.
ISBN 0-13-608331-5 Pbk : £9.45
1.Ti
(B79-16099)

A(XA1600/B) — History, to 1600. Periodicals
Plainsong and Mediaeval Music Society
Journal of the Plainsong & Mediaeval Music Society. — Englefield
Green (46 Bond St., Englefield Green, Surrey TW20 0PY) : The
Society.
Vol.1- ; 1978-. — 1978-. — music ; 22cm.
Annual. — [3],120p. in 1st issue. — Bibl.
Sd : £1.50(free to members)
ISSN 0143-4918
1.Ti
(B79-36420)

A(XFWE101) — History, 1725-1825
Farmer, Paul
Into the classics / [by] Paul Farmer. — London : Longman, 1979.
— 24p : ill, facsim, music, ports ; 23cm. — (Longman music
topics)
Text on inside covers.
ISBN 0-582-21576-5 Sd : £0.65
1.Ti
(B79-33549)

A(XFY101) — History, 1760-1860
Middleton, Richard
From Liszt to music hall / prepared by Richard Middleton ; for
the [Open University] Course Team. — Milton Keynes : Open
University Press, 1978[i.e.1979]. — 68p : ill, facsims, music,
ports ; 30cm. — (An arts foundation course : arts and society in
an age of industrialization ; units 30-31) (A101 ; 30-31)
With answers. — Col. ill. on front cover. — Bibl.: p.66.
ISBN 0-335-05423-4 Pbk : Unpriced
1.Ti 2.Open University 3.Sr
(B79-36911)

A(XFYK151) — History, 1770-1920
Blume, Friedrich
Classic and Romantic music : a comprehensive survey / [by]
Friedrich Blume ; translated [from the German] by M.D. Herter
Norton. — London [etc.] : Faber, 1979. — ix,213p ; 22cm.
This translation originally published: New York : Norton, 1970 ; London :
Faber, 1972. — Translation of two essays in 'Die Musik in Geschichte und
Gegenwart'. Kassel : Bärenreiter, 1949. — Bibl.: p.195-198. — Index.
ISBN 0-571-11354-0 Pbk : £2.50 : CIP rev.
1.Ti
(B79-05246)

A(XPK19) — History, 1950-1978
Neue Musik und die Tradition (Conference), Darmstadt, 1978
Die neue Musik und die Tradition : sieben Kongressbeiträge und
eine analytische Studie / herausgegeben von Reinhold Brinkmann.
— Mainz ; London [etc.] : Schott, 1978. — 152p : music ; 24cm.
— (Internationales Musikinstitut Darmstadt. Institut für Neue
Musik und Musikerziehung. Veröffentlichungen ; Bd 19)
'... sieben Referat-Texte den Kongress "Die neue Musik und die Tradition"
der 32. Hauptarbeitstagung des Instituts vom 18. bis 23. März 1978 in
Darmstadt ...' - Vorbemerkung.
Pbk : £10.80
ISBN 3-7957-1759-0
1.Brinkmann, Reinhold 2.Sr
(B79-11940)

A(XR9) — History, 1970-1978
Internationale Ferienkurse für Neue Musik, 29, Darmstadt, 1978
Ferienkurse '78 / herausgegeben von Ernst Thomas. — Mainz ;
London [etc.] : Schott, 1978. — 99,[11]p,[4]p of plates : facsims,
music, ports ; 25 cm. — (Darmstädter Beiträge zur neuen Musik ;
17)
'Stadt Darmstadt - Internationales Musikinstitut 29. Internationale
Ferienkurse für Neue Musik [30.7. bis 15.8.1978]' - p.7.
Pbk : £9.60
ISBN 3-7957-1574-1
1.Ti 2.Thomas, Ernst 3.Internationales Musikinstitut Darmstadt 4.Sr
(B79-14011)

A(YB/XG151) — Europe, 1800-1950
Dahlhaus, Carl
Die Idee der absoluten Musik / [von] Carl Dahlhaus. — Kassel
[etc.] ; London ([12 Bucklesbury, Hitchin, Herts. SG5 1BB]) :
Bärenreiter-Verlag [etc.], 1978. — 152p ; 18cm.
Pbk : £2.31
ISBN 3-7618-0599-3
1.Ti
(B79-17758)

A(YC/BC) — Great Britain. Directories
Music trades international buyers guide, yearbook & directory. —
[Watford] ([4 Local Board Rd, Watford, Herts.]) : Music Trades
International.
1979. — [1979]. — [1],73p : ill ; 30cm.
Previously published: as 'Music trades international directory'.
Pbk : £6.75
ISSN 0143-2575
(B79-23760)

A(YC/MM) — Great Britain. Incorporated Society of Musicians
Incorporated Society of Musicians
Professional register of artists / Incorporated Society of Musicians. — London (10 Stratford Place, W1N 9AE) : The Society. 1977. — [1977]. — [2],72p ; 21cm.
Sd : £1.00
1.Ti
(B79-27780)

A(YC/Q/MM) — Great Britain. Organizations. Graduate and professional education
Incorporated Society of Musicians
Handbook and register of members / the Incorporated Society of Musicians. — London (10 Stratford Place, W1N 9AE) : The Society.
1978-79. — 1978. — [2],230p : ill, map ; 21cm.
Pbk : £7.00
1.Ti
(B79-17756)

A(YC/WE/Q/BC) — Great Britain. Festivals. Organizations. Yearbooks
British Federation of Music Festivals
Year book / the British Federation of Music Festivals (incorporating The Music Teachers' Association). — London (106 Gloucester Place, W1H 3DB) : [The Federation].
1979. — [1979]. — [1],111p : ill ; 21cm.
Sd : £1.50
ISSN 0309-8044
1.Ti
(B79-18561)

A(YDDS/XF101) — Norfolk, 1700-1800
Fawcett, Trevor
Music in eighteenth-century Norwich and Norfolk / by Trevor Fawcett. — Norwich ([Norwich NR4 7TJ]) : Centre of East Anglian Studies, University of East Anglia, 1979. — [4],73p : facsims, map, music ; 15x21cm.
Text on inside covers.
Sd : £1.75
1.Ti 2.University of East Anglia. Centre of East Anglian Studies
(B79-33550)

A(YT/X) — United States. History
Kingman, Daniel
American music : a panorama / [by] Daniel Kingman. — New York : Schirmer ; London : Collier Macmillan, 1979. — xxx, 577p : ill, music ; 24cm.
Ill. on inside covers. — Bibl. — Index.
ISBN 0-02-871260-9 Pbk : £7.45
1.Ti
(B79-25329)

A(Z) — Music-related to babies
Cass-Beggs, Barbara
Your baby needs music / [by] Barbara Cass-Beggs. — London : Ward Lock, 1979. — 144p : ill, music ; 22cm.
Originally published: North Vancouver : Douglas and McIntyre, 1978. — Bibl.: p.134-136. — Index.
ISBN 0-7063-5900-3 : £4.95
1.Ti
(B79-50405)

A(ZE) — Music - expounded through postage stamps
Senior, Geoffrey
Music and musicians on postage stamps / [compiled by Geoffrey Senior]. — [Orrell] ([299 Gathurst Rd, Orrell, Greater Manchester]) : [The compiler], [1979]. — [147]p ; 26cm.
Limited ed. of 100 copies. — Bibl.: p.[143]-[147].
Sp : £3.00
1.Ti
(B79-16833)

A/AM — Theory
Winold, Allen
Introduction to music theory / [by] Allen Winold,John Rehm. — 2nd ed. — Englewood Cliffs ; London [etc.] : Prentice-Hall, 1979. — xviii,377p : ill, music ; 28cm.
Previous ed.: Englewood Cliffs : Prentice-Hall, 1971. — Index.
ISBN 0-13-489666-1 Pbk : £8.40
1.Ti 2.Rehm, John
(B79-30253)

A/AM(XDYAK181) — Theories, 1570-1750
Walker, Daniel Pickering
Studies in musical science in the late Renaissance / [by] D.P. Walker. — London : Warburg Institute [etc.], 1978. — vii,174p : ill, music ; 26cm. — (Warburg Institute. Studies ; vol.37)
Index.
ISBN 0-85481-056-0 : £15.00
1.Ti 2.Sr
(B79-17759)

A/B — Physics
Lloyd, Llewelyn Southworth
Intervals, scales and temperaments ... / [by] Ll.S. Lloyd and Hugh Boyle. — [New] ed. — London : Macdonald and Jane's, 1978. — xix,322p : ill, music ; 23cm.
'Srticles by the late Ll. S. Lloyd selected and edited with an introduction and bibliography by Hugh Boyle. Definitions, experiments, measurements, calculations, various appendices and tables by Hugh Boyle'. — Previous ed.: London : Macdonald and Co., 1963. — Bibl.: p.112-114. — Index.
ISBN 0-354-04229-7 : £9.95
1.Ti 2.Boyle, Hugh
(B79-50003)

A/C — Appreciation
Baker, Richard, b.1925
Richard Baker's music guide. — Newton Abbot [etc.] : David and Charles, 1979. — 144p ; 23cm.
Bibl.: p.138-140. — Index.
ISBN 0-7153-7782-5 : £3.95 : CIP rev.
1.Music gudie
(B79-12528)

Bamberger, Jeanne Shapiro
The art of listening : developing musical perception / [by] Jeanne Shapiro Bamberger, Howard Brofsky ; with a foreword by Roger Sessions. — 4th ed. — New York [etc.] ; London : Harper and Row, 1979. — xx,396p : ill, music, ports ; 24cm.
Previous ed.: 1975. — Bibl. — Index.
ISBN 0-06-040943-6 Pbk : £8.15
1.Ti 2.Brofsky, Howard
(B79-28895)

Hopkins, Antony
Understanding music / [by] Antony Hopkins. — London [etc.] : Dent, 1979. — 255p : ill, music ; 25cm.
Bibl.: p.249. — Index.
ISBN 0-460-04376-5 : £6.95 : CIP rev.
1.Ti
(B79-15552)

A/CB — Analytical guides
Kresky, Jeffrey
Tonal music : twelve analytic studies / [by] Jeffrey Kresky. — Bloomington ; London : Indiana University Press, 1977. — xv, 167p : ill, music ; 24cm.
ISBN 0-253-37011-6 : £8.75
1.Ti
(B79-10475)

A/CC — Aesthetics
Hamel, Peter Michael
Through music to the self : how to appreciate and experience music anew / [by] Peter Michael Hamel ; translated from the German by Peter Lemesurier. — Tisbury : Compton Press, 1978. — ix,228p : ill, music ; 23cm. — (An element book)
Translation of: 'Durch Musik zum Selbst'. Bern : Scherz, 1976. — Bibl.: p.223-225. — List of sound discs : p.227-228.
ISBN 0-900193-53-0 : £5.95
1.Ti 2.Sr
(B79-08926)

Smith, F Joseph
The experiencing of musical sound : prelude to a phenomenology of music / [by] F. Joseph Smith. — New York ; London [etc.] : Gordon and Breach, 1979. — 256p : ill, music ; 23cm. — (Musicology series)
ISBN 0-677-04430-5 : £8.10
1.Ti 2.Sr
(B79-02983)

A/D(M/C) — Composers. Encyclopaedias
Ingman, Nicholas
Gifted children of music : the young lives of the great musicians / [by] Nicholas Ingman ; illustrations by Bernard Brett. — London : Ward Lock, 1978. — 96p : ill(some col) ; 29cm.
ISBN 0-7063-5721-3 : £3.95 : CIP rev.
1.Ti
(B78-27520)

Stern, Susan
Women composers : a handbook / by Susan Stern. — Metuchen ; London : Scarecrow Press ; [Folkestone] : [Distributed by Bailey and Swinfen], 1978. — viii,191p ; 23cm.
Bibl.
ISBN 0-8108-1138-3 : £6.00
1.Ti
(B79-02985)

A/D(M/FD) — Composers. Recorded music
Salter, Lionel
The 'Gramophone' guide to classical composers and recordings / [by] Lionel Salter. — London : Salamander Books, 1978. — [1], 217,[4]p(2 fold) : ill(chiefly col), facsims(some col), ports(some col) ; 31cm. — (A Salamander book)
Spine title: Classical composers and recordings. — Facsims. on lining papers. — Index.
ISBN 0-86101-025-6 : £6.95
1.Ti 2.Classical composers and recordings 3.Sr
(B79-00562)

A/D(M/YB) — Composers. Europe
Burnham, Howard
    Grones dictionary of music, or, A golden treasury of musical
    rubbish, or, Misleading lives of the great composers / [text by
    Howard Burnham and illustrations by Richard Butterworth]. —
    Ampleforth (Windmill Farm, Ampleforth, Yorkshire) : Emerson
    Edition, 1978. — 2-85p : ill, ports ; 28cm.
    Index.
    ISBN 0-9506209-0-4 Pbk : £2.95
    1.Ti 2.Butterworth, Richard
                                                        (B79-04539)

Rapoport, Paul
    Opus est. — London : Kahn and Averill, Oct. 1978. — [200]p.
    ISBN 0-900707-48-8 : £5.75 : CIP entry
    1.Ti
                                                        (B78-29830)

A/D(M/YX/XM76) — Composers. Australia, 1900-1975
Australian composition in the twentieth century / edited by Frank
    Callaway and David Tunley. — Melbourne ; Oxford [etc.] :
    Oxford University Press, 1978[i.e.1979]. — x,248p : music, ports ;
    26cm.
    Published in Australia: 1978. — Bibl. — Lists of works. — Lists of sound
    discs. — Index.
    ISBN 0-19-550522-0 : £18.50
    1.Callaway, Frank 2.Tunley, David
                                                        (B79-33552)

A/D(VF) — Composition. Schools
Paynter, John
    Sound tracks / devised and written by John Paynter ; designed
    and illustrated by Eve Mathews. — Cambridge [etc.] : Cambridge
    University Press.
    [3] : Sound poems. — 1978. — 1v. : ill(some col), music ; 30cm.
    Booklet (iii,12p.), sheet ([2]sides), 5 folders ([20]p.) in plastic envelope. —
    Bibl.
    ISBN 0-521-20580-8 : £1.95
    1.Ti 2.Mathews, Eve
                                                        (B78-23591)

A/E(XQP4) — Performance, 1974-1977
Porter, Andrew
    Music of three seasons, 1974-1977. — London : Chatto and
    Windus, Jan. 1979. — [672]p.
    ISBN 0-7011-2340-0 : £12.50 : CIP entry
    1.Ti
                                                        (B78-37093)

A/EC — Conducting
Conductors on conducting / [compiled and edited by] Bernard
    Jacobson. — London : Macdonald and Jane's, 1979. — 238p :
    ports ; 24cm. — (The performance and interpretation of music)
    Originally published: Frenchtown, N.J. : Columbia Publishing Co., 1978. —
    Index.
    ISBN 0-354-04416-8 : £6.95
    1.Jacobson, Bernard, b.1936 2.Sr
                                                        (B79-32716)

A/EC(P) — Beecham, Sir Thomas, bt. Biographies
Beecham, *Sir* Thomas, *bart*
    A mingled chime : leaves from an autobiography / by Sir Thomas
    Beecham. — London : Hutchinson, 1979. — 272p ; 23cm.
    Originally published: 1944. — Index.
    ISBN 0-09-138430-3 : £5.95 : CIP rev.
    1.Ti
                                                        (B79-08131)

Jefferson, Alan
    Sir Thomas Beecham : a centenary tribute / [by] Alan Jefferson ;
    foreword Sir Robert Mayer. — London : Macdonald and Jane's,
    1979. — 256p,[24]p of plates : ill, facsim, ports ; 24cm.
    Bibl.: p.244-246. — Index.
    ISBN 0-354-04205-x : £6.50
                                                        (B79-11942)

A/EC(P) — Boult, Sir Adrian. Biographies
Music and friends : seven decades of letters to Adrian Boult from
    Elgar, Vaughan Williams, Holst, Bruno Walter, Yehudi Menuhin
    and other friends / annotated by Jerrold Northrop Moore ;
    foreword by Keith Falkner. — London : H. Hamilton, 1979. —
    xv,207p,[4]p of plates : ill, facsims, music, ports ; 23cm.
    Index.
    ISBN 0-241-10178-6 : £6.95 : CIP rev.
    1.Boult, Sir Adrian 2.Moore, Jerrold Northrop
                                                        (B79-08128)

A/EC(P) — Harty. Sir. Hamilton. Biographies
Hamilton Harty : his life and music / edited by David Greer. —
    Belfast : Blackstaff Press, [1979]. — iii-xi,161p : ill, facsims,
    music, ports ; 23cm.
    Ill. on lining papers. — Bibl.: p.153. — List of works: p.141-151. — List of
    discs: p.133-140. — Index.
    ISBN 0-85640-131-5 : £7.50
    1.Greer, David
                                                        (B79-10480)

A/EC(P) — Solti, Sir Georg. Biographies
Robinson, Paul
    Solti / [by] Paul Robinson ; discography by Bruce Surtees. —
    London : Macdonald and Jane's, 1979. — [5],168p,[8]p of plates :
    1 ill, music, ports ; 23cm. — (The art of the conductor)
    Bibl.: p.165. — List of sound discs: p.151-164. — Index.
    ISBN 0-354-04288-2 : £5.95
    1.Sr
                                                        (B79-24592)

A/EC(P) — Tausky, Vilem. Biographies
Tausky, Vilem
    Vilem Tausky tells his story : a two-part setting / recounted by
    Margaret Tausky. — London : Stainer and Bell, 1979. — 160p :
    ill, music, ports ; 23cm.
    ISBN 0-85249-478-5 : £6.00
    1.Tausky, Margaret
                                                        (B79-25860)

A/EC/FD(P/WT) — Godfrey. Sir. Dan. Recorded music. Lists
Upton, Stuart
    Sir Dan Godfrey & the Bournemouth Municipal Orchestra : a
    biographical discography, copiously illustrated with pictures and
    facsimile reproductions covering countless famous personalities
    and related material / compiled by Stuart Upton. — New
    enlarged ed. — West Wickham (4 Harvest Bank Rd, West
    Wickham, Kent) : Vintage Light Music Society, 1979. — [1],34p :
    ill, facsims, ports ; 21cm.
    Previous ed.: s.l. : Mascotte Society, 1970. — List of sound discs: p.14-20;
    34.
    Sd : Unpriced
    1.Ti 2.Vintage Light Music Society
                                                        (B79-11941)

A/EF — Ear training
Trubitt, Allen R
    Ear training and sight-singing : an integrated approach / [by]
    Allen R. Trubitt, Robert S. Hines. — New York : Schirmer
    Books ; London : Collier Macmillan.
    Book 1. — 1979. — xii,330p : chiefly music ; 28cm.
    With answers.
    ISBN 0-02-870810-5 Pbk : £8.25
    Also classified at AB/EG
    1.Ti 2.Hines, Robert S
                                                        (B79-25327)

A/FD — Recorded music
Building a library. — London : Oxford University Press, Oct. 1979.
    — [160]p.
    ISBN 0-19-311324-4 Pbk : £2.95 : CIP entry
    1.Lade, John
                                                        (B79-25861)

A/FD(BC) — Recorded music. Yearbooks
British Phonographic Industry
    BPI year book : a review of the British record and tape industry.
    — London ([33 Thurloe Pl., SW7 2HQ]) : BPI.
    1977 : Centenary ed. : one hundred years of recorded sound. — [1977]. —
    224p : ill(some col), col maps, ports ; 26cm.
    ISBN 0-906154-00-6 Pbk : £2.95
    ISSN 0142-7636
    1.Ti
                                                        (B79-19927)

A/FD(QB/WT) — Recorded music. Organisations. Lists
British record company & music industry index. — Staverton
    (Hamilton House, Nelson Close, Staverton, Totnes, Devon TQ9
    6PG) : R.S. Productions, [1979]. — [10]p ; 30cm.
    Sd : £1.00
                                                        (B79-35264)

A/FD(WT) — Recorded music. Lists
Music master. — Hastings (1 De Cham Ave., Hastings, Sussex) :
    John Humphries.
    1979 / [edited by John Humphries]. — 1979. — 29-735p ; 31cm.
    ISBN 0-904520-07-2 : £30.00
    ISSN 0308-9347
    1.Humphries, John, b.1941
                                                        (B79-28369)

A/FE(QB/WT) — Blue Amberol Cylinders. Lists
Carter, Sydney Horace
    'Blue Amberol' cylinders : a catalogue / compiled by Sydney H.
    Carter. — Bournemouth (19 Glendale Rd, Bournemouth BH6
    4JA) : 'Talking machine review', [1978]. — 130,[33]p : facsims ;
    26cm.
    ISBN 0-902338-30-7 Sd : £4.00
    1.Ti 2.'Talking machine review'
                                                        (B79-05450)

A/FF/ER — Discothèques
Blackford, Andy
    Disco dancing tonight : clubs, dances, fashion, music / [by] Andy
    Blackford. — [London] : Octopus Books, [1979]. — 80p :
    ill(chiefly col), ports(chiefly col) ; 30cm.
    Index.
    ISBN 0-7064-1019-x Pbk : £1.50
    1.Ti
                                                        (B79-16105)

A/FG — Tape recording
Anderton, Craig
Home recording for musicians / by Craig Anderton. — [Saratoga] : Guitar Player Books ; Farnham (25 East St., Farnham, Surrey) : [Distributed by] Omnibus Book Service, 1978. — 182p : ill ; 28cm.
Sound disc (1s. 7in. 33 1/3 rpm) bound in. — Bibl.: p.172-173. — Index.
ISBN 0-89122-019-4 Pbk : £7.95
1.Ti

(B79-12532)

A/FK — Barrel organ
Ord-Hume, Arthur Wolfgang Julius Gerald
Barrel organ : the story of the mechanical organ and its repair / [by] Arthur W.J.G. Ord-Hume. — London [etc.] : Allen and Unwin, 1978. — 567p,[54]p of plates : ill, facsims, map, music, ports ; 26cm.
Bibl.: p.548-552. — Index.
ISBN 0-04-789005-3 : £18.50

1.Ti

(B79-01356)

A/FP(BC) — Recorded music. Yearbooks
British Phonographic Industry
BPI year book : a review of the British record and tape industry. — [London] ([33 Thurloe Place, SW7 2HQ]) : BPI.
1978. — 1978. — 224p : ill(some col), col maps, ports ; 26cm.
ISBN 0-906154-01-4 Pbk : £2.95
ISSN 0142-7636
1.Ti

(B79-19928)

A/G — Folk music
Woods, Fred
Folk revival : the rediscovery of a national music / [by] Fred Woods. — Poole : Blandford Press, 1979. — 133p,[8]p of plates : ports ; 20cm.
Index.
ISBN 0-7137-0970-7 : £3.95 : CIP rev.
ISBN 0-7137-0993-6 Pbk : £1.95
1.Ti

(B79-14913)

A/GB — Popular music
Dann, Allan
How to succeed in the music business / [by] Allan Dann & John Underwood]. — New York ; London [etc.] : Wise Publications ; London (78 Newman St., W1P 3LA) : [Distributed by] Music Sales Limited, 1978. — 87p : ill, forms, 2 ports ; 26cm.
Bibl.: p.76-77. — Index.
ISBN 0-86001-454-1 Pbk : £2.50
1.Ti 2.Underwood, John, b.1934

(B79-10119)

Farmer, Paul
Pop / [by] Paul Farmer. — [London] : Longman, [1979]. — 24p : ill, music ; 23cm. — (Longman music topics)
Text on inside covers.
ISBN 0-582-21577-3 Sd : £0.65
1.Ti

(B79-32712)

A/GB(B) — Popular music. Periodicals
Pop star weekly. — [London] : [Spotlight Publications].
24 Mar. 1979-. — [1979]-. — ill(some col), ports(some col) ; 41cm.
Thirty-two p. in 1st issue.
Sd : £0.20(£20.00 yearly)
ISSN 0143-0653

(B79-27779)

Superpop. — London (1B Parkfield St., N1 0PR) : 'Superpop'.
No.1- ; Jan. 27, 1979-. — [1979]-. — ill, ports ; 42cm.
Weekly. — 28p. in 1st issue.
Sd : £0.15

(B79-24588)

A/GB(YC/BC) — Popular music. Great Britain. Yearbooks
Kemps music & recording industry year book international. — London : Kemps.
1979 / [editor Peter W. Gamble]. — 1979. — [4],320,110p : ill, maps ; 21cm.
Index.
ISBN 0-905255-52-6 Pbk : £10.50
ISSN 0305-7100
1.Gamble, Peter William 2.Music & recording industry year book international

(B79-22267)

A/GB/FD(YC/BC) — Popular music. Recorded music. Great Britain. Yearbooks
British Phonographic Industry
BPI year book : a survey of the British record and tape industries. — London (350 Kilburn High Rd, N.W.6) : Parkway Publications Ltd.
1976. — 1976. — 3-242p : ill(some col), maps, ports ; 26cm.
Pbk : £2.50
ISSN 0142-7636
1.Ti

(B79-19926)

A/GC(B) — Country music. Periodicals
Country people. — [London] : [IPC Magazines].
[No.1]- ; 1979-. — [1979]-. — ill, ports(some col) ; 28cm.
67p. in 1st issue.
Sd : £0.80

(B79-27777)

A/GR(VG) — Activities. Primary schools
Sing a song. — Sunbury-on-Thames [etc.] : Nelson ; London : ILEA Learning Materials Service.
1. [Teacher's book] / compilers Wendy Bird, David Evans, Gary McAuliffe ; editor Sue Chapple]. — 1978. — [110]p : music ; 22x28cm.
Bibl. (1p). — Index.
ISBN 0-17-413002-3 Sp : £2.75
1.Bird, Wendy 2.Evans, David, b.1940 (May) 3.McAuliffe, Gary 4.Inner London Education Authority. Learning Materials Service

(B79-07467)

A/HKR/FD(WT) — Rock. Records. Lists
Gambaccini, Paul
Critics' choice top 200 albums / compiled by Paul Gambaccini with Susan Ready ; with contributions from ... [others]. — London [etc.] : Omnibus Press ; London (78 Newman St., W1P 3LA) : Distributed by Book Sales Limited, 1978. — 96p : ill, ports ; 26cm.
ISBN 0-86001-494-0 Pbk : £2.25
1.Ti 2.Ready, Susan

(B79-09962)

A/JT(P) — Race, Steve. Biographies
Race, Steve
Musician at large / [by] Steve Race. — London : Eyre Methuen, 1979. — 224p,leaf of plate,[8]p of plates : 1 ill, ports ; 23cm.
Index.
ISBN 0-413-39740-8 : £6.50 : CIP rev.
1.Ti

(B79-17755)

A/JT(XQQ) — Radio, 1975
British Broadcasting Corporation
Catalogue of music broadcast on Radio 3 / British Broadcasting Corporation. — London : B.B.C.
1975 / researched and compiled by Mary Wiegold and Caroline Wilkinson ; edited by Stephen Plaistow. — 1978. — [3],293p ; 30cm.
Previously published: as 'Catalogue of music broadcast on Radio 3 and Radio 4'.
ISBN 0-563-17372-6 Pbk : £4.50
1.Ti 2.Wiegold, Mary 3.Wilkinson, Caroline 4.Plaistow, Stephen 5.Catalogue of music broadcast on Radio 3 and Radio 4

(B79-29149)

A/JV(YDHDB) — Music hall. Bristol
Barker, Kathleen
Early music hall in Bristol / [by] Kathleen Barker. — Bristol (74 Bell Barn Rd, Stoke Bishop, Bristol BS9 2DG) : Historical Association, Bristol Branch, 1979. — [2],20p,[4]p of plates : 1 ill, 3 facsims ; 22cm. — (Historical Association. Bristol Branch. Local history pamphlets ; 44)
Sd : £0.60
1.Ti 2.Sr

(B79-23405)

A/M — Rudiments
Lally, Maureen
Listen, sing and play / [by] Maureen Lally. — Dublin : Educational Company of Ireland.
1 : Senior infants, lessons 1-10. Workbook. — 1977. — [2],12p : ill, music ; 19x25cm.
Sd : £0.35
1.Ti

(B79-02026)

A/M(VG) — Rudiments. Primary schools
Andrews, J Austin
Introduction to music fundamentals : a programmed textbook for the elementary classroom teacher / musical contents [by] J. Austin Andrews ; programming specialist Jeanne Foster Wardian. — 4th ed. — Englewood Cliffs ; London [etc.] : Prentice-Hall, 1978. — viii,208,40p : ill, music ; 22x28cm.
Fill-in book. — With answers to self-tests. — Previous ed.: New York : Appleton-Century-Crofts, 1972. — Index.
ISBN 0-13-489575-4 Sp : £8.00
1.Ti 2.Wardian, Jeanne Foster

(B79-00564)

A/PF — Tonality
Avantgarde, Jazz, Pop : Tenderzen zwischen Tonalität und Atonalität : neun Vorragstexte / herausgegeben von Reinhold Brinkmann. — Mainz ; London [etc.] : Schott, 1978. — 119p : music ; 24cm. — (Institut für Neue Musik und Musikerziehung. Veröffentlichungen ; Band 18)
Pbk : £7.20
ISBN 3-7957-1758-2
1.Brinkmann, Reinhold 2.Sr

(B79-11128)

Warfield, Gerald
Layer analysis : a primer of elementary tonal structures / [by]
Gerald Warfield. — New York ; London : Longman, 1978. — xv,
158p : music ; 28cm.
Fill-in book. — Originally published: New York : McKay, 1976. — Bibl.:
p.106. — Index.
ISBN 0-582-28069-9 Sp : £6.35
1.Ti
(B79-50004)

A/R — Harmony
Benjamin, Thomas
Techniques and materials of tonal music : with an introduction to
twentieth-century techniques / [by] Thomas Benjamin, Michael
Horvit, Robert Nelson. — 2nd ed. — Boston [Mass.] [etc.] ;
London : Houghton Mifflin, 1979. — xiii,268p : ill, music ; 26cm.
Previous ed.: 1975. — Bibl.: p.262-263. — Index.
ISBN 0-395-27066-9 : £9.75
1.Ti 2.Horvit, Michael 3.Nelson, Robert
(B79-18563)

Mickelsen, William C
Hugo Riemann's 'Theory of harmony' : a study / by William C.
Mickelsen. And, History of music theory, Book III / by Hugo
Riemann ; translated [from the German] and edited by William C.
Mickelsen. — Lincoln [Neb.] ; London : University of Nebraska
Press, 1977. — xv,263p : ill, music ; 24cm.
Includes footnotes in Italian and French. — 'Geschichte der Musiktheorie
im IX-XIX Jahrhundert' originally published: Leipzig : M. Hesse, 1898. —
Bibl.: p.239-251. — Index.
ISBN 0-8032-0891-x : £10.50
1.Ti 2.Riemann, Hugo. [Geschichte der Musiktheorie im IX-XIX
Jahrhundert. Bd 3 : Die Harmonielehre. English]. History of music theory,
Book III
(B79-04541)

Warburton, Annie Osborne
Harmony : a textbook for class use on aural foundations / [by]
Annie O. Warburton. — New ed. — London : Longman, 1979. —
vi,322p : music ; 20cm.
Previous ed.: i.e. New ed., 1952.
ISBN 0-582-33071-8 Pbk : £1.95
1.Ti
(B79-35972)

A/RM — Counterpoint
Benjamin, Thomas
The craft of modal counterpoint : a practical approach / [by]
Thomas Benjamin. — New York : Schirmer Books ; London :
Collier Macmillan, 1979. — ix,230p : music ; 23cm.
Bibl.: p.230.
ISBN 0-02-870480-0 Pbk : £7.45
1.Ti
(B79-30799)

A/S — Form
Green, Douglas Marshall
Form in tonal music : an introduction to analysis / [by] Douglas
M. Green. — 2nd ed. — New York ; London [etc.] : Holt,
Rinehart and Winston, 1979. — xi,324p : ill, music ; 25cm.
Previous ed.: 1965. — Index.
ISBN 0-03-020286-8 : £10.00
1.Ti
(B79-24591)

AB — MUSICAL LITERATURE. VOCAL MUSIC
AB/E — Singing
Hammar, Russell A
Singing - : an extension of speech / by Russell A. Hammar. —
Metuchen ; London : Scarecrow Press ; [Folkestone] : [Distributed
by Bailey and Swinfen], 1978. — vii,208p : ill, music ; 23cm.
Index.
ISBN 0-8108-1182-0 : £6.75
1.Ti
(B79-17764)

Husler, Frederick
Singer : die physische Natur des Stimmorganes : Anleitung zum
Aufschliessen der Singstimme / [von] Frederick Husler, Yvonne
Rodd-Marling ; Abbildungen von Frederick Husler. — 2.Aufl. —
Mainz ; London [etc.] : Schott, 1978. — 187p,plate : ill(chiefly
col), port ; 24cm.
Translation of: 'Singing'. Revised ed. London : Hutchinson, 1976. -- Bibl.:
p.179-180. — List of sound discs: p.173-178. — Index.
Pbk : £9.60
ISBN 3-7957-0065-5
1.Ti 2.Rodd-Marling, Yvonne
(B79-13063)

Who wants to sing? : (what it's all about) / by Two Singers [i.e.
John and Minna Patterson]. — [2nd and enlarged ed.]. —
[Belfast] ([9 Kinnaird Terrace, Antrim Rd, Belfast BT14 6BN]) :
[John Patterson], [1978]. — [16],146p : ill, music ; 21cm.
Previous ed.: Belfast : Jordan, 1974.
Pbk : £3.80
Also classified at AL/E
1.Patterson, John 2.Patterson, Minna
(B79-06707)

AB/EDD — Diction
Grubb, Thomas
Singing in French : a manual of French diction and French vocal
repertoire / [by] Thomas Grubb ; with a foreword by Pierre
Bernac. — New York : Schirmer Books ; London : Collier
Macmillan, 1979. — xvii,221p : music ; 24cm.
With answers. — Sound disc (2s. 7in. 33 1/3rpm) as insert. — Bibl.: p.217.
ISBN 0-02-870790-7 Pbk : £7.45
1.Ti
(B79-25332)

AB/EG — Sight reading
Trubitt, Allen R
Ear training and sight-singing : an integrated approach / [by]
Allen R. Trubitt, Robert S. Hines. — New York : Schirmer
Books ; London : Collier Macmillan.
Book 1. — 1979. — xii,330p : chiefly music ; 28cm.
With answers.
ISBN 0-02-870810-5 Pbk : £8.25
Primary classification A/EF
1.Ti 2.Hines, Robert S
(B79-25327)

ABN — Stories
Hosier, John
The sorcerer's apprentice, and other stories / by John Hosier ;
illustrated by Bettina. — London [etc.] : Oxford University Press,
1978. — [7],64p ; 21cm. — (The young reader's guides to music ;
11)
Originally published: 1960.
ISBN 0-19-314922-2 Pbk : £1.50
1.Ti 2.Bettina, b.1903 3.Sr
(B79-50005)

AC — MUSICAL LITERATURE. OPERA
AC(C) — Encyclopaedias
Rosenthal, Harold
The concise Oxford dictionary of opera / by Harold Rosenthal
and John Warrack. — 2nd ed. — London [etc.] : Oxford
University Press, 1979. — [14],561p : music ; 21cm.
Previous ed.: 1964. — Bibl.: p.[9-10].
ISBN 0-19-311318-x : £6.95
1.Ti 2.Warrack, John
(B79-23401)

AC(WB/P) — Tucker, Norman
In memoriam N.W.G.T., 1910-1978 / [edited by J. Audrey Ellison].
— [London] ([74 Doneraile St., SW6 6EP]) : J.A. Ellison, 1978.
— [2],30p : 2 ports ; 22cm.
Sheet as insert.
ISBN 0-904677-09-5 Sd : £1.30
1.Ellison, J Audrey
(B79-16101)

AC(WB/P) — Tucker, Norman. Biographies
Tucker, Norman, *b.1910*
Norman Tucker, musician : before and after two decades at
Sadler's Wells : an autobiography. — London (74 Doneraile St.,
SW6 6EP) : J.A. Ellison, 1978. — [7],211p,leaf of plate,[8]p of
plates : ill, ports ; 22cm.
Index.
ISBN 0-904677-08-7 Pbk : £4.95
(B79-17760)

AC/CC(YE/XE201) — Criticism and aesthetics. Germany, 1600-1800
Flaherty, Gloria
Opera in the development of German critical thought / [by]
Gloria Flaherty. — Princeton ; Guildford : Princeton University
Press, 1978. — xi,383p ; 23cm.
Bibl.: p.335-363. — Index.
ISBN 0-691-06370-2 : £11.70
1.Ti
(B79-14914)

AC/E(X25344) — Performance. History, 1597-1940
Loewenburg, Alfred
Annals of opera, 1597-1940 / compiled from the original sources
by Alfred Loewenburg ; with an introduction by Edward J. Dent.
— 3rd ed., revised and corrected. — London : J. Calder, 1978. —
xxvi,1756 columns ; 26cm.
Previous ed.: Geneva : Societas Bibliographica, 1955. — Index.
ISBN 0-7145-3657-1 : £30.00
1.Ti
(B79-02988)

AC/E(YC/QB/K) — Royal Opera House, Covent Garden. Economics
Blaug, Mark
  Why are Covent Garden seat prices so high? / by Mark Blaug. —
  London (Royal Opera House Covent Garden, WC2 7QA) : Royal
  Opera House Covent Garden Ltd, 1976. — 13,[2]p : ill, plans ;
  28cm.
  Sd : Unpriced
  1.Ti 2.Royal Opera House
                                                                            (B79-04908)

AC/E(YDKP/X) — Llandudno. History
Jones, Ivor Wynne
  Llandudno's operatic tradition / [by] Ivor Wynne Jones. —
  Llandudno (71 Llandudno Rd, Penrhyn Bay. Llandudno,
  Gwynedd) : Pegasus, 1979. — 15p : facsims, port ; 22cm.
  'Reprinted from "Welsh music", vol.6, no.1, Spring 1979' - title page verso.
  Sd : £0.50
  1.Ti
                                                                            (B79-27786)

ACF — MUSICAL LITERATURE. OPERETTA
ACF(YH) — Operetta. France
Harding, James, *b.1929*
  Folies de Paris : the rise and fall of French operetta / [by] James
  Harding. — London : Chappell : Elm Tree Books, 1979. — 183p,
  [8]p of plates : ill, ports ; 26cm.
  Bibl.: p.174-176. — Index.
  ISBN 0-903443-28-7 : £7.95
  1.Ti
                                                                            (B79-19445)

ACM — MUSICAL LITERATURE. MUSICAL PLAYS
ACM(YD/XMR53) — Musical plays. England, 1916-1978
Parker, Derek
  The story and the song : a survey of English musical plays,
  1916-78 / [by] Derek and Julia Parker. — London : Chappell :
  Elm Tree Books, 1979. — xv,184p : ill, ports ; 26cm.
  Bibl.: p.171-172. — Index.
  ISBN 0-903443-25-2 : £7.50
  1.Ti 2.Parker, Julia
                                                                            (B79-35973)

ACM/JR(WT) — Musical plays. Films. Lists
Woll, Allen L
  Songs from Hollywood musical comedies, 1927 to the present : a
  dictionary / [by] Allen L. Woll. — New York ; London :
  Garland, 1976. — x;vii,251p ; 23cm. — (Garland reference library
  in the humanities ; vol.44)
  Index.
  ISBN 0-8240-9958-3 : £15.00
  1.Ti 2.Sr
                                                                            (B79-50406)

AD — MUSICAL LITERATURE. CHORAL MUSIC
AD(VF/YC/WT) — Choral music. Schools. Great Britain. Lists
Choir Schools Association
  Choir schools / [Choir Schools Association]. — Ripon (c/o The
  Honorary Secretary, Cathedral Choir School, Whitcliffe La.,
  Ripon, N. Yorkshire HG4 2LA) : The Association, [1978?]. —
  Folder ([4]p) : map ; 27cm.
  Unpriced
  1.Ti
                                                                            (B79-19102)

AD(YDGB/WE/X) — Three Choirs Festival. History
  Two hundred and fifty years of the Three Choirs Festival : a
  commemoration in words and pictures / edited by Barry Still. —
  [London] ([c/o Arts Council of Great Britain, 105 Piccadilly,
  W1V 0AU]) : Three Choirs Festival Association, 1977. — 67p :
  ill, facsims, music, ports ; 28cm.
  Bibl.: p.65.
  Pbk : £2.00
  1.Still, Barry 2.Three Choirs Festival Association
                                                                            (B79-07463)

AD/E — Choral music. Performance
Hofbauer, Kurt
  Praxis der chorischen Stimmbildung / [von] Kurt Hofbauer. —
  Mainz ; London [etc.] : Schott, 1978. — 107p : ill, music ; 21cm.
  — (Bausteine für Musikerziehung und Musikpflege ;
  Schriftenreiche B33)
  Bibl.: p.106-107. — Index.
  Pbk : £6.00
  ISBN 3-7957-1033-2
  1.Ti 2.Sr
                                                                            (B79-11133)

AD/LD(YD/D) — Church music. England. Essays
  English church music : a collection of essays. — Croydon
  (Addington Palace, Croydon CR9 5AD) : Royal School of Church
  Music.
  1979. — [1979]. — 54p,[2]leaves of plates : facsim, music, port ; 22cm.
  ISBN 0-85402-081-0 Pbk : £2.24
  1.Royal School of Church Music
                                                                            (B79-33554)

AD/LD(YD/XDXJ112) — Church music. England, 1549-1660
Le Huray, Peter
  Music and the Reformation in England, 1549-1660 / [by] Peter le
  Huray. — Cambridge [etc.] : Cambridge University Press, 1978.
  — xvii,454p,[12]p of plates : ill, facsims, music ; 24cm. —
  (Cambridge studies in music)
  Originally published: London : Jenkins, 1967. — Bibl.: p.427-442. — List of
  music: p.406-426. — Index.
  ISBN 0-521-21958-2 : £19.50
  ISBN 0-521-29418-5 Pbk : £5.95
  1.Ti 2.Sr
                                                                            (B79-16102)

ADFF/EDD — Roman Catholic liturgy. Diction
Hines, Robert S
  Singer's manual of Latin diction and phonetics / [by] Robert S.
  Hines. — New York : Schirmer Books ; London : Collier
  Macmillan, 1975. — xvii,86p ; 24cm.
  Includes a chapter in Latin with English translation. — Bibl.: p.85-86.
  ISBN 0-02-870800-8 : £6.75
  1.Ti
                                                                            (B79-08691)

ADGTCW(YE/XE151) — Protestant church music. Germany,
    1600-1750
Krummacher, Friedhelm
  Die Choralbearbeitung in der protestantischen Figuralmusik
  zwischen Praetorius und Bach / [von] Friedhelm Krummacher. —
  Kassel [etc.] ; London ([17 Bucklesbury, Hitchin, Herts. SG51
  BB]) : Bärenreiter, 1978. — xvi,546p : music ; 24cm. — (Kieler
  Schriften zur Musikwissenschaft ; Bd 22)
  Pbk : Unpriced
  ISBN 3-7618-0526-8
  1.Ti 2.Sr
                                                                            (B79-17763)

ADK(XEYK37) — Anthems, 1670-1706
  The **Gostling** manuscript / compiled by John Gostling ; foreword
  by Franklin B. Zimmerman. — Austin ; London : University of
  Texas Press, 1977. — xvi,205,213,[4]p : music ; 26cm.
  Facsimile reproduction of 'The original Gostling Manuscript ... in the
  Humanities Research Center, the University of Texas at Austin' - title page
  verso. — Second sequence of pages printed tête beche.
  ISBN 0-292-72713-5 : £24.50
  1.Gostling, John 2.University of Texas at Austin. Humanities Research
  Center
                                                                            (B79-04542)

ADM — Hymns
  Sing to God / compiled by Margaret V. Old and Elspeth M.
  Stephenson. — London : Scripture Union, 1978. — [126]p ; 16cm.
  Originally published: 1971. — Index.
  ISBN 0-85421-722-3 : £0.75
  1.Old, Margaret Valerie 2.Stephenson, Elspeth Mary 3.Scripture Union
                                                                            (B79-31511)

ADM(X) — Hymns. History
Reynolds, William Jensen
  A joyful sound : Christian hymnody / [by] William Jensen
  Reynolds. — 2nd ed. / prepared by Milburn Price. — New
  York ; London [etc.] : Holt, Rinehart and Winston, 1978. — xii,
  308p : music ; 25cm.
  Previous ed.: published as 'A survey of Christian hymnody'. 1963. — Bibl.:
  p.119-124. — Index.
  ISBN 0-03-040831-8 : £8.75
  1.Ti 2.Price, Milburn 3.Survey of Christian hymnody
                                                                            (B79-05497)

ADM/D(M/WT) — Hymns. Composers. Lists
Hayden, Andrew J
  British hymn writers and composers : a check-list, giving their
  dates & places of birth & death / by Andrew J. Hayden and
  Robert F. Newton. — [1st ed. reprinted] / [with appendix of
  revisions]. — Croydon (c/o Addington Palace, Croydon CR9
  5AD) : Hymn Society of Great Britain and Ireland, 1977 [i.e.
  1979]. — [100]p ; 21cm.
  First ed. originally published: 1977. — Bibl.: p.[4].
  Pbk : £3.00
  1.Ti 2.Newton, Robert F 3.Hymn Society of Great Britain and Ireland
                                                                            (B79-15556)

ADM/LSF — Hymns. Presbyterian
  Handbook to 'The church hymnary'. — 3rd ed. / edited by John
  M. Barkley. — London [etc.] : Oxford University Press, 1979. —
  viii,411p ; 22cm.
  Previous ed.: / edited by James Moffatt and Millar Patrick. 1927. — Index.
  ISBN 0-19-146811-8 : £3.50
  1.Barkley, John Monteith 2.Church hymnary
                                                                            (B79-31512)

ADW(YDK) — Songs, etc. Wales
Williams, Huw
  Canu'r bobol / gan Huw Williams. — Dinbych [i.e. Denbigh] :
  Gwasg Gee, 1978. — 232p ; 23cm.
  Index.
  £4.00
  1.Ti
                                                                            (B79-04543)

ADW/GB — Popular songs
Rock file. — St Albans : Panther.
5 / edited by Charlie Gillett and Simon Frith. — 1978. — 286p ; 18cm.
ISBN 0-586-04680-1 Pbk : £1.25
1.Gillett, Charlie 2.Frith, Simon
(B79-03804)

ADW/GB(XNU7) — Popular songs, 1939-1945
Huggett, Frank Edward
Goodnight sweetheart : songs and memories of the Second World War / [by] Frank E. Huggett. — London : W.H. Allen, 1979. — 192p : ill, facsims, ports ; 25cm.
With answers. — Bibl.: p.192.
ISBN 0-491-02308-1 : £5.95
1.Ti
(B79-37421)

AJFDW/GR(VJ) — Unison female voices, children's voices. Songs, etc. Activities. Junior schools
Singing rhymes / [compiled] by Dorothy Taylor ; with illustrations by Brian Price Thomas and photographs by John Moyes. — Loughborough : Ladybird Books, 1979. — 52p : chiefly col ill, music ; 18cm. — (Learning with traditional rhymes ; book 7)
ISBN 0-7214-0537-1 : £0.30
1.Taylor, Dorothy 2.Price-Thomas, Brian 3.Moyes, John, b.1924 4.Sr
(B79-06706)

AK — MUSICAL LITERATURE. VOCAL SOLOS
AK/E(VC/XFYS201) — Singing. Teaching, 1777-1927
Monahan, Brent Jeffrey
The art of singing : a compendium of thoughts on singing published between 1777 and 1927 / by Brent Jeffrey Monahan. — Metuchen ; London : Scarecrow Press ; [Folkestone] : [Distributed by Bailey and Swinfen], 1978. — xiv,342p ; 23cm.
Bibl. — Index.
ISBN 0-8108-1155-3 : £9.35
1.Ti
(B79-08929)

AKDH/LSC(YM/XFX31) — Motets, Anthems, Hymns, etc. Orthodox Eastern Church. Russia, 1740-1770
Akademiía nauk SSSR. *Biblioteka. MSS. (33.3.5)*
An unpublished religious song-book of mid-eighteenth century Russia / edited by J. Sullivan and C.L. Drage. — London (c/o C.L. Drage, 94 Inverness Terrace, W.2) : The editors, 1978. — iv, 114p,[6] leaves of plates : facsims ; 22cm.
'The manuscript of the song-book is preserved in the Manuscript Department of the Library of the Academy of Sciences of the USSR in Leningrad under the reference 33.3.5'. — Introduction.
Pbk : £2.00
1.Ti 2.Sullivan, J 3.Drage, Charles Lovell
(B79-37420)

AKDW/G(YC) — Folk songs. England
Everyman's book of English country songs / edited by Roy Palmer. — London [etc.] : Dent, 1979. — viii,256p,[8]p of plates : ill, facsims, music ; 25cm.
Index.
ISBN 0-460-12048-4 : £7.95 : CIP rev.
1.Palmer, Roy
(B79-15558)

AKDW/G(YM/XCE751) — Folk songs. Russia, 900-1650
Zguta, Russell
Russian minstrels : a history of the skomorokhi / [by] Russell Zguta. — Oxford : Clarendon Press, 1978. — xv,160p : ill ; 24cm.
Index.
ISBN 0-19-815652-9 : £8.95
1.Ti
(B79-24590)

AKDW/GB(YT/WT) — Popular songs. United States. Lists
Craig, Warren
Sweet and lowdown : America's popular song writers / by Warren Craig ; with a foreword by Milton Ager. — Metuchen ; London : Scarecrow Press ; [Folkestone] : [Distributed by Bailey and Swinfen], 1978. — xi,645p ; 23cm.
Index.
ISBN 0-8108-1089-1 : £18.75
1.Ti
(B79-11129)

AKDW/GB/E(M/DE) — Popular songs. Singers. Questions and answers
Discowords. — St Leonards On Sea : Dormbourne Limited ; Horsham : Distributed by Wells Gardner Darton.
Vol.1, no.1- ; [1978]-. — 1978-. — 25cm.
Quarterly. — 36p. in 1st issue.
Sd : £0.20
(B79-00580)

AKDW/GB/E(P) — Aznavour, Charles. Biographies
Aznavour, Charles
Yesterday when I was young / [by] Charles Aznavour. — London : W.H. Allen, 1979. — [6],202p,[16]p of plates : ports ; 23cm.
Index.
ISBN 0-491-02446-0 : £5.95
1.Ti
(B79-36914)

AKDW/GB/E(P) — Beatles
'**Mersey** beat', the beginnings of the Beatles / edited and introduced by Bill Harry. — London [etc.] : Omnibus Press ; London (78 Newman St., W1P 3LA) : Distributed by Book Sales Limited, 1977. — 96p : chiefly facsims, ports ; 33cm.
Consists chiefly of facsimile reprints from 'Mersey beat', July 1961-Nov. 1964.
ISBN 0-86001-415-0 Pbk : £2.95
1.Harry, Bill
(B79-36913)

AKDW/GB/E(P) — Beatles. Biographies
Beatles, The
Beatles in their own words / compiled by Miles ; edited by Pearce Marchbank. — London [etc.] : Omnibus Press, 1978. — 125,[3]p : ill, ports ; 26cm.
ISBN 0-86001-540-8 Pbk : £2.50
1.Ti 2.Miles 3.Marchbank, Pearce
(B79-26552)

Schaffner, Nicholas
The Beatles forever / [by] Nicholas Schaffner. — New York ; London [etc.] : McGraw-Hill, 1978. — 224p,[4]p of plates : ill(some col), facsims, ports(some col) ; 28cm.
Originally published: Harrisburg, Pa. : Stackpole, 1977. — Bibl.: p.217-219. — List of sound discs: p.206-213. — Index.
ISBN 0-07-055087-5 Pbk : £4.95
1.Ti
(B79-20268)

AKDW/GB/E(P) — Bee Gees. Biographies
Bee Gees, *Group*
Bee Gees : the authorized biography / by Barry, Robin and Maurice Gibb ; as told to David Leaf. — London : Octopus Books, 1979. — 160p : ill, facsims, ports ; 28cm.
Col. poster (fold. sheet) tipped in and perforated at inside edge.
ISBN 0-7064-1091-2 Pbk : £2.99
1.Leaf, David
(B79-20269)

Pryce, Larry
The Bee Gees / [by] Larry Pryce. — London [etc.] : Panther, 1979. — 141p,[16]p of plates : ports ; 18cm.
List of sound discs: p.129-141.
ISBN 0-586-04854-5 Pbk : £0.80
1.Ti
(B79-10478)

AKDW/GB/E(P) — Bowlly, Al. Biographies
Colin, Sid
Al Bowlly. — London : Elm Tree Books, Jan. 1979. — [192]p.
ISBN 0-241-10057-7 : £5.95 : CIP entry
1.Staveacre, Tony
(B78-37099)

AKDW/GB/E(P) — Denver, John. Biographies
Martin, James
John Denver : Rocky Mountain wonderboy / [by] James Martin. — London : Everest, 1977. — [4],148p,[16]p of plates : ports ; 18cm.
Also published: New York : Pinnacle Books, 1977.
ISBN 0-905018-56-7 Pbk : £0.75
(B79-50006)

AKDW/GB/E(P) — Fields. *Dame. Gracie.* Biographies
Rochdale Museum
Our Gracie / [text by Elizabeth Pollitt]. — [Rochdale] ([c/o Rochdale Museum Esplanade, Rochdale, Lancs.]) : [Rochdale Arts and Entertainments Services], [1978]. — [25]p : 2 ill, facsims, ports ; 21x30cm.
'[accompanies an exhibition held at] Rochdale Museum, September 9th-October 7th, 1978'. — Bibl.(1p.).
Sd : £0.70
1.Ti 2.Pollitt, Elizabeth 3.Rochdale (Metropolitan District). Arts and Entertainments Services
(B79-08928)

AKDW/GB/E(P) — Harrison, George. Biographies
Michaels, Ross
George Harrison : yesterday and today / by Ross Michaels. — New York ; London : Flash Books ; London (78 Newman St., W.1) : [Distributed by] Book Sales Ltd, 1977. — 96p : ill, ports ; 26cm.
List of sound discs: p.91-96.
ISBN 0-8256-3913-1 Pbk : £1.95
(B79-11130)

AKDW/GB/E(P) — Richard, Cliff. Biographies
Richard, Cliff
The illustrated 'Which one's Cliff?'. — Sevenoaks : Hodder and
Stoughton, Oct. 1978. — [192]p.
Originally published: as 'Which one's Cliff?'. 1977.
ISBN 0-340-23413-x Pbk : £2.95 : CIP entry
1.Ti 2.Latham, Bill

(B78-29837)

AKDW/GB/E(P/EM/XRF) — Wings, 1976
Powell, Aubrey
Wings tour USA / ... all photographs by Aubrey Powell ; graphics
and illustration by George Hardie ; edited by Storm Thorgerson &
Peter Christopherson. — Limpsfield (High St., Limpsfield, Surrey
RH8 0DY) : Paper Tiger, 1978. — [156]p : chiefly ill(some col),
ports ; 29cm.
At head of title: Hands across the water.
ISBN 0-905895-10-x Pbk : £3.25
1.Ti 2.Thorgerson, Storm 3.Christopherson, Peter 4.Hands across the water
(B79-05872)

AKDW/GB/FD(P/WT) — Dylan, Bob. Recorded music. Lists
Cable, Paul
Bob Dylan : his unreleased works / [by] Paul Cable. — [London]
(P.O. Box 1, W.C.2) : Scorpion Publications Ltd/Dark Star, 1978.
— 192p : ports ; 22cm.
Index.
ISBN 0-905906-17-9 : Unpriced
ISBN 0-905906-16-0 Pbk : £2.95

(B79-18867)

**AKDW/GB/FD(P/WT) — Popular songs. Recorded music. The
             Shadows. Lists**
Geddes, George Thomson
Foot tapping : the Shadows, 1958-1978 / [by] George T. Geddes.
— Glasgow (102 Dorchester Ave., Glasgow G12 0EB) : The
author, 1978. — [3],54p ; 30cm.
Bibl.: p.53-54.
Sp : £1.00
1.Ti

(B79-00884)

AKDW/GB/FD(WT) — Popular songs. Recorded music. Lists
The Guinness book of British hit singles : (the Guinness book of
records records). — 2nd ed. / [compiled by] Jo Rice ... [et al.]. —
Enfield : Guinness Superlatives, 1979. — 319p : col ill, ports ;
21cm.
Text, ill., col. ports. on front cover and inside covers. — Previous ed.: /
compiled by Jo and Tim Rice. 1977.
ISBN 0-900424-89-3 : £5.25
ISBN 0-900424-99-0 Pbk : £3.95
1.Rice, Jo

(B79-22108)

AKDW/GBSR — Reggae
Davis, Stephen
Reggae bloodlines : in search of the music and culture of
Jamaica / text by Stephen Davis ; photographs by Peter Simon. —
London [etc.] : Heinemann Educational, 1979. — [8],216p : ill,
facsim, music, ports ; 28cm.
Originally published: Garden City, N.Y. : Anchor Press, 1977. — Bibl.:
p.210. — List of sound discs : p.211-216.
ISBN 0-435-98190-0 Pbk : £4.95
1.Ti 2.Simon, Peter

(B79-31926)

AKDW/GC(BC) — Country music. Yearbooks
British Country Music Association
Yearbook / British Country Music Association. — Newton Abbot
([PO Box 2, Newton Abbot, Devon TQ12 4HT]) : The
Association.
1979. — 1979. — [2],80p : ill, ports ; 21cm.
Pbk : Unpriced
ISSN 0308-4698
1.Ti

(B79-34987)

AKDW/GC/E(P) — Parton, Dolly. Biographies
Nash, Alanna
Dolly / [by] Alanna Nash. — London [etc.] : Panther, 1979. —
397,[8]p of plates : ports ; 18cm.
List of sound discs: p.395-397.
ISBN 0-586-05051-5 Pbk : £1.25
1.Ti

(B79-33546)

AKDW/GNL(P) — Scott, Joe. Biographies
Ives, Edward D
Joe Scott : the woodsman-songmaker / [by] Edward D. Ives. —
Urbana [etc.] ; London : University of Illinois Press, 1978. —
xxxvii,473p : ill, maps, music, ports ; 24cm. — (Music in America
life)
Bibl.: p.455-462. — Index.
ISBN 0-252-00683-6 : £15.75
1.Sr

(B79-22639)

AKDW/HHW — Blues
Farmer, Paul
Ragtime & blues / [by] Paul Farmer. — London : Longman,
1979. — 24p : ill, facsims, map, music, ports ; 23cm. —
(Longman music topics)
Text on inside covers.
ISBN 0-582-21579-x Sd : £0.65
Primary classification AQPHXJ
1.Ti

(B79-36912)

AKDW/HHW/E(M) — Blues. Singers. Biographies
Guralnick, Peter
Feel like going home : portraits in blues & rock'n'roll / [by] Peter
Guralnick. — London [etc.] : Omnibus Press, [1978]. — 256p : ill,
ports ; 23cm.
Originally published: New York : Outerbridge and Dienstfrey, 1971. — Bibl.
: p.253-256. — List of sound discs: p.248-251.
ISBN 0-86001-493-2 Pbk : £2.95
Also classified at AKDW/HK/E(M)
1.Ti

(B79-10476)

AKDW/HK/E(M) — Rock 'n' roll. Singers. Biographies
Guralnick, Peter
Feel like going home : portraits in blues & rock'n'roll / [by] Peter
Guralnick. — London [etc.] : Omnibus Press, [1978]. — 256p : ill,
ports ; 23cm.
Originally published: New York : Outerbridge and Dienstfrey, 1971. — Bibl.
: p.253-256. — List of sound discs: p.248-251.
ISBN 0-86001-493-2 Pbk : £2.95
Primary classification AKDW/HHW/E(M)
1.Ti

(B79-10476)

AKDW/HK/E(M) — Rock'n'roll. Musicians
Oxtoby, David
Oxtoby's rockers : the eternal fan / [text by] David Sandison. —
Oxford : Phaidon, 1978. — 80p : ill, chiefly ports(chiefly col) ;
30cm.
ISBN 0-7148-1854-2 Pbk : £4.95
1.Sandison, David 2.Rockers

(B79-15543)

AKDW/HK/E(P) — Presley, Elvis
Elvis lives!. — London : Galaxy Publications Ltd ; Horsham :
[Distributed] by Wells Gardner Darton, 1978. — [1],49p : ill,
facsims, chiefly ports(some col) ; 30cm.
'A Galaxy special'.
Sd : £0.75

(B79-02989)

AKDW/HKR(B) — Rock. Periodicals
Black dwarf. — [Bristol] ([7 Ivywell Rd, Bristol BS9 1NX]) :
['Black dwarf'].
1- ; [1978]-. — [1978]-. — ill ; 21cm.
Published at irregular intervals. — [2],14p. in 1st issue.
Sd : £0.23
ISSN 0142-2804

(B79-01354)

AKDW/HKR(P) — Genesis
Genesis *(Group)*
Genesis lyrics / illustrated by Kim Poor ; introductions by Jo
Durden-Smith and Chris Welch. — London : Sidgwick and
Jackson, 1979. — 100[i.e.98]p(2 fold) : ill(some col), ports ; 31cm.
List of sound discs: p.93. — Index.
ISBN 0-283-98526-7 : £8.95 : CIP rev.
ISBN 0-283-98527-5 Pbk : £5.50
1.Poor, Kim

(B79-14920)

AKDW/HKR(X) — Rock. History
Doney, Malcolm
Summer in the city : rock music and way of life / [by] Malcolm
Doney. — Berkhamsted : Lion Publishing, 1978. — x,133p : ill,
ports ; 20cm. — (An Aslan lion book)
ISBN 0-85648-085-1 Pbk : £1.25
1.Ti 2.Sr

(B79-04538)

AKDW/HKR/E(M) — Rock. Singers
It's - rock scene. — Maidenhead : Purnell, 1979. — 4-61p :
ports(some col) ; 27cm.
Cover title: Rock scene. — Ports. on lining papers.
ISBN 0-361-04558-1 : £1.50
1.Rock scene

(B79-28896)

AKDW/HKR/E(M) — Songs, etc. Rock. Singers
Burchill, Julie
'The boy looked at Johnny' : the obituary of rock and roll / [by]
Julie Burchill and Tony Parsons. — London : Pluto Press, 1978.
— 96p : ports ; 20cm.
ISBN 0-86104-030-9 Pbk : £1.25
1.Ti 2.Parsons, Tony

(B79-02984)

AKDW/HKR/E(P) — Bowie, David
Claire, Vivian
David Bowie! / by Vivian Claire. — New York ; London : Flash
Books ; London (78 Newman St., W.1) : [Distributed by] Books
Sales Ltd, 1977. — 80p : ports ; 26cm.
List of sound discs: p.77.
ISBN 0-8256-3911-5 Pbk : £1.95

(B79-11131)

AKDW/HKR/E(P) — Bylan, Bob. Biographies
Dylan, Bob
Bob Dylan in his own words / compiled by Miles ; edited by
Pearce Marchbank. — London [etc.] : Omnibus Press, 1978. —
128p : ill, ports ; 26cm.
ISBN 0-86001-542-4 Pbk : £2.50

(B79-31930)

AKDW/HKR/E(P) — Led Zeppelin. Biographies
Mylett, Howard
Led Zeppelin / [by] Howard Mylett. — London [etc.] : Panther,
1978. — 172p,[8]p of plates : ports ; 18cm.
Originally published: St Albans : Panther, 1976.
Pbk : £0.75
ISBN 0-586-04390-x
1.Ti

(B79-10479)

AKDW/HKR/E(P) — Moon, Keith. Biographies
Waterman, Ivan
Keith Moon : the life and death of a rock legend / [by] Ivan
Waterman. — London : Arrow Books, 1979. — 142,[16]p of
plates : ill, ports ; 18cm.
ISBN 0-09-920930-6 Pbk : £1.00

(B79-31933)

AKDW/HKR/E(P) — Wakeman, Rick. Biographies
Wooding, Dan
Rick Wakeman : the caped crusader / [by] Dan Wooding. —
London [etc.] : Panther, 1979. — 206p,[16]p of plates : ill, ports ;
18cm.
Originally published: London : Hale, 1978. — List of sound discs: p.201. —
List of films: p.202. — Index.
ISBN 0-586-04853-7 Pbk : £0.95

(B79-19446)

AKDW/HKR/E(P/YC) — Rock. Performance. Great Britain
Gorman, Clem
Backstage rock : behind the scenes with the bands / [by] Clem
Gorman ; photographs by Jan Turvey. — London [etc.] : Pan
Books, 1978. — 205p,[8]p of plates : ill, ports ; 18cm.
Index.
ISBN 0-330-25583-5 Pbk : £0.90
1.Ti

(B79-50007)

AKDW/HKR/FD(WT) — Rock. Recorded music. Lists
Rockmaster. — Southampton (13 Stanton Rd, Regents Park,
Southampton, Hants.) : Rockmaster.
1978 / edited by Terry Hounsome and Tim Chambre. — [1978]. — iv,309,
[1]p ; 25cm.
Index.
Sd : Unpriced
1.Hounsome, Terry 2.Chambre, Tim

(B79-35642)

AKDW/HKRJ — Jazz rock
Coryell, Julie
Jazz-rock fusion : the people - the music / [by] Julie Coryell &
Laura Friedman ; preface by Ramsey Lewis. — London [etc.] :
Boyars : [Distributed by Calder and Boyars], 1978. — xvii,297,[4]
p,[32]p of plates : ports(some col) ; 22x29cm.
'A Marion Boyars special'. — Bibl.: p.263. — List of sound discs: p.265-297.
ISBN 0-7145-2667-3 : £12.00
ISBN 0-7145-2662-2 Pbk : £6.95
1.Ti 2.Friedman, Laura

(B79-32718)

AKDW/JV/FD(B) — Music hall. Recorded music. Periodicals
Music hall records. — London (50 Reporton Rd, S.W.6) : Tony
Barker.
No.1- ; June 1978-. — 1978-. — ports ; 21cm.
Six issues a year. — p.41-61 in 3rd issue. — Lists of sound discs.
Sd : £0.60(£3.60 yearly)
ISSN 0142-6737

(B79-15561)

AKDW/K/G(YD) — Ballads. England
A **ballad** history of England : from 1588 to the present day /
[compiled by] Roy Palmer. — London : Batsford, 1979. — 192p :
ill, facsims, 2 maps, music, ports ; 26cm.
Bibl.: p.186-187. — Index.
ISBN 0-7134-0968-1 : £6.50
1.Palmer, Roy

(B79-11132)

AKDW/K/G/KDX — Ballads. Bawdy
Burns, Robert
[The merry muses of Caledonia]. The secret cabinet of Robert
Burns : merry muses of Caledonia. — [New ed.]. — Edinburgh :
P. Harris, 1979. — 92,[1]p : ill, map, 2 ports ; 18cm. — (Gems of
British social history series ; no.3)
Scots text, English notes.
ISBN 0-904505-84-7 : £3.50
1.Ti 2.Ti 3.Sr

(B79-36915)

The **gentleman's** bottle companion. — Edinburgh : P. Harris, Feb.
1979. — [88]p.
Facsimile reprint of: 1st ed. London : s.n., 1768.
ISBN 0-904505-60-x : £4.50 : CIP entry

(B79-00568)

AKFL/E(P) — Slobodskaya, Oda. Biographies
Leonard, Maurice
Slobodskaya : a biography of Oda Slobodskaya / by Maurice
Leonard. — London : Gollancz, 1979. — 142p,[8]p of plates :
ports ; 23cm.
Index.
ISBN 0-575-02622-7 : £6.50
1.Ti

(B79-22638)

AKFL/E(P) — Söderström, Elizabeth. Biographies
Söderström, Elisabeth
In my own key. — London : H. Hamilton, Oct. 1979. — [128]p.
Translation of: 'I min tonart'. Stockholm : Benniers, 1978.
ISBN 0-241-10318-5 : £5.95 : CIP entry
1.Ti

(B79-25330)

AKFL/E(P) — Teyte, Maggie, Dame. Biographies
O'Connor, Garry
The pursuit of perfection : a life of Maggie Teyte / by Garry
O'Connor. — London : Gollancz, 1979. — 327p,leaf of plate,[22]p
of plates : ill, facsims, ports ; 24cm.
List of sound discs: p.300-314. — Index.
ISBN 0-575-02562-x : £7.95
1.Ti

(B79-15555)

AL — MUSICAL LITERATURE. INSTRUMENTAL MUSIC
AL(YTGLB/WJ) — Harold E. Cook. Collection. Catalogues
Bucknell University. *Music Department*
The Harold E. Cook collection of musical instruments / [compiled
by] Jackson Hill. — Lewisburg [Penn.] : Bucknell University
Press ; London : Associated University Press, 1975. — 69p,xxxii p
of plates : ill, music ; 29cm.
This collection was bequeathed to the Music Department of Bucknell
University. — Bibl.: p.59-60. — Index.
ISBN 0-8387-1574-5 : £5.75
1.Ti 2.Cook, Harold E 3.Hill, Jackson

(B79-02987)

AL/B — Instruments
Ardley, Neil
Musical instruments / [by] Neil Ardley ; illustrated by Annette
Wade and Angus McBride. — [London] : Macmillan, 1978. —
2-23p : col ill ; 21cm. — (Fact finders)
Index.
ISBN 0-333-24465-6 : £0.95
1.Ti 2.Sr

(B79-50008)

Ardley, Neil
Musical instruments / [by] Neil Ardley ; illustrated by Annette
Wade and Angus McBride ; designed by Faulkner/Marks
Partnership. — [London] : Macmillan, 1978[i.e.1979]. — 2-23p :
col ill ; 20cm. — (Fact finders)
Originally published: 1978. — Index.
ISBN 0-333-26156-9 Pbk : £0.50
1.Ti 2.Wade, Annette 3.McBride, Angus 4.Sr

(B79-22637)

Goffe, Toni
Wonder why book of XYZ of musical instruments / written and
illustrated by Toni Goffe. — London : Transworld, 1978. — 32,[3]
p : col ill ; 28cm.
ISBN 0-552-57030-3 Sd : £0.75
1.Ti 2.XYZ of musical instruments

(B79-16838)

AL/B(XEG194) — Instruments, 1607-1800
Montagu, Jeremy
The world of baroque & classical musical instruments / [by]
Jeremy Montagu. — Newton Abbot [etc.] : David and Charles,
1979. — 136p,plate : ill(some col), music, ports ; 26cm.
Ill. on lining papers. — Bibl.: p.130-131. — Index.
ISBN 0-7153-7593-8 : £8.95 : CIP rev.
1.Ti

(B79-07466)

AL/BC — Instrument making
De Paule, Andy
Makin' your own country instruments / [by] Andy De Paule. —
New York ; London [etc.] : Van Nostrand Reinhold, 1979. — vii,
213p : ill ; 22cm.
Cover title: Country instruments : makin' your own. — Fold. sheet (of ill.)
as insert. — Index. — Contains chapters on Appalachian dulcimer,
mandolin, guitar, and violin.
ISBN 0-442-26117-9 Pbk : £4.45
1.Ti 2.Country instruments
(B79-32720)

Making musical instruments, strings and keyboard / edited by
Charles Ford ; with a foreword by Anthony Baines. — London
[etc.] : Faber, 1979. — 3-192p,[8]p of plates : ill ; 31cm.
Bibl.: p.179-188. — Index.
ISBN 0-571-10870-9 : £15.00 : CIP rev.
1.Ford, Charles
(B79-00571)

Who wants to sing? : (what it's all about) / by Two Singers [i.e.
John and Minna Patterson]. — [2nd and enlarged ed.]. —
[Belfast] ([9 Kinnaird Terrace, Antrim Rd, Belfast BT14 6BN]) :
[John Patterson], [1978]. — [16],146p : ill, music ; 21cm.
Previous ed.: Belfast : Jordan, 1974.
Pbk : £3.80
Primary classification AB/E
1.Patterson, John 2.Patterson, Minna
(B79-06707)

AL/E — Instrumental music. Performance
Choose your instrument : a beginner's guide to making music /
edited and with an introduction by Jeremy Montagu ; illustrated
by Lilla Fox. — London : Gollancz, 1979. — 144p : ill ; 21cm.
Index.
ISBN 0-575-02495-x : £2.95
1.Montagu, Jeremy
(B79-08927)

AL/E(WT/BC) — Instrumentalists. Lists. Yearbooks
Register of early music. — [London] ([Journals Department, Press
Rd, NW10 0DD]) : [Oxford University Press].
1977. — [1977]. — [2],34p ; 24cm.
Sd : £1.50
ISSN 0307-0816
(B79-14012)

ALP(WT) — Instrument(s) & piano. Lists
Hinson, Maurice
The piano in chamber ensemble. — Hassocks : Harvester Press,
Sept. 1978. — [605]p.
ISBN 0-85527-634-7 : £10.50 : CIP entry
1.Ti
(B78-23117)

AM — MUSICAL LITERATURE. ORCHESTRAL MUSIC
AM/DF — Orchestration
Piston, Walter
Orchestration / by Walter Piston. — London : Gollancz, 1978. —
ix,477p : ill, music ; 22cm.
Originally published: 1975. — Index.
ISBN 0-575-02602-2 Pbk : £3.95
1.Ti
(B79-01355)

AM/E(QB) — Orchestras. Organization
Van Horn, James
The community orchestra : a handbook for conductors, managers
and boards / [by] James Van Horn. — Westport, Conn. ;
London : Greenwood Press, 1979. — xii,127,[1]p ; 25cm.
Bibl.: p.117-120. — Index.
ISBN 0-313-20562-0 : £11.75
1.Ti
(B79-33555)

AMM/E — Symphony orchestras
Orchestra / edited by André Previn ; interviews by Michael Foss ;
photographs by Richard Adeney. — London : Macdonald and
Jane's, 1979. — 224p : ill(some col), ports(some col) ; 26cm.
Ill. on lining papers. — Index.
ISBN 0-354-04420-6 : £7.95
1.Previn, André 2.Foss, Michael 3.Adeney, Richard
(B79-35974)

AMME(X) — Symphonies. History
Stedman, Preston
The symphony / [by] Preston Stedman. — Englewood Cliffs ;
London [etc.] : Prentice-Hall, 1979. — ix,429p : ill, facsims,
music, ports ; 24cm.
Index.
ISBN 0-13-880062-6 : £9.70
1.Ti
(B79-32717)

AMT — MUSICAL LITERATURE. JAZZ
Nanry, Charles
The jazz text / [by] Charles Nanry, with Edward Berger. — New
York ; London [etc.] : D. Van Nostrand, 1979. — xi,276p : ill,
facsims, music, ports ; 23cm.
Bibl.: p.256-267. — Index.
ISBN 0-442-25908-5 Pbk : £6.70
1.Ti 2.Berger, Edward
(B79-21878)

AMT(M) — Musicians
Jazz at Ronnie Scott's / [compiled] by Kitty Grime ; photography
by Val Wilmer. — London : Hale, 1979. — 192p : ports ; 26cm.
Index.
ISBN 0-7091-6907-8 : £5.80
1.Grime, Kitty 2.Wilmer, Valerie
(B79-16103)

AMT(P) — Brown, Sandy. Biographies
Brown, Sandy
The McJazz manuscripts : a collection of the writings of Sandy
Brown / compiled and introduced by David Binns. — London
[etc.] : Faber, 1979. — 168p,[8]p of plates : facsims, music, ports ;
23cm.
List of sound discs: p.151-164. — Index.
ISBN 0-571-11319-2 : £6.95 : CIP rev.
1.Ti
(B79-10483)

AMT(P) — Charles, Ray. Biographies
Charles, Ray
Brother Ray : Ray Charles' own story / [by] Ray Charles and
David Ritz. — London : Macdonald and Jane's, 1979. — xii,340p,
[8]p of plates : 1 ill, ports ; 24cm.
Originally published: New York : Dial Press, 1978. — List of records:
p.318-340.
ISBN 0-354-04393-5 : £5.95
1.Ti 2.Ritz, David
(B79-21877)

AMT(P) — Coltrane, John. Biographies
Cole, Bill
John Coltrane / by Bill Cole. — New York : Schirmer ; London :
Collier Macmillan, 1978. — viii,264p : ill, music, ports ; 21cm.
Originally published: 1976. — Bibl.: p.241-250. — Index.
ISBN 0-02-870500-9 Pbk : £3.25
(B79-12531)

AMT(P) — Scott, Ronnie. Biographies
Scott, Ronnie
Some of my best friends are blues / [by] Ronnie Scott ; with Mike
Hennessey ; cartoons by Mel Calman. — London : W.H. Allen,
1979. — 125p : ill ; 21cm.
ISBN 0-491-02239-5 : £3.50
1.Ti 2.Hennessey, Mike
(B79-28900)

AMT(P) — Waller, Fats. Biographies
Vance, Joel
Fats Waller : his life and times / [by] Joel Vance. — London :
Robson, 1979. — [1],ix,179p,[6]p of plates,leaf of plate : ports ;
24cm.
Originally published: Chicago : Contemporary Books, 1977. — Bibl.:
p.171-172. — Index.
ISBN 0-86051-077-8 : £5.50 : CIP rev.
(B79-16104)

AMT(X) — History
Chilton, John
Jazz / [by] John Chilton ; foreword by George Melly. —
Sevenoaks : Teach Yourself Books, 1979. — [6],186p,[8]p of
plates : music, ports ; 20cm. — (Teach yourself books)
Bibl.: p.169-173. — List of sound discs: p.164-168. — Index.
ISBN 0-340-23847-x Pbk : £1.95 : CIP rev.
1.Ti 2.Sr
(B79-15559)

AMT(YT/X) — United States. History
Ostransky, Leroy
Jazz city : the impact of our cities on the development of jazz /
[by] Leroy Ostransky. — Englewood Cliffs ; London [etc.] :
Prentice-Hall, 1978. — xiv,274p ; 21cm.
'A Spectrum book'. — Bibl.: p.250-256. — List of sound discs: p.258-264. —
Index.
ISBN 0-13-509380-5 : £8.00
ISBN 0-13-509372-4 Pbk : £4.35
1.Ti
(B79-04544)

AMT(Z) — Jazz-related to psychological perspectives
Dollase, Rainer
Das Jazzpublikum : zur Sozialpsychologie einer kulturellen
Minderheit / Rainer Dollase, Michael Rüsenberg, Hans J.
Stollenwerk. — Mainz ; London [etc.] : Schott, 1978. — 234p : ill,
facsims, forms, ports ; 24cm. — (ED6813)
Bibl.: p.231-234.
Pbk : £9.60
ISBN 3-7957-2411-2
1.Ti 2.Rüsenberg, Michael 3.Stollenwerk, Hans J

(B79-10482)

AMT/FD(XPE26) — Recorded music, 1945-1970
Modern jazz, the essential records : a critical selection / by Max
Harrison ... [et al.]. — London : Aquarius Books ; Watford :
Distributed by Argus Books, 1978. — [8],140p ; 22cm.
Originally published: 1975. — Index.
Pbk : £2.90
ISBN 0-904619-01-x
1.Harrison, Max

(B79-15562)

AN — MUSICAL LITERATURE. CHAMBER MUSIC
AN(T) — Chamber music. Bibliographies of scores
Forsyth, Ella Marie
Building a chamber music collection : a descriptive guide to
published scores / by Ella Marie Forsyth. — Metuchen ;
London : Scarecrow Press ; [Folkestone] : [Distributed by Bailey
and Swinfen], 1979. — xix,191p ; 23cm.
Bibl.: p.143-165. — Index.
ISBN 0-8108-1215-0 : £6.30
1.Ti

(B79-32195)

ANXNSE — Strings & keyboard quartet. Sonatas
Hogwood, Christopher
The trio sonata / [by] Christopher Hogwood. — London : British
Broadcasting Corporation, 1979. — 128p : music ; 20cm. —
(British Broadcasting Corporation. BBC music guides)
Bibl.: p.125-126. — Index.
ISBN 0-563-17095-6 Pbk : £2.50
1.Ti 2.Sr

(B79-33556)

**AP — MUSICAL LITERATURE. INDIVIDUAL INSTRUMENTS
& INSTRUMENTAL GROUPS**
APV — Electronic music
Anderton, Craig
Electronic projects for musicians / by Craig Anderton ;
illustrations by Vesta Copestakes. — [Saratoga] : Guitar Player
Productions ; Farnham (25 East St., Farnham, Surrey) :
[Distributed by] Omnibus Book Service, [1977]. — [1],133p : ill ;
28cm.
Sound disc (20. 7ins. 33 1/3 rpm) bound in. — Originally published:
Saratoga : Guitar Player Productions, 1975.
ISBN 0-89122-011-9 Pbk : £5.95
1.Ti

(B79-09656)

Berry, M K
Electronic music and creative tape recording / by M.K. Berry. —
London : Babani, 1978. — 87p : ill ; 19cm. — (BP 51)
ISBN 0-900162-72-4 Pbk : £1.25
1.Ti

(B79-32721)

APV/BC — Electronic instruments. Manufacture
Flind, A J
Electronic projects in music / [by] A.J. Flind. — London [etc.] :
Newnes Technical Books, 1979. — [6],81p : ill(some col) ; 22cm.
— (Newnes constructors projects)
ISBN 0-408-00391-x Pbk : £2.25 : CIP rev.
1.Ti

(B79-17724)

APV/FD(WT) — Electronic music. Recorded music. Lists
Kondracki, Miroslaw
Internationale Diskographie elektronischer Musik = International
electronic music discography = Discographie internationale de la
musique electronique / [compiled by] Miroslaw Kondracki, Marta
Stankiewicz, Frits C. Weiland. — Mainz ; London [etc.] : Schott,
1979. — 174p ; 24cm.
Spine title: International electronic music discography. — German, English
and French text.
Pbk : £11.20
ISBN 3-7957-0150-3
1.Ti 2.Stankiewicz, Marta 3.Weiland, Frits C 4.International electronic
music discography

(B79-35641)

**APW — MUSICAL LITERATURE. KEYBOARD
INSTRUMENTS**
APW/E — Performance
Lewendon, Vanessa
Play keyboards today / [by] Vanessa Lewendon. — London
[etc.] : Hamlyn, 1979. — 64p : ill(chiefly col), music, ports(chiefly
col) ; 28cm.
ISBN 0-600-37201-4 : £3.50
ISBN 0-600-37180-8 Pbk : £1.95
1.Ti

(B79-24593)

AQ (TC) — Piano. Bibliographies of scores
The pianist's resource guide : piano music in print and literature on
the pianistic art. — Park Ridge, Ill. [etc.] : Pallma Music ;
London (20 Earlham St., WC2H 9LN) : [Distributed by]
Breitkopf and Härtel (London) Ltd.
1978-79 / [by] Joseph Rezits, Gerald Deatsman. — 1978. — xi,1491p ;
30cm.
Index.
ISBN 0-8497-7800-x Pbk : £32.50

1.Rezits, Joseph 2.Deatsman, Gerald

(B79-24852)

AQ/B — Piano. Instruments
Shead, Herbert A
The anatomy of the piano / [by] Herbert A. Shead ; illustrated by
the author. — Old Woking (The Gresham Press, Old Woking,
Surrey) : Unwin Brothers Ltd, 1978. — [8],177p : ill ; 24cm.
Bibl.: p.175-177.
ISBN 0-905418-20-4 Pbk : £8.50
1.Ti

(B79-15560)

AQ/B(XFWK122) — Piano. Instruments, 1730-1851
Harding, Rosamond Evelyn Mary
The piano-forte : its history traced to the Great Exhibition of
1851 / by Rosamond E.M. Harding. — 2nd ed. — Old Woking
(Unwin Brothers Ltd, The Gresham Press, Old Woking, Surrey) :
Gresham Books, 1978. — xxii,450p,[32] leaves of plates(1
fold),[10]p of plates : ill, music, 2 ports ; 24cm.
English text, some French and German notes. — Previous ed.: Cambridge :
Cambridge University Press, 1933. — Bibl.: p.311-316. — Index.
ISBN 0-905418-31-x : £11.50
1.Ti

(B79-14922)

AQ/BC(P) — Piano. Double keyboard piano. Makers. Emanuel Moór
Shead, Herbert A
The history of the Emanuel Moór double keyboard piano / [by]
Herbert A. Shead. — [London?] : Emanuel Moór Double
Keyboard Piano Trust ; Old Woking (The Gresham Press, Old
Woking, Surrey GU22 9LH) : Distributed by Unwin Brothers
Ltd, 1978. — 310p,[2]fold of plates : ill, facsim, music, ports ;
24cm.
Spine title: The Emanuel Moór double keyboard piano. — Includes reprints
of articles by others, written between 1921 and 1959. — Bibl. — Index.
ISBN 0-9506023-0-2 Pbk : £15.00
1.Ti 2.Emanuel Moór Double Keyboard Piano Trust

(B79-08930)

AQ/BT — Piano. Maintenance
Kennedy, Kenneth Thomas
Piano action repairs and maintenance / [by] K.T.Kennedy. —
London : Kaye and Ward [etc.], 1979. — 101p : ill ; 24cm.
ISBN 0-7182-1205-3 : £7.95
1.Ti

(B79-11135)

AQ/E(P) — Gould, Glenn. Biographies
Payzant, Geoffrey
Glenn Gould : music & mind / [by] Geoffrey Payzant. —
Toronto ; London [etc.] : Van Nostrand Reinhold, 1978. — xiii,
192p,[16]p of plates : ports ; 24cm.
Bibl.: p.173-175. — List of works: p.176. — List of films: p.176. — List of
sound discs: p.177-182. — Index.
ISBN 0-442-29802-1 : £10.45

(B79-16841)

AQ/E(P) — Schnabel, Artur
Wolff, Konrad
Schnabel's interpretation of piano music / [by] Konrad Wolff. —
2nd ed. — London : Faber, 1979. — [2],187p : music, port ;
19cm.
Previous ed.: published as 'The teaching of Artur Schnabel'. 1972. — Index.
ISBN 0-571-10029-5 Pbk : £2.50
1.Ti 2.Teaching of Artur Schnabel

(B79-36916)

AQ/E(VC) — Piano. Performance
Bastien, James W
  How to teach piano successfully / by James W. Bastien. — 2nd
  ed. — Park Ridge, Ill. : General Words and Music [etc.] ; London
  (20 Earlham St., WC2H 9LN) : [Distributed by] Breitkopf and
  Hartel (London) Ltd, 1977. — [5],x,574p : ill, forms, music,
  ports ; 25cm.
  Previous ed.: Park Ridge, Ill. : General Words and Music, 1973. — Bibl.:
  p.475-487. — Index.
  ISBN 0-8497-6109-3 Pbk : £7.90
  1.Ti
                                                                (B79-25333)

AQPHXJ — Ragtime
Farmer, Paul
  Ragtime & blues / [by] Paul Farmer. — London : Longman,
  1979. — 24p : ill, facsims, map, music, ports ; 23cm. —
  (Longman music topics)
  Text on inside covers.
  ISBN 0-582-21579-x Sd : £0.65
  Also classified at AKDW/HHW
  1.Ti
                                                                (B79-36912)

AQR/E — Harpsichord. Performance
Schott, Howard
  Playing the harpsichord / [by] Howard Schott. — [1st ed.,
  reprinted] ; with a new introduction by the author. — London
  [etc.] : Faber, 1979. — 3-223p,8p of plates : ill, music ; 21cm.
  This ed. originally published: 1971. — List of music: p.215-216. — Index.
  ISBN 0-571-11375-3 Pbk : £2.95 : CIP rev.
  1.Ti
                                                                (B79-05250)

AR(QB/DFEB/X) — Bristol & District Organists' Association.
                                           History
Lawrance, F W J
  The Bristol and District Organists' Association : a brief history /
  by F.W.J. Lawrance. — [Weston-super-Mare] ([57 Burnham
  Drive, Bleadon Hill, Weston-super-Mare, Avon BS24 9LF]) : [The
  author], 1979. — 51,[13]p : ill, facsims, ports ; 21cm.
  Sd : £1.00
  1.Ti
                                                                (B79-27792)

AR(YC/VP/Q/BC) — Organists. Great Britain. Royal College of
                                           Organists. Yearbooks
Royal College of Organists
  Year book / Royal College of Organists. — [London]
  ([Kensington Gore, SW7 2QS]) : [The College].
  1978-1979. — [1978]. — [1],x,41p : ill, port ; 30cm.
  Sd : £1.15
  ISSN 0080-4320
  1.Ti

AR/E(P) — Thalben-Ball, George. Biographies
Rennert, Jonathan
  George Thalben-Ball. — Newton Abbot : David and Charles,
  Sept. 1979. — [144]p.
  ISBN 0-7153-7863-5 : £5.95 : CIP entry
                                                                (B79-21879)

ARW — MUSICAL LITERATURE. STRING INSTRUMENTS
ARW/E(VC) — Bowed string instruments. Performance. Teaching
Young, Phyllis
  Playing the string game : strategies for teaching cello and strings /
  by Phyllis Young ; illustrations by Sally Blakemore. — Austin ;
  London : University of Texas Press, 1978. — xii,102p : ill ; 29cm.
  Index.
  ISBN 0-292-73814-5 : £10.50
  ISBN 0-292-73815-3 Pbk : £7.00
  1.Ti
                                                                (B79-20274)

AS/E(P) — Menuhin, Yehudi. Biographies
Menuhin, Yehudi
  Unfinished journey / [by] Yehudi Menuhin. — London : Futura
  Publications, 1978. — 508p,[16]p of plates : music, ports ; 18cm.
  Originally published: London : Macdonald and Jane's, 1977. — Index.
  ISBN 0-7088-1329-1 Pbk : £1.60
  1.Ti
                                                                (B79-11136)

ASQQ/B — Viola d'amore. Instruments
Danks, Harry
  The viola d'amore / by Harry Danks. — 2nd ed. — Halesowen (7
  Summit Gardens, Halesowen, West Midlands B63 4SP) : Stephen
  Bonner, 1979. — 128p,[14]p of plates : ill, music, 2 ports(1 col,
  tipped in) ; 31cm.
  'Casadesus centenary edition' - Limited ed. of 500 numbered copies. —
  Previous ed.: Halesowen : Bois de Boulogne, 1976. — Bibl.: p.123-127. —
  Index.
  Unpriced
  1.Ti
                                                                (B79-09707)

AT — MUSICAL LITERATURE. PLUCKED STRING
               INSTRUMENTS
ATS/E — Guitar. Performance
Butterfield, Arthur
  Play guitar today / [by] Arthur and Graham Butterfield. —
  London [etc.] : Hamlyn, 1979. — 64p : col ill, music, ports(chiefly
  col) ; 28cm.
  ISBN 0-600-37200-6 : £3.50
  ISBN 0-600-37178-6 Pbk : £1.95
  1.Ti 2.Butterfield, Graham
                                                                (B79-22642)

Laine, Denny
  Denny Laine's guitar book. — London : G. Whizzard : Deutsch,
  1979. — 3-109,[1]p : ill(some col), ports ; 30cm.
  Text, ports on lining papers.
  ISBN 0-233-97101-7 : £4.95
  1.Guitar book
                                                                (B79-33558)

ATSPV/B(X) — Electric guitars. History
Brosnac, Donald
  The electric guitar : its history and construction / by Donald
  Brosnac. — London [etc.] : Omnibus Press, 1975. — 96p : ill,
  ports ; 28cm.
  Bibl.: p.90.
  ISBN 0-86001-491-6 Pbk : £3.50
  1.Ti
                                                                (B79-33557)

ATSPV/E — Electric guitar. Performance
Butterfield, Graham
  Play rock guitar today / [by] Graham Butterfield. — London
  [etc.] : Hamlyn, 1979. — 64p : ill(chiefly col), music, ports(chiefly
  col) ; 28cm.
  ISBN 0-600-37202-2 : £3.50
  ISBN 0-600-37181-6 Pbk : £1.95
  1.Ti
                                                                (B79-24594)

AU — MUSICAL LITERATURE. WIND INSTRUMENTS
AUMM/E(QB/P) — Royal Artillery Band. Bandsmen. Mason, H.B.
                                           Biographies
Mason, H B
  Memoirs of a gunner bandsman, 1907-1932 / [by] H.B. Mason. —
  Orpington : The author ; [Ilfracombe] : [Distributed by Stockwell],
  1978. — 31p,[2]p of plates : 2 ports ; 18cm.
  ISBN 0-7223-1185-0 Pbk : Unpriced
  1.Ti
                                                                (B79-06708)

AVYR/BT — Irish bagpipes. Maintenance
Garvin, Wilbert
  The Irish bagpipes : their construction and maintenance / [by]
  Wilbert Garvin ; foreword by Breandán Breathnach. — Belfast :
  Blackstaff Press [for] Na Píobairí Uileann, 1978. — xiv,40,[1]p :
  ill ; 30cm.
  Bibl.: p.40.
  ISBN 0-85640-149-8 Pbk : £3.95
  1.Ti 2.Píobairí Uileann, Na
                                                                (B79-17765)

AWM(X) — Brass band. History
Taylor, Arthur Richard
  Brass band / [by] Arthur R. Taylor. — London [etc.] :
  Hart-Davis MacGibbon, 1979. — x,356p : ill, ports ; 24cm.
  Bibl.: p.338-344. — List of sound discs: p.323-332. — Index.
  ISBN 0-246-11082-1 : £10.00
  1.Ti
                                                                (B79-06709)

AX — MUSICAL LITERATURE. PERCUSSION
               INSTRUMENTS
AXQ/E — Drums. Performance
Brown, Ashley
  Play drums today / [by] Ashley Brown. — London [etc.] :
  Hamlyn, 1979. — 64p : ill(chiefly col), music, ports(chiefly col) ;
  28cm.
  ISBN 0-600-37199-9 : £3.50
  ISBN 0-600-37179-4 Pbk : £1.95
  1.Ti
                                                                (B79-24596)

AXSR(YDDEBO) — Church bells. Essex. Boreham. St. Andrew's Church
Smith, William Joseph Thomas
    Bells, clocks & ringers / [by William J.T. Smith]. — [Chelmsford] ([Boreham Vicarage, Chelmsford CM3 3EG]) : [The author], 1979. — 48[i.e.57]p : ill, facsims, geneal tables ; 26cm. — (Boreham histories ; no.5)
    Bibl.: p.46. — Index.
    Pbk : £0.50
    1.Ti 2.Sr

(B79-31934)

AXSR/E(QB/X) — Cambridge University Guild of Change Ringers. History
Cook, William T
    The Cambridge University Guild of Change Ringers, 1879-1979 : a centenary history / by William T. Cook. — [Cambridge] ([c/o B.D. Threlfall, 106 High St., Bottisham, Cambridge, Cambs.]) : C.U.G.C.R., 1979. — [2],45p ; 21cm.
    Sd : Unpriced
    1.Ti 2.Cambridge University Guild of Change Ringers

(B79-30802)

B — INDIVIDUAL COMPOSERS
BAPACP — Aman, David. The golden bond. Librettos
Barrow, Kenneth
    The golden bond : a spectacular revue / devised and written by Kenneth Barrow to celebrate the Golden Jubilee of the National Union of Townswomen's Guilds ; original music by David Aman. — London (2 Cromwell Place, SW7 2JG) : National Union of Townswomen's Guilds, 1978. — [8],68 leaves : plan ; 28cm.
    Pbk : £1.50
    1.Ti 2.Aman, David 3.National Union of Townswomen's Guilds

(B79-27787)

BARGAC — Argento, Dominic. Miss Havisham's fire. Librettos
Olon-Scrymgeour, John
    Miss Havisham's fire : opera in two acts / [music by] Dominick Argento ; libretto (after Dickens) by John Olon-Scrymgeour. — [London] : Boosey and Hawkes, [1979]. — 40p ; 27cm.
    Sd : £1.00
    1.Ti 2.Argento, Dominick

(B79-26551)

BBC(N) — Bach, Johann Sebastian. Biographies
    Johann Sebastian Bach : life, times, influence / edited by Barbara Schwendowius and Wolfgang Dömling ; [translated from the German by John Coombs, Lionel Salter, Gaynor Nitz]. — Kassel [etc.] ; London ([17 Bucklersbury, Hitchin, Herts. SG5 1BB]) : Bärenreiter, 1977. — 179p : ill(some col), facsims(1 col), geneal table, maps, music, plan, ports(some col) ; 31x32cm.
    'The essays making up this collection were all written in 1974 and 1975. They first appeared as separate articles, each with its own series of illustrations, in the booklets accompanying Archiv Produktion's eleven-page Bach Edition' - Editors' note. — Bibl.: p.172-173. — Index.
    £21.12
    ISBN 3-7618-0589-6
    1.Schwendowius, Barbara 2.Dömling, Wolfgang

(B79-11127)

BBCADD/LK — Bach, Johann Sebastian. Passions
Steinitz, Paul
    Bach's passions / [by] Paul Steinitz. — London : Elek, 1979. — ix,137p : facsim, music ; 23cm. — (Masterworks of choral music)
    Facsim. on lining papers. — Bibl.: p.131-132. — List of sound discs: p.133-134. — Index.
    ISBN 0-236-40132-7 : £5.95
    1.Ti 2.Sr

(B79-14916)

BBCN — Baines, William
Carpenter, Roger
    Goodnight to Flamboro' : the life and music of William Baines / by Roger Carpenter ; with decorations by Richard A. Bell. — Rickmansworth (22 Pheasants Way, Rickmansworth, Herts.) : Triad Press, 1977. — 132p : ill, music, port ; 30cm. — (Triad Press bibliographical series ; no.7)
    Bibl.: p.124-126. — List of sound recordings: p.126-127. — List of works: p.116-123.
    ISBN 0-902070-22-3 Pbk : £6.95 : CIP rev.
    1.Ti

(B77-21345)

BBGAC — Bartók, Béla. Bluebeard's castle. Librettos
Ország-Land, Thomas
    Prince Bluebeard's castle : a libretto / adapted from the Hungarian of Béla Balázs, and The splendid stags : a Bartók companion / by Thomas Ország-Land ; prints by Nicholas Parry. — [London] ([Top Floor, 64 Highgate High St., N6 5HX]) : [The author], 1978. — 47p : ill ; 21cm.
    '... new performing scripts of the texts of Béla Bartók's "Prince Bluebeard's Castle" and "Cantata Profana" ...' - note.
    ISBN 0-906057-07-8 Sd : £2.10
    1.Ti 2.Balázs, Béla. Kékszakállú herceg vara. Adaptations 3.Bartók, Béla

(B79-30800)

BBJ(N) — Beethoven, Ludwig van. Biographies
Kendall, Alan, *b.1939*
    Beethoven and his world / [by] Alan Kendall ; [illustrators Roger Payne, Roger Phillips]. — London : Ward Lock, Oct. 1979. — [32]p. — (Great masters) ([Kingfisher library])
    Bibl.: p.29. — List of works: p.28. — Index.
    ISBN 0-7063-5867-8 : £2.95 : CIP rev.
    1.Ti 2.Payne, Roger 3.Phillips, Roger 4.Sr5.Sr

(B79-30252)

BBJ(QVB) — Beethoven, Ludwig van. Autograph manuscripts. Sketchbooks
Nottebohm, Gustav
    Two Beethoven sketchbooks : a description with musical extracts / by Gustav Nottebohm ; translated [from the German] by Jonathan Katz ; with a foreword by Denis Matthews. — London : Gollancz, 1979. — xi,130p : music ; 23cm.
    Translation of: 'Zwei Skizzenbücher von Beethoven aus den Jahren 1801 bis 1803'. Neue Ausg., Leipzig : s.n., 1924. — Index.
    ISBN 0-575-02583-2 : £4.95
    1.Ti 2.Beethoven, Ludwig von

(B79-14912)

BBJADG — Beethoven, Ludwig van. Missa solemnis
Fiske, Roger
    Beethoven's Missa solemnis / [by] Roger Fiske. — London : Elek, 1979. — [7],123p : facsim, music ; 23cm. — (Masterworks of choral music)
    Facsim. on lining papers. — Bibl.: p.116-117. — List of sound discs: p.118-119. — Index.
    ISBN 0-236-40146-7 : £5.95
    1.Ti 2.Sr

(B79-14016)

BBJAMME — Beethoven, Ludwig van. Symphonies
Pike, Lionel
    Beethoven, Sibelius and the 'profound logic'. — London : Athlone Press, Nov.78. — [264]p.
    ISBN 0-485-11178-0 : £12.95 : CIP entry
    Also classified at BSHAMME
    1.Ti

(B78-37102)

BBKR — Berg, Alban
Jarman, Douglas
    The music of Alban Berg. — London : Faber, Jan. 1979. — [272] p.
    ISBN 0-571-10956-x : £18.00 : CIP entry
    1.Ti

(B78-37095)

BBMM(TC) — Bernstein, Leonard. Bibliographies of scores
Gottlieb, Jack
    Leonard Bernstein : a complete catalogue of his works / compiled by Jack Gottlieb. — New York : Amberson Enterprises ; New York ; London : [Distributed by] Boosey and Hawkes, 1978. — 68p : ill, facsim, ports ; 25cm.
    'Celebrating His 60th birthday, August 25, 1978'. — Bibl.: p.60. — Index.
    ISBN 0-913932-40-x Sd : £2.50

(B79-06192)

BBRO — Boulez, Pierre
Griffiths, Paul
    Boulez / [by] Paul Griffiths. — London [etc.] : Oxford University Press, 1978 [i.e. 1979]. — 64p : music ; 22cm. — (Oxford studies of composers ; (16))
    Bibl.: p.64. — List of works: p.62-63.
    ISBN 0-19-315442-0 Pbk : £3.50
    1.Sr

(B79-18562)

BBS(WJ) — Boyce, William. Exhibitions
Bodleian Library
    William Boyce, 1711-1779 : a bicentenary exhibition / [Bodleian Library]. — Oxford ([Broad St., Oxford OX1 3BG]) : The Library, 1979. — [2],15p ; 21cm.
    [Catalogue of] ... an exhibition of ... works from ... the Bodleian holdings of Boyce's manuscripts and printed material ...' - Preface.
    ISBN 0-900177-69-1 Sd : £0.15

(B79-26827)

BBT(N) — Brahms, Johannes. Biographies
McLeish, Kenneth
    Brahms / [by] Kenneth and Valerie McLeish. — London : Heinemann, 1979. — [5],90p : ill, facsims, music, ports ; 21cm. — (Composers and their world)
    Index.
    ISBN 0-434-95128-5 : £2.50
    1.McLeish, Valerie 2.Sr

(B79-27782)

BBTNADX — Brian, Havergal. Gothic symphony
Truscott, Harold
Havergal Brian's 'Gothic symphony' : two studies / by Harold
Truscott, Paul Rapoport ; with How the 'Gothic symphony' came
to be written, by Havergal Brian. — Potters Bar (33 Coopers Rd,
Little Heath, Potters Bar, Herts. EN6 1JQ) : Havergal Brian
Society, 1978. — 87p : ill, music, ports ; 30cm.
ISBN 0-9505185-1-4 Pbk : £6.95(£4.75 to members of the Havergal Brian
Society)
1.Ti 2.Rapoport, Paul 3.Havergal Brian Society 4.Gothic symphony
(B79-10481)

BBU — Britten, Benjamin. *Baron Britten*
Evans, Peter, *b.1929*
The music of Benjamin Britten. — London : Dent, Feb. 1979. —
[560]p.
ISBN 0-460-04350-1 : £15.00 : CIP entry
1.Ti
(B79-00563)

Benjamin Britten, 1913-1976 : pictures from a life : a pictorial
biography / compiled by Donald Mitchell with the assistance of
John Evans. — London [etc.] : Faber, 1978. — viii,[192],16p :
ill(some col), facsims, chiefly ports(some col) ; 26cm.
Ill. on lining papers. — Bibl.: p.12. — Index.
ISBN 0-571-11261-7 : £15.00 : CIP rev.
1.Mitchell, Donald 2.Evans, John, b.1953
(B78-29832)

BBUAC — Britten, Benjamin, Baron Britten
The **operas** of Benjamin Britten : the complete librettos illustrated
with designs of the first productions / edited by David Herbert
... ; preface by Peter Pears. — London : H. Hamilton, 1979. —
xxxi,384p : ill(some col) ; 29cm.
Bibl.: p.377. — Index.
ISBN 0-241-10256-1 : £30.00
1.Herbert, David
(B79-34989)

BBUE — Bruckner, Anton
Newlin, Dika
Bruckner, Mahler, Schoenberg / [by] Dika Newlin. — [Revised
ed.]. — London : Boyars [Distributed by Calder and Boyars],
1979. — xi,308p : music ; 25cm.
This ed. originally published: New York : Norton, 1978. — Bibl.: p.293-301.
— Index.
ISBN 0-7145-2658-4 : £9.95
Also classified at BME; BSET
1.Ti
(B79-05247)

BBVT(N) — Butterworth, George. Biographies
Angus-Butterworth, Lionel Milner
Sir Alex K. Butterworth, LL.B. (1854-1946) and Captain G.S.K.
Butterworth, M.C.,B.A. (1885-1916) / by L.M.
Angus-Butterworth. — [Buxton] ([Old Hall Hotel, Buxton,
Derbyshire]) : [The author], 1979. — 12p : geneal table, 2 ports ;
22cm. — (Belfield papers ; no.5)
Sd : £0.50
1.Ti 2.Sr
(B79-27781)

BCE(N) — Chopin, Frédéric. Biographies
Marek, George Richard
Chopin / [by] George R. Marek, Maria Gordon-Smith. —
London : Weidenfeld and Nicolson, 1979. — xi,289p,[8]p of
plates : ill, ports ; 25cm.
Originally published: New York : Harper and Row, 1978. — Bibl.:
p.277-282. — Index.
ISBN 0-297-77616-9 : £8.50
1.Gordon-Smith, Maria
(B79-11134)

BCE(N) — Chopin, Frédéric. Biographies
Orga, Ateş
Chopin. — Revised 2nd ed. — Tunbridge Wells : Midas Books,
Mar. 1978. — [144]p.
Previous ed.: 1976.
ISBN 0-85936-116-0 : £6.50 : CIP entry
ISBN 0-85936-127-6 Pbk : £3.25
(B78-05411)

Zamoyski, Adam
Chopin : a biography / [by] Adam Zamoyski. — London :
Collins, 1979. — 336p,[16]p of plates : ill, music, ports ; 24cm.
Bibl.: p.320-324. — Index.
ISBN 0-00-216089-7 : £7.95
(B79-32719)

BCMTADW — Cotton, Reynell. Hambledon Cricket Song
Knight, Ronald David
Hambledon's cricket glory / [by Ronald David Knight]. —
Weymouth (40 Abbotsbury Rd, Weymouth, Dorset DT4 0AE) :
The author.
Vol.6 : The Hambledon cricket song. — 2nd (revised) ed. — 1977. — 28,7p,
[4]p of plates : 1 ill, facsim, geneal table, 2 ports ; 21cm.
Song on fold. sheet ([33]p.;music) as insert. — Song by Reynell Cotton. —
Previous ed.: 1975. — Bibl.: p.26.
ISBN 0-903769-06-9 Pbk : £0.50
1.Ti 2.Cotton, Reynell
(B79-29607)

BDJ(N) — Debussy, Claude. Biographies
Lockspeiser, Edward
Debussy : his life and mind / [by] Edward Lockspeiser. — 2nd
ed. — Cambridge [etc.] : Cambridge University Press.
In 2 vols.
Vol.1 : 1862-1902. — 1978. — xvi,275p,leaf of plate,[16]p of plates : ill,
geneal table, music, ports ; 23cm.
This ed. originally published: London : Cassell, 1966. — Bibl.: p.245-255. —
Index.
ISBN 0-521-22053-x : £12.00
ISBN 0-521-29341-3 Pbk : £3.95
(B79-20263)

Lockspeiser, Edward
Debussy : his life and mind / [by] Edward Lockspeiser. —
Cambridge [etc.] : Cambridge University Press.
In 2 vols.
Vol.2 : 1902-1918. — 1978. — xiv,337p,leaf of plate,[16]p of plates : ill,
music, ports ; 23cm.
Originally published: London : Cassell, 1965. — Bibl.: p.301-311. — List of
works: p.287-293. — Index.
ISBN 0-521-22054-8 : £15.00
ISBN 0-521-29342-1 Pbk : £4.95
(B79-20264)

BDJ(Z) — Debussy, Claude - related to Richard Wagner
Holloway, Robin
Debussy and Wagner / [by] Robin Holloway. — London (48
Great Marlborough St., W1V 2BN) : Ernst Eulenburg Ltd, 1979.
— 235p : music ; 23cm.
ISBN 0-903873-25-7 : £5.50
ISBN 0-903873-26-5 Pbk : £4.00
Also classified at BWC(Z)
1.Ti
(B79-35970)

BDX(N) — Dvořák, Antonín. Biographies
Clapham, John, *b.1908*
Dvořák. — Newton Abbot : David and Charles, Sept. 1979. —
[2245]p.
ISBN 0-7153-7790-6 : £8.95 : CIP entry
(B79-22636)

BEP(B) — Elgar, Sir Edward, 1st bart. Periodicals
Elgar Society
The Elgar Society journal. — [New Barnet] ([104 Crescent Rd,
New Barnet, Herts.]) : ['The Elgar Society Journal'].
Supersedes: Elgar Society newsletter, new series.
[Vol.1, no.1]- ; Jan. 1979-. — [1979]-. — ports ; 21cm.
Three times a year. — 32p. in 1st issue.
Sd : Free to members
ISSN 0143-1269
(B79-23400)

BFB — Falla, Manuel de
James, Burnett
Manuel de Falla and the Spanish musical renaissance / by Burnett
James. — London : Gollancz, 1979. — 172p,[8]p of plates :
ports ; 22cm.
Bibl.: p.161-165. — Index.
ISBN 0-575-02645-6 : £6.95
1.Ti
(B79-16837)

BFD — Fauré, Gabriel
Orledge, Robert
Gabriel Fauré / [by] Robert Orledge. — London (48 Great
Marlborough St., W1V 2BN) : Eulenberg Books, 1979. — xv,
367p,[31]p of plates : ill, facsims, music, ports ; 24cm.
Bibl.: p.330-344. — List of works: p.272-326. — Index.
ISBN 0-903873-40-0 : £7.00
ISBN 0-903873-41-9 Pbk : £5.50
(B79-35971)

BGK — Glazunov, Aleksandr Konstantinovich
Steane, Leonard
Glazounov : an assessment of the value of Glazounov's orchestral
music, with tributes from various sources / [by] Leonard Steane.
— [1st ed.] reprinted and revised. — Coventry (57 Burns Rd,
Coventry, Warwickshire CV2 4AD) : The author, 1979. — [15]p ;
22cm.
This ed. originally published: 1974.
Sd : £0.50
(B79-27791)

BHE(N) — Haydn, Joseph. Biographies
Butterworth, Neil
Haydn. — Tunbridge Wells : Midas Books, Mar. 1978. — [141]p.
Originally published: 1977.
ISBN 0-85936-030-x : £6.50 : CIP entry
ISBN 0-85936-128-4 Pbk : £3.25

(B78-05400)

BJRP(N) — Joplin, Scott. Biographies
Haskins, James
Scott Joplin. — London : Robson Books, Jan. 1979. — [264]p.
Originally published: Garden City, N.Y. : Doubleday, 1978.
ISBN 0-86051-058-1 : £4.50 : CIP entry
1.Benson, Kathleen

(B78-38608)

BKDEACM — Kander, John. Chicago. Librettos
Ebb, Fred
Chicago : a musical vaudeville / book by Fred Ebb and Bob
Fosse ; music by John Kander ; lyrics by Fred Ebb. — New
York ; London [etc.] : French, [1976]. — 123p : 2 plans ; 22cm.
— (French's musical library)
'Based on the play "Chicago" by Maurine Dallas Watkins'. — Nine men, 10
women.
ISBN 0-573-68081-7 Sd : £1.65
1.Fosse, Bob 2.Kander, John 3.Watkins, Maurine Dallas. Chicago.
Adaptations

(B79-06704)

BME — Mahler, Gustav
Newlin, Dika
Bruckner, Mahler, Schoenberg / [by] Dika Newlin. — [Revised
ed.]. — London : Boyars : [Distributed by Calder and Boyars],
1979. — xi,308p : music ; 25cm.
This ed. originally published: New York : Norton, 1978. — Bibl.: p.293-301.
— Index.
ISBN 0-7145-2658-4 : £9.95
Primary classification BBUE
1.Ti

(B79-05247)

BME(N) — Mahler, Gustav. Biographies
Mahler, Gustav
Selected letters of Gustav Mahler / the original edition selected by
Alma Mahler, enlarged and edited with new introduction,
illustrations and notes by Knud Martner ; translated from the
original German by Eithne Wilkins & Ernst Kaiser and Bill
Hopkins. — London [etc.] : Faber, 1979. — 3-480p,[8]p of plates :
2 ill, facsims, ports ; 24cm.
Translation and revision of: 'Briefe, 1879-1971' / edited by Alma Mahler.
Berlin : Paul Zsolnay, 1924. — Bibl.: p.23-24. — Index.
ISBN 0-571-08643-8 : £15.00 : CIP rev.
1.Mahler, Alma 2.Martner, Knud

(B79-14911)

BMN — Monteverdi, Claudio
Stevens, Denis
Monteverdi : sacred, secular and occasional music / [by] Denis
Stevens. — Rutherford [etc.] : Fairleigh Dickinson University
Press ; London : Associated University Presses, 1978. — 147p :
music ; 22cm.
Bibl.: p.139-141. — Index.
ISBN 0-8386-1937-1 : £4.95

(B79-32715)

BMS(N) — Mozart, Wolfgang Amadeus. Biographies
Ottaway, Hugh
Mozart / [by] Hugh Ottaway. — London : Orbis Books, 1979. —
208p : ill(some col), facsims, music, ports(some col) ; 26cm.
Facsim. on lining papers. — Bibl.: p.203-204. — Index.
ISBN 0-85613-069-9 : £10.00

(B79-21148)

Woodford, Peggy
Mozart. — Tunbridge Wells : Midas Books, Mar. 1978. — [144]p.
Originally published: 1977.
ISBN 0-85936-050-4 : £6.50 : CIP entry
ISBN 0-85936-128-4 Pbk : £3.25

(B78-05401)

BMS(TC) — Mozart, Wolfgang Amadeus. Bibliographies of scores
Wiener Stadt- und Landesbibliothek
Verzeichnis der Schubert-Handschriften in der Musiksammlung
der Wiener Stadt- und Landesbibliothek / [von] Ernst Hilmar. —
Kassel [etc.] ; London ([17 Bucklersbury, Hutchin, Herts. SG5
1BB]) : Bärenreiter [for] the International Association of Music
Libraries and the International Musicological Society, 1978. — xv,
144p,105[i.e.135]p of plates : ill, music ; 27cm. — (Catalogus
musicus ; 8)
Index.
Pbk : £28.05
ISBN 3-7618-0346-x
1.Ti 2.Hilmar, Ernst 3.Sr

(B79-10755)

**BMSAQPE/E — Mozart, Wolfgang Amadeus. Sonatas.
          Interpretation**
Richner, Thomas
Interpreting Mozart's piano sonatas / by Thomas Richner. —
London : Paterson's Publications, 1978. — viii,96p : 1 ill, music,
ports ; 22cm.
Originally published: as 'Orientation for interpreting Mozart's piano sonatas'.
New York : Bureau of Publications, Teacher's College, Columbia University,
1953. — Bibl.: p.95-96.
Pbk : £2.00
1.Ti

(B79-04545)

BNEACN — Nield, David. Helen come home. Librettos
Taylor, Jeremy James
Helen comes home, or, Achilles the heel. — London : French,
July 1979. — [48]p.
ISBN 0-573-15004-4 : £1.50 : CIP entry
1.Ti 2.Nield, David

(B79-17762)

BN1(N) — Nielsen, Carl. Biographies
Simpson, Robert
Carl Nielsen : symphonist / [by] Robert Simpson ; biographical
appendix by Torben Meyer. — Completely revised ed. —
London : Kahn and Averill, 1979. — 260p : facsims, music,
ports ; 23cm.
Previous ed.: London : Dent, 1952. — List of works: p.251-257. — Index.
ISBN 0-900707-46-1 : £6.95 : CIP rev.

(B79-13062)

BPDRACM — Parr, Andrew. Big Al. Librettos
Gardiner, John
'Big Al' : a new musical based on the life and times of the
infamous Chicago gangster Al Capone / book & lyrics by John
Gardiner ; music by Andrew Parr. — [Hitchin] ([6 Friday
Furlong, Hitchin, Herts. SG5 2ND]) : [Gardiner-Parr Musicals],
[1977]. — [5],51 leaves : ill, map ; 30cm.
Music available separately.
Pbk : £1.50
1.Ti

(B79-31928)

BPO — Poulenc, Francis
Audel, Stéphane
My friends and myself : conversations [with] Francis Poulenc /
assembled by Stéphane Audel ; translated [from the French] by
James Harding. — London : Dobson, 1978. — 152p,leaf of
plate,[8]p of plates : 1 ill, ports ; 23cm.
Translation of: 'Moi et mes amis'. Genève : La Palatine, 1963. — Index.
ISBN 0-234-77251-4 : £4.95
1.Ti 2.Poulenc, Francis

(B78-39780)

BPPAMBN — Prokofiev, Sergei. Peter and the wolf. Stories
Voigt, Erna
Peter and the wolf / adapted from the musical tale by Sergei
Prokofiev [by] Erna Voigt ; [translated from the German]. —
Glasgow [etc.] : Blackie, 1979. — [28]p : ill(chiefly col), music ;
25x27cm.
This adaptation published: in German. Vienna : Betz, 1979.
ISBN 0-216-90875-2 : £3.75
1.Prokof'ev, Sergeĭ Sergeevich. Peter and the wolf. Adaptations

(B79-35567)

BQI(N) — Quilter, Roger. Biographies
Hold, Trevor
The walled-in garden : a study of the songs of Roger Quilter
(1877-1953) / [by] Trevor Hold. — Rickmansworth (22 Pheasants
Way, Rickmansworth, Herts.) : Triad Press, 1978. — 72p :
facsims, music, ports ; 30cm. — (Triad Press bibliographical
series ; no.8)
Bibl.: p.55-56. — List of works: p.48-51. — List of sound discs: p.57-60. —
Index.
Pbk : £4.95
1.Ti

(B79-05249)

BSET — Schoenberg, Arnold
Newlin, Dika
Bruckner, Mahler, Schoenberg / [by] Dika Newlin. — [Revised
ed.]. — London : Boyars : [Distributed by Calder and Boyars],
1979. — xi,308p : music ; 25cm.
This ed. originally published: New York : Norton, 1978. — Bibl.: p.293-301.
— Index.
ISBN 0-7145-2658-4 : £9.95
Primary classification BBUE
1.Ti

(B79-05247)

BSF(N) — Schubert, Franz. Biographies
McLeish, Kenneth
Schubert / [by] Kenneth and Valerie McLeish. — London :
Heinemann, 1979. — [5],82p : ill, facsims, music, ports ; 21cm. —
(Composers and their world)
Index.
ISBN 0-434-95127-7 : £2.50
1.Ti 2.McLeish, Valerie 3.Sr

(B79-26550)

BSF(TE) — Schubert, Franz. Bibliographies of manuscripts
Wiener Stadt- und Landesbibliothek
Verzeichnis der Schubert-Handschriften in der Musiksammlung
der Wiener Stadt- und Landesbibliothek / [von] Ernst Hilmar. —
Kassel [etc.] ; London ([17 Bucklersbury, Hutchin, Herts. SG5
1BB]) : Bärenreiter [for] the International Association of Music
Libraries and the International Musicological Society, 1978. — xv,
144p,105[i.e.135]p of plates : ill, music ; 27cm. — (Catalogus
musicus ; 8)
Index.
Pbk : £28.05
ISBN 3-7618-0346-x
1.Ti 2.Hilmar, Ernst 3.Sr

(B79-10755)

BSGNHACM — Sharkey, Jack. Operetta! Librettos
Sharkey, Jack
Operetta! : (a stampede through nostalgia) / book, music and
lyrics by Jack Sharkey and Dave Reiser. — New York ; London
[etc.] : French, 1979. — 85p ; 19cm.
Five men, 4 women, supers.
ISBN 0-573-61358-3 Sd : £1.80
1.Ti 2.Reiser, Dave

(B79-37419)

BSGR(N) — Shostakovich, Dmitriĭ Dmitrievich. Biographies
Shostakovich, Dmitriĭ Dmitrievich
Testimony. — London : H. Hamilton, Oct. 1979. — [320]p.
ISBN 0-241-10321-5 : £7.95 : CIP entry
1.Ti

(B79-25857)

BSH — Sibelius, Jean
Layton, Robert
Sibelius. — 2nd ed. — London : Dent, Jan. 1979. — [224]p. —
(The master musicians series)
Previous ed.: 1965.
ISBN 0-460-03169-4 : £4.50 : CIP entry
1.Sr

(B78-37096)

BSHAMME — Sibelius, Jean. Symphonies
Pike, Lionel
Beethoven, Sibelius and the 'profound logic'. — London : Athlone
Press, Nov.78. — [264]p.
ISBN 0-485-11178-0 : £12.95 : CIP entry
Primary classification BBJAMME
1.Ti

(B78-37102)

BSOTACF — Straus, Oscar. Walzertraum. Librettos
Dunn, Bernard
A waltz dream : operetta in three acts / new book by Bernard
Dunn ; new lyrics by Michael Flanders and Edmund Tracey ;
additional lyrics by Bernard Dunn ; original book and lyrics by
Felix Dörmann and Leopold Jacobson ; music by Oscar Straus ;
adapted and arranged by Ronald Hanmer. — London (10
Rathbone St., W1P 2BJ) : Josef Weinberger, 1978. — [1],iii,123p ;
20cm.
Pbk : £1.25
1.Ti 2.Flanders, Michael 3.Tracey, Edmund 4.Straus, Oscar

(B79-06705)

BSV — Stravinsky, Igor
White, Eric Walter
Stravinsky. — 2nd ed. — London : Faber, Oct. 1979. — [640]p.
Previous ed.: 1966.
ISBN 0-571-04923-0 : £13.50 : CIP entry

(B79-25328)

BSV(N) — Stravinsky, Igor. Biographies
Stravinsky, Vera
Stravinsky in pictures and documents / by Vera Stravinsky and
Robert Craft. — London : Hutchinson, 1979. — 688p,31p of
plates : ill(some col), facsims(some col), geneal table, map,
music(some col), ports(some col) ; 29cm.
Originally published: New York : Simon and Schuster, 1978. — Bibl.:
p.559-600. — Index.
ISBN 0-09-138000-6 : £16.00
1.Ti 2.Craft, Robert

(B79-15553)

Vlad, Roman
Stravinsky / [by] Roman Vlad. — 3rd ed. / translated from the
Italian by Frederick Fuller. — London [etc.] : Oxford University
Press, 1978. — viii,288p : music ; 23cm.
Translation of: 'Strawinsky'. Nuova ed. Torino : Einaudi, 1973. — Previous
ed. of this translation: / translated by Frederick and Ann Fuller. 1968. —
Bibl.: p.281-284. — Index.
ISBN 0-19-315444-7 : £5.95

(B79-11126)

BSWACF — Sullivan. Sir. Arthur Seymour. The Mikado. Librettos
Gilbert, Sir William Schwenck
The Mikado, or, The town of Titipu / by Sir W.S. Gilbert ; with
eight illustrations in colour by W. Russell Flint & drawings in pen
and ink by Charles E. Brock. — London (42 Bloomsbury St.,
W.C.1) : Godfrey Cave Associates, 1979. — vi,96p,[8]p of plates :
ill(some col) ; 25cm. — (Facsimile classics series)
Facsimile reprint of: 1928 ed. London : Macmillan, 1928.
ISBN 0-906223-05-9 : £5.50
1.Ti 2.Sr

(B79-16839)

BSWACF — Sullivan,. Sir. Arthur. The yeomen of the guard.
Librettos
Gilbert, Sir William Schwenck
The yeomen of the guard, or, The merryman and his maid / by
Sir W.S. Gilbert ; with eight illustrations in colour by W. Russell
Flint & drawings in pen and ink by Charles E. Brock. — London
(42 Bloomsbury St., W.C.1) : Godfrey Cave Associates Ltd. 1979.
— vi,102p,[8]p of plates : ill(some col) ; 25cm. — (Facsimile
classics series)
Facsimile reprint of: 1929 ed. London : Macmillan, 1929.
ISBN 0-906223-06-7 : £5.50
1.Ti 2.Sr

(B79-16840)

BTCE
Hand, Colin
John Taverner : his life and music / [by] Colin Hand. — London
(48 Great Marlborough St., W1V 2BN) : Eulenberg Books, 1978.
— 128p : 1 ill, music ; 23cm.
Bibl.: p.120-122. — Index.
ISBN 0-903873-52-4 Pbk : £2.00

(B79-06702)

BTD(N) — Tchaikovsky, Peter
Strutte, Wilson
Tchaikovsky : his life and times / [by] Wilson Strutte. —
Tunbridge Wells : Midas Books, 1979. — [10],158p : ill, 2 facsims,
ports ; 26cm.
Bibl.: p.153. — Index.
ISBN 0-85936-113-6 : £6.50

(B79-27783)

BTD(N) — Tchaikovsky, Peter. Biographies
Brown, David, b.1929
Tchaikovsky : a biographical and critical study / by David Brown.
— London : Gollancz.
Vol.1 : The early years (1840-1874). — 1978. — 348p,[8]p of plates : 1 ill,
music, ports ; 24cm.
List of works: p.339-342. — Index.
ISBN 0-575-02454-2 : £8.50

(B79-05248)

BTDAM/HM — Tchaikovsky, Peter. Ballet
Warrack, John
Tchaikovsky ballet music / [by] John Warrack. — London :
British Broadcasting Corporation, 1979. — 72p : music ; 20cm. —
(British Broadcasting Corporation. BBC music guides)
ISBN 0-563-12860-7 Pbk : £1.40
1.Ti 2.Sr

(B79-31929)

BVD(YDCHD/P — Vaughan Williams, Ralph. Dorking. Biographies
Dorking and Leith Hill District Preservation Society. Local History
Group
Vaughan Williams in Dorking : a collection of personal
reminiscences of the composer Dr Ralph Vaughan Williams,
O.M. / [Dorking and Leith Hill District Preservation Society,
Local History Group] ; edited by Celia Newbery. — Dorking
([c/o C. Newbery, 'Wrencot', Partridge La., Newdigate, Dorking,
Surrey]) : The Group, 1979. — [4],42p : ill, facsims, music, ports ;
30cm.
Bibl.: p.42.
Sd : £0.80
1.Ti 2.Newbery, Celia

(B79-21875)

BVJ(N) — Vivaldi, Antonio. Biographies
Kendall, Alan, b.1939
Vivaldi / [by] Alan Kendall. — London [etc.] : Panther, 1979. —
255p,[8]p of plates : ill, facsims, music, plan, ports ; 18cm.
Originally published: London : Chappell : Elm Tree Books, 1978. — List of
works: p.205-235. — Bibl.: p.237-238. — Index.
ISBN 0-586-05065-5 Pbk : £1.50

(B79-33548)

BWC — Wagner, Richard
The Wagner companion / edited by Peter Burbidge and Richard
Sutton. — London [etc.] : Faber, 1979. — 3-462p : music ; 23cm.
Bibl.: p.441-453. — Index.
ISBN 0-571-10471-1 : £12.50 : CIP rev.
ISBN 0-571-11450-4 Pbk : Unpriced
1.Burbidge, Peter 2.Sutton, Richard

(B78-40353)

BWC(N) — Wagner, Richard. Biographies
Culshaw, John
Wagner : the man and his music / [by] John Culshaw. —
London : Hutchinson, 1979. — x,181p : ill(some col), facsims,
plans, ports(some col) ; 24cm. — (Metropolitan Opera Guild.
Composer series)
Originally published: New York ; E.P. Dutton, 1978. — Index.
ISBN 0-09-136210-5 : £5.95 : CIP rev.
1.Sr
(B78-37864)

Taylor, Ronald, b.1924
Richard Wagner : his life, art and thought / [by] Ronald Taylor.
— London : Elek, 1979. — 3-285p,[16]p of plates : ill, facsims,
music, ports ; 24cm.
Bibl.: p.267-275. — Index.
ISBN 0-236-40071-1 : £7.95
(B79-08130)

Watson, Derek
Richard Wagner : a biography / [by] Derek Watson. — London
[etc.] : Dent, 1979. — 352p,[32]p of plates : ill, facsims, ports ;
24cm.
Bibl.: p.335-339. — Index.
ISBN 0-460-03166-x : £15.00 : CIP rev.
(B79-21149)

Westernhagen, Curt von
Wagner : a biography / [by] Curt von Westernhagen ; translated
[from the German] by Mary Whittall. — Cambridge [etc.] :
Cambridge University Press.
In 2 vols. — Translation of: 'Wagner'. 2nd, rev. and enlarged ed. Zürich :
Atlantis Musikbuch-Verlag, 1978.
Vol.2 : [1864-83]. — 1978. — x p,p329-654,[16]p of plates : ill, facsim,
music, ports ; 24cm.
Bibl.: p.629-637. — Index to vols 1-2.
ISBN 0-521-21932-9 : £12.50
(B79-17761)

BWC(Z) — Wagner, Richard - related to Claude Debussy
Holloway, Robin
Debussy and Wagner / [by] Robin Holloway. — London (48
Great Marlborough St., W1V 2BN) : Ernst Eulenburg Ltd, 1979.
— 235p : music ; 23cm.
ISBN 0-903873-25-7 : £5.50
ISBN 0-903873-26-5 Pbk : £4.00
Primary classification BDJ(Z)
1.Ti
(B79-35970)

BWC(ZD) — Wagner, Richard - influencing the English
Sessa, Anne Dzamab
Richard Wagner and the English / [by] Anne Dzamba Sessa. —
Rutherford [etc.] : Fairleigh Dickinson University Press ;
London : Associated University Presses, 1979. — 191p : 1 ill ;
22cm.
Bibl.: p.172-185. — Index.
ISBN 0-8386-2055-8 : £7.00
1.Ti
(B79-50407)

BWCAC — Wagner, Richard. Der Ring des Nibelungen
Cooke, Deryck
I saw the world end : a study of Wagner's 'Ring' / [by] Deryck
Cooke. — London [etc.] : Oxford University Press, 1979. — [7],
360p : music ; 21cm.
Bibl.: p.354-355. — Index.
ISBN 0-19-315318-1 : £6.50
Pbk : £3.95
1.Ti
(B79-15554)

Penetrating Wagner's Ring : an anthology / edited by John Louis
DiGaetani. — Rutherford [etc.] : Fairleigh Dickinson University
Press ; London : Associated University Presses, 1978. — 453p : ill,
music ; 24cm.
Bibl.: p.447-453.
ISBN 0-8386-1795-6 : £12.00
1.DiGaetani, John Louis
(B79-14015)

BWCAC — Wagner, Richard. Opera
Dahlhaus, Carl
Richard Wagner's music dramas / [by] Carl Dahlhaus ; translated
[from the German] by Mary Whittall. — Cambridge [etc.] :
Cambridge University Press, 1979. — [5],161p : music ; 24cm.
Translation of: 'Richard Wagners Musikdramer'. Velber : Friedrich, 1971.
ISBN 0-521-22397-0 : £7.50
1.Ti
(B79-33553)

BWM(N) — Webern, Anton. Biographies
Moldenhauer, Hans
Anton von Webern : a chronicle of his life and work / by Hans
Moldenhauer in collaboration with Rosaleen Moldenhauer. —
London : Gollancz, 1978. — 803p,leaf of plate,xiv p of plates : ill,
coat of arms, facsims, music, ports ; 24cm.
Bibl.: p.757-773. — Index.
ISBN 0-575-02436-4 : £20.00
1.Moldenhauer, Rosaleen
(B79-02986)

BWY — Wynne, David
Jones, Richard Elfyn
David Wynne / [by] Richard Elfyn Jones. — [Cardiff] :
University of Wales Press [for the Welsh Arts Council], 1979. —
73p : music ; 24cm. — (Composers of Wales ; 3)
List of works and recordings: p.65-73.
ISBN 0-7083-0714-0 Pbk : £1.50 : CIP rev.
1.Welsh Arts Council 2.Sr
(B79-09705)

BZ — LITERATURE ON NON-EUROPEAN MUSIC
BZMQTADW — Nigeria. Tiv tribe. Songs, etc
Keil, Charles
Tiv song / [by] Charles Keil. — Chicago ; London : University of
Chicago Press, 1979. — xiii,301p,[16]p of plates : ill, music,
ports ; 25cm.
Bibl.: p.285-289. — Index.
ISBN 0-226-42962-8 : £7.00
1.Ti
(B79-26553)

BZNM — Rhodesia
Berliner, Paul
The soul of Mbira : music and traditions of the Shona people of
Zimbabwe / [by] Paul Berliner. — Berkeley [etc.] ; London :
University of California Press, 1978. — xx,280p,[30]p of plates :
ill, map, music ; 24cm. — (Perspectives on southern Africa ; 26)
Bibl.: p.263-268. — List of sound discs: p.269. — List of films: p.273. —
Index.
ISBN 0-520-03315-9 : £12.00
1.Ti 2.Sr
(B79-19448)

C/AC — Musicianship
Russell-Smith, Geoffry
Let's explore music : the Russell-Smith method based on Kodály
and Orff principles. — London : EMI.
Piano accompaniment (36p.), Teacher's handbook (80p.).
Book 1 : Junior. — 1979. — 4to & 8vo.
Unpriced
1.Ti 2.Russell-Smith, Geoffry
(B79-50408)

C/AY — Collections
Music in the classic period : an anthology with commentary /
[compiled by] F.E. Kirby. — New York : Schirmer ; London :
Collier Macmillan, 1979. — viii,928p ; 8vo.
ISBN 0-02-870710-9 : £11.20
1.Kirby, Frank Eugene
(B79-50409)

C/AYD — Collections. England
Musica Britannica : a national collection of music. — London :
Stainer and Bell.
Vol.42 : The judgement of Paris / [by] Thomas Augustine Arne ; edited by
Ian Spink ; a masque written by William Congreve. — 1978. — xxviii,99p ;
fol.
Unpriced
Also classified at CQPF
1.Spink, Ian 2.Congreve, William
(B79-50009)
Vol.43 : English songs, 1800-1860 / edited by Geoffrey Bush and Nicholas
Temperley. — 1979. — xxvi,144p : facsim ; fol.
ISBN 0-85249-439-4 : Unpriced
Also classified at KDW/AYD
1.Bush, Geoffrey 2.Temperley, Nicholas
(B79-50814)

C/AZ — Collected works of individual composers
Purcell, Henry
[Works]. The works of Henry Purcell. — Sevenoaks : Novello.
Vol.3 : Dido and Aeneas / edited under the supervision of the Purcell
Society by Margaret Laurie. — 1979. — xxi,106p. ; 8vo. —
£10.00
Also classified at CQC
1.Ti
(B79-50815)

C/M — Rudiments
Russell-Smith, Geoffry
Let's explore music : the Russell-Smith method based on Kodaly and Orff principles. — London : EMI.
Book 1 : Junior, pupils edition. — 1979. — 48p ; 8vo.
Unpriced
1.Ti

(B79-50410)

CB — VOCAL MUSIC
CB/AF — Exercises
Nobis, Herbert
Hören und Singen : ein Solfège-Übungsbuch zur Gehörbildung / von Herbert Nobis. — Mainz ; London : Schott, 1977. — 56p ; 4to. — (Bausteine für Musikerziehung und Musikpflege ; 34)
£5.60
1.Ti 2.Sr

(B79-50816)

CB/AY — Vocal music. Collections. History 1450-1500
Monte Cassino (*Monastery*). *Biblioteca. MSS. (Codex 871)*
The musical manuscript Montecassino 871 : a Neapolitan repertory of sacred and secular music of the late fifteenth century / edited by Isabel Pope and Masakata Kanazawa. — Oxford : Clarendon Press, 1978. — xxiii,676p,[16]p of plates : music ; 4to.
Includes songs in Latin, Italian, Spanish and French. — With bibliography. — List of music. — Index.
ISBN 0-19-816132-8 : £25.00
1.Ti 2.Pope, Isabel 3.Kanazawa, Masakata

(B79-50411)

CB/EG — Sight reading
Gould, Murray Joseph
Paths to musical thought : an approach to ear singing through sight singing / by Murray Joseph Gould. — New York ; London : Holt, Rinehart and Winston, 1979. — ix,308p ; 4to.
With glossaries.
ISBN 0-03-020421-6 : Unpriced
1.Ti

(B79-50412)

CC — OPERA. VOCAL SCORES
Argento, Dominick
[The voyage of Edgar Allan Poe. *Vocal score*]. The voyage of Edgar Allan Poe : opera in two acts / [by] Dominick Argento ; libretto by Charles Nolte. — New York ; [London] : Boosey and Hawkes, 1979. — [8],405p ; 4to.
Unpriced
1.Ti 2.Ti 3.Nolte, Charles

(B79-50413)

Delius, Frederick
[The magic fountain. *Vocal score*]. The magic fountain : lyric drama in 3 acts / words and music by Frederick Delius ; vocal score by Eric Fenby. — London : Delius Trust, Boosey and Hawkes, 1979. — iv,192p ; 4to.
Duration 98 min.
Unpriced
1.Ti 2.Fenby, Eric

(B79-50010)

Hoddinott, Alun
[The magician. Op.88. *Vocal score*]. The magician : an opera in one act / [by] Alun Hoddinott ; libretto by John Morgan. — London : Oxford University Press, 1978. — [3],59p ; 8vo.
Duration 35 min.
ISBN 0-19-336839-0 : Unpriced
1.Ti 2.Morgan, John

(B79-50011)

Olive, Leslie
[The Master of Ashmore. *Vocal score*]. The Master of Ashmore : opera in three acts / by Leslie Olive ; book by Jon Adams. — Sittingbourne : Jon Adams, 1978. — 4to.
Unpriced
1.Ti 2.Ti 3.Adams, Jon

(B79-50012)

Philidor, François André Danican
[Tom Jones. *Vocal score*]. Tom Jones : comic opera in three acts based on the novel by Henry Fielding = opera comique en trois actes d'aprés le roman de Henry Fielding / [by] François-André Philidor ; libretto by Antoine Alexandre Henri Poinsinet ... ; revised by Jean-Michel Sedaine ... ; English version by Adrian Salter ; edited by Nicolas McGegan and Adrian Salter. — London : Boosey and Hawkes, 1978. — x,185p ; 4to.
£7.50
1.Ti 2.Poinsinet, Antoine Alexandre Henri 3.Sedaine, Jean-Michel 4.Salter, Adrian 5.McGegan, Nicolas

(B79-50013)

Tavener, John
[Thérèse. *Vocal score*]. Thérèse ... / music by John Tavener ; words by Gerard McLarnon ; piano reduction by Lionel Friend. — London : Chester Music, 1979. — 219p ; 4to.
Unpriced
1.Ti 2.McLarnon, Gerard 3.Friend, Lionel

(B79-50817)

CF — OPERETTAS. VOCAL SCORES
Britten, Benjamin, *Baron Britten*
[Paul Bunyan. Op.17. *Vocal score*]. Paul Bunyan : an operetta in two acts and a prologue, op.17 / [by] Benjamin Britten ; libretto by W.H. Auden, piano reduction by David Matthews. — London : Faber Music, 1978. — xii,172p ; fol.
Unpriced
1.Ti 2.Auden, Wysten Hugh 3.Matthews, David

(B79-50014)

Suppé, Franz von
[Das Pensionat. *Vocal score*]. The finishing school : comic operetta in one act (two scenes) / music by Franz von Suppé ; English version by Vilem Tausky. — London : Weinberger, 1978. — 97p ; 8vo.
Unpriced
1.Ti 2.Ti 3.Tausky, Vilem

(B79-50414)

CM — MUSICAL PLAYS. VOCAL SCORES
Buckley, Joss
[Gunslinger. *Vocal score*]. Gunslinger / music by Joss Buckley ; book and lyrics by Richard Crane. — London : Chappell, 1979. — 48p. ; 4to.
Unpriced
1.Ti 2.Ti 3.Crane, Richard

(B79-50820)

Glen, Robert
[Out of this world. *Vocal score*]. Out of this world : musical in two scenes / words and music by Robert Glen and Maureen McAfferty. — London : Weinberger, 1979. — [2],54p ; 4to.
Unpriced
1.Ti 2.McAfferty, Maureen

(B79-50818)

Valenti, Michael
[Snow White and the seven dwarfs. *Vocal score*]. Snow White and the seven dwarfs / [by] Michael Valenti ; book and lyrics Elsa Rael. — New York ; London : Associated Music, 1979. — [8], 48p : ill ; 4to.
Unpriced
1.Ti 2.Rael, Elsa

(B79-50819)

CM/L — Religious musical plays. Vocal score
Burgon, Geoffrey
[The fall of Lucifer. *Vocal score*]. The fall of Lucifer : for countertenor, tenor and bass soloists, chamber choir and instrumental ensemble / [by] Geoffrey Burgon. — London : Chester Music, 1979. — 34p ; 4to.
The text is of the first play of the Chester Mystery Cycle.
Unpriced
1.Ti

(B79-50015)

CN — Children's musical plays with keyboard accompaniment
Davies, Peter Maxwell
[The two fiddlers. *Vocal score*]. The two fiddlers = Die beiden Musikanten : opera in two acts = Oper in zwei Akten / [von] Peter Maxwell Davies ; libretto by the composer from an idea by George Mackay Brown. — London : Boosey and Hawkes, 1978. — v,81p ; 4to.
Inscribed on a sticky label on the title page 'Deutsche Übersetzung von Werner Kilian'.
Unpriced
1.Ti 2.Ti 3.Kilian, Werner

(B79-50016)

Parker, Jim
[The shepherd king. *Vocal score*]. The shepherd king : a musical play in eight scenes / music by Jim Parker ; book and lyrics by Tom Stanier. — London : Weinberger, 1979. — iv,36p ; 4to.
Unpriced
1.Ti 2.Stanier, Tom

(B79-50415)

CN/L — Children's religious musical plays
Lebowsky, Stanley
[The children's crusade]. The children's crusade : a morality play for the young, for four-part chorus of mixed voices, three soloists, narrator, piano and guitar accompaniment / [by] Stanley Lebowsky ; lyrics and text by Fred Tobias. — New York ; London : Schirmer, 1978. — [2],88p ; 4to.
£5.15
1.Ti 2.Ti 3.Tobias, Fred

(B79-50416)

CN/LF — Children's musical plays. Christmas
Swann, Donald
Wacky and his fuddlejig : a chidren's Christmas musical play / music, Donald Swann ; original story, Stanford Summers ; adaptation and lyrics, Arthur Scholey ; percussion parts, Lyn Howe. — London : Universal, 1978. — 52p ; 8vo.
Unpriced
1.Ti 2.Scholey, Arthur 3.Howe, Lyn

(B79-50017)

Walker, Sue
The day the animals sang : a musical for children / [by] Sue Walker. — Great Wakering : Mayhew-McCrimmon, 1977. — 31p ; 8vo.
For solo voices, chorus and piano.
ISBN 0-85597-202-5 : Unpriced
1.Ti

(B79-50821)

CPP — Pantomimes. Vocal scores
Astell, Betty
Aladdin / by Betty Astell. — [London] : [Evans], 1978. — [3], 56p ; 4to.
Pantomime.
ISBN 0-237-75044-9 : Unpriced
1.Ti

(B79-50018)

Astell, Betty
Cinderella / by Betty Astell. — [London] : /Evans], 1978. — [2], 77p ; 4to.
Pantomime.
ISBN 0-237-75045-7 : Unpriced
1.Ti

(B79-50019)

Astell, Betty
Dick Whittington / by Betty Astell. — [London] : [Evans], 1978. — [3],64p ; 4to.
Pantomime.
ISBN 0-237-75046-5 : Unpriced
1.Ti

(B79-50020)

Astell, Betty
Mother goose / by Betty Astell. — [London] : [Evans], 1978. — [3],115p ; 4to.
Pantomime.
ISBN 0-237-75042-2 : Unpriced
1.Ti

(B79-50021)

Astell, Betty
Queen of hearts / by Betty Astell. — [London] : [Evans], 1978. — [2],81p ; 4to.
Pantomime.
ISBN 0-237-75047-3 : Unpriced
1.Ti

(B79-50022)

Astell, Betty
The sleeping beauty / by Betty Astell. — [London] : [Evans], 1978. — [2],101p ; 4to.
Pantomime.
ISBN 0-237-75043-0 : Unpriced
1.Ti

(B79-50023)

CQC — OPERA. FULL SCORES
Prokofiev, Sergei
[Love of three oranges]. L'amour des trois oranges. Opus 33 : opéra en 4 actes et 10 tableaux avec un prologue d'après Carlo Gozzi / [par] Serge Prokofieff; traduction française par Véra Janacopoulos et l'auteur; deutsche Neufassung von Dr. Jürgen Bythien und Eberhard Sprink. — London : Boosey and Hawkes, 1979. — [8],628p ; 8vo. — (Hawkes pocket scores ; 917)
Miniature score. — Duration 107 min.
Unpriced
1.Ti 2.Ti 3.Janacopoulos, Véra 4.Bythier, Jürgen 5.Sprink, Eberhard 6.Sr

(B79-50822)

Purcell, Henry
[Works]. The works of Henry Purcell. — Sevenoaks : Novello.
Vol.3 : Dido and Aeneas / edited under the supervision of the Purcell Society by Margaret Laurie. — 1979. — xxi,106p. ; 8vo. —
£10.00
Primary classification C/AZ
1.Ti

(B79-50815)

Reimann, Aribert
Lear : Oper in zwei Teilen nach William Shakespeare eingerichtet von Claus H. Henneberg (1976/1978) / von Aribert Reimann. — Mainz ; London : Schott, 1979. — [8],460p ; fol.
Unpriced
1.Ti 2.Henneberg, Claus H

(B79-50823)

CQM — MUSICAL PLAYS. FULL SCORES
CQM/L — Religious musical plays. Full scores
The **Play** of Daniel : a 13th century liturgical drama from Beauvais Cathedral / edited by Mark Brown. — Ilkley ((Lyndhurst, Denton Rd, Ben Rhydding)) : Pro Cantione Antiqua ; [London] : [Breitkopf und Härtel], 1978. — [1],74p ; 4to.
£2.95
1.Brown, Mark

(B79-50417)

CQN — Children's musical plays. Full scores
Adams, Chris
The lollipop lady : a musical play for primary schools / [by] Chris Adams and Michael Sullivan. — Kingston-upon-Thames (43 Clifton Rd.) : Youngsong, 1979. — 16p. ; 4to.
Unpriced
1.Ti 2.Sullivan, Michael

(B79-50825)

Hess, Reimund
Dampflok-Story : ein Kinder - Musical : für Sprecher, 1-3 stg. Kinderchor und Begleitinstrumente auf Text von James Krüss / [von] Reimund Hess. — Mainz ; London : Schott, 1979. — 67p ; 4to.
£10.00
1.Ti 2.Krüss, James

(B79-50418)

Withams, Eric
The gorgon's head / words and music by Eric Withams ; (with additional text adapted from Charles Kingsley) based on the Greek myth of 'Perseus and Medusa'. — London : Universal, 1979. — 52p ; 8vo.
Musical play for soloists, chorus and instrumental ensemble. — Duration 35 min.
Unpriced
1.Ti 2.Kingsley, Charles

(B79-50824)

CQPF — MASQUES. FULL SCORES
Musica Britannica : a national collection of music. — London : Stainer and Bell.
Vol.42 : The judgement of Paris / [by] Thomas Augustine Arne ; edited by Ian Spink ; a masque written by William Congreve. — 1978. — xxviii,99p ; fol.
Unpriced
Primary classification C/AYD
1.Spink, Ian 2.Congreve, William

(B79-50009)

DADH — MOTETS, ANTHEMS, HYMNS. CHORAL SCORES
Martin, Frank
[Ode à la musique. *Choral score*]. Ode à musique / [par] Frank Martin. — Kassel ; [London] : Bärenreiter, 1977. — 16p ; 4to.
French and German text.
£1.16
1.Ti

(B79-50419)

DE — RELIGIOUS CANTATAS WITH KEYBOARD ACCOMPANIMENT
Roxburgh, Edwin
[The rock. *Vocal score*]. The rock : for soli, choir and orchestra / [by] Edwin Roxburgh. — London : United Music, 1979. — [4], 112p ; 4to.
Facsimile of the composer's autograph.
Unpriced
1.Ti

(B79-50826)

Schubert, Franz
[Lazarus. *Vocal score*]. Lazarus : an Easter cantata, for solo, mixed chorus and orchestra / [by] Franz Schubert ; edited by Paul White. — New York ; London : Schirmer, 1978. — [2],54p ; 8vo.
£1.80
1.Ti 2.Ti

(B79-50420)

DE/LF — Christmas
Bach, Wilhelm Friedemann
[Ach, dass du den Himmel zerrissest. *Vocal score*]. Ach, dass du den Himmel zerrissest = Oh! you who doth rend heav'n asunder : festo nativit Christi, Weihnachtskantate von, Christmas cantata / by Wilhelm Friedemann Bach ; General bass - Aussetzung, musikalische Ergänzungen, Bearbeitung und kritische Bericht ... von ... Oscar Foellmer und ... Friedrich Schall, ins Englische übersetzt von ... Fred Flindell. — Melville ; [Croydon] : Belwin Mills, 1978. — 43p ; 8vo.
Duration 22 min.
£2.25
1.Ti 2.Fuellmer, Oscar 3.Schall, Friedrich 4.Flindell, Fred

(B79-50421)

Chamberlain, Ronald
Herod and the rooster : a legend for all seasons, a dramatic
cantata / music, Ronald Chamberlain ; words, Arthur Scholey. —
Pinner ((125 Waxwell Lane)) : The Grail, 1979. — 32p ; 4to.
Soloists, choir and piano.
ISBN 0-901829-51-x : Unpriced
1.Ti 2.Scholey, Arthur

(B79-50827)

Hurd, Michael
[This day to man. *Vocal score*]. This day to man : six hymns for
the Nativity for SATB and orchestra / by Michael Hurd. —
Sevenoaks : Novello, 1979. — [2],37p ; 8vo.
Duration 21 min.
Unpriced
1.Ti

(B79-50828)

Palmer, David
[Holy Boy. *Vocal score*]. Holy Boy : a folk oratorio / with words
and music by David Palmer. — London : EMI, 1979. — 63p ;
4to.
Arranged for a two part choir, soloists and accompaniment of piano and/or
guitar with suggestions for recorders and melodic percussion instruments.
ISBN 0-86175-078-0 : Unpriced
1.Ti

(B79-50829)

DE/LFP — Epiphany
Bach, Wilhelm Friedemann
[Wie schön leuchtet der Morgenstern. *Vocal score*]. Wie schon
leuchtet der Morgenstern = How fair the morning star doth
glow : Kantate Dom. II. p. Epiph. / von Wilhelm Friedemann
Bach ; Generalbass-Aussetzung, musikalische Ergänzungen,
Bearbeitung und kritischer Bericht ... von Oscar Foellmer und ...
Friedrich Schall ; ins Englische ubersetzt von ... Fred Flindell. —
Melville ; [Croydon] : Belwin-Mills, 1978. — 47p ; 8vo.
Duration 23 min.
£2.25
1.Ti 2.Foellmer, Oscar 3.Schall, Friedrich 4.Flindell, Fred

(B79-50422)

DE/LK — Good Friday
Stainer, *Sir* John
[The crucifixion. *arr*]. The crucifixion : a meditation on the Sacred
Passion of the Holy Redeemer / [by] John Stainer ; arranged for
tenor (or soprano) and bass (or alto) soli, SSA and organ, with
hymns for congregational participation by Desmond Ratcliffe;
words selected and written by the Reverend J. Sparrow-Simpson,
M.A. — Sevenoaks : Novello, 1978. — [2],77p ; 8vo.
The organ part has been edited by the arranger. — Duration 50 min.
£1.55
Primary classification FDE/LK
1.Ti 2.Ti 3.Sparrow-Simpson, J

(B79-50100)

DE/LL — Easter
Bach, Wilhelm Friedemann
[Erzittert und fallet. *Vocal score*]. Erzittert und fallet = Oh,
tremble and falter : Kantate zum Ostersonntag von, Easter
cantata / by Wilhelm Friedemann Bach ; Generalbassaussetzung,
musikalische ergaenzungen, Bearbeitung und kritischer Bericht -
von ... Oscar Fuellmer und ... Friedrich Schall : ins Englische
ubersetzt [sic] von ... Fred Flindell. — Melville ; [Croydon] :
Belwin-Mills, 1978. — 55p ; 8vo.
Duration 30 min.
£2.25
1.Ti 2.Foellmer, Oscar 3.Schall, Friedrich 4.Flindell, Fred

(B79-50423)

**DFF — ROMAN LITURGY WITH KEYBOARD
       ACCOMPANIMENT**
DG — Ordinary of the Mass
Reinhardt, Stephen
Mass for Elizabeth Seton. Missa brevis : for SATB chorus with
organ or piano accompaniment / [by] Stephen Reinhardt. — New
York : Broude ; [London] : [Breitkopf und Härtel], 1979. — [1],
28p ; 8vo.
£2.10
1.Ti

(B79-50424)

DGKHB — Divine Office. Matins. Te Deum
Berlioz, Hector
[Te Deum. Op.22. *Vocal score*]. Te Deum. Op.22 / [von] Hector
Berlioz ; Klavierauszug ... Otto Taubmann. — Kassel ; London :
Bärenreiter, 1978. — [2],99p ; 4to.
£3.96
1.Ti 2.Taubmann, Otto

(B79-50425)

Ferris, William
Te Deum : for unison, boys', and mixed choirs combined, with
organ / [by] William Ferris. — New York ; [London] : Oxford
University Press, 1979. — 12p ; 8vo.
English text.
Unpriced

(B79-50426)

DGKJ — Divine Office. Vespers
Handel, George Frideric
[Dixit Dominus. *Vocal score*]. Dixit Dominus : Psalm 110, for two
sopranos, alto, tenor and bass soli, SSATB, strings and continuo /
[by] G.F. Handel ; edited by Watkins Shaw. — Sevenoaks :
Novello, 1979. — vii,95p ; 8vo.
£2.25
Primary classification DR
1.Ti 2.Shaw, Watkins

(B79-50448)

DGKJ/LF — Divine Office. Vespers. Christmas
Monteverdi, Claudio
[Choral music. *Selections : arr*]. Christmas vespers : antiphons,
psalms and hymns for soloists, double choir, instruments and
organ continuo / [by] Claudio Monteverdi ; edited by Denis
Stevens. — Sevenoaks : Novello, 1979. — 118p ; 8vo.
£3.50
Primary classification DJ/LF
1.Ti

(B79-50437)

DGKJ/LNC — Divine Office. Vespers. Corpus Christi
Gabrieli, Giovanni
[Sacrae symphoniae, bk.2. O quam suavis]. O quam suavis : for
eight-part chorus of mixed voices with organ accompaniment /
[by] Giovanni Gabrieli ; edited by Dale Jergenson and Daniel
Wolfe. — New York ; London : Schirmer, 1978. — iv,19p ; 8vo.
— (Gregg Smith choral series)
£0.75
Also classified at DJ/LNC
1.Ti 2.Ti 3.Jergenson, Dale 4.Wolfe, Daniel 5.Sr

(B79-50427)

DGKK — Divine Office. Vespers. Magnificat
Bach, Johann Christian
[Magnificat, D major, (1758)]. Magnificat / [von] Johann
Christian Bach ; herausgegeben von Akos Fodor. — Budapest :
Editio musica ; Zurich ; [London] : Eulenburg, 1978. — [4],32p ;
4to.
For S.S.A.A.T.T.B.B. and orchestra. — With keyboard reduction.
Unpriced
Primary classification EMDGKK
1.Fodor, Akos

(B79-50044)

**DGM — ANGLICAN LITURGY WITH KEYBOARD
       ACCOMPANIMENT**
Festival service book. — Addington : Royal College of Church
Music.
9 : Voice and verse : a meditation with words and music. — 1979. — 64p ;
8vo.
ISBN 0-85402-079-9 : Unpriced

(B79-50428)

DGNQ — Anglican liturgy. Morning prayer. Te Deum
Croft, William
[Te Deum. *Vocal score*]. Te Deum : for soloists, chorus, and
orchestra / [by] William Croft ; edited by Watkins Shaw. —
London : Oxford University Press, 1979. — [8],56p ; 8vo.
ISBN 0-19-335585-x : Unpriced
1.Shaw, Watkins

(B79-50429)

DGS — Communion
Shephard, Richard
The Wiltshire service : Holy Communion series 3, for
congregation and choir (SATB) with organ or piano / [by]
Richard Shephard. — Croydon : Royal School of Church Music,
1979. — 16p ; 8vo.
Unpriced
1.Ti

(B79-50430)

Wills, Arthur
Missa in memoriam Benjamin Britten : Holy Communion series 3
for S.A.T.B. and organ / [by] Arthur Wills. — [Croydon] :
Addington Press, 1978. — 15p ; 8vo.
Unpriced
1.Ti

(B79-50830)

**DH — MOTETS, ANTHEMS, HYMNS, ETC. WITH
       KEYBOARD ACCOMPANIMENT**
Bernstein, Leonard
[Symphony no.3, 'Kaddish'. Yit'ga dal. *arr*]. Canon in five parts
... : for boys chorus with piano accompaniment / [by] Leonard
Bernstein. — New York ; London : Amberson : Schirmer (dist.),
1979. — 8p ; 8vo.
Text in Hebrew.
£0.35
1.Ti 2.Ti

(B79-50831)

Hoiby, Lee
Hear us, O hear us, Lord : anthem for S.A.T.B. and organ / [by] Lee Hoiby ; [words by] John Donne. — New York : Broude ; [London] : [Breitkopf und Härtel], [1979]. — 13p ; 8vo.
£0.55
1.Ti 2.Donne, John

(B79-50431)

Ives, Grayston
Let all the world in every corner sing / [by] Grayston Ives ; words by George Herbert ... ; anthem for SATB and organ. — Sevenoaks : Novello, 1978. — [1],21p ; 8vo. — (Novello church music ; no.46)
Duration 7 1/2 min.
£0.61
1.Ti 2.Herbert, George 3.Sr

(B79-50024)

Kirk, Theron
Let all on earth their voices raise : for four-part chorus of mixed voices with piano accompaniment / [by] Theron Kirk ; [words by] Isaac Watts. — New York ; London : Schirmer, 1979. — 8p ; 8vo.
Unpriced
1.Ti 2.Watts, Isaac

(B79-50832)

Nelson, Ron
Oh, God, invent a word for us : for two-part children's chorus and SAB adult chorus with organ and/or piano / [by] Ron Nelson ; [words by] Shirley Nelson. — [New York] ; [London] : Boosey and Hawkes, 1979. — 19p ; 8vo.
Unpriced
1.Ti 2.Nelson, Shirley

(B79-50833)

Rutter, John
A Gaelic blessing / [by] John Rutter ; words adapted from an old Gaelic tune. — Croydon : Royal School of Church Music, 1978. — 4p ; 8vo.
For SATB with organ.
Unpriced
1.Ti

(B79-50432)

Young, Donald J
[Sermon on the mount. *Vocal score*]. Sermon on the mount : for four-part chorus of mixed voices with piano accompaniment / [by] Donald J. Young. — New York ; London : Schirmer, 1979. — 12p ; 8vo.
£0.45
1.Ti 2.Ti

(B79-50433)

DH/LF — Christmas
Mendelssohn, Felix
[Christus. *Selections : arr*]. There shall a star from Jacob come forth : three excerpts from Christus / [by] Felix Mendelssohn ... ; vocal score re-edited from the full score by Ivor Keys. — [Croydon] : Addington Press, 1979. — 20p ; 8vo.
Unpriced
1.Ti 2.Ti 3.Keys, Ivor

(B79-50834)

DH/LL — Easter
Earnest, David
The Son has risen : mixed chorus and organ / [by] David Earnest ; words by Tray Christopher. — New York : Broude ; [London] : [Breitkopf und Härtel], 1979. — 12p ; 8vo.
£0.45
1.Ti 2.Christopher, Tray

(B79-50434)

Kingsbury, John
Jesus, our Lord, doth live again : Easter anthem, for mixed voices, S.A.T.B. / German folk melody, ed. and accomp. by John Kingsbury. — New York : Broude ; [London] : [Breitkopf und Härtel], 1979. — 7p ; 8vo.
£0.42
1.Ti

(B79-50435)

DJ — MOTETS WITH KEYBOARD ACCOMPANIMENT
Caldara, Antonio
Regini coeli laetare = Freu dich, Maria, Himmelsköningin : für vierstimmigen gemischten Chor und Basso continuo = for four-part mixed chorus and basso continuo / [von] Antonio Caldara ; herausgegeben von ... Thomas Kohlhase ; original Text, lateinische Marienantiphon, zusätzlicher deutscher text von Th.K. — Kassel ; London : Bärenreiter, 1978. — 20p ; 4to. — (Chor-Archiv)
£2.97
1.Ti 2.Kohlhase, Thomas 3.Sr

(B79-50436)

Grandi, Alessandro
[Il quatro libro de motetti. Plorabo die ac nocte]. Plorabo die ac nocte / [by] Alessandro Grandi ; edited by Deborah Roberts. — London (36 Ranelagh Gdns W.6) : Cathedral Music, 1978. — 11p ; 8vo.
For S.A.T.B. and organ.
Unpriced
1.Ti 2.Roberts, Deborah

(B79-50025)

Shephard, Richard
Three short anthems / by Richard Shephard. — Croydon : Royal School of Church Music, 1979. — 11p ; 8vo.
Contents: 1: Jesus! dulcis memoria, SATB with organ - 2: Prayer for a new mother, unison voices - 3: The birds, SATB unaccompanied.
Unpriced
Also classified at EZDH; JFDP/LF
1.Ti

(B79-50835)

DJ/LF — Motets. Christmas
Monteverdi, Claudio
[Choral music. *Selections : arr*]. Christmas vespers : antiphons, psalms and hymns for soloists, double choir, instruments and organ continuo / [by] Claudio Monteverdi ; edited by Denis Stevens. — Sevenoaks : Novello, 1979. — 118p ; 8vo.
£3.50
Also classified at DGKJ/LF
1.Ti

(B79-50437)

DJ/LNC — Corpus Christi
Gabrieli, Giovanni
[Sacrae symphoniae, bk.2. O quam suavis]. O quam suavis : for eight-part chorus of mixed voices with organ accompaniment / [by] Giovanni Gabrieli ; edited by Dale Jergenson and Daniel Wolfe. — New York ; London : Schirmer, 1978. — iv,19p ; 8vo. — (Gregg Smith choral series)
£0.75
Primary classification DGKJ/LNC
1.Ti 2.Ti 3.Jergenson, Dale 4.Wolfe, Daniel 5.Sr

(B79-50427)

DK — ANTHEMS WITH KEYBOARD ACCOMPANIMENT
Bullard, Alan
Praise the Lord out of heaven : S.A.T.B. / [by] Alan Bullard ; [text] from Psalm 148, New English Bible, second edition. — York : Banks, 1979. — 12p ; 8vo. — (Eboracum choral series ; 69)
Unpriced
1.Ti 2.Sr

(B79-50438)

Gibbons, Orlando
[Church music]. Orlando Gibbons II : full anthems, hymns and fragmentary verse anthems / transcribed and edited by David Wulstan. — London : Stainer and Bell, 1978. — xvi,208p ; 8vo.
ISBN 0-85249-517-x : Unpriced
1.Ti 2.Wulstan, David

(B79-50026)

Handel, George Frideric
[Let God arise. *Vocal score*]. Let God arise : anthem for soprano and tenor soli, SATB and orchestra / [by] G.F. Handel ; edited by Janet Beat. — Sevenoaks : Novello, 1978. — vi,61p ; 8vo.
The B flat version. — The symphony is printed in score.
£1.65
1.Ti 2.Beat, Janet

(B79-50027)

Rorem, Ned
Surge, illuminare / [by] Ned Rorem ; [text from] the third song of Isaiah, text from the draft proposed Book of Common Prayer. — [New York] ; [London] : Boosey and Hawkes, 1979. — 15p ; 8vo.
For S.A.T.B. and organ. — Text in English - Duration 4 min.
Unpriced
1.Ti

(B79-50439)

Sumsion, Herbert
They that go down to the sea in ships : anthem for S.A.T.B. and organ / by Herbert Sumsion ; [from] Psalm 107. — Croydon : Addington Press, 1979. — 16p ; 8vo.
Unpriced
1.Ti

(B79-50836)

Tomkins, John
The King shall rejoice / [by] John Tomkins ; edited by Maurice Bevan. — London (36 Ranelagh Gdns, W.6) : Cathedral Music, 1978. — 7p ; 8vo. — (Saint Paul's series ; no.14)
For SSAATB.
Unpriced
1.Ti 2.Bevan, Maurice 3.Sr

(B79-50028)

DK/AY — Collections
Anthems from Addington. — Croydon : Royal School of Church
  Music.
  1 : O sing unto the Lord a new song, by Peter Aston. God is gone up, by
  Anthony Hedges. Think on these things, by Arthur Wills. Daughters of
  Zion, by Francis Jackson. Thou art Peter, by Tony Hewitt-Jones. — 1978.
  — 47p ; 8vo. —
  Unpriced

(B79-50440)

DM — HYMNS WITH KEYBOARD ACCOMPANIMENT
Rubbra, Edmund
  [Three hymn tunes. Op.114]. Three hymns tunes / [by] Edmund
  Rubbra. — South Croydon : Lengnick, [1979]. — [4]p ; 8vo.
  S.A.T.B. — Contents: 1: Prayer to Jesus (Richard de Castre) - 2: That
  Virgin's Child (Gwyneth) - 3: Queen of Mercy (Foley).
  Unpriced

(B79-50441)

Wilson, Alan J
  [Charlton]. Take my life : tune, Charlton, words, Frances Ridley
  Havergal [and] Come, Holy Ghost : tune, Pentecost, words,
  Bishop J. Cosin, based on 'Veni creator spiritus' / [two hymns by]
  Alan J. Wilson. — London : Weinberger, 1979. — 7p ; 8vo.
  The first hymn for S.A.T.B. solo or unison voices and piano, the second for
  SATB, congregation and organ.
  Unpriced
  1.Ti 2.Ti 3.Pentecost 4.Come, Holy Ghost

(B79-50442)

DM/AY — Hymns. Collections
  [Australian hymn book]. With one voice : a hymn book for all the
  churches with Catholic supplement / editor, Wesley Milgate. —
  London : Collins, 1979. — lxii,784p ; 8vo.
  Unpriced
  1.Milgate, Wesley

(B79-50443)

Living Lord : eighty hymns for the eighties / edited by Patrick
  Appleford. — London : Weinberger, 1979. — 8vo.
  Harmony ed. ([171]p.), melody ed. ([93]p.).
  Unpriced
  1.Appleford, Patrick

(B79-50838)

  [Sound of living waters]. Combined Sound of living waters - Fresh
  sounds / compiled by Betty Pulkingham and Jeanne Harper. —
  London : Hodder and Stoughton, 1978. — 463p ; 8vo.
  ISBN 0-340-23262-5 : £6.95
  1.Pulkingham, Betty 2.Harper, Jeanne

(B79-50029)

Youth songs : a collection for soloists and groups. — London :
  Salvationist Publishing & Supplies, 1979. — [127p.] ; 8vo.
  £2.95

(B79-50837)

DM/LSJ/AY — Methodist Church. Collections
Partners in praise. — London : Stainer & Bell : Chester House
  Publications [for the Methodist Church Division of Education and
  Youth], 1979. — xii,164p ; 8vo.
  Music edited by Allen Percival and T. Brian Coleman, words edited by Fred
  Pratt Green and Bernard Braley.
  £5.50
  1.Percival, Allen 2.Coleman, T. Brian 3.Methodist Church. Division of
  Education and Youth

(B79-50444)

DP — CAROLS WITH KEYBOARD ACCOMPANIMENT
DP/AY — Collections
Chormusik für Kinder. — London : Bärenreiter.
  Heft 3 : Passion, Ostern, Pfingsten / herausgegeben von Landesverband der
  evangelischen Kindenmusiker Badens. — 1979. — [1],48p ; 8vo. —
  £3.96

(B79-50445)

DP/LF — Christmas
Ehret, Walter
  Hush! My dear. (Nettleton carol) : for mixed chorus and piano /
  arranged and edited by Walter Ehret ; [words by] Isaac Watts. —
  New York : Broude ; [London] : [Breitkopf and Härtel], 1979. —
  7p ; 8vo.
  £0.42
  1.Ti

(B79-50839)

Ehret, Walter
  My masters, be merry! : for mixed voices (SATB) and
  accompaniment / English carol ed. and arr. by Walter Ehret. —
  New York : Broude ; [London] : [Breitkopf and Härtel], 1979. —
  8p ; 8vo.
  £0.42
  1.Ti

(B79-50840)

Goldman, Maurice
  Sleep, little Jesus, sleep : Spanish-American folk song for full
  chorus of mixed voices with soprano solo and piano / arranged by
  Maurice Goldman ; text by M.C. — Wendover : Roberton, 1978.
  — 7p ; 8vo. — (Roger Wagner choral series)
  £0.20
  1.Ti 2.Sr

(B79-50446)

Kingsbury, John
  Rejoice, then, Christ is born : Christmas song for mixed voices,
  optional a cappella S.A.T.B., Italian carol-tune (traditional) / arr.
  and ed. by John Kingsbury ; [words by] G.P. Grantham. — New
  York : Broude ; [London] : [Breitkopf and Härtel], 1979. — 8p ;
  8vo.
  £0.42
  1.Ti 2.Grantham, G P

(B79-50841)

Swale, David
  This endris night : S.A.T.B. / [by] David Swale ; [text] anon. —
  York : Banks, 1979. — 4p ; 8vo. — (Eboracum choral series ; 91)
  With piano and/or organ.
  Unpriced
  1.Ti 2.Sr

(B79-50842)

Wichmann, Russell G
  Once in royal David's city : carol for two-part mixed chorus and
  organ with optional chimes / [by] Russell G. Wichmann ; works
  by C.F. Alexander ; tune 'Irby', by H.J. Gauntlett ... — New
  York ; London : Oxford University Press, 1979. — 7p ; 8vo.
  Unpriced
  1.Ti 2.Alexander, Cecil Frances

(B79-50030)

Willcocks, Sir David
  What Child is this? S.A.T.B. (acc. or unacc.), English traditional
  melody / arranged by David Willcocks ; words by W.C. Dix. —
  London : Oxford University Press, 1978. — 3p ; 8vo. — (Oxford
  choral songs ; X270)
  ISBN 0-19-343071-1 : Unpriced
  1.Ti 2.Sr

(B79-50447)

DP/LF/AY — Christmas. Collections
Carols for choirs. — London : Oxford University Press.
  3 : Fifty carols ; edited and arranged by David Willcocks and John Rutter.
  — 1978. — 198p ; 8vo.
  ISBN 0-19-353570-x : Unpriced
  1.Willcocks, Sir David 2.Rutter, John

(B79-50031)

Carols in concert : six carols for SATB with divisions and organ or
  piano / composed and arranged by Donald Cashmore. —
  Sevenoaks : Novello, 1979. — 40p ; 4to.
  Includes another version of 'Rocking', to be distinguished from his earlier
  arrangement.
  Unpriced
  1.Cashmore, Donald

(B79-50843)

DR — PSALMS WITH KEYBOARD ACCOMPANIMENT
Handel, George Frideric
  [Dixit Dominus. Vocal score]. Dixit Dominus : Psalm 110, for two
  sopranos, alto, tenor and bass soli, SSATB, strings and continuo /
  [by] G.F. Handel ; edited by Watkins Shaw. — Sevenoaks :
  Novello, 1979. — vii,95p ; 8vo.
  £2.25
  Also classified at DGKJ
  1.Ti 2.Shaw, Watkins

(B79-50448)

Porta, Constanzo
  [Psalmodia vespertina. lauda Hierusalem Dominum]. Lauda
  Hierusalem Dominum / [by] Costanzo Porta ; transcribed and
  edited by Martyn Imrie. — London (72 Brewery Rd, N.7) : Mapa
  mundi, 1978. — 4to. — (Italian church music ; no.4)
  For S.A.T.B. — Choral score (8p.) & organ part (3p.).
  Unpriced
  1.Ti 2.Ti 3.Imrie, Martyn 4.Sr

(B79-50032)

Stocker, David
  Shout for joy : for four-part chorus of mixed voices with piano
  accompaniment / [by] David Stocker ; [words] Psalm 47. — New
  York ; London : Schirmer, 1979. — 17p ; 8vo.
  £0.75
  1.Ti

(B79-50844)

DW — SONGS, ETC. WITH KEYBOARD ACCOMPANIMENT

Albert, *Prince Consort of Victoria, Queen of Great Britain*
[Wachst, Liebchen, Du. *arr*]. Serenade : for four-part chorus of mixed voices with piano accompaniment / [by] Albert, Prince Consort ; arranged by John McCarthy, English version by John McCarthy. — Wendover : Roberton, 1978. — 10p ; 8vo.
The original text was by Prince Ernst of Saxe-Coburg-Gotha.
£0.24
1.Ti 2.Ti

(B79-50449)

Blackley, Terry J
[Blues on the run. *arr*]. Blues on the run : for SATB chorus and piano with optional bass and drums / music by Terry Blackley ; arranged by Terry Blackley ; words by Karen Ray Blackley. — New York : Warner ; [London] : [Blossom], 1979. — 8vo.
Vocal score (6p.) & 2 parts.
Unpriced
1.Ti 2.Ti 3.Blackley, Karen Ray

(B79-50845)

Blackley, Terry J
[Circles. *arr*]. Circles : for SATB chorus and piano with optional bass and drums / music by Terry J. Blackley ; words by Karen Ray Blackley ; arranged by Terry J. Blackley. — New York : Warner ; [London] : [Blossom], 1979. — 8vo.
Vocal score (9p.) & 2 parts.
Unpriced
1.Ti 2.Ti 3.Blackley, Karen Ray

(B79-50846)

Blackley, Terry J
[Empty arms. *arr*]. Empty arms : for SATB chorus and piano with optional bass and drums / music by Terry J. Blackley ; arranged by Terry J. Blackley ; lyrics by Karen Ray Blackley. — New York : Warner ; [London] : [Blossom], 1979. — 8vo.
Vocal score (8p.) & 2 parts.
Unpriced
1.Ti 2.Ti 3.Blackley, Karen Ray

(B79-50847)

Ferguson, Barry
Aubade : song cycle for speaker, SATB and piano (or harp) / [by] Barry Ferguson ; words by Judith Rose. — Sevenoaks : Novello, 1979. — [8],24p ; 8vo.
Duration 17 min.
Unpriced
1.Ti 2.Rose, Judith

(B79-50033)

Ferris, William
Indian summer : for mixed chorus and piano / [by] William Ferris ; poem by Emily Dickinson. — New York ; London : Oxford University Press, 1979. — 15p ; 8vo.
Unpriced
1.Ti 2.Dickinson, Emily

(B79-50848)

Gershwin, George
[Porgy and Bess. Summertime. *arr*]. Summertime : S.A.C.(T.) B. with piano / music by George Gershwin ; arranged by Walter Ehret; lyrics by Dubose Heyward. — [New York] ; [London] : Chappell, 1978. — 5p. ; 8vo. — (Broadway showcase choral series)
Unpriced
1.Ti 2.Ti 3.Heyward, Du Bose 4.Ehret, Walter 5.Sr

(B79-50849)

Loewe, Frederick
[Paint your wagon. They call the wind Maria. *arr*]. They call the wind Maria : S.A.C.(T.) B. with piano / music by Frederic Loewe ; arranged by Walter Ehret ; words by Alan Jay Lerner. — [New York] ; [London] : Chappell, 1978. — 5p ; 8vo. — (Broadway showcase choral series)
Unpriced
1.Ti 2.Ti 3.Lerner, Alan Jay 4.Ehret, Walter 5.Sr

(B79-50850)

McCartney, Paul
[Mull of Kintyre. *arr*]. Mull of Kintyre / words and music by McCartney-Laine ; arranged by Clive Sanson [sic]. — London : Music Sales, 1978. — 8p ; 8vo.
Duration 3 min. — Arranged for S.A.T.B.
Unpriced
1.Ti 2.Laine, Denny 3.Sansom, Clive

(B79-50034)

Pierce, Brent
I will always need you : for vocal solo, SATB chorus and piano with optional bass and drums / by Brent Pierce. — New York : [London] : [Blossom], 1979. — 8vo.
Vocal score (14p.) & 2 parts.
Unpriced
1.Ti

(B79-50851)

Porter, Cole
[Kiss me, Kate. Another op'nin', another show. *arr*]. Another op'nin', another show : for S.A. cambiata, B. or S.A.T.B. with piano / words and music by Cole Porter; arranged by Walter Ehret. — Bryn Mawr ; [London] : Chappell, 1979. — 6p ; 4to. — (Broadway showcase choral series)
Unpriced
1.Ti 2.Ti 3.Ehret, Walter 4.Sr

(B79-50852)

Radlbauer, Dan
[I wanna share. *arr*]. I wanna share : for vocal solo, SATB chorus and piano with optional bass and drums / words and music by Dan Radlbauer. — New York : Warner ; [London] : [Blossom], 1979. — 8vo.
Vocal score (9p.) & 2 parts.
Unpriced
1.Ti 2.Ti

(B79-50853)

Rhein, Robert
The de'il's awa wi'th' exiseman : for four-part chorus of mixed voices with piano accompaniment / traditional Scottish melody arranged by Robert Rhein ; [words by] Robert Burns ... — New York ; London : Schirmer, 1979. — 7p ; 8vo.
£0.35
1.Ti 2.Burns, Robert

(B79-50854)

Rocherolle, Eugénie R
Little bitty baby : for SAB-SA chorus and piano / words and music by Eugénie R. Rocherolle. — [New York] : Warner ; [London] : [Blossom], 1978. — 8p ; 8vo.
Unpriced
1.Ti

(B79-50035)

Rodgers, Richard
[The King and I. Getting to know you. *arr*]. Getting to know you : for S.A. cambiata, B. or S.A.T.B. / music by Richard Rodgers ; arranged by Walter Ehret; words by Oscar Hammerstein. — Bryn Mawr ; [London] : Williamson, 1979. — 6p. ; 4to. — (Broadway showcase choral series)
Unpriced
1.Ti 2.Ti 3.Ehret, Walter 4.Hammerstein, Oscar, b.1895 5.Sr

(B79-50855)

Rodgers, Richard
[Oklahoma!. Oh, what a beautiful mornin'. *arr*]. Oh, what a beautiful mornin' : S.A.C.(T)B. with piano / music by Richard Rodgers ; arranged by Walter Ehret : words by Oscar Hammerstein. — Bryn Mawr ; [London] : Williamson Music, 1978. — 7p. ; 8vo. — (Broadway showcase choral series)
Unpriced
1.Ti 2.Ti 3.Hammerstein, Oscar, .1895 4.Ehret, Walter 5.Sr

(B79-50856)

Rodgers, Richard
[The sound of music. Climb ev'ry mountain. *arr*]. Climb ev'ry mountain : for S.A. cambiata, B. or S.A.T.B. with piano / music by Richard Rodgers ; arranged by Walter Ehret ; lyrics by Oscar Hammerstein II. — Bryn Mawr ; [London] : Williamson Music, 1979. — 5p ; 8to. — (Broadway showcase choral series)
Unpriced
1.Ti 2.Ti 3.Ehret, Walter 4.Hammerstein, Oscar, b.1895 5.Sr

(B79-50857)

Rodgers, Richard
[State fair. Its a grand night for singing. *arr*]. Its a grand night for singing : S.A.C.(T).B, with piano / music by Richard Rodgers ; arranged by Walter Ehret ; words by Oscar Hammerstein II. — Bryn Mawr ; [London] : Williamson, 1978. — 7p. ; 8to. — (Broadway showcase choral series)
Unpriced
1.Ti 2.Ti 3.Ehret, Walter 4.Hammerstein, Oscar, b.1895 5.Sr

(B79-50858)

Ruby, Harry
[Broadway Joe. *arr*]. She was an acrobat's daughter, an English music hall song : for four-part chorus of mixed voices with piano accompaniment / [by Harry Ruby] ; arr. John McCarthy. — Wendover : Roberton, 1979. — 15p ; 8vo.
Unpriced
1.Ti 2.Ti 3.McCarthy, John

(B79-50450)

Styne, Jule
[Gypsy. Everything's coming up roses. *arr*]. Everything's coming up roses : for S.A. cambiata, B. or S.A.T.B, with piano / music by Jules Styne ; arranged by Walter Ehret ; lyrics by Stephen Sondheim. — Bryn Mawr ; [London] : Williamson, 1979. — 8p ; 4to. — (Broadway showcase choral series)
Unpriced
1.Ti 2.Ti 3.Ehret, Walter 4.Sondheim, Stephen 5.Sr

(B79-50859)

Tepper, Albert
[4 American settings. Song of Thyrsis]. Song of Thyrsis : S.A.T.B. & piano / [by] Albert Tepper ; poem by Philip Morin Freneau. — [New York] ; [London] : Boosey and Hawkes, 1979. — 12p. ; 8vo. — (Brown University choral series)
Duration 31/2 min.
£0.35
1.Ti 2.Ti 3.Freneau, Philip Morin 4.Four American settings. Song of Thyrsis 5.Sr

(B79-50860)

Tepper, Albert
The sycophantic fox and the gullible raven : S.A.T.B. & piano / [by] Albert Tepper ; poem by Guy Wetmore Carryl. — [New York] ; [London] : Boosey and Hawkes, 1979. — 28p. ; 8vo. — (Brown University choral series)
Duration 51/2 min.
£0.90
1.Ti 2.Carryl, Guy Wetmore 3.Sr

(B79-50861)

Townsend, Douglas
Sleeping innocence : a lullaby, for mixed chorus and piano / [by] Douglas Townsend ; [words by] Bonnie Bowman. — New York : Broude ; [London] : [Breitkopf and Härtel], 1979. — 8vo.
Op.15, no.1.
£0.42
1.Ti 2.Bowman, Bonnie

(B79-50451)

Tull, Fisher
An Indian prayer / [by] Fisher Tull. — [New York] ; [London] : Boosey and Hawkes, 1979. — 14p ; 8vo.
S.A.T.B. and piano.
Unpriced
1.Ti

(B79-50452)

Yancy, Marvin
[Our love. *arr*]. Our love / words and music by Marvin Yancy and Chuck Jackson ; arranged for S.A.B. with piano and optional drums by Jacques Rizzo. — Bryn Marw ; [London] : Chappell, 1978. — 10p ; 8vo.
Unpriced
1.Ti 2.Jackson, Chuck 3.Rizzo, Jacques

(B79-50036)

Yancy, Marvin
[Our love. *arr*]. Our love / words and music by Marvin Yancy and Chuck Jackson ; arranged for S.A.T.B. with piano and optional drums by Jacques Rizzo. — Bryn Mawr ; [London] : Chappell, 1978. — 9p ; 8vo.
Unpriced
1.Ti 2.Jackson, Chuck 3.Rizzo, Jacques

(B79-50037)

Zimmermann, Heinz Werner
Drei Nestroy-Collagen : für gemischten Chor und zwei Klaviere / [von] Heinz Werner Zimmermann. — Kassel ; [London] : Bärenreiter, 1978. — [2],40p ; fol.
No.1 based on 'Mein' Fru, dieser Engel' by A. Müller (the Elder). No.2 based on 'Die Werber' by J.F.C. Lanner.
£13.20
1.Ti

(B79-50038)

DW/GBB — Pop songs
Goodrum, Randy
[You needed me. *arr*]. You needed me : S.A.B. with piano and optional drums / words and music by Randy Goodrum; arranged by Jacques Rizzo. — Bryn Mawr ; [London] : Chappell, 1978. — 8p. ; 8vo.
Unpriced
1.Ti 2.Rizzo, Jacques

(B79-50862)

DW/LC/LF — Spirituals. Christmas
Ehret, Walter
Wasn't that a mighty day! : Christmas spiritual for mixed voices, accompanied (S.A.T.B.) / ed. and arr. by Walter Ehret ; trad. adapted W.S. — New York : Broude ; [London] : [Breitkopf and Härtel], 1979. — 8p ; 8vo.
With piano.
£0.42
1.Ti 2.Ehret, Walter

(B79-50863)

DX — SECULAR CANTATAS WITH KEYBOARD ACCOMPANIMENT
Tate, Phyllis
[All the world's a stage. *Vocal score*]. All the world's a stage : prologue, six variations, and epilogue for chorus and orchestra / [by] Phyllis Tate ; works by Shakespeare. — London : Oxford University Press, 1979. — 28p ; 8vo.
Duration 16 min.
ISBN 0-19-338344-6 : Unpriced
1.Ti 2.Shakespeare, William

(B79-50864)

E — CHORAL WORKS WITH ACCOMPANIMENT OTHER THAN KEYBOARD
EJQPLRDTF — With harp & organ. Lord's Prayer
Janáček, Leoš
[Our father]. Otčenáš = Our Father : for full chorus of mixed voices, tenor or soprano solo, organ and harp / by Leoš Janáček ... ; edited and adapted by Antonín Tučapský ... — Wendover : Roberton, 1979. — 8vo.
Score (28p.), Chorus score (12p.).
£0.75 (Chorus score £0.28)
1.Ti 2.Ti 3.Tučapský, Antonín

(B79-50865)

ELDM — With instruments. Hymns
Carter, Sydney
[9 carols or ballads. Lord of the dance. *arr*]. Lord of the dance / [by] Sydney Carter. — London : Galliard, 1979. — [1],4p ; 4to.
Arranged for any number of singers and players.
Unpriced
1.Ti 2.Ti 3.Nine carols or ballads. Lord of the dance. arr

(B79-50453)

EM — With orchestra
Feldman, Morton
Chorus and orchestra / [by] Morton Feldman. — Toronto ; [London] : Universal, 1978. — [3],32p ; 4to.
Duration 15 min.
Unpriced

(B79-50039)

EM/JM — With orchestra. Incidental music
Delius, Frederick
Hassan : the incidental music to the play by James Elroy Flecker / [by] Frederick Delius. — London : Boosey and Hawkes, 1978. — [4],211p ; 8vo. — (Hawkes pocket scores ; 916)
With S.A.T.B. chorus. — Edited by Robert Threlfall.
Unpriced
1.Ti 2.Flecker, James Elroy 3.Threlfall, Robert 4.Sr

(B79-50040)

EMDD — With orchestra. Oratorios
Walton, *Sir* William
Belshazzar's feast : for baritone solo, mixed choir, and orchestra / the text selected and arranged from the Bible by Osbert Sitwell; the music by William Walton; [foreword by] Michael Kennedy. — Limited ed. — London : Oxford University Press, 1978. — xxv, 165p ; fol.
One of three hundred and fifty copies signed by the composer.
ISBN 0-19-338463-9 : £60.00
1.Ti

(B79-50041)

EMDE — With orchestra. Religious cantatas
Halffter, Cristóbal
Officium defunctorum (1978) / [by] Cristóbal Halffter. — London : Universal, 1978. — [6]p ; fol.
For 13 soloists, mixed chorus and orchestra. — Reproduction of the composer's manuscript.
Unpriced
1.Ti

(B79-50866)

Schuller, Gunther
The power within us : a narrative oratorio for baritone, narrator, chorus and orchestra / [by] Gunther Schuller. — New York ; London : Associated Music, 1978. — [2],111p ; 4to.
Unpriced
1.Ti

(B79-50454)

EMDGKADD/LN — With orchestra. Veni sancte spiritus
Burgon, Geoffrey
[Veni spiritus. *Vocal score*]. Veni spiritus : for soprano and baritone soloists, chorus and orchestra / [by] Geoffrey Burgon. — London : Chester Music, 1979. — [3],62p ; 4to.
Unpriced
1.Ti 2.Ti

(B79-50042)

EMDGKAV — With orchestra. Requiems
Verdi, Giuseppe
[Messa di requiem]. Requiem / [by] Giuseppe Verdi ; in full score. — New York : Dover Publications ; [London] : [Constable], 1978. — [4],204p ; fol.
Edited by Kurt Soldan. Originally published Leipzig, Peters, s.d.: glossary of German terms found in the score specially prepared.
ISBN 0-486-23682-x : Unpriced
1.Ti 2.Soldan, Kurt

(B79-50043)

EMDGKK — With orchestra. Divine Office. Vespers. Magnificat

Bach, Johann Christian
[Magnificat, D major, (1758)]. Magnificat / [von] Johann
Christian Bach ; herausgegeben von Akos Fodor. — Budapest :
Editio musica ; Zurich ; [London] : Eulenburg, 1978. — [4],32p ;
4to.
For S.S.A.A.T.T.B.B. and orchestra. — With keyboard reduction.
Unpriced
Also classified at DGKK
1.Fodor, Akos

(B79-50044)

EMDX — With orchestra. Secular cantatas

Brahms, Johannes
Schicksalslied = Song of destiny. Op.54 / [by] Johannes Brahms ;
foreword by Joan Chissell. — London : Eulenberg, 1979. — xi,
53p ; 8vo.
For mixed voices and orchestra. — Words by J.C.F. Hölderlin. — Miniature
score.
Unpriced
1.Ti 2.Hölderlin, Johann Christian Friedrich

(B79-50867)

Eloy, Jean Claude
Kāmakalā. Le triangle des énergies : pour trois ensembles
d'orchestres et de choeurs / [par] Jean-Claude Eloy. — London :
Universal, 1978. — vii,56p ; fol.
Reproduction of the composer's manuscript.
Unpriced
1.Ti

(B79-50868)

Hovhaness, Alan
[Symphony no.24, op.273, 'Majnun']. Majnun symphony.
(Symphony no.24). Op.273 : for tenor solo, four-part chorus of
mixed voices, trumpet in C, solo violin and string orchestra / [by]
Alan Hovhaness. — New York ; London : Associated Music,
1978. — 88p ; 4to.
Text from Salaman and Absal by Jami, translated from the Persian by
Edward Fitzgerald. — Duration 25 min.
£9.10
1.Ti 2.Ti 3.Jāmi 4.Fitzgerald, Edward

(B79-50869)

Rachmaninoff, Sergei
The bells : Opus 35 : poem for soprano, tenor and baritone soli,
chorus and orchestra / [by] S. Rachmaninoff ; text, from the
poem of Edgar Allan Poe, by K. Balmont, retranslated into
English by Fanny S. Copeland. — London : Boosey and Hawkes,
[1979]. — [4],140p ; 8vo.
Miniature score. — Text in Russian and English.
Unpriced
1.Balmont, Konstantin Dmitrievich 2.Copeland, Fanny S

(B79-50455)

Spinner, Leopold
Cantata, op.20 on German folksong texts : for mezzo-soprano
solo, chorus and chamber orchestra / [by] Leopold Spinner. —
London : Boosey and Hawkes, 1978. — iv,40p ; fol.
Duration 18 min.
Unpriced
1.Ti

(B79-50045)

ENYLDE — With keyboard & percussion. Religious cantatas

Fanshawe, David
African sanctus ... : for soprano solo, mixed chorus, instrumental
ensemble and pre-recorded tape / [by] David Fanshawe. —
London : Chappell, 1979. — 223p : ill ; 4to.
Miniature score. — Facsimile of the composer's autograph - Duration 60
min.
Unpriced
1.Ti

(B79-50456)

**ERPLXDH/KDN — With organ & percussion. Motets, Anthems,
Hymns, etc. Funerals**

Zimmermann, Udo
Psaslm der Nacht : für sechzehnstimmigen Frauenchor,
Männerstimmen, Schlagwerk und Orgel / [von] Udo
Zimmermann ; nach Texten von Nelly Sachs und des 129. (130.)
Psalms ('De profundis'). — Kassel ; London : Bärenreiter, 1978.
— 32p ; fol.
£7.92
1.Ti 2.Sachs, Nelly

(B79-50046)

ETQDW — With harp. Songs, etc

Binkerd, Gordon
Sorrow hath a double voice : for solo high voice, unison male or
female chorus and harp / by Gordon Binkerd ; based on a
thirteenth century melody by Adam de la Hale ; text, Christina
Rossetti. — [New York] ; [London] : Boosey and Hawkes, 1978.
— 11p ; 8vo.
Score (11p.) & harp part. - 'The harp part is sold separately'.
Unpriced
1.Ti 2.Rossetti, Christina 3.Adam de la Halle

(B79-50047)

EVRPLXDW — With flute & percussion. Songs, etc

Sohal, Naresh
... Surya : for S.A.T Bar. B. soli, chorus, flute and percussion /
[by] Naresh Sohal. — Sevenoaks : Novello, 1979. — [6],34p ; 4to.
Verses by Kalidas and from Rig Veda. — Duration 11 min.
Unpriced
1.Ti 2.Kalidas

(B79-50048)

EWSNTPLRDR — With trumpets (2) & organ. Psalms

Badarak, Mary Lynn
Psalm 100 : (anthem), for four-part chorus of mixed voices with
organ and 2 trumpets accompaniment / [by] Mary Lynn Badarak.
— New York ; London : Schirmer, 1979. — 16p ; 8vo.
Unpriced
1.Ti

(B79-50870)

EXRVDP/LF — With tambourines. Carols. Christmas

Whitter, Mark
Stardance carol : S.A.T.B. / [by] Mark Whitter ; [words by]
David Whitter. — York : Banks, 1979. — 3p ; 8vo. — (Eboracum
choral series ; 89)
With tambourine or tabor.
Unpriced
1.Ti 2.Sr

(B79-50871)

EZ — UNACCOMPANIED CHORAL WORKS

EZDD/LK — Oratorios. Good Friday

Peranda, Marco Giuseppe
[St. Mark's Passion]. Markus-Passion für Solostimmen und
vierstimmigen Chor a cappella / von Marco Giuseppe Peranda ;
herausgegeben vom Kirchenchorwerk der
Evangelisch-Lutherischen Landeskirche Sachsens ; Einrichtung,
Wolfram Steude. — Leipzig : VEB Deutscher Verlag ; [London] :
[Breitkopf and Härtel], 1978. — 40p ; 4to.
£2.70
1.Ti 2.Ti 3.Steude, Wolfram

(B79-50872)

**EZDFF/AYD — Unaccompanied voices. Roman liturgy. Collections.
England**

Fifteenth-century liturgical music. — London : Stainer and Bell.
2 : Four anonymous masses / transcribed and edited by Margaret Bent. —
1979. — xvii,193p ; 8vo.
ISBN 0-85249-544-7 : Unpriced
1.Bent, Margaret

(B79-50873)

EZDG — Ordinary of the Mass

Guerrero, Francisco
[Missarum liber secundo. Missa de la batalla escoutez]. Missa de
la batalla escoutez : for 5 voices / [by] Francisco Guerrero ;
transcribed and edited by Martyn Imrie. — London : Mapa
mundi, 1978. — 28p ; 4to. — (Spanish church music ; no.7)
Unpriced
1.Ti 2.Ti 3.Imrie, Martyn 4.Sr

(B79-50049)

Peñalosa, Francisco de
Missa El ojo : for 4 voices / [by] Francisco de Peñalosa ;
transcribed and edited by Martyn Imrie. — London (72 Brewery
Rd, N.7) : Mapa mundi, 1978. — 28p ; 4to. — (Spanish church
music ; no.9)
Unpriced
1.Ti 2.Imrie, Martyn 3.Sr

(B79-50050)

Tye, Christopher
The Mass Euge bone : for 6 voices / [by] Christopher Tye ;
transcribed and edited by Nigel Davison. — London (72 Brewery
Rd, N.7) : Mapa mundi, 1978. — 23p ; 4to. — (English church
music ; no.1)
Unpriced
1.Ti 2.Davison, Nigel 3.Sr

(B79-50051)

Victoria, Tomás Luis de
[Motecta. O quam gloriosum est regnum]. Motet and mass, O
quam gloriosum est regnum / [by] Tomás Luis de Victoria ;
edited by Thomas Rive. — London : Eulenburg, 1978. — xii,31p ;
8vo.
The mass which is here published with the motet is taken from 'Missarum
libri duo'. — Miniature score.
Unpriced
Primary classification EZDJ/LQ
1.Ti 2.Ti 3.Rive, Thomas

(B79-50091)

EZDG — Unaccompanied voices. Roman liturgy. Ordinary of the Mass
Josquin des Prés
Missa Pange lingua : for voices / by Josquin des Prez ; edited and arranged for modern use by Nigel Davison. — London : Chester Music, 1979. — [2],40p ; 4to.
Unpriced
1.Ti 2.Davison, Nigel

(B79-50874)

EZDGKADD/LK — Stabat mater
Laburda, Jiří
Stabat mater : for four-part chorus of mixed voices a cappella / [by] Jiří Laburda. — New York ; London : Schirmer, 1978. — 40p ; 8vo.
Latin & English text.
£2.75

(B79-50457)

EZDGKAV — Requiems
Okeghem, Jean
Missa pro defunctis : for 2,3 and 4 voices / [by] Johannes Ockeghem ; transcribed and edited by Bruno Turner. — London (72 Brewery Rd, N.7) : Mapa mundi, 1978. — 19p ; 4to. — (Franco-Flemish church music ; no.1)
Unpriced
1.Ti 2.Turner, Bruno 3.Sr

(B79-50052)

Victoria, Tomás Luis de
[Officium defunctorum. Missa pro defunctis]. Requiem à 6 (1605) / [by] Tomás Luis de Victoria ; edited by David Wulstan. — Oxford : Oxenford Imprint, 1978. — 44p ; 8vo.
For S.S.A.T.T.B.
Unpriced
1.Ti 2.Wulstan, David

(B79-50053)

EZDGKH — Divine Office. Matins
Lobo, Alfonso
[Liber primus missarum. Credo quod redemptor mens vivit]. Credo quod redemptor mens vivit : pro defunctis, for 4 voices / [by] Alfonso Lobo ; transcribed and edited by Bruno Turner. — [London] : Mapa mundi, 1978. — 4p ; 4to. — (Spanish choral music ; no.15)
Unpriced
Primary classification EZDJ/KDN
1.Ti 2.Ti 3.Turner, Bruno 4.Sr

(B79-50068)

EZDGKH/LEZ — Divine Office. Matins. Advent
Handl, Jacob
[Tomus primus operis musici. Rorate coeli]. Rorate coeli : motet for the Advent season, for 6 voices / [by] Jakob Handl ; transcribed and edited by Martyn Imrie. — [London] : Mapa mundi, 1978. — 4p ; 4to. — (German-Slav church music ; no.4)
Unpriced
Primary classification EZDJ/LEZ
1.Ti 2.Ti 3.Imrie, Martyn 4.Sr

(B79-50072)

EZDGKH/LHM — Divine Office. Tenebrae. Maundy Thursday
Lasso, Orlando di
[Hieremiae prophetae lamentationes, et alia piae cantiones. *Selections*]. Lamentations for Tenebrae on Maundy Thursday, Feria V in Coena Domini ad Matatinum / [by] Orlandus Lassus ; transcribed and edited by Clive Wearing. — London (72 Brewery Rd, N.7) : Mapa Mundi, 1978. — 23p ; 4to. — (London Lassus series ; no.1)
For SATTB.
Unpriced
Primary classification EZDJ/LHM
1.Ti 2.Ti 3.Sr

(B79-50081)

Lasso, Orlando di
[Hieremiae prophetae lamentationes, et alia piae cantiones. *Selections*]. Six responsories for Tenebrae on Maundy Thursday, feria V in Coena Domini ad Matatinum / [by] Orlandus Lassus ; transcribed and edited by Clive Wearing. — London (72 Brewery Rd, N.7) : Mapa mundi, 1978. — 14p ; 4to. — (London Lassus series ; no.2)
Unpriced
Primary classification EZDJ/LHM
1.Ti 2.Ti 3.Sr

(B79-50082)

EZDGKH/LK — Divine Office. Tenebrae. Good Friday
Ammon, Blasius
[Sacrae cantiones. Tenebrae factae sunt]. Tenebrae factae sunt : for 4 voices / [by] Blasius Ammon ; transcribed and edited by Martyn Imrie. — London (72 Brewery Rd, N.7) : Mapa mundi, 1978. — 4p ; 4to. — (German-Slav church music ; no.2)
Unpriced
Primary classification EZDJ/LK
1.Ti 2.Ti 3.Imrie, Martyn 4.Sr

(B79-50083)

EZDGKJ — Divine Office. Vespers. Christmas
Law, Ronald
Hodie Christus natus est / [by] Ronald Law. — London (36 Ranelagh Gdns W.6) : Cathedral Music, 1978. — [2]p ; 8vo.
For unaccompanied mixed voices.
Unpriced
Primary classification EZDJ/LF
1.Ti

(B79-50077)

Marenzio, Luca
[Motecta festorum totius anni ... liber primus. Hodie Christus natus est]. Hodie Christas natus est / [by] Luca Marenzio ; transcribed and edited by Martyn Imrie. — London (72 Brewery Rd, N.7) : Mapa mundi, 1978. — 4p ; 4to. — (Italian church music ; no.2)
For S.A.T.B.
Unpriced
Primary classification EZDJ/LF
1.Ti 2.Ti 3.Imrie, Martyn 4.Sr

(B79-50073)

EZDGKJ/LNC — Divine Office. Vespers. Corpus Christi
Marenzio, Luca
[Motecta festorum totius anni ... liber primus. O sacrum convivium]. O sacrum convivium : motet for the Feast of Corpus Christi, for 4 voices / [by] Luca Marenzio ; transcribed and edited by Martyn Imrie. — London (72 Brewery Rd, N.7) : Mapa mundi, 1978. — 4p ; 4to. — (Italian church music ; no.1)
Unpriced
Primary classification EZDJ/LNC
1.Ti 2.Ti 3.Imrie, Martyn 4.Sr

(B79-50089)

EZDGKK — Divine Office. Vespers. Magnificat
Gagliano, Marco da
[Sacra cantiones, lib. 2. Magnificat]. Magnificat / [by] Marco da Gagliano ; edited by James Erber. — London : Cathedral Music, 1978. — 9p ; 8vo.
For SSST.
Unpriced
1.Ti 2.Erber, James

(B79-50054)

Lasso, Orlando di
Magnificat praetur rerum seriem : upon the motet by Josquin, for 6 voices / [by] Roland de Lassus ; transcribed and edited by Bruno Turner. — London (72 Brewery Rd, N.7) : Mapa mundi, 1978. — 15p ; 4to. — (Franco-Flemish church music ; no.2)
Unpriced
1.Ti 2.Turner, Bruno 3.Sr

(B79-50055)

Vivanco, Sebastian de
[Liber magnificarum. Magnificat octavi toni]. Magnificat octavi toni : for 8 voices / [by] Sebastian de Vivanco ; transcribed and edited by Bruno Turner. — London : Mapa mundi, 1978. — 20p ; 4to. — (Spanish church music ; no.18)
Unpriced
1.Ti 2.Ti 3.Turner, Bruno 4.Sr

(B79-50056)

EZDGKR/LF — Divine Office. Compline. Christmas
Lobo, Alfonso
[Liber primus missarum. Ave regina coelorum]. Ave regina coelorum : Compline and votive antiphon for the season from Christmas to the Purification / [by] Alfonso Lobo ; transcribed and edited by Bruno Turner. — London (72 Brewery Rd, N.7) : Mapa mundi, 1978. — 4p ; 4to. — (Spanish choral music ; no.13)
For S.S.A.T.B.
Unpriced
1.Ti 2.Ti 3.Turner, Bruno 4.Sr

(B79-50057)

EZDGKRM/LF — Divine Office. Compline. Office hymns. Christmas
Shepherd, John
Salvator mundi, Domine : Compline hymn for the Vigil of Christmas in the Sarum Use / [by] John Sheppard ; transcribed and edited by Bruno Turner. — London (72 Brewery Rd, N.7) : Mapa mundi, 1978. — 4p ; 4to. — (English church music ; n.2)
Unpriced
Primary classification EZDJ/LF
1.Ti 2.Turner, Bruno 3.Sr

(B79-50078)

EZDGMM — Anglican liturgy. Preces & responses
Fletcher, Andrew
Versicles and responses : Series 3 Morning and Evening Prayer / by Andrew Fletcher. — Croydon : Royal School of Church Music, 1978. — 8p ; 8vo.
For (a) SATB unaccompanied. (b) SATTB unaccompanied - 2nd tenors singing People's part (c) SATB and people (d) People and organ.
Unpriced
Also classified at JDGMM

(B79-50458)

Jackson, Francis
Versicles and responses (including the Sovereign's Accession) : S.A.(T.)T.B. / [by] Francis Jackson. — York : Banks, 1979. — 8p ; 8vo. — (Eboracum choral series ; 73)
Unpriced
1.Ti 2.Sr

(B79-50459)

Neary, Martin
Preces and responses / [by] Martin Neary. — Croydon : Royal School of Church Music, 1978. — [3]p ; 8vo.
Unpriced
1.Ti

(B79-50460)

EZDGPP — Anglican liturgy. Evening prayer. Canticles
Saunders, Neil
Magnificat and Nunc dimittis for five-part chorus of mixed voices unaccompanied / by Neil Saunders. — Wendover : Roberton, 1979. — 12p ; 8vo. — (Sacred music for mixed voices)
Duration 6 min.
£0.24
1.Sr

(B79-50461)

EZDH — Motets, Anthems, Hymns, etc
Argento, Dominick
A thanksgiving to God, for his house / [by] Dominick Argento ; poem by Robert Herrick. — [New York] ; [London] : Boosey and Hawkes, 1979. — 12p. ; 8vo.
For S.A.T.B. unaccompanied. — Duration 4 min.
Unpriced
1.Ti 2.Herrick, Robert

(B79-50875)

Howells, Herbert
I would be true / [by] Herbert Howells. — Croydon : Addington Press, 1978. — 7p ; 8vo.
For SATB and organ.
Unpriced
1.Ti

(B79-50876)

Nelson, Ron
Here we come as in the beginning / [by] Ron Nelson ; [text by] James Schevill. — [New York] ; [London] : Boosey and Hawkes, 1979. — 20p. ; 8vo.
For S.A.T.B. unaccompanied. — Duration 6 min.
Unpriced
1.Ti 2.Schevill, James

(B79-50877)

Praetorius, Michael
[Musae Sioniae Tl.3. Allein Gott in der Höh sei Ehr]. Allein Gott in der Höh sei Ehr : Choralbearbeitung für zwei vierstimmige Chöre / [von] Michael Praetorius ; herausgegeben von Friedel W. Böhler. — Kassel ; London : Bärenreiter, 1978. — 7p ; 8vo. — (Werkreihe für Bläser und Sänger)
£1.16
1.Ti 2.Ti 3.Böhler, Friedel W 4.Sr

(B79-50462)

Purcell, Daniel
[Bow down thine ear. I will thank thee, O Lord]. I will thank thee, O Lord / [by] Daniel Purcell ; transcribed by Christopher Dearnley from Bodleian Library Ms. mus. d.22C. — London (36 Ranelagh Gdns W.6) : Cathedral Music, 1978. — [2]p ; 8vo.
For SATB.
Unpriced
1.Ti 2.Ti 3.Dearnley, Christopher

(B79-50058)

Rose, Bernard
Three Addison anthems : for soprano, alto, tenor and bass / [by] Bernard Rose ; [words by] Joseph Addison. — [Croydon] : Addington Press, 1979. — 24p ; 8vo.
Unpriced
1.Ti 2.Addison, Joseph

(B79-50878)

Saetveit, Adolph
Spirit of peace : for four-part chorus of mixed voices a cappella / [by] Adolph Saetveit. — New York ; London : Schirmer, 1979. — 11p ; 8vo.
£0.45
1.Ti

(B79-50879)

Shephard, Richard
Three short anthems / by Richard Shephard. — Croydon : Royal School of Church Music, 1979. — 11p ; 8vo.
Contents: 1: Jesu! dulcis memoria, SATB with organ - 2: Prayer for a new mother, unison voices - 3: The birds, SATB unaccompanied.
Unpriced
Primary classification DJ
1.Ti

(B79-50835)

Snyder, Wesley
I love thy church, O God : for four-part chorus of mixed voices with optional piano accompaniment / [by] Wesley Snyder ; [words by] Timothy Dwight. — New York ; London : Schirmer, 1979. — 8p ; 8vo.
Based on 'Saint Thomas' by A. Williams.
Unpriced
1.Ti 2.Dwight, Timothy 3.Williams, A

(B79-50880)

EZDH/LK — Motets, Anthems, Hymns, etc. Good Friday
Schubert, Franz
[Stabat mater. Amen. *arr*]. Hallelujah amen ... : for four-part chorus of mixed voices a cappella / [by] Franz Schubert ; edited by Maynard Klein. — New York ; London : Schirmer, 1979. — 15p ; 8vo.
£0.45
1.Ti 2.Ti 3.Klein, Maynard

(B79-50463)

EZDH/LL — Motets, Easter
Beadell, Robert
I saw water flowing = Vidi aquam : anthem for Eastertide for four-part chorus of mixed voices a cappella / [by] Robert Beadell. — New York ; London : Schirmer, 1979. — 5p ; 8vo. — (Gordon H. Lamb conductors choral series)
Unpriced
1.Ti 2.Sr

(B79-50881)

EZDJ — Motets
Copland, Aaron
Four motets / [by] Aaron Copland ; texts drawn from Biblical sources. — [New York] ; [London] : Boosey and Hawkes.
For S.A.T.B. — Duration 2 min 40 secs.
[No.1] : Help us, O Lord ... — [1979]. — 7p ; 8vo.
Unpriced
1.Ti

(B79-50464)

[No.2] : Thou, O Jehovah ... — [1979]. — 8p ; 8vo.
Unpriced
1.Ti

(B79-50465)

[No.3] : Have mercy on us, O my Lord ... — [1979]. — 8p ; 8vo.
Unpriced
1.Ti

(B79-50466)

[No.4] : Sing ye praises to our King ... — [1979]. — 10p ; 8vo.
Unpriced
1.Ti

(B79-50467)

Escribano, Juan
Paradisi porta : motet for 6 voices / [by] Juan Escribano ; transcribed and edited by Martyn Imrie from Rome, Biblioteca Apostolica Vaticana Capp, Sist. ... — London (72 Brewery Rd, N.7) : Mapa mundi, 1978. — 4p ; 4to. — (Spanish church music ; no.8)
Unpriced
1.Ti 2.Imrie, Martyn 3.Sr

(B79-50059)

Esquivel, Juan
[Motecta festorum. Sancta Maria]. Sancta Maria / [by] Juan Esquivel ; transcribed and edited by Bruno Turner. — London (72 Brewery Rd, N.7) : Mapa mundi, 1978. — 4p ; 4to. — (Spanish church music ; no.5)
For S.S.A.T. — S.A.T.B.
Unpriced
1.Ti 2.Ti 3.Turner, Bruno 4.Sr

(B79-50060)

Fayrfax, Robert
Aeternae laudis lilium : for 5 voices / [by] Robert Fayrfax ; transcribed and edited by Peter Phillips. — London (72 Brewery Rd, N.7) : Mapa mundi, 1978. — 12p ; 4to. — (English church music ; no.5)
Unpriced
1.Ti 2.Phillips, Peter 3.Sr

(B79-50061)

Guerrero, Francisco
[Motecta. Duo seraphim]. Duo seraphim / [by] Francisco Guerrero ; transcribed and edited by Bruno Turner. — London : Mapa mundi, 1978. — 4p ; 4to. — (Spanish church music ; no.6)
For S.S.A.T. — S.A.T.B.
Unpriced
1.Ti 2.Ti 3.Turner, Bruno 4.Sr

(B79-50062)

Joubert, John
[Pro pace motets. Op.19, 32, 29]. Pro pace motets : for unaccompanied chorus / [by] John Joubert. — Sevenoaks : Novello, 1979. — [8],47p ; 8vo.
Previously published separately. — Contents: 1: Libera plebem, Op.19-2 : O tristia secla priora. Op.32-3 : Solus ad victiman. Op.29.
£1.95
1.Ti 2.Ti

(B79-50468)

Lobo, Alfonso
[Liber primus missarum. Ave maria]. Ave Maria : for 8 voices / [by] Alfonso Lobo ; transcribed and edited by Bruno Turner. — London (72 Brewery Rd, N.7) : Mapa mundi, 1978. — 8p ; 4to. — (Spanish church music ; no.11)
Unpriced
1.Ti 2.Ti 3.Turner, Bruno 4.Sr

(B79-50063)

Lobo, Alfonso
[Liber primus missarum. Quam pulchri sunt gressus tui]. Quam pulchri sunt gressus tui / [by] Alfonso Lobo ; transcribed and edited by Bruno Turner. — [London] : Mapa mundi, 1978. — 4p ; 4to. — (Spanish church music ; no.12)
For S.S.A.T.T.B.
Unpriced
1.Ti 2.Ti 3.Turner, Bruno 4.Sr

(B79-50064)

Philips, Peter
[Cantiones sacrae, octonis vocibus. Tu es Petrus]. Tu es Petrus : for 8 voices / [by] Peter Philips ; transcribed and edited by Peter Phillips. — [London] : Mapa mundi, 1978. — 7p ; 4to. — (English church music ; no.3)
Unpriced
1.Ti 2.Ti 3.Phillips, Peter 4.Sr

(B79-50065)

Tallis, Thomas
Sancte Deus / [by] Thomas Tallis ; transcribed and edited by Peter Phillips. — London (72 Brewery Rd, N.7) : Mapa mundi, 1978. — 4p ; 4to. — (English church music ; no.4)
For S.S.T. Bar.
Unpriced
1.Ti 2.Phillips, Peter 3.Sr

(B79-50066)

Tallis, Thomas
Videte miraculum : for 6 voices / [by] Thomas Tallis ; transcribed and edited by John Milsom. — London (72 Brewery Rd, N.7) : Mapa Mundi, 1978. — 7p ; 4to. — (English church music ; no.6)
Unpriced
1.Ti 2.Milsom, John 3.Sr

(B79-50067)

Victoria, Tomás Luis de
[Motecta, Sancta Maria]. Sancta Maria, and, Ecce sacerdos magnus : for four part chorus of mixed voices unaccompanied / Tomas Luis de Victoria ... ; edited by Martin Banner. — Wendover : Roberton, 1978. — 15p ; 8vo. — (Lawson-Gould sacred choral series)
£0.28
1.Ti 2.Banner, Martin 3.Ecce sacerdos magnus 4.Sr

(B79-50469)

EZDJ/AY — Motets. Collections
The **Chester** book of motets : sacred renaissance motets, with Latin texts / edited by Anthony G. Petti. — London : Chester Music.
7 : Motets for 3 voices. — 1979. — 45p ; 8vo.
Unpriced
1.Petti, Anthony Gaetano

(B79-50882)

EZDJ/KDN — Motets. Funerals
Lobo, Alfonso
[Liber primus missarum. Credo quod redemptor mens vivit]. Credo quod redemptor mens vivit : pro defunctis, for 4 voices / [by] Alfonso Lobo ; transcribed and edited by Bruno Turner. — [London] : Mapa mundi, 1978. — 4p ; 4to. — (Spanish choral music ; no.15)
Unpriced
Also classified at EZDGKH
1.Ti 2.Ti 3.Turner, Bruno 4.Sr

(B79-50068)

Lobo, Alfonso
[Liber primus missarum. Versa est in luctum]. Versa est in luctum : ad exsequias Philip II, cathol. regis Hisp. = for the funeral of Philip II, Catholic King of Spain / [by] Alfonso Lobo ; transcribed and edited by Bruno Turner. — London (72 Brewery Rd, N.7) : Mapa mundi, 1978. — 4p ; 4to. — (Spanish church music ; no.10)
Unpriced
1.Ti 2.Ti 3.Turner, Bruno 4.Sr

(B79-50069)

EZDJ/LEZ — Motets. Advent
Esquivel, Juan
Veni Domine : motet for the Advent season for 5 voices / [by] Juan Esquivel ; transcribed and edited by Bruno Turner. — London (72 Brewery Rd, N.7) : Mapa mundi, 1978. — 4p ; 4to. — (Spanish church music ; no.21)
Unpriced
1.Ti 2.Turner, Bruno 3.Sr

(B79-50070)

Esquivel, Juan
Vox clamantis in deserto : motet for the Advent season for 4 voices / [by] Juan Esquivel ; transcribed and edited by Bruno Turner. — London (72 Brewery Rd, N.7) : Mapa mundi, 1978. — [2p] ; 4to. — (Spanish church music ; no.22)
Unpriced
1.Ti 2.Turner, Bruno 3.Sr

(B79-50071)

Handl, Jacob
[Tomus primus operis musici. Rorate coeli]. Rorate coeli : motet for the Advent season, for 6 voices / [by] Jakob Handl ; transcribed and edited by Martyn Imrie. — [London] : Mapa mundi, 1978. — 4p ; 4to. — (German-Slav church music ; no.4)
Unpriced
Also classified at EZDGKH/LEZ
1.Ti 2.Ti 3.Imrie, Martyn 4.Sr

(B79-50072)

EZDJ/LF — Motets. Christmas
Ammon, Blasius
[Sacrae cantiones. Parvulus filius]. Parvulus filius : for 6 voices / [by] Blasius Ammon ; transcribed and edited by Martyn Imrie. — London (72 Brewery Rd, N.7) : Mapa mundi, 1978. — 4p ; 4to. — (German-Slav church music ; no.1)
Unpriced
1.Ti 2.Ti 3.Imrie, Martyn 4.Sr

(B79-50074)

Cristo, Pedro de
Quaeramus cum pastoribus : for 4 voices / [by] Pedro de Cristo ; transcribed and edited by Bruno Turner. — London (72 Brewery Rd, N.7) : Mapa mundi, 1978. — 4p ; 4to. — (Spanish church music ; no.20)
Unpriced
1.Ti 2.Turner, Bruno 3.Sr

(B79-50075)

Guerrero, Francisco
[Motecta ... liber secundus. Pastores loquebantur]. Pastores loquebantur / [by] Francisco Guerrero ; transcribed and edited by Martyn Imrie. — London (72 Brewery Rd, N.7) : Mapa mundi, 1978. — 8p ; 4to. — (Spanish church music ; no.17)
For S.S.A.T.B.B.
Unpriced
1.Ti 2.Ti 3.Imrie, Martyn 4.Sr

(B79-50076)

Law, Ronald
Hodie Christus natus est / [by] Ronald Law. — London (36 Ranelagh Gdns W.6) : Cathedral Music, 1978. — [2]p ; 8vo.
For unaccompanied mixed voices.
Unpriced
Also classified at EZDGKJ/LF
1.Ti

(B79-50077)

Marenzio, Luca
[Motecta festorum totius anni ... liber primus. Hodie Christus natus est]. Hodie Christas natus est / [by] Luca Marenzio ; transcribed and edited by Martyn Imrie. — London (72 Brewery Rd, N.7) : Mapa mundi, 1978. — 4p ; 4to. — (Italian church music ; no.2)
For S.A.T.B.
Unpiced
Also classified at EZDGKJ
1.Ti 2.Ti 3.Imrie, Martyn 4.Sr

(B79-50073)

Shepherd, John
Salvator mundi, Domine : Compline hymn for the Vigil of Christmas in the Sarum Use / [by] John Sheppard ; transcribed and edited by Bruno Turner. — London (72 Brewery Rd, N.7) : Mapa mundi, 1978. — 4p ; 4to. — (English church music ; n.2)
Unpriced
Also classified at EZDGKRM/LF
1.Ti 2.Turner, Bruno 3.Sr

(B79-50078)

Victoria, Tomás Luis de
[Motectas festorum. Quem vidistis, pastores?]. Quem vidistis, pastores? / [by] Tomás Luis de Victoria ; transcribed and edited by Bruno Turner. — London (72 Brewery Rd, N.7) : Mapa mundi, 1978. — 8p ; 4to. — (Spanish church music ; no.19)
For S.S.A.T.T.B.
Unpriced
1.Ti 2.Ti 3.Turner, Bruno 4.Sr

(B79-50079)

THE BRITISH CATALOGUE OF MUSIC

EZDJ/LG — Motets. Lent

Lobo, Alfonso
[Liber primus missarum. Vivo ego, dicit Dominus]. Vivo ego, dicit Dominus : motet for Lent for 4 voices / [by] Alfonso Lobo ; transcribed and edited by Bruno Turner. — London (72 Brewery Rd, N.7) : Mapa mundi, 1978. — 4p ; 4to. — (Spanish choral music ; no.16)
Unpriced
1.Ti 2.Ti 3.Turner, Bruno 4.Sr
(B79-50080)

EZDJ/LHM — Motets. Maundy Thursday

Lasso, Orlando di
[Hieremiae prophetae lamentationes, et alia piae cantiones. *Selections*]. Lamentations for Tenebrae on Maundy Thursday, Feria V in Coena Domini ad Matatinum / [by] Orlandus Lassus ; transcribed and edited by Clive Wearing. — London (72 Brewery Rd, N.7) : Mapa Mundi, 1978. — 23p ; 4to. — (London Lassus series ; no.1)
For SATTB.
Unpriced
Also classified at EZDGKH/LHM
1.Ti 2.Ti 3.Sr
(B79-50081)

Lasso, Orlando di
[Hieremiae prophetae lamentationes, et alia piae cantiones. *Selections*]. Six responsories for Tenebrae on Maundy Thursday, feria V in Coena Domini ad Matatinum / [by] Orlandus Lassus ; transcribed and edited by Clive Wearing. — London (72 Brewery Rd, N.7) : Mapa mundi, 1978. — 14p ; 4to. — (London Lassus series ; no.2)
Unpriced
Also classified at EZDGKH/LHM
1.Ti 2.Ti 3.Sr
(B79-50082)

EZDJ/LK — Motets. Good Friday

Ammon, Blasius
[Sacrae cantiones. Tenebrae factae sunt]. Tenebrae factae sunt : for 4 voices / [by] Blasius Ammon ; transcribed and edited by Martyn Imrie. — London (72 Brewery Rd, N.7) : Mapa mundi, 1978. — 4p ; 4to. — (German-Slav church music ; no.2)
Unpriced
Also classified at EZDGKH/LK
1.Ti 2.Ti 3.Imrie, Martyn 4.Sr
(B79-50083)

Gabrieli, Andrea
Maria stabat / [by] Andrea Gabreli ; [text from] St John XX. — London (36 Ranelagh Gdns W.6) : Cathedral Music, 1978. — 7p ; 8vo.
For SAATBB. — Edited by R. Barnes.
Unpriced
1.Ti
(B79-50084)

EZDJ/LM — Motets. Ascension

Byrd, William
[Gradualia, lib. 2. Alleluia, ascendit Deus]. Alleluia, our Lord is risen : for mixed chorus SSATB / [by] William Byrd ; arranged and edited by John Kingsbury ; English text by J.K. — New York : Broude ; [London] : [Breitkopf und Härtel], 1979. — 6p ; 8vo.
£0.42
1.Ti 2.Ti 3.Kingsbury, John
(B79-50470)

Handl, Jacob
[Secundus tomus musici operis. Ascendens Christus]. Ascendens Christus : motet for the Ascension of our Lord, for 4 voices / [by] Jakob Handl ; transcribed and edited by Martyn Imrie. — London (72 Brewery Rd, N.7) : Mapa mundi, 1978. — 3p ; 3to. — (German-Slav church music ; no.3)
Unpriced
1.Ti 2.Ti 3.Imrie, Martyn 4.Sr
(B79-50085)

Silva, Andreas de
Omnis pulchritudo Domini : motet for the Ascension of our Lord, for 5 voices / [by] Andreas de Silva ; transcribed and edited by Martyn Imrie. — London (72 Brewery Rd, N.7) : Mapa mundi, 1978. — 8p ; 4to. — (Franco-Flemish church music ; no.6)
Unpriced
1.Ti 2.Imrie, Martyn 3.Sr
(B79-50086)

EZDJ/LN — Motets. Whitsun

Gagliano, Marco da
[Sacra cantiones, lib.2. Veni creator spiritus]. Veni creator spiritus / [by] Marco da Gagliano ; edited by James Erber. — London : Cathedral Music, 1978. — 6p ; 8vo.
Unpriced
1.Ti 2.Erber, James
(B79-50087)

EZDJ/LNC — Motets. Corpus Christi

Lobo, Alfonso
[Liber primus missarum. O quam suavis est, Domine]. O quam suavis est, Domine : motet for the Feast of Corpus Christi, for 6 voices / [by] Alfonso Lobo ; transcribed and edited by Bruno Turner. — London (72 Brewery Rd, N.7) : Mapa mundi, 1978. — 7p ; 4to. — (Spanish choral music ; no.14)
Unpriced
1.Ti 2.Ti 3.Turner, Bruno 4.Sr
(B79-50088)

Marenzio, Luca
[Motecta festorum totius anni ... liber primus. O sacrum convivium]. O sacrum convivium : motet for the Feast of Corpus Christi, for 4 voices / [by] Luca Marenzio ; transcribed and edited by Martyn Imrie. — London (72 Brewery Rd, N.7) : Mapa mundi, 1978. — 4p ; 4to. — (Italian church music ; no.1)
Unpriced
Also classified at EZDGKJ/LNC
1.Ti 2.Ti 3.Imrie, Martyn 4.Sr
(B79-50089)

EZDJ/LQ — Motets. All Saints

Porta, Constanzo
[Liber primus motectorum quatuor vocum. Vidi turbam magnam]. Vidi turbam magnam : motet for All Saints' Day, for 4 voices / [by] Costanzo Porta ; transcribed and edited by Martyn Imrie. — London (72 Brewery Rd, N.7) : Mapa mundi, 1978. — 4p ; 4to. — (Italian church music ; no.3)
Unpriced
1.Ti 2.Ti 3.Imrie, Martyn 4.Sr
(B79-50090)

Victoria, Tomás Luis de
[Motecta. O quam gloriosum est regnum]. Motet and mass, O quam gloriosum est regnum / [by] Tomás Luis de Victoria ; edited by Thomas Rive. — London : Eulenburg, 1978. — xii,31p ; 8vo.
The mass which is here published with the motet is taken from 'Missarum libri duo'. — Miniature score.
Unpriced
Also classified at EZDG
1.Ti 2.Ti 3.Rive, Thomas
(B79-50091)

EZDK — Anthems

Dearnley, Christopher
The isles of the sea : anthem for unaccompanied choir ... / [by] Christopher Dearnley ; [text from] Isaiah XXIV ... — London (36 Ranelagh Gdns W.6) : Cathedral Music, 1978. — 5p ; 8vo. — (Saint Paul's series ; no.12)
Earlier numbers issued without series title. — For SATB.
Unpriced
1.Ti 2.Sr
(B79-50092)

Reimann, Aribert
John III, 16 = Johannes III, 16 : for mixed chorus a capp;ella = für gemischten Chor a cappella / [by] Aribert Reimann. — Mainz ; London : Schott, 1976. — 36p ; 4to.
Multilingual text.
Unpriced
1.Ti
(B79-50093)

Vance, Margaret
I will give thanks : for four-part chorus of mixed voices with piano accompaniment / [by] Margaret Vance ; [from] Psalm 9. — New York ; London : Schirmer, 1979. — 11p ; 8vo.
£0.45
1.Ti
(B79-50883)

EZDP/LF — Carols. Christmas

Carter, Andrew
De Virgin Mary : West Indian traditional carol. S.A.T.B. unacc. / arr. Andrew Carter. — York : Banks, 1979. — 8vo. — (Eboracum choral series ; 86)
Unpriced
1.Ti 2.Sr
(B79-50884)

Cary, Tristram
Two nativity songs / arranged from 'Piae cantiones' for unaccompanied mixed voices by Tristram Cary. — London : Oxford University Press, 1979. — 15p ; 8vo.
Latin text.
ISBN 0-19-343536-5 : Unpriced
1.Ti
(B79-50885)

Grüber, Franz Xaver
[Stille Nacht, heilige Nacht. *arr*]. Silent night / music, Franz Grüber ; arr. Barry Rose ; words, J. Mohr ; tr. various. — London (36 Ranelagh Gdns W.6) : Cathedral Music, 1978. — s. sh ; 8vo.
Unpriced
1.Ti 2.Ti 3.Mohr, J 4.Rose, Barry
(B79-50094)

Hedges, Anthony
Mary's carol / words and music by Anthony Hedges. — London : Universal, 1979. — 8p ; 8vo.
Voices only, or with the addition of instrumental parts.
Unpriced
1.Ti
(B79-50886)

Kirkpatrick, William Jerome
[Away in a manger. *arr*]. Away in a manger / melody, W.K. Kirkpatrick ; arr. Barry Rose, words, anon. — London (36 Ranelagh Gdns W.6) : Cathedral Music, 1978. — s.sh ; 8vo.
For SATB.
Unpriced
1.Ti 2.Rose, Barry
(B79-50095)

Law, Ronald
Joy on this day / words and music, Ronald Law. — London (36 Ranelagh Gdns W.6) : Cathedral Music, 1978. — [2]p ; 8vo.
For S.A.T.B.
Unpriced
1.Ti
(B79-50096)

EZDR — Psalms
Brumel, Antoine
Laudate Dominum de caelis : for 4 voices / [by] Antoine Brumel ; transcribed and edited by Martyn Imrie. — London (72 Brewery Rd, N.7) : Mapa mundi, 1978. — 12p ; 4to. — (Franco-Flemish church music ; no.4)
Unpriced
1.Ti 2.Imrie, Martyn 3.Sr
(B79-50097)

Haydn, Joseph
[Sechs englische Psalmen. Hob. XXIII Anhang, Nachtrag]. Sechs Psalmen = Six psalms : für dreistimmigen gemischten Chor = for three-part mixed chorus, Hob. XXIII Anhang, Nachtrag / [von] Joseph Haydn ; auf englische Nachdichtungen von James Merrick mit neuen deutschen Texten von Eva Rechlin herausgegeben von Ulrich W. Zimmer. — Kassel ; London : Bärenreiter, 1979. — 23p ; 4to. — (Chor-Archiv)
English & German text.
£2.31
1.Ti 2.Ti 3.Zimmer, Ulrich W 4.Sr
(B79-50471)

Richafort, Jean
Ecce quam bonum : See how good, how right : for four-part chorus of mixed voices a cappella / [by] Jean Richafort ; edited by Maynard Klein ; Psalm 133 adapted by M.K. — New York ; London : Schirmer, 1978. — 4p ; 8vo.
Latin & English text.
£0.30
1.Ti 2.Klein, Maynard
(B79-50472)

EZDU — Madrigals
Bennet, John
Madrigals to foure voices (1599) / [by] John Bennet ; edited by Edmund H. Fellowes, revised by Davitt Moroney. — London : Stainer and Bell, 1979. — x,131p ; 8vo. — (The English madrigalists ; no.23)
ISBN 0-85249-456-4 : Unpriced
1.Ti 2.Fellowes, Edmund Horace 3.Moroney, Davitt 4.Sr
(B79-50473)

Lasso, Orlando di
[Libro de villanelle. O occhi manza mia]. O occhi manza mia = Thine eyes, oh, my beloved : for four-part chorus of mixed voices a cappella / [by] Orlando di Lasso ... ; edited by Maynard Klein ; English text by M.K. — New York ; London : Schirmer, 1979. — 4p ; 8vo.
£0.35
1.Ti 2.Ti 3.Klein, Maynard
(B79-50887)

Lasso, Orlando di
[Libro de villanelle. Tutto lo di]. Day after day, they all say 'sing' : Tutto lo di mi dici : for eight-part chorus of mixed voices a cappella / [by] Orlando di Lasso ; edited by Maynard Klein, English text by M.K. — New York ; London : Schirmer, 1978. — 16p ; 8vo.
.£0.45
1.Ti 2.Ti 3.Klein, Maynard
(B79-50474)

Vecchi, Horatio
[Canzonetti ... libro quarto a quattro voci. Partiro si]. Partirò sì = Parting is pain : for four-part chorus of mixed voices a cappella / [by] Orazio Vecchi ; edited by Maynard Klein ; English text by M.K. — New York ; London : Schirmer, 1978. — 8p ; 8vo.
£0.35
1.Ti 2.Ti 3.Klein, Maynard
(B79-50475)

EZDW — Songs, etc
Binkerd, Gordon
Promises like pie-crust : SATB / [by] Gordon Binkerd ; texts Christina Rossetti and Dante Gabriel Rossetti. — [New York] ; [London] : Boosey and Hawkes, 1978. — 20p ; 8vo.
Unpriced
1.Ti 2.Rossetti, Christina 3.Rossetti, Dante Gabriel
(B79-50098)

Brahms, Johannes
[Es ist ein Ros entsprungen. Op. 122, no.8. *arr*]. Es ist ein Ros entsprungen = Now blooms a rose so tender / adapted by Gordon Binkerd from Johannes Brahms' organ chorale prelude (op.122, no.8) based on the Michael Praetorius chorale; German text anonymous; English translation by Gordon Binkerd. — [New York] ; [London] : Boosey and Hawkes, 1979. — 7p ; 8vo.
Unpriced
1.Ti 2.Binkerd, Gordon 3.Praetorius, Michael
(B79-50888)

Brown, Christopher
Even such is time : for mixed chorus / music by Christopher Brown ; words by Walter Raleigh. — London : J. and W. Chester, 1979. — 8p ; 8vo. — (Contemporary choral series)
For S.A.T.B.
Unpriced
1.Ti 2.Raleigh, Sir Walter 3.Sr
(B79-50476)

Burkhard, Willy
Fünf Gesänge für gemischten Chor nach Gedichten von Richard Dehmel, Opus 26 / [von] Willy Burkhard. — Kassel ; [London] : Bärenreiter, 1978. — 8p ; 8vo. — (Bärenreiter - Chorreihe)
Contents: 1: Freudenruf - 2: Vorgefühl - 3: Ständchen - 4: Die stille Stadt - 5: Werkspruch.
£1.16
1.Ti 2.Dehmel, Richard 3.Sr
(B79-50477)

De Cormier, Robert
Frankie and Johnny : for four-part chorus of mixed voices with soprano, alto, baritone and tenor solos a cappella / adapted by Robert de Cormier. — Wendover : Roberton, 1978. — 14p ; 8vo. — (Robert de Cormier choral series)
£0.28
1.Ti 2.Sr
(B79-50478)

Diemer, Emma Lou
Tell me, dearest, what is love? : for mixed chorus a cappella / [by] Emma Lou Diemer ; [words by] John Fletcher ... — New York : Broude ; [London] : [Breitkopf and Härtel], 1979. — 8p ; 8vo.
£0.42
1.Ti 2.Fletcher, John
(B79-50889)

Dvořák, Antonín
[Amid nature. Op.63. A song went to my heart]. So many songs = Es zog manch Lied : for four-part chorus of mixed voices a cappella / [by] Antonín Dvořák ; English text by Jane May. — New York ; London : Schirmer, 1979. — 8p ; 8vo.
Text in German and English.
£0.35
1.Ti 2.Ti 3.May, Jane
(B79-50890)

Dvořák, Antonín
[Amid nature. Op.63. Birch tree by the verdant slope]. Birch tree on green hill = Birke am grünen Bergeshang : for four-part chorus of mixed voices a cappella / [by] Antonín Dvořák ... ; English text by Jane May. — New York ; London : Schirmer, 1979. — 11p ; 8vo.
Text by Vítězslav Hálek, translated from the Czech.
£0.45
1.Ti 2.Ti 3.May, Jane 4.Hálek, Vítězslav
(B79-50891)

Dvořák, Antonín
[Amid nature. Op.63. Golden fields]. Golden meadows = Goldne Fluren : for four-part chorus of mixed voices a cappella / [by] Antonín Dvořák ; English text by Jane May. — New York ; London : Schirmer, 1979. — 7p ; 8vo.
Text in German and English.
£0.35
1.Ti 2.Ti 3.May, Jane
(B79-50892)

Dvořák, Antonín
[Amid nature. Op.63. This is in truth a day of joy]. A summer
day = Ein Sommertag : for four-part chorus of mixed voices a
cappella / [by] Antonín Dvořák ... ; English text by Jane May. —
New York ; London : Schirmer, 1979. — 12p ; 8vo.
Text by Vitězslav Hálek, translated from the Czech.
£0.45
1.Ti 2.Ti 3.May, Jane 4.Hálek, Vitězslav

(B79-50893)

Elgar, Sir Edward, bart
[Part-songs. Selections]. The early part-songs 1890-1891 : for
SATB with divisions / [by] Edward Elgar. — Sevenoaks :
Novello, 1979. — [2],29p ; 8vo.
Contents: O happy eyes. Op.18, no.1 - Love. Op.18, no.2 - My love dwelt in
a northern land - Spanish serenade. Op.23.
£1.15
1.Ti

(B79-50894)

Genzmer, Harald
Lied des Vogelstellers : drei leichte Chorlieder No.1 / [von]
Harald Genzmer ; [Text von] Jacques Prévert. — Mainz ;
London : Schott, 1979. — 4p ; 8vo. — (Schott's Chorverlag)
For mixed voices.
£0.72
1.Ti 2.Prévert, Jacques 3.Sr

(B79-50895)

Genzmer, Harald
Rechenstunde : drei leichte Chorlieder, für gemischten Chor
No.3 / von Harald Genzmer ; [Text von] Jacques Prévert. —
Mainz ; London : Schott, 1979. — 8p ; 8vo.
£0.72
1.Ti 2.Prévert, Jacques

(B79-50896)

Genzmer, Harald
Stadturlaub : drei leichte Chorlieder No.2 / [von] Harald
Genzmer ; [Text von] Jacques Prévert. — Mainz ; London :
Schott, 1979. — 4p ; 8vo. — (Schott's Chorverlag)
For mixed voices.
£0.72
1.Ti 2.Prévert, Jacques 3.Sr

(B79-50897)

Maconchy, Elizabeth
Four miniatures for unaccompanied chorus SATB / words by
Eleanor Farjeon ; music by Elizabeth Maconchy. — London :
Chester Music, 1979. — [2],21p ; 8vo. — (Contemporary choral
series)
Contents: Light the lamps up, lamplighter - For snow - The night will never
stay - For a mocking voice.
Unpriced
1.Ti 2.Farjeon, Eleanor 3.Sr

(B79-50479)

Monteverdi, Claudio
[L'Orfeo. Vieni Imeneo. arr]. Zwei Chöre aus 'Orpheus' = Two
chorusses [sic] from 'Orpheus' / [von] Claudio Monteverdi ;
[bearbeitet von] Carl Orff; [deutscher Text von] Dorothee
Günther; englischer Text... Robert Hess. — Mainz ; [London] :
Schott, 1979. — 11p ; 4to. — (Schott's Chorverlag)
Contents: 1. Preist diesen Tag der Freude = Praised be this day - 2. Froher
Tag, lichter Tag = Joyous day, shining day.
£0.80
1.Ti 2.Orff, Carl 3.Günther, Dorothee 4.Hess, Robert 5.Sr

(B79-50898)

Nelson, Havelock
Kitty of Coleraine : traditional Irish, S.A.T.B. unacc. / arr.
Havelock Nelson. — York : Banks, 1979. — 7p ; 8vo. —
(Eboracum choral series ; 75)
Unpriced
1.Ti 2.Sr

(B79-50899)

Pierce, Brent
One dream : for a cappella SATB chorus / by Brent Pierce. —
New York : Warner ; [London] : [Blossom], 1979. — 8p ; 8vo.
Unpriced
1.Ti

(B79-50900)

Rhein, Robert
Ae fond kiss : for four-part chorus of mixed voices with baritone
solo a cappella / traditional Scottish melody arranged by Robert
Rhein ; [words by] Robert Burns. — New York ; London :
Schirmer, 1979. — 6p ; 8vo.
£0.35
1.Ti 2.Burns, Robert

(B79-50901)

Rhein, Robert
Kelvingrove : for four-part chorus of mixed voices a cappella with
optional piano / traditional Scottish melody arranged by Robert
Rhein ; [words by] Thomas Lyle. — New York ; London :
Schirmer, 1979. — 7p ; 8vo.
£0.55
1.Ti 2.Lyle, Thomas

(B79-50902)

Schallehn, Hilger
Steht auf und singt : festlicher Spruch / [von] Hilger Schallehn ;
[Text] Max Barthel. — Mainz ; [London] : Schott, 1979. — 10p. ;
8vo. — (Schottes Chorverlag)
£0.80
1.Ti 2.Sr

(B79-50903)

Trojahn, Manfred
Madrigal : für achtstimmigen Chor, 1975 / [von] Manfred
Trojahn. — Kassel ; London : Bärenreiter, 1978. — [2],12p ; fol.
Based on 'Ecco, moriro dunque' by Gesualdo.
£3.96
1.Ti

(B79-50099)

EZDW/AYDK — Songs, etc. Collections. Wales
Welsh popular songs : a collection of some of the most popular
Welsh songs and hymns ... / by Nick Roberts ... ; with Welsh and
English words [and] tonic sol-fa and chord symbols. —
Manchester ((82 Princess St.)) : Music Exchange, 1978. — 23p ;
4to.
Unpriced

(B79-50480)

EZDW/G/AYD — Folk songs. Collections. England
Suite nach englischen Volksliedern / Satz und deutsche
Textfassung, Heinrich Poos. — Mainz ; [London] : Schott. —
(Schott's Chorverlag)
English and German text.
No.1 : The keel row. Einst kam ich nach Sandgate. — 1979. — 8p ; 8vo.
£0.72
1.Poos, Heinrich 2.Sr

(B79-50481)

No.2 : The old true love. Ach komm, tritt ein. — 1979. — 4p ; 8vo.
£0.48
1.Poos, Heinrich 2.Sr

(B79-50482)

No.3 : The keeper. Ein Jager wollte jagen gehn. — 1979. — 12p ; 8vo.
£0.80
1.Poos, Heinrich 2.Sr

(B79-50483)

No.4 : There's none to soothe. Wo weilst du, Lieb. — 1979. — 4p ; 8vo.
£0.48
1.Poos, Heinrich 2.Sr

(B79-50484)

No.5 : The miller of Dee. War einst ein braver Mullersmann. — 1979. —
7p ; 8vo.
£0.72
1.Poos, Heinrich 2.Sr

(B79-50485)

Suite nach englischen Volksliedern / Satzund deutsche Textfassung,
Heinrich Poos. — Mainz ; [London] : Schott. — (Schott's
Chorverlag)
English and German text.
No.6 : Cock a doodle doo. — 1979. — 4p ; 8vo.
£0.48
1.Poos, Heinrich 2.Sr

(B79-50486)

EZDW/LC — Spirituals
Clements, John
Weepin' Mary : negro spiritual, S.A.T.B. unaccompanied /
arranged by John Clements. — London : EMI, 1978. — 4p ; 8vo.
Unpriced
1.Ti

(B79-50487)

EZDW/LF — Songs, etc. Christmas
Carter, Andrew
The twelve days of Christmas : English traditional carol, S.A.T.B.
unacc. / arr. Andrew Carter. — York : Banks, 1979. — 12p ;
8vo. — (Eboracum choral series ; 85)
Unpriced
1.Ti 2.Sr

(B79-50904)

EZDX — Secular cantatas
Berger, Jean
The fruit of the vine : for full chorus of mixed voices a cappella /
[by] Jean Berger ; on texts by Sir Walter Raleigh, George
Saintsbury, Book of Proverbs. — New York ; London : Schirmer,
1979. — 26p ; 8vo.
Unpriced
1.Ti

(B79-50905)

F — FEMALE VOICES, CHILDREN'S VOICES
FADW — Songs, etc. Choral scores
Binkerd, Gordon
[On the king's highway. *Chorus score*]. On the king's highway :
for children's chorus and chamber orchestra / [by] Gordon
Binkerd ; poems by James Stephens. — New York ; [London] :
Boosey and Hawkes, 1979. — 12p ; 8vo.
Unpriced
1.Ti 2.Ti 3.Stephens, James

(B79-50488)

Schubert, Heino
[Die kleinen Jahreszeiten. *Choral score*]. Die kleinen Jahreszeiten :
Fraunchor und Klavier / [von] Heino Schubert. — Mainz ;
[London] : Schott, 1979. — 16p ; 8vo.
£1.00
1.Ti 2.Ti

(B79-50906)

FDE/LK — Religious cantatas. Good Friday
Stainer, *Sir* John
[The crucifixion. *arr*]. The crucifixion : a meditation on the Sacred
Passion of the Holy Redeemer / [by] John Stainer ; arranged for
tenor (or soprano) and bass (or alto) soli, SSA and organ, with
hymns for congregational participation by Desmond Ratcliffe;
words selected and written by the Reverend J. Sparrow-Simpson,
M.A. — Sevenoaks : Novello, 1978. — [2],77p ; 8vo.
The organ part has been edited by the arranger. — Duration 50 min.
£1.55
Also classified at DE/LK
1.Ti 2.Ti 3.Sparrow-Simpson, J

(B79-50100)

FDE/LP — Religious cantatas. Harvest
Cartwright, Kenneth
Harvest jazz : a cantata for schools / [by] Kenneth Cartwright ;
words by Leighton Stubbs. — London : Boosey and Hawkes,
1979. — 4to.
Vocal score & 4 parts.
Unpriced
1.Ti 2.Stubbs, Leighton

(B79-50489)

FDGPP — Anglican liturgy. Evening Prayer. Canticles
Burgon, Geoffrey
Magnificat and Nunc dimittis / [by] Geoffrey Burgon. —
London : Chester Music, 1979. — 11p. ; 4to. — (Contemporary
church music series)
Magnificat for two-part chorus. — Nunc dimittis originally published
separately..
Unpriced
1.Ti 2.Sr

(B79-50907)

FDH/LF — Motets, Anthems, Hymns, etc. Christmas
Campbell, Sidney Schofield
[Praise to God in the highest. *arr*]. Praise to God in the highest :
Russian melody / arranged by S.S. Campbell ; adapted, two-part
with some divisi, by John Ottley ; words translated by A.F.D. —
London : Oxford University Press, 1979. — 4p ; 8vo. — (Oxford
easy anthems ; E141)
ISBN 0-19-351126-6 : Unpriced
1.Ti 2.Ottley, John 3.D., A F 4.Sr

(B79-50490)

FDP/LF — Carols. Christmas
Price, Beryl
Two songs of the nativity : for two-part choir and piano / words
and music by Beryl Price. — Wendover : Roberton, 1979. —
11p ; 8vo.
Duration 2 min. — Contents: 1: Bethlehem. Star. 2: Glory to God.
£0.24
1.Ti

(B79-50491)

FDR — Psalms
How, Martin
Psalm 23 / [by] Martin How. — London : Weinberger, 1979. —
4p ; 8vo.
For S.A., unison voices or baritone solo with organ.
Unpriced
Also classified at JDR
1.Ti

(B79-50908)

FDW — Songs, etc
Arch, Gwen
The spinning wheel : S.S.A.A. (with divisi) / Irish folk song
arranged by Gwyn Arch. — London : Oxford University Press,
1979. — 12p ; 8vo. — (Oxford choral songs ; W99)
ISBN 0-19-342599-8 : Unpriced
1.Ti 2.Sr

(B79-50909)

Benger, Richard
Fare well / music by Richard Benger ; words by Walter de la
Mare. — London : Edwin Ashdown, 1978. — 7p ; 8vo. — (Vocal
trios ; no.73)
Duration 2 1/2 min.
£0.20
1.Ti 2.De la Mare, Walter 3.Sr

(B79-50101)

Benger, Richard
Music : for S.S.C. / music by Richard Benger ; words by Walter
de la Mare. — London : Edwin Ashdown, 1979. — 11p ; 8vo. —
(Vocal trios ; no.74)
Duration 3 1/2 min.
£0.25
1.Ti 2.De la Mare, Walter 3.Sr

(B79-50102)

Brahms, Johannes
[Komm'bald. Op.97, no.5. *arr*]. Come soon = Komm bald : for
three-part chorus of women's voices with piano accompaniment /
[by] Johannes Brahms ; arranged by J.R. Carroll ; [text by] Klaus
Groth ; English text by J.R.C. — New York ; London : Schirmer,
1978. — 6p ; 8vo.
English text.
£0.35
1.Ti 2.Ti 3.Carroll, Joseph Robert 4.Groth, Klaus

(B79-50492)

Brahms, Johannes
[Wie die Wolke. Op.6, no.5. *arr*]. As the clouds with longing
wander : Wie die Wolke : for three-part chorus of women's voices
with piano accompaniment / [by] Johannes Brahms ; arranged by
J.R. Carroll, [words by] von Fallersleben, English text by J.R.C.
— New York ; London : Schirmer, 1978. — 7p ; 8vo.
English text only.
£0.35
1.Ti 2.Ti 3.Fallersleben, Hoffmann von 4.Carroll, Joseph Robert

(B79-50493)

Bresgen, Cesar
[Tiertanzburlesken. *Vocal score*]. Tiertanzburlesken / [von] Cesar
Bresgen ; nach Texten von Eva Rechlin ; für ein-bis dreistimmigen
Kinderchor und Klavier (weitere Instrumente ad lib.). — Mainz ;
London : Schott, 1979. — 40p ; 8vo. — (Bausteine für
Musikerziehung und Musikpflege ; Werkreihe B.187)
Unpriced
1.Ti 2.Rechlin, Eva 3.Sr

(B79-50103)

De Cormier, Robert
The Erie Canal, and, Great grandad : American folk songs, for
two-part chorus of equal voices and piano / arranged by Robert
de Cormier. — Wendover : Roberton, 1978. — 15p ; 8vo. —
(Robert de Cormier choruses for young voices)
The Erie Canal has piano and percussion accompaniment.
£0.28
1.Ti 2.Great grandaad 3.Sr

(B79-50494)

Franz, Robert
[Mutter, o sing 'mich zur Ruh', op.10, no.3. *arr*]. Mother, O sing
me to sleep = Mutter, O sing mich zur ruh' : for three-part
chorus of female voices and piano / by Robert Franz ... ; arranged
by Robert S. Hines. — Wendover : Roberton, 1979. — 7p ; 8vo.
— (Treble clef choral series)
£0.24
1.Ti 2.Ti 3.Hines, Robert S 4.Sr

(B79-50910)

Holst, Gustav
[Part-songs. *Selections*]. Songs of land, sea and air : a collection of
part songs and canons for equal voices with piano
accompaniment / by Gustav Holst. — Sevenoaks : Novello, 1979.
— [3],28p ; 8vo.
Works comprise H.110-2, 110-3, 138-1, 138-2, 110-1, 40, 150.
Unpriced
1.Ti

(B79-50104)

Hudson, Hazel
Will you be my partner? : a quodlibet / arranged, from
well-known melodies, by Hazel Hudson. — London : Edwin
Ashdown, 1979. — 12p ; 8vo. — (Ashdown vocal duets ; no.393)
For 2 voices, optional percussion and piano. — Duration 21/4 min.
£0.25
1.Ti 2.Sr

(B79-50911)

Laburda, Jiří
[Dobry den]. What a day : Dobry den : a choral cycle, for
two-part chorus of young voices with piano accompaniment or a
cappella / [by] Jiří Laburda ; [words by] Josef Bursík ; English
version by Jane May. — New York ; London : Schirmer, 1978. —
22p ; 8vo.
£2.10
Also classified at FEZDW
1.Ti 2.Ti 3.Bursík, Josef 4.May, Jane

(B79-50495)

Ross, Colin
Gently the breeze blows : two-part / [by] Colin Ross ; [words by]
Madeline Chase. — York : Banks, 1979. — 4p ; 8vo. —
(Eboracum choral series ; 81)
Unpriced
1.Ti 2.Chase, Madeline 3.Sr
(B79-50496)

Yancy, Marvin
[Our love. *arr*]. Our love / words and music by Marvin Yancy
and Chuck Jackson ; arranged for S.S.A. with piano and optional
drums by Jacques Rizzo. — Bryn Mawr ; [London] : Chappell,
1978. — 10p ; 8vo.
Unpriced
1.Ti 2.Jackson, Chuck 3.Rizzo, Jacques
(B79-50105)

FDW/GBB — Pop songs
Goodrum, Randy
[You needed me. *arr*]. You needed me : S.S.A. with piano and
optional drums / words and music by Randy Goodrum; arranged
by Jacques Rizzo. — Bryn Maur ; [London] : Chappell, 1979. —
8p. ; 8vo.
Unpriced
1.Ti 2.Rizzo, Jacques
(B79-50912)

FDW/JR — Songs, etc. Films
Lerner, Samuel
[Popeye the sailor. I'm Popeye the sailorman. *arr*]. I'm Popeye the
sailor man : for two-part chorus and piano / words and music by
Sammy Lerner ; arranged by Andrew Balent. — New York :
Warner ; [London] : [Blossom], 1978. — 6p ; 8vo. —
(Supersounds series for young chorus)
Unpriced
1.Ti 2.Ti 3.Balent, Andrew 4.Sr
(B79-50106)

FDX — Secular cantatas
Schubert, Heino
Die kleinen Jahreszeiten : Fra nuenchur und Klavier / [von]
Heino Schubert. — Mainz ; London : Schott, 1979. — 20p ; 8vo.
£4.10
1.Ti
(B79-50497)

**FE/NYHSDE/LF — With recorders & percussion. Religious
cantatas. Christmas**
Leaper, Kenneth
Yule : for two speakers, children's voices, games players, piano,
with occasional recorders : melodicas, tuned and untuned
percussion / [by] Kenneth Leaper. — London : Chappell, 1979.
— 36p. ; 4to.
Unpriced
1.Ti
(B79-50913)

FE/SQPLRDR — With cello & organ. Psalms
Goehr, Alexander
Psalm 4 : for soprano, alto, female chorus, viola solo, and organ /
[by] Alexander Goehr. — London : Schott, 1979. — [2],15p ; 4to.
£1.85
1.Ti
(B79-50914)

FE/XMDW/JN — With percussion. Songs, etc. Mime
Wesley-Smith, Martin
Machine : a music mime, for choir, percussion and tape / by
Martin Wesley-Smith. — [Sydney] ; [London] : Universal, 1978.
— [4],12p ; obl. 4to.
The tape is optional.
Unpriced
1.Ti
(B79-50915)

FE/XTPLXTQWDK — With glockenspiel & triangle. Anthems
Wienhorst, Richard
Bless the Lord, O my soul : for two-part chorus of women's voices
with glockenspiel and triangle accompaniment / [by] Richard
Wienhorst ; [text from] Psalm 103 ... — New York ; London :
Associated Music, 1978. — 4p ; 8vo.
£0.30
1.Ti
(B79-50498)

Wienhorst, Richard
Taste and see : for two-part chorus of women's voices with
glockenspiel and triangle / [by] Richard Wienhorst ; [text from]
Psalm 34 ... — New York ; London : Associated Music, 1978. —
5p ; 8vo.
£0.35
1.Ti
(B79-50499)

FEZDH — Unaccompanied voices. Motets, Anthems, Hymns, etc
Staden, Johann
[Hauss-Musik, Tl.3. Danket dem Herren. *arr*]. Give thanks to the
Lord : for three-part chorus of women's voices a cappella / [by]
Johann Staden ; arranged by Ed Thompson. — New York ;
London : Schirmer, 1979. — 6p ; 8vo.
£0.35
1.Ti 2.Ti 3.Thompson, Ed
(B79-50500)

Verdi, Giuseppe
[Quattro pezzi sacri. Laudi alla vergine Maria]. Laudi alla vergine
Maria = Prayer to the Virgin Mary : for four-part chorus of
female voices / by Giuseppe Verdi ... ; edited by John Rogers,
and, Domine Deus rex coelestis : Almighty Father, King of
Heaven : for three-part chorus of female voices by Giovanni
Battista Borri ; edited by Jack Boyd. — Wendover : Roberton,
1979. — 14p ; 8vo.
£0.32
1.Ti 2.Ti 3.Boyd, Jack 4.Rogers, John 5.Borri, Giovanni Battista. Domine
Deus, rex coelestis
(B79-50916)

FEZDW — Unaccompanied voices. Songs, etc
Diemer, Emma Lou
Weep no more : for women's chorus a cappella / [by] Emma Lou
Diemer ; [words by] John Fletcher ... — New York : Broude ;
[London] : [Breitkopf and Härtel], 1979. — 8p ; 8vo.
£0.42
1.Ti 2.Fletcher, John
(B79-50917)

Holst, Gustav
Songs from 'The princess' : for unaccompanied equal voices
(SSA-SSSAA) / words by Alfred Lord Tennyson ; music by
Gustav Holst, opus 20 (1905). — Sevenoaks : Novello, 1979. —
23p ; 8vo.
Published in the same volume for the first time.
£1.15
1.Ti 2.Tennyson, Alfred, Baron Tennyson
(B79-50918)

Klefisch, Walter
Lasset uns singen : Volkslied von Tahiti / Textfassung und Satz,
Walter Klefisch. — Mainz ; London : Schott, 1979. — s.sh ; 8vo.
— (Schott's Chorblätter ; 616)
For S.S.A. unaccompanied.
£0.24
1.Ti 2.Sr
(B79-50501)

Laburda, Jiří
[Dobry den]. What a day : Dobry den : a choral cycle, for
two-part chorus of young voices with piano accompaniment or a
cappella / [by] Jiří Laburda ; [words by] Josef Bursík ; English
version by Jane May. — New York ; London : Schirmer, 1978. —
22p ; 8vo.
£2.10
Primary classification FDW
1.Ti 2.Ti 3.Bursík, Josef 4.May, Jane
(B79-50495)

Poos, Heinrich
Tanzlied. (Ritmo di joropo) / Textfassung und Satz, Heinrich
Poos. — Mainz ; [London] : Schott, 1972. — 4p ; 4to. —
(Schott's Chorverlag)
For S.S.A.A. unaccompanied.
£0.48
1.Ti 2.Sr
(B79-50502)

FLDGPP — Treble voices. Evening Prayer. Canticles
Blatchly, Mark
Magnificat and Nunc dimittis / [by] Mark Blatchly. — London
(36 Ranelagh Gdns, W.6) : Cathedral Music, 1978. — 16p ; 8vo.
S.S. and organ.
Unpriced
(B79-50107)

FLDW — Treble voices. Songs, etc
Benger, Richard
Requiescat : S.S. and piano / music by Richard Benger ; words by
Oscar Wilde. — London : Edwin Ashdown, 1979. — 7p ; 8vo. —
(Ashdown vocal duets ; no.394)
£0.20
1.Ti 2.Wilde, Oscar 3.Sr
(B79-50919)

G — MALE VOICES
GDW — Songs, etc
Davies, Bryan
Hava nagila : Israeli folk song / arranged for four-part chorus of
male voices and piano duet by Bryan Davies; English words by
Bryan Jones; tonic solfa transcription by John Cynan Jones. —
Wendover : Roberton, 1979. — 16p. ; 8vo.
£0.32
1.Ti 2.Jones, John Cynan
(B79-50920)

Larbalestier, Philip George
The little place where I was born : setting for male voices
(T.T.B.B.) / music by P.G. Larbalestier ; words by Arthur Jones.
— Rhuthun ((Fford yr Osaf)) : Cyngor Gwasanaethau Gwirfoddol
Clwyd (Clwyd Voluntary Services Council), 1979. — 4to.
Unpriced
1.Ti 2.Jones, Arthur

(B79-50503)

Larbalestier, Philip George
The little place where I was born : setting for male voices,
T.T.B.B. / music by P.G. Larbalestier ; words by Arthur Jones.
— Rhuthun (Ffordd yr osaf) : Cyngor Gwasanapthau Gwiyfiddol
Clwyd = Clwyd Voluntary Services Council, 1979. — 7p ; 4to.
Staff and tonic sol-fa notation.
Unpriced
1.Ti 2.Jones, Arthur

(B79-50921)

GE/UMDW — With wind band. Songs, etc
Scheck, Helmut
Die Musik kommt : Männerchor und kleines Blasorchester / [von]
Helmut Scheck ; [Text] (Deflev von Liliencron). — Mainz ;
[London] : Schott, 1979. — 25p ; 4to. — (Schott's Chorverlag)
With keyboard reduction of the accompaniment.
£5.60
1.Ti 2.Liliencron, Detlev von 3.Sr

(B79-50922)

GE/XTBDW/X — With bell lyra. Canons
Salieri, Antonio
[Scherzi armonici. arr]. Two Salieri canons / arranged by Gordon
Binkerd. — [New York] ; [London] : Boosey and Hawkes, 1978.
— 11p ; 8vo.
For male voices. — The bell - lyra is used in no.2 only. — Contents: 1:
Milton (Tennyson) - 2: Das Glockenspiel.
Unpriced
1.Ti 2.Ti 3.Binkerd, Gordon

(B79-50108)

GEZDG — Unaccompanied voices. Ordinary of the Mass
La Rue, Pierre de
Missa cum iucunditate : for 4 and 5 voices / [by] Pierre de la
Rue ; transcribed and edited by Nigel Davison. — London (72
Brewery Rd, N.7) : Mapa mundi, 1978. — 29p ; 4to. —
(Franco-Flemish church music ; no.3)
For ATTB.
Unpriced
1.Ti 2.Davison, Nigel 3.Sr

(B79-50109)

GEZDJ — Unaccompanied voices. Motets
Anchieta, Juan de
Salve Regina / [by] Juan de Anchieta ; source, Seville, Bibl.
Colombina, transcribed and edited by Martyn Imrie. — London
(72 Brewery Rd, N.7) : Mapa mundi, 1978. — 8p ; 4to. —
(Spanish church music ; no.4)
For ATTB.
Unpriced
1.Ti 2.Imrie, Martyn 3.Sr

(B79-50110)

Escobar, Pedro de
Clamabat autem mulier / [by] Pedro de Escobar ; source, Seville,
Bibl. Colombina ... ; transcribed and edited by Martyn Imrie. —
London (72 Brewery Rd, N.7) : Mapa mundi, 1978. — 4p ; 4to.
— (Spanish church music ; no.3)
For ATTB.
Unpriced
1.Ti 2.Imrie, Martyn 3.Sr

(B79-50111)

Josquin des Prés
[Domine, ne in furore tuo arguas me]. Oh my Lord, let not your
blinding fury - My heart = Domine, ne in furore - Cor meum :
for four-part chorus of men's voices a cappella / [by] Josquin des
Prez ; edited by F. John Adams ; English version by Jane May. —
New York ; London : Schirmer, 1978. — 24p ; 8vo.
My heart (Cor meum) is the second part of the work.
£0.75
1.Ti 2.Ti 3.Adams, F John 4.May, Jane

(B79-50504)

Martìn de Rivafrencha
[Vox dilecti mei]. Two motets [sic] : for four voices / [by] Martìn
de Rivafrencha ; source, Seville, Bibl. Colombina, transcribed and
edited by Martyn Imrie. — London (72 Brewery Rd, N.7) : Mapa
mundi, 1978. — 4p ; 4to. — (Spanish church music ; no.1)
The same motet in two sections for ATTB.
Unpriced
1.Imrie, Martyn 2.Sr

(B79-50112)

Okeghem, Jean
Salve regina : for 4 voices / [by] Johannes Ockeghem ; transcribed
and edited by John Milsom. — London (72 Brewery Rd, N.7) :
Mapa mundi, 1978. — 8p ; 4to. — (Franco-Flemish church
music ; no.5)
Unpriced
1.Ti 2.Milson, John 3.Sr

(B79-50113)

Peñalosa, Francisco de
Sancta mater / [by] Francisco de Peñalosa ; source, Seville, Bibl.
Colombina ; transcribed and edited by Martyn Imrie. — London
(72 Brewery Rd, N.7) : Mapa mundi, 1977. — 4p ; 4to. —
(Spanish church music ; no.2)
For ATTB.
Unpriced
1.Ti 2.Sr

(B79-50114)

GEZDP/LF — Unaccompanied voices. Carols. Christmas
Chorbajian, John
My gift : for four-part chorus of men's voices a cappella / [by]
John Chorbajian ; [words by] Christina Rossetti. — New York ;
London : Schirmer, 1979. — 7p ; 8vo.
£0.35
1.Ti 2.Rossetti, Christina

(B79-50923)

GEZDU — Unaccompanied voices. Madrigals
Lawes, William
Gather your rosebuds / [by] William Lawes, [with] Though I am
young / [by] Nicholas Laniere ; edited by Mark Brown. —
Ilkley : Pro Cantione Antiqua ; [London] : [Breitkopf und Härtel],
1975. — [2]p ; 8vo. — (PCA partsongs)
For ATB and TTB.
Unpriced
1.Ti 2.Brown, Mark 3.Laniere, Nicholas 4.Though I am young 5.Sr

(B79-50505)

GEZDW — Unaccompanied voices. Songs, etc
Desch, Rudolf
Putze dich mit meinem Tüchlein : Kastilianisches Volkslied aus
Avila (Spanien) / Satz, Rudolf Desch ; deutsche Nachdichtung,
Rudolf Desch. — Mainz ; London : Schott, 1979. — 4p ; 4to. —
(Schott's Chorverlag)
T.T.B.B.
£0.48
1.Ti 2.Sr

(B79-50507)

Diemer, Emma Lou
Away, delights : for men's chorus a cappella / [by] Emma Lou
Diemer ; words by John Fletcher ... — New York : Broude ;
[London] : [Breitkopf and Härtel], 1979. — 7p ; 8vo.
£0.42
1.Ti 2.Fletcher, John

(B79-50924)

Dvořák, Antonín
[Bouquet of Czech folk songs. B72. The betrayed shepherd]. The
abducted shepherd = Der entführte Hirt : for four-part chorus of
men's voices a cappella / [by] Antonín Dvořák ; English text by
Jane May. — New York ; London : Schirmer, 1979. — 8p ; 8vo.
Text in German and English.
£0.35
1.Ti 2.Ti 3.May, Jane

(B79-50925)

Dvořák, Antonín
[Bouquet of Czech folk songs. B72. The sweetheart's resolve]. If
you should go away = Wenn du fortgehst : for four-part chorus
of men's voices a cappella / by Antonín Dvořák ; English text by
Jane May. — New York ; London : Schirmer, 1979. — 8p ; 8vo.
£0.35
1.Ti 2.Ti 3.May, Jane

(B79-50926)

Elgar, *Sir* **Edward,** *bart*
[5 part songs. Op.45]. From the Greek Anthology : five
unaccompanied part-songs for TTBB. Opus 45 / [by] Edward
Elgar. — Sevenoaks : Novello, 1979. — 23p ; 8to.
This edition published for the first time as one volume.
£1.15
1.Ti 2.Ti 3.Five part-songs. Op.45

(B79-50927)

Huber, Klaus
['... inwendig voller Figur ...'. Traumgesicht]. Traumgesicht : für
Männerstimme allein (1971) / [von] Klaus Huber ; [Text]
Apocalypsis 8, 9. — Mainz : Ars viva ; [London] : [Schott], 1976.
— [4p] ; 4to.
Text in Latin. — Facsimile of the composer's autograph.
£3.00
1.Ti 2.Ti

(B79-50506)

Partsongs. — Ilkley ((Lyndhurst, Denton Rd, Ben Rhydding)) : Pro
Cantione Antiqua ; [London] : [Breitkopf and Härtel].
Partsongs by Ravenscroft and one song by Edward Piers.
Vol.1 : for unaccompained [i.e. unaccompanied] male voices
(A(A)T(T)B(B)) / edited by Mark Brown ; historical research, Richard
Townsend. — 1975. — [1],31p ; 8vo.
£2.40
1.Brown, Mark 2.Townsend, Richard

(B79-50508)

Schubert, Franz
Lied im Freien. D.572 / [von] Franz Schubert ; [Text von] Johann
Gaudenz von Salis-Seewis. — Kassel ; [London] : Bärenreiter,
1978. — 8p ; 4to. — (The 19th century)
For T.T.B.B.
£0.99
1.Ti 2.Salis-Seewis, Johann Gaudenz von 3.Sr

(B79-50115)

J — VOICES IN UNISON
JADM — Hymns. Melody part
[**Australian** hymn book. *Melody part*]. With one voice : a hymn
book for all the churches, with Catholic supplements / editor,
Wesley Milgate. — London : Collins, 1979. — xxxiv,744p ; 8vo.
ISBN 0-00-599636-8 : Unpriced
1.Milgate, Wesley

(B79-50929)

[**With** one voice. *Congregation part*]. With one voice : a hymn book
for all the churches / [editor] Wesley Milgate. — 2nd ed. —
London : Collins, 1979. — xxxiv,679p ; 8vo.
1st ed. entitled 'Australian hymn book'.
ISBN 0-00-599581-7 : Unpriced
1.Milgate, Wesley

(B79-50116)

JDGMM — Anglican liturgy. Preces & responses
Fletcher, Andrew
Versicles and responses : Series 3 Morning and Evening Prayer /
by Andrew Fletcher. — Croydon : Royal School of Church
Music, 1978. — 8p ; 8vo.
For (a) SATB unaccompanied. (b) SATTB unaccompanied - 2nd tenors
singing People's part (c) SATB and people (d) People and organ.
Unpriced
Primary classification EZDGMM

(B79-50458)

JDGS — Anglican liturgy. Communion
Osborne, Hayward
Holy communion, series 3 ... / [by] Hayward Osborne. —
London : Weinberger, 1979. — 8p ; 8vo.
For congregational singing. — In two staves, organ and voice part
incorporated.
Unpriced
1.Ti

(B79-50117)

JDH — Motets, Anthems, Hymns, etc
Hamble, William R
Father of mercies : for chorus of unison voices with organ
accompaniment / Silesian melody ... arranged by William R.
Hamble ; [text by] St. Elisabeth. — New York ; London :
Chappell, 1979. — 4p ; 8vo.
Unpriced
1.Ti 2.Elisabeth, Saint

(B79-50930)

JDR — Psalms
How, Martin
Psalm 23 / [by] Martin How. — London : Weinberger, 1979. —
4p ; 8vo.
For S.A., unison voices or baritone solo with organ.
Unpriced
Primary classification FDR
1.Ti

(B79-50908)

JE/TSDM — With guitar. Hymns
Cowgill, Samuel C
The peacemakers gospel songs and choruses / compiled by S.C.
Cowgill. — Bradford ((Elim Pentecostal Church, Wakefield Rd)) :
S.C. Cowgill, 1979. — 18p ; 8vo.
Music by S.C. Cowgill and V.J. Cowgill, arr. A. Jarvis.
Unpriced
1.Ti 2.Cowgill, V J

(B79-50509)

JE/TSDP/LF/AY — With guitar. Carols. Christmas. Collections
Fröhliche Weihnacht : Weihnachtslieder aus aller Welt /
herausgegeben von Karl Haus, Illustrationen von Isi Huber. —
Mainz ; London : Schott, 1978. — 27p ; obl.8vo.
£2.40
1.Haus, Karl

(B79-50118)

JE/TSDW/AYDM — With guitar. Songs, etc. Collections, Ireland
Comic songs of Ireland / collected and annotated by James N.
Healy ; music written out by Con O'Donovan with chords suitable
for guitar, piano and organ. — Dublin [etc.] : Mercier Press, 1978.
— 48p ; 8vo.
ISBN 0-85342-529-9 : Unpriced
1.Healy, James N 2.O'Donovan, Con

(B79-50510)

JE/TSDW/G/AYDL — With guitar. Folk songs. Collections. Scotland
The **Scottish** folksinger : 118 modern and traditional folksongs /
collected and edited by Norman Buchan and Peter Hall. — New
ed. — Glasgow ; London : Collins, 1978. — 159p ; 8vo.
Also available in paperback.
ISBN 0-00-411125-7 : Unpriced
1.Buchan, Norman 2.Hall, Peter

(B79-50119)

JE/VSNQDW — With recorder sextet. Songs, etc
Sullivan, *Sir* **Arthur Seymour**
[The pirates of Penzance. *Selections : arr*]. Suite from Gilbert and
Sullivan's 'The pirates of Penzance / arranged by Michael D.
Stratford for voices, 2 descant, 2 treble, tenor & bass recorders. —
South Croydon : Lengnick, 1979. — 4to & obl. 8vo.
Score (19p.) & 5 parts.
£1.10
1.Ti 2.Ti 3.Stratford, Michael D

(B79-50931)

JE/XSQDH — With handbells. Motets, Anthems, Hymns, etc
McCray, James
Four introits : unison chorus and hand bells / [by] James
McCray. — New York : Broude ; [London] : [Breitkopf und
Härtel], 1979. — 5p ; 8vo.
£0.42
1.Ti

(B79-50511)

JEZDG/AY — Unaccompanied voices. Ordinary of the Mass. Collections
A **plainsong** mass book. — London : Catholic Truth Society, 1979.
— [6],77p ; 8vo.
Unpriced
Also classified at JEZDGK/AY; JEZDTD/AY
1.Higham, David 2.Wright, Benedict

(B79-50512)

JEZDGK/AY — Unaccompanied voices. Proper of the Mass. Collections
A **plainsong** mass book. — London : Catholic Truth Society, 1979.
— [6],77p ; 8vo.
Unpriced
Primary classification JEZDG/AY

(B79-50512)

JEZDGNPE — Unaccompanied voices. Morning Prayer. Canticles. Antiphons
Communities Consultative Council. *Anglican Office Book Committee*
Ferial antiphons on Venite, Benedictus and Magnificat with simple
tones / [compiled by] Anglican Office Book Committee. —
Richmond : Communities Consultative Council, 1978. — 13p ;
8vo.
Unpriced
Also classified at JEZDGPPE
1.Ti

(B79-50932)

JEZDGPPE — Unaccompanied voices. Evening Prayer. Canticles. Antiphons
Communities Consultative Council. *Anglican Office Book Committee*
Ferial antiphons on Venite, Benedictus and Magnificat with simple
tones / [compiled by] Anglican Office Book Committee. —
Richmond : Communities Consultative Council, 1978. — 13p ;
8vo.
Unpriced
Primary classification JEZDGNPE
1.Ti

(B79-50932)

JEZDM/LSJ/AY — Unaccompanied voices. Hymns. Methodist Church. Collections
One world songs : Methodist World Development Action
  Campaign. — London : Methodist Church (Division of Social
  Responsibility), 1978. — [125p] ; 8vo.
  With errata slip.
  £1.40
                                                                      (B79-50120)

JEZDTD — Unaccompanied voices. Plainsong. Gregorian chant
Cantors : a collection of Gregorian chants / selected and edited by
  Mary Berry ... with new English words for singing by Rose Mary
  McCabe. — Cambridge : Cambridge University Press, 1979. —
  48p ; 8vo. — (The resources of music)
  ISBN 0-521-22149-8 : Unpriced
  1.Berry, Mary 2.McCabe, Rose Mary 3.Sr
                                                                      (B79-50933)

JEZDTD/AY — Unaccompanied voices. Gregorian plainsong. Collections
A plainsong mass book. — London : Catholic Truth Society, 1979.
  — [6],77p ; 8vo.
  Unpriced
  Primary classification JEZDG/AY
                                                                      (B79-50512)

JEZDW/G/AYDM — Unaccompanied voices. Folk songs. Collections. Ireland
Songs of the Irish in America / edited by Bill Meek. — Skerries (25
  Shonick Rd. Skerries) : Gilbert Dalton, 1978. — 64p ; 8vo.
  'The land of libertie'. — Cover. — Music transcriptions by Manus O'Boyle.
  Unpriced
  1.Meek, Bill 2.O'Boyle, Manus
                                                                      (B79-50121)

JEZDW/G/AYDN — Unaccompanied voices. Folk songs. Collections. Dublin
Songs of Dublin / edited by Frank Harte. — Skerries (25 Shenick
  Rd. Skerries) : Gilbert Dalton, 1978. — 64p ; 8vo.
  Music transcriptions by Manus O'Boyle.
  Unpriced
  1.Harte, Frank 2.O'Boyle, Manus
                                                                      (B79-50122)

JEZDW/G/AYDQC — Unaccompanied voices. Folk songs. Collections. Cork
Songs of Cork / edited by Tomás Ó Canainn. — Skerries (25
  Shonick Rd. Skerries) : Gilbert Dalton, 1978. — 127p ; 8vo.
  'Down Erin's lovely lee'. — Cover.
  Unpriced
  1.Ó Canainn, Tomás
                                                                      (B79-50123)

JEZDW/G/AYDTB — Unaccompanied voices. Folk songs. Collections. Belfast
Songs of Belfast / edited by David Hammond. — Skerries (25
  Shenick Rd, Skerries) : Gilbert Dalton, 1978. — 63p ; 8vo.
  Music transcriptions by Manus O'Boyle.
  Unpriced
  1.Hammond, David 2.O'Boyle, Manus
                                                                      (B79-50124)

JFADM/AY — Female voices, Children's voices. Hymns. Melody part. Collections
[Someone's singing, Lord. Melody part]. Someone's singing, Lord :
  hymns and songs for children / chosen by Beatrice Harrop ;
  melody edition with chords for guitar, parts for voice or
  instrument and drawings by Bernard Cheese. — London : A & C
  Black, 1979. — [80]p ; 8vo.
  Guitar chords, Graham C. Westcott, additional instrument parts, Sarah
  Evans.
  ISBN 0-7136-1847-7 : Unpriced
  Also classified at JFE/TSDM/AY
  1.Westcott, Graham C 2.Harrop, Beatrice 3.Evans, Sarah
                                                                      (B79-50125)

JFADW — Female voices, Children's voices. Songs, etc. Melody part
Kingsbury, Roy
  [Seasons and people and other songs. Melody part]. Seasons and
  people and other songs / [by] Roy Kingsbury and Patrick O'Shea.
  — Oxford : Oxford University Press, 1979. — 31p ; 8vo.
  In a box, with a tape cassette.
  ISBN 0-19-450558-8 : Unpriced
  1.Ti 2.Ti 3.O'Shea, Patrick
                                                                      (B79-50513)

JFADW/GJ — Female voices, Children's voices. Children's songs. Melody part
Milne, Lorraine
  [The fix-it man. Melody part]. The fix-it man : songs for schools /
  [by] Lorraine Milne ; illustrated by Roland Harvey. — South
  Melbourne ; London : Macmillan, 1979. — 33p ; 8vo.
  ISBN 0-333-25190-3 : Unpriced
  1.Ti
                                                                      (B79-50514)

[Yip-i-addy-i-ay yip-i-addy-i-ay. Melody part]. Yip-i-addy-i-ay
  yip-i-addy-i-ay : songs for junior and middle school with optional
  parts for recorder and percussion / arranged by Bert Brewis. —
  London : Chappell, 1979. — 37p. ; 8vo.
  Unpriced
  1.Brewis, Bert
                                                                      (B79-50934)

JFDH — Female voices, Children's voices. Motets, Anthems, Hymns, etc
Kidd, J Michael
  Thou madest all things well : anthem for unison voices and
  organ / music, J. Michael Kidd ; a tribute to the Admiral of the
  Fleet, The Earl Mountbatten of Burma; words by Lewis
  Beckerley. — London : Weinberger, 1979. — 4p. ; 8vo.
  Unpriced
  1.Ti 2.Beckerley, Lewis
                                                                      (B79-50935)

JFDM/GJ — Female voices, Children's voices. Children's hymns
Murcott, Peter
  Complete sing for Jesus : songs for children / words and music by
  Peter Murcott ; guitar chords by David and Isabel Abbott. —
  Ilkeston ((23 Park Rd)) : Moorley's Bible and Bookshop, [1979].
  — [40]p ; 4to.
  ISBN 0-86071-055-6 : £1.00
  1.Ti 2.Abbott, Isabel 3.Abbott, David
                                                                      (B79-50515)

Murcott, Peter
  More sing for Jesus : songs for children / words and music by
  Peter Murcott ; guitar chords by David and Isabel Abbott. —
  Ilkeston ((23 Park Rd)) : Moorley's Bible and Bookshop, 1979. —
  [20]p ; 4to.
  ISBN 0-86071-054-8 : £0.55
  1.Ti 2.Abbott, David 3.Abbott, Isabel
                                                                      (B79-50516)

JFDP/LF — Female voices, Children's voices. Carols. Christmas
Barsham, Eve
  Come give your hearts to joy this day / music by Eve Barsham ;
  words by H.J. Smith. — London : Ashdown, 1979. — 4p ; 8vo.
  — (Ashdown unison songs ; no.109)
  Voices in unison. — Duration 1 1/4 min.
  Unpriced
  1.Ti 2.Smith, H J 3.Sr
                                                                      (B79-50936)

Berkeley, Michael
  3 Christmas carols : for unison voices and piano / [by] Michael
  Berkeley. — London : Schirmer, 1978. — 4p ; 8vo.
  Contents: 1: The oxen (Hardy) - 2: Cradle song - 3: Christmas bells
  (Longfellow).
  Unpriced
  1.Ti 2.Three Christmas carols
                                                                      (B79-50126)

Hudson, Hazel
  Go go Gabriel : unison with optional descant / words and music
  by Hazel Hudson. — London : Ashdown, 1979. — 4p ; 8vo. —
  (Ashdown unison songs ; no.107)
  Duration 1 1/4 min.
  Unpriced
  1.Ti 2.Sr
                                                                      (B79-50937)

Hughes-Jones, Llifon
  How far is it to Bethlehem? Pa mor bell yur Bethlehem? : unison
  voices and piano / by Llifon Hughes-Jones ; English words by
  Frances Chesterton ; geirian [sic] Cymraeg cyf G. Wynne Griffith
  ... — Wendover : Roberton, 1979. — 7p ; 8vo.
  £0.20
  1.Ti 2.Chesterton, Frances 3.Griffith, G Wynne
                                                                      (B79-50517)

Shephard, Richard
  Three short anthems / by Richard Shephard. — Croydon : Royal
  School of Church Music, 1979. — 11p ; 8vo.
  Contents: 1: Jesus! dulcis memoria, SATB with organ - 2: Prayer for a new
  mother, unison voices - 3: The birds, SATB unaccompanied.
  Unpriced
  Primary classification DJ
  1.Ti
                                                                      (B79-50835)

JFDP/LF/AY — Female voices, Children's voices. Christmas carols. Collections
Christmas carols for young children : for piano, guitar and
  recorder / edited by Dawn and Peter Cope ; story retold by Timm
  Jenns ; musical arrangements by Bradford Thompson and Jess
  Curtis ; illustrated by Henriette Willebeek le Mair. — London :
  East West : Breitkopf and Härtel, 1979. — 31p ; obl. 8vo.
  £1.50
  Primary classification JFE/NUSNTDP/LF/AY
  1.Cope, Dawn 2.Cope, Peter 3.Jenns, Timm 4.Thompson, Bradford 5.Curtis,
  Jess
                                                                      (B79-50943)

JFDW — Female voices, Children's voices. Songs, etc
Fraser, Shena
   [Grannies to sell]. Grannies to sell, and, Boating / music by Shena
   Fraser ; words by James Reeves. — Wendover : Roberton, 1979.
   — 8p ; 8vo.
   £0.20
   1.Ti 2.Ti 3.Reeves, James 4.Boating
                                                       (B79-50518)

Harper, Don
   Songs for Alice : Alice in Wonderland and Through the looking
   glass / words by Lewis Carroll ; set to music by Don Harper ;
   with illustrations by Charles Folkard. — London : Adam &
   Charles Black, 1978. — 48p ; 8vo.
   ISBN 0-7136-1879-5 : Unpriced
   1.Ti 2.Carroll, Lewis
                                                       (B79-50127)

Hurd, Michael
   Round the town : five Charles Causley poems / with music by
   Michael Hurd. — Sevenoaks : Novello, 1978. — [2],18p ; 8vo.
   £0.74
   1.Ti 2.Causley, Charles
                                                       (B79-50128)

McNess-Eames, Vera
   I want to walk like an elephant : musical fun for 'tinies' with
   chord symbols for piano, piano accordion and guitar / music and
   lyrics by Vera McNess-Eames. — Ilfracombe : Stockwell, 1979. —
   29p : ill, chiefly music ; obl.8vo.
   ISBN 0-7223-1256-3 Pbk : £0.65
   1.Ti
                                                       (B79-50938)

JFDW/GJ — Female voices, Children's voices. Children's songs
Dainton, Marie Cleeve
   10 'swingalong' songs : for the primaries / by Marie Cleeve
   Dainton. — Leeds : Regina Music, 1978. — 16p ; 4to.
   Unpriced
   1.Ti 2.Ten 'swingalong' songs
                                                       (B79-50129)

Olive, Vivienne
   Children's songs / music by Vivienne Olive ; words by Vicky
   Olive. — London : Edwin Ashdown, 1979. — 7p ; 8vo. —
   (Ashdown unison songs ; no.108)
   Unpriced
   1.Ti 2.Olive, Vicky 3.Sr
                                                       (B79-50519)

Page, Ian
   Learning tree songbook / words and music by Ian Page;
   illustrated by Keith Aldred and Bridget Appleby. — London :
   Chappell, 1979. — 40p. ; 4to.
   Unpriced
   1.Ti
                                                       (B79-50939)

White, Estelle
   Good morning, Jesus : twenty-four songs for children / by Estelle
   White. — Leigh-on-Sea ((55 Leigh Rd)) : Kevin Mayhew, 1979.
   — 32p ; 4to.
   Unpriced
   1.Ti
                                                       (B79-50940)

JFDW/JN — Female voices, Children's voices. Songs, etc. Mime
Diamond, Eileen
   Find a bin : a song/mime for children / words and music by
   Eileen Diamond. — London : Chappell, in association with Keep
   Britain Tidy, 1978. — 4p ; 4to.
   Unpriced
   1.Ti
                                                       (B79-50941)

Diamond, Eileen
   The toyshop : a song/mime for all children / words and music by
   Eileen Diamond. — London : Chappell, 1979. — 8p ; 4to.
   Unpriced
   1.Ti
                                                       (B79-50520)

JFE/LDM/GJ — Female voices, Children's voices. With instruments.
   Children's hymns
Auckland, Bessie H
   Joyful songs / [by] Bessie H. Auckland ; illustrated by Ann
   Axworthy. — Edinburgh : Oliver and Boyd, 1979. — 49p ; 4to.
   Hymns for children with instrumental accompaniment.
   ISBN 0-05-003260-7 : Unpriced
   1.Ti
                                                       (B79-50521)

JFE/LDP/AY — Female voices, Childrens voices. With instruments.
   Carols. Collections
Sociable carols : fifteen Christmas carols / arranged for young
   singers and players by Anne Mendoza and Pat Shaw. — London :
   Oxford University Press, 1979. — 30p ; obl. 8vo.
   ISBN 0-19-330595-x : Unpriced
   1.Shuldham-Shaw, Patrick
                                                       (B79-50522)

JFE/LDW/G/AYK — Female voices, Children's voices. With
   instruments. Folk songs. Collections. Spain
Olé : twelve Spanish songs / arranged for young singers and players
   by Anne Mendoza. — London : Oxford University Press, 1977. —
   [2],22p ; obl. 8vo.
   ISBN 0-19-330597-6 : Unpriced
   1.Mendoza, Anne
                                                       (B79-50523)

JFE/NUSNTDP/LF/AY — Female voices, Children's voices with
   recorders, strings & keyboard. Christmas carols.
   Collections
Christmas carols for young children : for piano, guitar and
   recorder / edited by Dawn and Peter Cope ; story retold by Timm
   Jenns ; musical arrangements by Bradford Thompson and Jess
   Curtis ; illustrated by Henriette Willebeek le Mair. — London :
   East West : Breitkopf and Härtel, 1979. — 31p ; obl. 8vo.
   £1.50
   Also classified at JFDP/LF/AY
   1.Cope, Dawn 2.Cope, Peter 3.Jenns, Timm 4.Thompson, Bradford 5.Curtis,
   Jess
                                                       (B79-50943)

JFE/NYDSDX — Female voices, Children's voices. With recorders,
   strings, keyboard & percussion. Secular cantatas
Winch, Richard
   The pedlar of Swaffham : a children's cantata with simple
   accompaniments for piano and classroom instruments / words and
   music by Richard Winch. — London : Chappell, 1979. — 24p. ;
   4to. — (Ways with music)
   Unpriced
   1.Ti 2.Sr
                                                       (B79-50944)

JFE/NYFSDX — Female voices, Children's voices. With recorders,
   keyboard & percussion. Secular cantatas
Atkins, John G
   A country day : a festival piece / words and music arranged by
   John G. Atkins. — London : EMI, 1979. — [1],16p ; 8vo.
   With voices, recorders, percussion and piano.
   Unpriced
   1.Ti
                                                       (B79-50945)

JFE/NYLDP/LF — Female voices, Children's voices. With keyboard
   & percussion. Carols. Christmas
Brown, Gerald Edgar
   Five nativity carols : for unison voices, piano and simple
   percussion / by Gerald E. Brown. — London (7 Garrick St.
   W.C.2) : Middle Eight Music, 1979. — 12p. ; 8vo.
   Unpriced
   1.Ti
                                                       (B79-50946)

JFE/TSDM/AY — Female voices, Children's voices. With guitar.
   Hymns. Collections
[Someone's singing, Lord. Melody part]. Someone's singing, Lord :
   hymns and songs for children / chosen by Beatrice Harrop ;
   melody edition with chords for guitar, parts for voice or
   instrument and drawings by Bernard Cheese. — London : A & C
   Black, 1979. — [80]p ; 8vo.
   Guitar chords, Graham C. Westcott, additional instrument parts, Sarah
   Evans.
   ISBN 0-7136-1847-7 : Unpriced
   Primary classification JFADM/AY
   1.Westcott, Graham C 2.Harrop, Beatrice 3.Evans, Sarah
                                                       (B79-50125)

JFE/XDW/GJ/AY — Female voices, Children's voices. With
   percussion. Children's songs. Collections
See-saw sacaradown : fourteen childrens [sic] songs with simple
   accompaniments for classroom instruments / [by] Anne Mendoza.
   — London : Chappell, 1979. — 22p. ; 4to. — (Ways with music)
   Unpriced
   1.Mendoza, Anne 2.Sr
                                                       (B79-50947)

JFEZDW/GR — Unaccompanied female voices, children's voices. Activity songs
Staton, Kathleen
Diddly, diddly, dumpty : finger plays, face games, action rhymes, fun songs, for nursery and infant schools / music by Kathleen Staton ; verses selected or written by Lilian McCrea. — London : EMI, 1979. — 56p. ; obl. 8vo.
Unpriced
1.Ti 2.McCrea, Lilian

(B79-50524)

JFLDW — Treble voices. Songs, etc
Smith, Gregg
[Beware of the soldier. Songs of innocence. Little lamb. *arr].* Little lamb : for unison treble choir with piano, four hands accompaniment / by Gregg Smith ; text by William Blake. — New York ; London : Schirmer, 1979. — 6p ; 8vo.
£0.35
1.Ti 2.Ti 3.Blake, Wiliam

(B79-50948)

JN — SINGLE VOICES IN COMBINATION
JNBE/MRDW/FT — Vocal quintet with chamber orchestra. Songs, etc. With tape
Harvey, Jonathan
Inner light (2) : for SSATB soli, instrumental ensemble and tape ... / [by] Jonathan Harvey ; texts are taken from Kipling, Blake, T.S. Eliot, St. John's Gospel, Rudolf Steiner. — London : Faber Music, 1979. — [6],121p ; fol.
Duration 35 mins.
Unpriced
1.Ti

(B79-50949)

JNFLEE/SNTPWDJ — Soprano duet. With violins (2) & keyboard. Motets
Monteverdi, Claudio
[Selva morale e spirituale. Ut queant laxis. *arr].* Hymn to Saint John the Baptist. Ut queant laxis / [by] Claudio Monteverdi ; arr. Neil Butterworth for two sopranos (or chorus), two violins and continuo. — London (36 Ranelagh Gdns W.6) : Cathedral Music, 1978. — 8p ; 8vo.
Unpriced
1.Ti 2.Ti 3.Butterworth, Neil

(B79-50130)

KDE — RELIGIOUS CANTATAS. SOLOS
KDGPR — Female voice. With guitar. Songs, etc
Burgon, Geoffrey
Sisters in song : a collection of new songs from the women's liberation movement / [compiled by] Tied Thompson, Andrea Webb and Janie Faychild. — London : Onlywomen Press, 1979. — 100p. ; 4to.
Vocal score (2p.) & part.
Unpriced
1.Ti 2.Thompson, Tierl 3.Webb, Andrea 4.Faychild, Junie

(B79-50951)

KDH — MOTETS, ANTHEMS, HYMNS, ETC. SOLOS
McDonough, Edward J
Come to me, your gentle shepherd. (Gentle shepherd) : theme song / written by Rev. Edward J. McDonough, C.S.S.R. for his radio, healing and restoration services. — New York : TRO ; [London] : [Essex Music], 1979. — 3p ; 4to.
Unpriced
1.Ti

(B79-50952)

KDP — CAROLS. SOLOS
KDP/LF/AY — Carols. Christmas Collections
BBC TV's Nationwide carols : winners 1978. — London : Chappell, 1979. — 36p. : ports ; 4to.
Unpriced

(B79-50953)

KDR — PSALMS. SOLOS
Ridout, Alan
Six songs from the psalms : six of the best songs from the BBC TV series 'Kossoff and company' / music by Alan Ridout ; words by David Kossoff. — London : Weinberger, 1979. — 12p ; 8vo.
Unpriced
1.Ti 2.Kossoff, David

(B79-50954)

KDW — SONGS, ETC. SOLOS
Ayres Netto, Marianinha
Sem dizer nada : canto e piano / letra e música de Marianinha C. Ayres Netto. — São Paulo : Fermata do Brasil ; [London] : [Clifford Essex], 1979. — [2p] ; fol.
Unpriced
1.Ti

(B79-50955)

Coward, *Sir* Noël
There will always be ... / words and music by Noël Coward ; piano arrangement by Norman Hackforth. — London : Chappell, 1979. — 5p ; 4to.
Unpriced
1.Ti 2.Hackforth, Norman

(B79-50525)

Gershwin, George
[Porgy and Bess. *Selections : arr].* Porgy and Bess / [by] George Gershwin ; a musical and pictorial journey book compiled, designed and edited by Lee Snider. — New York ; London : Elm Tree Books : Chappell, 1978. — 128p ; 4to.
Lyrics by Ira Gershwin and Dubose Heyward.
Unpriced
1.Ti 2.Ti 3.Gershwin, Ira 4.Heyward, Dubose

(B79-50131)

Hamlisch, Marvin
[They're playing our song. *Selections : arr].* They're playing our song / music by Marvin Hamlisch ; lyrics by Carole Bayer Sager. — Bryn Mawr ; [London] : Chappell, 1979. — 40p : ill,port ; 4to.
Unpriced
1.Ti 2.Ti 3.Sager, Carole Bayer

(B79-50956)

Lehár, Franz
[Die lustige Witwe. *Selections : arr].* Songs from The merry widow (Die lustige Witwe) / [by] Franz Lehár ; original book and lyrics by Victor Leon and Leo Stein, English lyrics by Sheldon Harnick. — London : Glocken, 1977. — [2],25p ; 4to.
Unpriced
1.Ti 2.Ti 3.Leon, Victor 4.Stein, Leo 5.Harnick, Sheldon

(B79-50957)

MacDonald, John
[High surge of the sea. *arr].* The song of the sea. An ataireachd ard = ('High surge of the sea') / music by John MacDonald ; adapted by Ian MacRae ; arr. Bob Nisbet ; Gaelic words by Donald MacIver ; English words by James MacPhee and Ian MacRae. — London : Bosworth and Co., 1979. — 4p ; 4to.
Song - English and Gaelic text.
Unpriced
1.Ti 2.Ti 3.MacIver, Donald 4.MacPhee, James 5.MacRae, Ian 6.Nisbet, Bob

(B79-50526)

Meira, Augusto
Ciranda do bom barqueiro : cantiga da infância / letra e música de Augusto Meira filho. — São Paulo : Sonata ; [London] : [Clifford Essex], 1979. — [3]p ; fol.
Unpriced
1.Ti

(B79-50958)

Moretti, Federico
[Doce canciones. Op.24]. Doce canciones = Twelve songs : with guitar accompaniment ... / [by] Federico Moretti ; with alternative piano accompaniment by Manuel Rücker ; complete facsimile edition with an introduction and English translation of the Spanish texts by Brian Jeffery. — London : Tecla, 1978. — xiv, 56p ; 4to.
Originally published: London : Clementi, Banger, Cullard, Davis & Cullard, 1812.
ISBN 0-8494-0140-2 : Unpriced
Primary classification KE/TSDW
1.Ti 2.Ti 3.Jeffery, Brian

(B79-50993)

Mullen, Brian
[Sweet Scottish isle. *arr].* Sweet Scottish isle / words and music by Brian Mullen ; piano arranged by Terance Bullard. — Lowestoft ((16 Mendip Rd)) : Autumn Publications, 1979. — 3p ; 4to.
Unpriced
1.Ti 2.Ti 3.Bullard, Terance

(B79-50959)

Mussorgsky, Modest
[Songs and dances of death. *arr].* Lieder und Tänze des Todes / [von] Modest P. Mussorgskij ; nach der Originalfassung für Gesang und Klavier bearbeitet für Gesang und Orgel von Wolfgang Dallmann. — Weisbaden ; [London] : Breitkopf und Härtel, 1979. — [4],31p ; obl. 4to.
Text in German.
£8.40
1.Ti 2.Ti 3.Dallmann, Wolfgang

(B79-50960)

Noble, Harold
Johnny : a Northumbrian fishergirl's song / words and music by Harold Noble. — South Croydon : Lengnick, 1979. — 5p ; 4to.
Unpriced
1.Ti
(B79-50132)

Schubert, Franz
[Songs]. Franz Schubert Lieder : Urtext der Neuen Schubert-Ausgabe / herausgegeben von Walther Dürr. — Kassel ; London : Bärenreiter.
Heft 1 : Die schöne Müllerin, op.25: Mittlere Stimme (Transposition). — 1977. — 79p ; 4to.
D.795. — Preface in German, English and French.
£5.28
1.Ti 2.Müller, Wilhelm
(B79-50133)

Heft 3 : Leider nach Texten von Goethe: Mittlere Stimme (Transposition). — 1978. — 80p ; 4to.
£4.80
1.Ti 2.Goethe, Johann Wolfgang von
(B79-50134)

Taylor, Cecil John
C. John Taylor's islands of beauty : ballad in English and Gaelic. — Oban (Isle of Seil, Oban, Argyll, Scotland) : Highland Arts Studios, 1978. — 3-8p : ports ; 4to.
For voice and piano. — Arranged by Gary Gordon.
Unpriced
1.Ti 2.Gordon, Gary 3.Islands of beauty
(B79-50527)

KDW/AY — Collections
The **English** recital song / compiled by David Patrick. — London : Chappell.
Vol.1. — 1979. — 79p ; 4to.
Includes works by C. Armstrong Gibbs, Eric Coates, Martin Shaw, Bax, Quilter, Graham Peel, Liza Lehmann, Elgar, Montague Phillips, Maud Valérie White, and Ireland.
Unpriced
1.Patrick, David
(B79-50528)

Das **europäische** Kunstlied : eine Auswahl von Klavierliedern aus vier Jahrhunderten für den Musikunterricht ... / herausgegeben von Margarete Jürgenson-Rupprecht und Kurt Suttner. — Mainz ; London : Schott, 1979. — 136p ; 4to.
£6.00
1.Jürgenson-Rupprecht, Margarete 2.Suttner, Kurt
(B79-50962)

Round the piano with Donald Swann : a collection of songs with piano accompaniments / selected and arranged by Donald Swann ; with drawings by Gaynor Chapman. — London : Bodley Head, 1979. — 93p ; 8vo.
ISBN 0-370-30173-0 : Unpriced
1.Swann, Donald
(B79-50961)

KDW/AYD — Songs, etc. Collections. England
Musica Britannica : a national collection of music. — London : Stainer and Bell.
Vol.43 : English songs, 1800-1860 / edited by Geoffrey Bush and Nicholas Temperley. — 1979. — xxvi,144p : facsim ; fol.
ISBN 0-85249-439-4 : Unpriced
Primary classification C/AYD
1.Bush, Geoffrey 2.Temperley, Nicholas
(B79-50814)

KDW/G/AYDJJ — Folk songs. Collections. Northumberland
Ma bonny lad : five traditional songs from Northumbria / arranged for voice and piano by René Atkinson. — Wendover : Roberton, 1979. — 16p ; 4to.
£1.50
1.Atkinson, René
(B79-50963)

KDW/G/AYEU — Folk songs. Collections. Germany. Judaeo. German
Jiddische Volkslieder : Liebeslieder, für Singstimme mit Klavier oder Gitarre / eingerichtet von Andre Asriel ; deutsche Nachdichtung und phonetische Transkription von Werner Gündzerodt ... — Berlin : Verlag Neue Musik ; [London] : [Breitkopf und Härtel], 1978. — 36p ; 4to.
Judaeo German and German text.
£3.60
1.Asriel, Andre 2.Günzerodt, Werner
(B79-50529)

KDW/G/AYH — Folk songs. Collections. France
Melusine. — Paris ; [London] : Chappell, 1979. — 43p. ; 4to. — (Collection rock et folk Chappell)
Folk songs arranged by the group 'Melusine'.
Unpriced
1.Sr
(B79-50964)

KDW/GB — Popular songs
Andersson, Benny
[Chiquitita. *arr*]. Chiquitita / words and music by Benny Anderson and Björn Ulvaens. — London : Chappell, 1979. — 5p ; 4to.
Unpriced
1.Ti 2.Ti 3.Ulvaens, Björn
(B79-50530)

Bush, Kate
[Lionheart. *arr*]. Lionheart / words and music by Kate Bush ; piano arrangements by Gordon Rees ; edited by Cecil Bolton ... — London : EMI, 1979. — 53p : ports ; 4to.
Unpriced
1.Ti 2.Rees, Gordon 3.Bolton, Cecil
(B79-50135)

Carmichael, Hoagy
[Songs. *Selections*]. The old music master : 23 great songs / [by] Hoagy Carmichael. — London : Chappell, 1979. — 68p. : port ; 4to.
Unpriced
1.Ti
(B79-50965)

Chinn, Nicky
Blockbuster / by Nick Chinn and Mike Chapman. — London : Chappell, 1979. — 176p ; 4to.
Unpriced
1.Ti 2.Chapman, Mike
(B79-50531)

McCartney, Paul
Back to the egg / words and music by McCartney [and others]. — London : MPL Communications, 1979. — 79p : ports ; 4to.
Unpriced
1.Ti
(B79-50966)

McCartney, Paul
[Back to the egg. Getting closer. *arr*]. Getting closer [and] Baby's request / words and music by McCartney. — London : MPL Communications, 1979. — 9p ; 4to.
Unpriced
1.Ti 2.Ti 3.Back to the egg. Baby's request. arr
(B79-50967)

McCartney, Paul
[B-side the seaside. Seaside woman. *arr*]. Seaside woman / words and music by McCartney. — London : MPL Communications, 1977. — [2p] ; 4to.
Unpriced
1.Ti 2.Ti
(B79-50968)

McCartney, Paul
Wings greatest / [mainly by Paul] McCartney. — London : MPL : Music Sales, 1979. — 60p ; 4to.
Unpriced
1.Ti
(B79-50136)

Richard, Keith
Some girls / [music mainly by Keith Richard] ; editor Cecil Bolton ; [words mainly by Mick Jagger]. — London : EMI, 1978. — 72p ; 4to.
Unpriced
1.Ti 2.Jagger, Mick
(B79-50137)

Ten CC
[Bloody tourists. *arr*]. Bloody tourists / [words and music by the group]. — London : Chappell, 1979. — 80p ; 4to.
Unpriced
1.Ti
(B79-50532)

Thin Lizzy
[Songs. *Selections : arr*]. Thin Lizzy : the best of ... / words and music by [the group]. — London : Chappell, 1979. — 88p : ill ; 4to.
Unpriced
1.Ti
(B79-50533)

Waller, Thomas
Fats Waller / editor Cecil Bolton. — London : EMI, 1978. — 64p ; 4to. — (Music makers)
Songs and piano solos by Waller and others.
Unpriced
1.Ti 2.Bolton, Cecil 3.Sr
(B79-50138)

Willis, Allee
Boogie wonderland / words and music by Allee Willis and Jon Lind. — London : Rondor : Chappell, 1979. — 7p ; 4to.
Song.
Unpriced
1.Ti 2.Lind, Jon

(B79-50534)

KDW/GB/AY — Popular songs. Collections
The **best** of popular music. — London : Chappell.
Songs.
Vol.1 : A-L. — 1979. — 175p. ; 4to.
Unpriced

(B79-50969)

Vol.2 : M-Z. — 1979. — 175-349p. ; 4to.
Unpriced

(B79-50970)

The **big** red fake book : giant hits of the 50's, 60's and 70's. — [Hollywood] : Screen Gems-EMI Music ; [London] : [EMI], 1978. — 318p ; 4to.
Unpriced

(B79-50535)

Headliners. — [London] : Chappell.
1. — 1977. — 52p ; 4to. —
Unpriced

(B79-50971)

2. — 1977. — 46p ; 4to. —
Unpriced

(B79-50972)

3. — 1978. — 30p ; 4to. —
Unpriced

(B79-50973)

5. — 1978. — 54p ; 4to. —
Unpriced

(B79-50974)

6. — 1979. — 46p ; 4to. —
Unpriced

(B79-50975)

Just friends, in print : Marian Montgomery with Richard Rodney Bennett in words, music and pictures / compiled by M. Easton. — Sevenoaks : Novello, 1979. — [2],70p : ports ; 4to.
Songs sung by Marian Montgomery and composed by Richard Rodney Bennett and others.
£2.95
1.Bennett, Richard Rodney 2.Easton, M

(B79-50536)

Singalongamax / edited and arranged by Cecil Bolton ; text by Peggy Jones. — London : EMI, 1979. — 87p ; 4to.
Songs in the repertory of Max Bygraves.
ISBN 0-86175-043-8 : Unpriced
1.Bolton, Cecil

(B79-50976)

KDW/GB/AY(XNU7) — Popular songs. Collections, 1939-1945
I'll be seeing you ... : featuring the songs, the artists and the memories of the Second World War. — London : EMI, 1979. — 119p ; 4to.
Editor and collator, Cecil Bolton.
ISBN 0-86175-042-x : Unpriced
1.Bolton, Cecil

(B79-50977)

KDW/GB/AYDL — Popular songs. Collections. Scotland
Scottish winners. — London : Campbell, Connelly and Connelly, 1979. — [1],13p ; 4to.
Songs. — Contents: 1: Catriona, by Roy Wilkie and Edin Millar - 2: God bless Caledonia, by Ronnie Bridges and Bob Halfin - 3: My Mary fair, by Robin Hall - 4: Rona, by Tom McClure - 5: Scotland, my Scotland, by W.P. Shannon.
Unpriced

(B79-50537)

KDW/GB/AYT — Popular songs. Collections, 1620-1958
The **songs** we sang : a treasury of American popular music / [by] Theodore Raph. — First paperback ed. — South Brunswick ; New York : Barnes ; London : Yoseloff, 1978. — 406p ; 4to.
Originally published: 1964.
ISBN 0-498-02050-9 : £4.00
1.Raph, Theodore

(B79-50538)

KDW/GC/AY — Country songs. Collection
Country crossroads : 15 dynamic hits. — Bryn Mawr ; [London] : Chappell, 1979. — 64p. ; 4to.
Unpriced

(B79-50980)

Don Williams : piano/vocal. — London : Chappell, 1979. — 48p. : ill,ports ; 4to.
Songs from the repertory of Don Williams.
Unpriced
1.Williams, Don

(B79-50979)

KDW/HKR — Rock
Ange
[Guet-apens. *arr*]. Guet-apens / [par] Ange. — Paris ; [London] : Chappell, 1979. — 30p. ; 4to.
Songs by the group 'Ange'.
Unpriced
1.Ti 2.Ti

(B79-50981)

Armatrading, Joan
[To the limit. *arr*]. To the limit / [words and music by] Joan Armatrading. — London : Chappell, 1979. — 48p : ports ; 4to.
Unpriced
1.Ti 2.Ti

(B79-50539)

Barclay James Harvest
[Gone to earth. *Selections: arr*]. Music from two hit albums, Gone to earth [and] XII / [by the group] Barclay James Harvest. — London : Chappell, 1979. — 80p ; 4to.
Unpriced
1.Ti 2.Ti

(B79-50982)

Beach Boys
Pet sound plus : 24 greatest hits ... / words and music by Brian Wilson ... [et al.]. — London : Chappell, 1979. — 64p : port ; 4to.
Songs in the repertory of the pop-group 'Beach boys'.
Unpriced
1.Ti 2.Wilson, Brian

(B79-50540)

Bee Gees
Spirits having flown / [words and music by the group]. — London : Chappell, 1979. — 47p ; 4to.
Unpriced
1.Ti

(B79-50541)

Clapton, Eric
[Backless. *arr*]. Backless / [by] Eric Clapton [et al.]. — Bryn Mawr ; [London] : Chappell, 1979. — 48p. : ill,ports ; 4to.
Songs.
Unpriced
1.Ti

(B79-50983)

Dire Straits
[Communiqué. *arr*]. Communiqué / [by] Dire Straits. — London : Chappell, 1979. — 72p. : ill ; 4to.
Unpriced
1.Ti

(B79-50984)

John, Elton
A single man / [words and music mainly by] Elton John and Gary Osborne. — London : Big Pig Music : Music Sales, 1978. — 53p ; 4to.
Unpriced
1.Ti 2.Osborne, Gary

(B79-50139)

Kiss
Double platinum. — Hollywood : Almo ; [London] : [EMI], 1978. — 95p ; 4to.
Album of songs by the group 'Kiss'.
Unpriced
1.Ti

(B79-50140)

Motorhead
[Overkill. *arr*]. Overkill / [by the group] Motorhead. — London : Chappell, 1979. — 47p. : ill ; 4to.
Unpriced
1.Ti 2.Ti

(B79-50985)

Nazareth
[No mean city. *arr*]. No mean city / [by the group] Nazareth. — London : Chappell, 1979. — 48p. : port ; 4to.
Unpriced
1.Ti 2.Ti

(B79-50986)

Queen
[Songs. *Selections : arr*]. Queen gold / [songs by the group
'Queen']. — London : EMI, 1979. — 172p ; 4to.
Comprising songs from their record albums 'News of the world' and 'Jazz'.
Unpriced
1.Ti

(B79-50987)

Steely Dan
[Songs. *Selections : arr*]. Steely Dan : the best of ... / words and
music by [the group]. — London : Chappell, 1978. — 72p ; 4to.
Unpriced
1.Ti

(B79-50542)

Stevens, Cat
[Back to earth. *arr*]. Back to earth / [by] Cat Stevens. —
[Hollywood] : Ashtar ; [London] : [EMI], 1979. — 98p : ill ; 4to.
Unpriced
1.Ti 2.Ti

(B79-50988)

Stewart, John
[Bombs away, dream babies. *arr*]. Bombs away, dream babies / all
words and music, John Stewart. — Bryn Mawr ; [London] :
Chappell, 1979. — 56p : ports ; 4to.
Unpriced
1.Ti 2.Ti

(B79-50989)

Stewart, Rod
[Songs. *Selections : arr*]. The vintage years / [by] Rod Stewart. —
London : Chappell, 1979. — 96p : ports ; 4to.
Unpriced
1.Ti

(B79-50990)

Thin Lizzy
Black rose : a rock legend / [by the group] Thin Lizzy. —
London : Chappell, 1979. — 52p : ports ; 4to.
Unpriced
1.Ti

(B79-50991)

Yes
Yes. Tormato / words and music by [the group]. — New York :
Warner ; [London] : [Music Sales], 1979. — 50p ; 4to.
Songs. — Contents: Arriving U.F.O. — Circus of heaven - Don't kill the
whale - Future times - Madrigal - On the silent wings of freedom -
Onward - Rejoice - Release, release.
Unpriced
1.Ti

(B79-50141)

Young, Neil
[After the gold rush. *arr*]. After the gold rush / words and music
by Neil Young. — London : Warner : Music Sales, 1978. — 63p ;
fol.
Unpriced
1.Ti

(B79-50142)

KDW/HKR/AY — Rock. Collections
Roots, rock and reggae / music selection by Nigel Burlinson, Mary
Jennings ; edited by Peter Foss. — London : Chappell, 1979. —
128p : ill ; 4to.
Songs by Bob Marley and others.
Unpriced
1.Burlinson, Nigel 2.Foss, Peter

(B79-50543)

KDW/JR — Films
Casey, Warren
[Grease. *arr*]. Grease : original soundtrack songs from the motion
picture / [by] Warren Casey and Jim Jacobs. — New York :
Warner ; [London] : [Blossom], 1978. — 103p ; 4to.
Songs by other composers included.
Unpriced
1.Ti 2.Jacobs, Jim

(B79-50143)

Casey, Warren
[Grease. *arr*]. Grease : original soundtrack songs from the motion
picture / [by] Warren Casey and Jim Jacobs. — Ilford : Chappell,
1978. — 103p ; 4to.
Songs by other composers included. — A cropped and slightly reduced
re-issue of the Warner edition.
Unpriced
1.Ti 2.Jacobs, Jim

(B79-50144)

Warren, Harry
[Songs. *Selections: arr*]. The works of Harry Warren / editor,
Cecil Bolton. — London : EMI, 1979. — 72p ; 4to. —
(Songsmiths)
Unpriced
1.Ti 2.Bolton, Cecil 3.Sr

(B79-50145)

**KE — VOCAL SOLOS WITH ACCOMPANIMENT OTHER
THAN KEYBOARD**
KE/LDW/AYD — With instruments. Songs, etc. Collections. England
Six 15th-century English songs : for voice with 1 and 2
instruments / edited by Ann-Marie Seaman and Richard Rastall.
— Newton Abbot : Antico, 1979. — [1],10p ; 4to.
Unpriced
1.Seaman, Ann-Marie 2.Rastall, Richard

(B79-50146)

KE/NXNRDW — With strings & keyboard quintet. Songs, etc
Eymwag, Joachim
Lamento / by Joachim Eymwag [or] Einweg ; edited by Ian
White. — Kings Langley ((Little Margaret, Penmans Green,
Chipperfield)) : E.L. White, 1979. — 5p ; fol.
Unpriced
1.Ti 2.White, Ian

(B79-50544)

KE/NXNTDW — With strings & keyboard trio. Songs, etc
Rorem, Ned
Serenade on five English poems : for voice, violin, viola and
piano / [by] Ned Rorem. — [New York] ; [London] : Boosey and
Hawkes, 1978. — 4to.
Duration 18 min. — Score ([5],25p.) & 2 parts.
Unpriced
1.Ti

(B79-50147)

KE/TSDW — With guitar. Songs, etc
Castelnuovo-Tedesco, Mario
Ballata dall'esilio : per voce e chitarra / [di] Mario
Castelnuovo-Tedesco ; [parole di] Guido Caralcanti. — Ancona ;
Milano : Bèrben ; [London] : [Breitkopf and Härtel], 1979. — 9p ;
4to.
£1.70
1.Ti 2.Caralcanti, Guido

(B79-50992)

Moretti, Federico
[Doce canciones. Op.24]. Doce canciones = Twelve songs : with
guitar accompaniment ... / [by] Federico Moretti ; with alternative
piano accompaniment by Manuel Rücker ; complete facsimile
edition with an introduction and English translation of the
Spanish texts by Brian Jeffery. — London : Tecla, 1978. — xiv,
56p ; 4to.
Originally published: London : Clementi, Banger, Cullard, Davis & Cullard,
1812.
ISBN 0-8494-0140-2 : Unpriced
Also classified at KDW
1.Ti 2.Ti 3.Jeffery, Brian

(B79-50993)

Swift, Dave
Living in the city : a songbook / by Dave Swift. — London ([59
Watney St., E.1]) : Basement Writers, 1975. — [24]p : ill, music ;
8vo.
Guitar tablature.
Sd : £0.15
1.Ti 2.Basement Writers

(B79-50545)

KE/TSDW/G/AYD — With guitar. Folk songs. Collections. England
The **English** folksinger : 159 modern and traditional folksongs /
collected and edited by Sam Richards and Tish Stubbs. —
Glasgow ; London : Collins, 1979. — 224p ; 8vo.
ISBN 0-00-411067-6 : £3.95(hardback), £1.95(pbk)
1.Richards, Sam 2.Stubbs, Tish

(B79-50994)

**KE/TSDW/K/G/AYDM — With guitar. Ballads. Collections.
Scotland**
Irische Lieder und Balladen / ausgewählt, herausgegeben und leicht
gesetzt für Gitarre solo von Klaus Buhé. — Mainz ; London :
Schott, 1979. — 27p ; 8vo.
£4.00
1.Buhé, Klaus

(B79-50995)

KEZ — UNACCOMPANIED VOCAL SOLOS
**KEZDW/G/AYDL — Unaccompanied voice. Folk songs. Collections.
Scotland**
Music and song from The Boys of the Lough : music and songs of
Ireland, Scotland and Shetland / [the songs and slow airs
transcribed by] Morag McLeod. — Edinburgh : Gilderoy, 1977.
— [5],56p ; 4to.
Songs from the repertoire of 'The Boys of the Lough'.
ISBN 0-9505982-0-8 : Unpriced
Also classified at KEZDW/G/AYDM
1.McLeod, Morag

(B79-50546)

KEZDW/G/AYDM — Unaccompanied voice. Folk songs. Collections. Ireland

Music and song from The Boys of the Lough : music and songs of Ireland, Scotland and Shetland / [the songs and slow airs transcribed by] Morag McLeod. — Edinburgh : Gilderoy, 1977. — [5],56p ; 4to.
Songs from the repertoire of 'The Boys of the Lough'.
ISBN 0-9505982-0-8 : Unpriced
Primary classification KEZDW/G/AYDL
1.McLeod, Morag

(B79-50546)

KEZDW/K/G/AYC — Unaccompanied ballads. Collections. Great Britain

Strike the bell : transport by road, canal, rail and sea in the nineteenth century through songs, ballads and contemporary accounts / selected and edited by Roy Palmer. — Cambridge : Cambridge University Press, 1978. — 64p : ill, facsims ; 4to. — (The resources of music)
With bibliography.
ISBN 0-521-21921-3 Sd : £2.25
1.Palmer, Roy 2.Sr

(B79-50547)

KF — FEMALE VOICE, CHILD'S VOICE
KFE/NYDPNPDW — Female voice. With woodwind, strings, keyboard & percussion septet. Songs, etc

Loevendie, Johannes Theodorus
Six Turkish folkpoems : for female voice and 7 instruments (1977) / [by] Theo Loevendie. — Amsterdam : Donemus ; [London] : [Lengnick], 1978. — 38p ; fol.
Unpriced
1.Ti

(B79-50548)

KFE/TSDW/AY — Female voice. With guitar. Songs, etc

Sisters in song : a collection of new songs from the women's liberation movement / [compiled by] Tierl Thompson, Andrea Webb and Janie Faychild. — London : Onlywoman Press, 1979. — 100p ; 4to.
Unpriced
1.Thompson, Tierl 2.Webb, Andrea 3.Faychild, Janie

(B79-50996)

KFLDJ — Soprano voice. Motets

Scarlatti, Domenico
[Salve regina. *Vocal score*]. Salve regina : sacred cantata for soprano and keyboard / [by] Domenico Scarlatti ; edited by Raymond Leppard. — London : Faber Music, 1979. — 19p ; 4to.
Unpriced
1.Ti 2.Leppard, Raymond

(B79-50148)

KFLDW — Soprano voice. Songs, etc

Bedford, David
An easy decision : soprano voice & piano / [by] David Bedford ; words by Kenneth Patchen. — London : Universal, 1978. — 3p ; 4to.
Unpriced
1.Ti 2.Patchen, Kenneth

(B79-50997)

Bedford, David
Some stars above magnitude 2.9 : soprano voice and piano / [by] David Bedford. — London : Universal, 1978. — [2],9p ; 4to.
Unpriced
1.Ti

(B79-50149)

Hoddinott, Alun
[A contemplation upon flowers. Op.90. *Vocal score*]. A contemplation upon flowers : 3 songs for soprano and orchestra / [by] Alun Hoddinott. — London : Oxford University Press, 1979. — 24p ; 8vo.
Duration 16 min. — Contents: 1: Life (Herbert) - 2: The flower (Herbert) - 3: A contemplation upon flowers (King).
ISBN 0-19-346719-4 : Unpriced
1.Ti 2.Ti

(B79-50998)

Rorem, Ned
Women's voices : eleven songs for soprano and piano / [by] Ned Rorem. — [New York] ; [London] : Boosey and Hawkes, 1979. — 40p ; 4to.
Text by various female poets - Duration 22 min.
Unpriced
1.Ti

(B79-50549)

Schonthal, Ruth
By the roadside : six songs to poems by Walt Whitman, for soprano and piano / [by] Ruth Schonthal. — New York ; [London] : Oxford University Press, 1979. — 12p ; 4to.
Duration 6 min.
Unpriced
1.Ti 2.Whitman, Walt

(B79-50150)

KFLE/MDW — Soprano voice. With orchestra. Songs, etc
Carter, Elliott
A mirror on which to dwell : six poems of Elizabeth Bishop, for soprano and chamber orchestra / [by] Elliott Carter. — New York ; London : Associated Music, 1977. — iv,96p ; 4to.
£24.20
1.Ti 2.Bishop, Elizabeth

(B79-50550)

Wagner, Richard
Wesendonk-Lieder : for soprano voice and orchestra / [by] Richard Wagner ; foreword by Lionel Salter. — London : Eulenburg, 1979. — xvii,52p ; 8vo.
The first four songs orchestrated by Felix Mottl. — Miniature score.
£2.15
1.Ti 2.Mottl, Felix

(B79-50999)

KFLE/MDX — Soprano voice with orchestra. Secular cantatas
Del Tredici, David
Vintage Alice : fantascene on a mad tea-party / [by] David Del Tredici. — New York ; [London] : Boosey and Hawkes, 1979. — [6],121p ; 8vo. — (Hawkes pocket scores ; 818)
Miniature score. — Duration 28 min. — Text by Lewis Carroll.
Unpriced
1.Ti 2.Carroll, Lewis 3.Sr

(B79-51000)

KFLE/NYENPDW — Soprano voice. With wind, strings & percussion septet. Songs, etc
Connolly, Justin
Poems of Wallace Stevens I : for soprano and seven players, opus 9 / [by] Justin Connolly. — Sevenoaks : Novello, 1979. — [8], 47p ; 8vo.
Duration 13 1/2 min.
£3.00
1.Ti 2.Stevens, Wallace

(B79-50151)

KFLE/RXNSDX — Soprano voice. With string quartet. Secular cantatas
Bauld, Alison
One pearl : a monody for soprano and string quartet / [by] Alison Bauld. — Sevenoaks : Novello, 1975. — [8],19p ; obl.4to.
Duration 16 min. — Facsimile of the composer's autograph.
£4.25
1.Ti

(B79-50152)

KFLE/VTDW — Soprano voice. With oboe. Songs, etc
Gerster, Ottmar
Die Amsel : für Sopranstimme und Oboe / [von] Ottmar Gerster ; text, Max Dauthendey. — Berlin : Neue Musik ; [London] : [Breitkopf und Härtel], 1977. — 8p ; 4to.
£1.20
1.Ti 2.Dauthendey, Max

(B79-50551)

KFLE/VVPLJ — Soprano voice with clarinet & piano. Motets
Cherubini, Luigi
[Hymnes sacrées. Ave Maria. *arr*]. Ave Maria. Offertorium / [by] Luigi Cherubini ; edited by Robin de Smet for 1. Soprano, B flat clarinet, (or flute) and piano, 2, two B flat clarinets and piano, 3, Flute, B flat clarinet and piano. — London : Fentone Music : Breitkopf und Härtel, 1979. — 4to.
Score (8p.) & 4 parts.
Unpriced
Also classified at VVNTQK/DJ; NWPNTK/DJ
1.Ti 2.Ti 3.De Smet, Robin

(B79-51001)

KFLEZDW — Unaccompanied soprano voice. Songs, etc. With tape
Rands, Bernard
Ballad 3 : for soprano and tape / [by] Bernard Rands. — London : Universal, 1978. — 5p ; obl. 4to.
Duration 12 min.
Unpriced
1.Ti

(B79-51003)

KFT — HIGH VOICE
KFTDW — Songs, etc
Arne, Thomas Augustine
[Songs. *Selections : arr*]. Twelve songs : for high voice / [by] Thomas Arne ; edited by Michael Pilkington. — London : Stainer and Bell.
Book 1. — 1979. — 31p ; 8vo.
ISBN 0-85249-461-0 : Unpriced
1.Pilkington, Michael
(B79-50552)

Book 2. — 1979. — 31p ; 8vo.
ISBN 0-85249-462-9 : Unpriced
1.Pilkington, Michael
(B79-50553)

Blow, John
[Songs. *Selections*]. Ten songs for high voice / [by] John Blow ; edited by Michael Pilkington. — London : Stainer and Bell, 1979. — 32p ; 8vo.
ISBN 0-85249-547-1 : Unpriced
1.Pilkington, Michael
(B79-51004)

Boyce, William
[Songs. *Selections : arr*]. Ten songs for high voice / [by] William Boyce ; edited by Michael Pilkington. — London : Stainer and Bell, 1979. — [1],32p ; 8vo.
ISBN 0-85249-493-9 : Unpriced
1.Ti 2.Pilkington, Michael
(B79-50554)

Britten, Benjamin, *Baron Britten*
[A birthday hansel. Op.92. *Selections : arr*]. Four Burns songs : for high voice and piano / [by] Benjamin Britten ; settings of poems by Robert Burns ; the piano arranged by Colin Matthews. — London : Faber Music, 1978. — 16p ; fol.
Unpriced
1.Ti 2.Ti 3.Burns, Robert 4.Matthews, Colin
(B79-50153)

Bush, Geoffrey
[Songs. *Selections*]. Eight songs for high voice and piano / [by] Geoffrey Bush. — Sevenoaks : Novello, 1979. — [2],30p ; 4to.
Published together for the first time.
£2.40
1.Ti 2.Ti
(B79-51005)

Chapple, Brian
Five Blake songs : for high voice and piano / [by] Brian Chapple. — London : Chester Music, 1979. — [2],27p ; 4to.
Facsimile of the composer's autograph.
1.Ti 2.Blake, William
(B79-50154)

Hook, James
[Songs. *Selections*]. Eight songs : for high voice / [by] James Hook ; edited by Michael Pilkington. — London : Stainer and Bell, 1979. — 32p ; 8vo.
ISBN 0-85249-494-7 : Unpriced
1.Pilkington, Michael
(B79-50555)

Parry, *Sir* **Charles Hubert,** *bart*
[English lyrics. *selections*]. Seven songs for high voice / edited by Geoffrey Bush. — London : Stainer and Bell, 1979. — 32p ; 8vo.
Unpriced
1.Ti 2.Ti 3.Bush, Geoffrey
(B79-51006)

Storace, Stephen
[Songs. *Selections*]. Seven songs : for high voice / [by] Stephen Storace ; edited by Michael Pilkington. — London : Stainer and Bell, 1979. — 32p ; 8vo.
ISBN 0-85249-510-2 : Unpriced
1.Pilkington, Michael
(B79-50556)

KFTDX — Secular cantatas
Sutermeister, Heinrich
[Consolatio philosophiae. *Vocal score*]. Consolatio philosophiae : scène dramatique voix haute et orchestre in memoriam Ernest Ansermet (1977) / [von] Heinrich Sutermeister ; argument de J.-Claude Piguet sur des poèmes de Boèce ; deutsche Übersetzung von Olof Gigon ; Klavierauszug vom Komponisten. — Mainz ; London : Schott, 1978. — 32p ; 4to.
Duration 18 min.
£10.80
1.Ti 2.Ti 3.Piguet, Jean Claude 4.Boethius 5.Gigon, Olof
(B79-50155)

KFTE/NWPNSDW — With woodwind & keyboard quartet. Songs, etc
Schürmann, Georg Caspar
[Operas. *Selections*]. Arien : für hohe Singstimme, Blockflöten, Fagott und Basso continuo / [von] Georg Caspar Schürmann ; herausgegeben von Nikolaus Delius ; Generalbass-Aussetzung, Gottfried Bach. — Erstausgabe. — Kassel ; London : Bärenreiter, 1978. — 4to.
Score & 3 parts.
£6.60
1.Ti 2.Ti 3.Delius, Nikolaus 4.Bach, Gottfried
(B79-50557)

KFV — MIDDLE VOICE
KFVDW — Songs, etc
Beeson, Jack
[The day's no rounder than its angles are. *arr*]. The day's no rounder than its angles are : three songs for medium voice and string quartet / [by] Jack Beeson ; words by Peter Viereck, voice and piano reduction. — New York ; [London] : Boosey and Hawkes, 1979. — 16p ; fol.
Unpriced
1.Ti 2.Viereck, Peter
(B79-50558)

Early Georgian songs / edited by Michael Pilkington. — London : Stainer and Bell.
Songs by Daniel Purcell, Eccles, Greene, Leveridge, Russel and Weldon.
Book 1 : Medium voice. — 1978. — 32p ; 8vo.
ISBN 0-85249-459-9 : Unpriced
1.Pilkington, Michael
(B79-50559)

Matthews, Colin
Un colloque sentimental = A sentimental conversation : cycle for medium voice and piano / [by] Colin Matthews ; poems by Paul Verlaine, Charles Baudelaire and Gérard de Nerval. — London : Faber Music, 1979. — 31p ; fol.
Unpriced
1.Ti
(B79-51007)

Stanford, *Sir* **Charles Villiers**
[Songs. *Selections*]. Six songs for medium voice / [by] C.V. Stanford ; edited by Geoffrey Bush. — London : Stainer and Bell, 1979. — 32p ; 8vo.
Contents: 1: The merry month of May - 2: Prospice - 3: O mistress mine - 4: The chapel on the hill - 5: The bold unbiddable child - 6: The pibroch.
ISBN 0-85249-526-9 : Unpriced
1.Bush, Geoffrey
(B79-51008)

KFVDX — Secular cantatas
Beeson, Jack
[A Creole mystery. *Vocal score*]. A Creole mystery : a short story for medium voice and string quartet / [by] Jack Beeson ; from the sketch by Lafcadio Hearn adapted by the composer. — New York ; [London] : Boosey and Hawkes, 1979. — 15p ; 4to.
Unpriced
1.Ti 2.Ti 3.Hearn, Lafcadio
(B79-50560)

KG — MALE VOICE
KGHDW — Tenor voice. Songs, etc
Martin, Frank
Dédicace de Pierre de Ronsard : 1945 : pour ténor et piano = für Tenor und Klavier / [par] Frank Martin. — Kassel ; London : Bärenreiter, 1978. — 8p ; 4to. — (Concerto vocale)
£2.64
1.Ti 2.Ronsard, Pierre de 3.Sr
(B79-50561)

KGNDW — Baritone voice. Songs, etc
Beeson, Jack
Senex / music by Jack Beeson ; poem by John Betjeman. — [New York] ; [London] : Boosey and Hawkes, 1979. — 7p ; 4to.
For baritone and piano. — Duration 2 1/4 min.
Unpriced
1.Ti
(B79-50562)

Hoddinott, Alun
Ancestor worship : four poems of Emyr Humphreys, for baritone and piano / [by] Alun Hoddinott. — London : Oxford University Press, 1979. — 19p ; 4to.
Duration 13 min.
ISBN 0-19-345433-5 : Unpriced
1.Ti 2.Humphreys, Emyr
(B79-51009)

KGNE/MDX — Baritone voice. With orchestra. Secular cantatas
Kelterborn, Rudolf
[Symphony no.3, 'Espansioni']. Espansioni : Sinfonie III für
grosses Orchester, Bariton und Tonband, 1974/1975 / [von]
Rudolf Kelterborn ; Texte von Giuseppe Ungaretti. — London :
Bärenreiter, 1978. — 47p ; 4to.
£11.55
1.Ti 2.Ti 3.Ungaretti, Giuseppe
                                                                                            (B79-50156)

KHYE/NYENQ — Speaker with wind, strings & percussion sextet
Walton, Sir William
Façade 2 : a further entertainment / with poems by Edith Sitwell
and music by William Walton. — London : Oxford University
Press, 1979. — [3],23p ; 4to.
Facsimile of the composer's autograph.
ISBN 0-19-359406-4 : Unpriced
1.Ti 2.Sitwell, Dame, Edith
                                                                                            (B79-51010)

LK — ARRANGEMENTS
LK/DP/LF/AY — Arrangements. Carols. Christmas. Collections
Christmas carols / [compiled by] Candida Tobin. — Bishop's
Stortford : Helison Press, 1976. — [14]p ; 8vo. — (Colour and
play books)
ISBN 0-905684-04-4 : Unpriced
1.Tobin, Candida 2.Sr
                                                                                            (B79-50157)

LK/DW/G/AY — Arrangements. Folk songs. Collections
Folksong book 1 / [compiled by] Candida Tobin. — Bishop's
Stortford : Helicon Press, 1976. — [14]p ; 8vo. — (Colour and
play books)
ISBN 0-905684-01-x : Unpriced
1.Tobin, Candida 2.Sr
                                                                                            (B79-50158)

LK/DW/GBB/AY — Arrangements. Pop songs. Collections
Stayin' alive, You need me, plus 12 hot hits / arranged by Bob
Lowden [for] flute (& other C instruments). — Bryn Mawr ;
[London] : Chappell, 1978. — 28p. ; 4to.
Unpriced
1.Lowden, Bob
                                                                                            (B79-51011)

LK/DW/GK/AY — Arrangements. Nursery rhymes. Collections
Nursery rhymes / [compiled by] Candida Tobin. — Bishop's
Stortford : Helicon Press, 1976. — [14]p ; 8vo. — (Colour and
play books)
ISBN 0-905684-03-6 : Unpriced
1.Tobin, Candida 2.Sr
                                                                                            (B79-50159)

LN — ENSEMBLES
Hoch, Peter
Ensemble/séparé : fur 1-4 Instrumentalspieler = for 1 to 4
players / [von] Peter Hoch. — Mainz ; London : Schott, 1979. —
obl.4to. — (Workshop ; 22)
The playing score consists of separate 'leaflets', and only the introduction
and instructions are paginated.
£6.00
1.Ti 2.Sr
                                                                                            (B79-50563)

LNK/AAY — Arrangements. Collections
The **elastic** band / [pieces compiled] by Atarah Ben-Tovim and
Douglas Boyd ; arrangements by John Harper. — London :
Novello, 1979. — obl.4to & 4to. — (Atarah's bandkit ; C1)
Four arrangements for school instrumental ensemble - Score ([1],29p.) & 11
parts with teachers' notes. — Contents: 1: Mazurka from 'Coppelia' by
Delibes - 2: Dozey Jack : traditional - 3: For he's a jolly muchacho - 4: The
rocking grenadiers.
Score, £5.00, Parts, Unpriced
1.Ben-Tovim, Atarah 2.Boyd, Douglas 3.Harper, John 4.Sr
                                                                                            (B79-50160)

MJ — MISCELLANEOUS WORKS
Gruber, Heinz Karl
Phantom-Bilder auf der Spur eines verdächtingen Themas. Op.30
= Photo-fit pictures on the tracks of a suspect theme = für
kleines Orchester = for small orchestra / [von] H.K. Gruber. —
London : Boosey and Hawkes, 1979. — fol. — (Hawkes school
series ; no.303)
Score ([4],30p.) & 23 parts, with several copies of various parts - Duration
12 1/2 min.
Unpriced
1.Ti 2.Sr
                                                                                            (B79-50564)

Maasz, Gerhard
Wir sind die Musikanten : eine kleine Instrumentenschau für
Orchester, Chor ad lib. (2 gl. Stimmen) und Sprecher ad lib. /
[von] Gerhard Maasz. — Mainz ; London : Schott, 1978. — 35p ;
4to. — (Concertino ; 184)
Duration 15 min.
£6.00
1.Ti 2.Sr
                                                                                            (B79-50161)

MK — ARRANGEMENTS
Ketelbey, Albert
[In a Persian market. arr]. Persian market swing. (In a Persian
market) / by Albert W. Ketelbey ; arranged by Frank Naylor. —
London : Bosworth & Co., 1979. — 16p ; 4to.
School orchestra and wind band.
£1.35
1.Ti 2.Ti 3.Naylor, Frank
                                                                                            (B79-50565)

MK/AGM — Arrangements. Marches
Suppé, Franz von
[Fatinitza march. arr]. Fatinitza march : based on themes from
the operetta 'Fatinitza' / by Franz von Suppé ; arr. by Frank
Naylor. — London : Bosworth & Co., 1979. — 16p ; 4to.
Duration 2 1/4 min.
£1.25
1.Ti 2.Ti 3.Naylor, Frank
                                                                                            (B79-51012)

Tchaikovsky, Peter
[Marche slave. Op.31. arr]. Marche slave / [by] Tchaikovsky ;
arranged by Geoffrey Tomlinson. — London : Oxford University
Press, 1978. — fol. — (Music for amateur orchestra)
Duration 5 min. — Score ([1],38p.) & 16 parts.
ISBN 0-19-367910-8 : Unpriced
1.Ti 2.Tomlinson, Geoffrey 3.Sr
                                                                                            (B79-50162)

Wagner, Josef Franz
[Unter dem Doppeladler. Op.159. arr]. Under the double eagle =
Unter dem Doppeladler : march, (op.159) / by J.F. Wagner ;
arranged [for school and amateur orchestra and wind band or
symphonic band by Frank Naylor]. — London : Bosworth & Co.,
1978. — 24p ; 4to.
Unpriced
1.Ti 2.Ti 3.Naylor, Frank
                                                                                            (B79-50163)

MK/AH/AYU — Arrangements. Dances. Collections. Latin America
Alla danza : lateinamerikanische Tänze (Cha-Cha, Tango argentino,
Bossa nova) zu vier Stimmen, Stabspiele, Schlagzeug und Klavier,
für Orchester, Streichorchester oder Instrumentalenensemble /
[von] Friedrich Zehm. — Mainz ; London : Schott, 1978. — 31p ;
4to.
Duration 12 min.
£8.00
Also classified at RXMK/AH/AYU
1.Zehm, Friedrich
                                                                                            (B79-50566)

MK/DP/LF/AY — Arrangements. Christmas carols. Collections
Christmas carol kit. — London : Middle Eight Music.
Set 1. — 1979. — 4to.
Conductor & 33 parts with several copies of various parts. — Contents : 1 :
Once in royal David's city - 2 : The first nowell - 3 : While shepherds
watched - 4 : O come, all ye faithful.
Unpriced
                                                                                            (B79-51013)

Set 2. — 1979. — 4to.
Conductor & 33 parts, with several copies of various parts. — Contents : 5 :
O little town of Bethlehem - 6 : Ding dong! merrily on high - 7 : Away in a
manger - 8 : Hark! the herald angels sing.
Unpriced
                                                                                            (B79-51014)

MK/HM — Arrangements. Ballet
Khachaturian, Aram
[Spartak. Adagio of Spartacus and Phrygia. arr]. Adagio / [by]
Aram Khachaturian ; arranged by David Stone. — London :
Boosey and Hawkes, 1979. — 35pt ; 4to. — (Hawkes school
series ; no.205)
Unpriced
1.Ti 2.Ti 3.Stone, David 4.Sr
                                                                                            (B79-50567)

Khachaturian, Aram
[Spartak. Adagio of Spartacus and Phrygia. arr]. Adagio / [by]
Aram Khachaturian ; arranged by David Stone. — London :
Boosey and Hawkes, 1979. — [1],36p ; fol. — (Hawkes school
series ; no.205)
Unpriced
1.Ti 2.Ti 3.Stone, David 4.Sr
                                                                                            (B79-50568)

MM — WORKS FOR SYMPHONY ORCHESTRA
MM/HM — Ballet music
Prokofiev, Sergei
[The prodigal son]. L'enfant prodigue. Opus 46 : ballet in three
scenes by Boris Kochno / [music by] Serge Prokofieff. — 1st ed.
— London : Boosey and Hawkes, 1978. — [4],195p ; 8vo. —
(Hawkes pocket scores ; 907)
Duration 35 min.
Unpriced
1.Ti 2.Ti 3.Sr
                                                                                            (B79-50164)

MM/JM — Incidental music

Grieg, Edvard
[Sigurd Jorsalfar. Op.56. *Selections*]. Three orchestral pieces from the incidental music to Sigurd Jorsalfar, op.56 / [by] Edvard Grieg ; foreword by John Horton. — London : Eulenburg, 1978. — vii,55p ; 8vo.
Miniature score.
Unpriced
1.Ti 2.Ti
(B79-50165)

MM/Y — Variations

Walton, *Sir* William
Varii capricci / [by] William Walton. — London : Oxford University Press, 1978. — [4],73p ; 8vo.
Foreword by Stephen Wikner. — Duration 14 min.
ISBN 0-19-368453-5 : Unpriced
1.Ti
(B79-50166)

MME — Symphonies

Klebe, Giselher
[Symphony, no.3, op.52]. Dritte Sinfonie für grosses Orchester, Op.52 = Third symphony for grand orchestra, Op.52 / [von] Giselher Klebe. — Kassel ; London : Bärenreiter, 1967[i.e.1979]. — [2],12p ; 8vo. — (Taschenpartituren ; 125)
Miniature score.
£13.20
1.Sr
(B79-50167)

Trojahn, Manfred
[Symphony, no.2]. II. Sinfonie, 1978 / [von] Manfred Trojahn. — Kassel ; London : Bärenreiter, 1978. — 64p ; 4to.
Duration 32 min. — Facsimile of the composer's autograph.
£12.54
1.Zweiter Sinfonie, 1978
(B79-50569)

Zimmermann, Ildo
Sinfonia come un grade lamento (1977). Dem Andenken Frederico [sic] García Lorca / von Ildo Zimmermann. — Leipzig : VEB Deutscher Verlag für Musik, 1979. — [4],30p ; fol.
£3.30
1.Ti 2.García Lorca, Federico
(B79-51015)

MMEM — Sinfoniettas

Janáček, Leoš
Sinfonietta / [by] Leoš Janáček ; edited by Jarmil Burghauser. — London : Eulenburg, 1979. — vi,116p ; 8vo.
Miniature score.
£2.50
1.Burghauser, Jarmil
(B79-50168)

MMF — Concertos

Bennett, Richard Rodney
Concerto, orchestra / [by] Richard Rodney Bennett. — Sevenoaks : Novello, 1974. — [6],70p ; 4to.
Based on the Tema seriale from Britten's Cantata academica. — Study score. — Facsimile of the composer's autograph. — Duration 23 min.
£4.85
1.Ti
(B79-50169)

Redel, Martin Christoph
[Concerto, orchestra, op.27]. Konzert für Orchester. Opus 27 / [von] Martin Christoph Redel. — Berlin : Bote and Bock ; [London] : [Schirmer], 1979. — 81p ; 4to.
Duration 21 min.
£14.40
(B79-51016)

MMG — Suites

Holst, Gustav
The planets : suite for large orchestra. Op.32 / [by] Gustav Holst ; new edition prepared by Imogen Holst & Colin Matthews. — London : Curwen, 1979. — [7],187p ; 4to.
Duration 45min..
Unpriced
1.Ti 2.Holst, Imogen 3.Matthews, Colin
(B79-51017)

Rimsky-Korsakoff, Nikolai
[The golden cockerel. *Suite*]. Suite from the opera, 'The golden cockerel' / [by] N.A. Rimsky-Korsakov ; foreword by David Lloyd-Jones. — London : Eulenburg, 1979. — vii,136p ; 8vo.
Miniature score.
Unpriced
1.Ti
(B79-51018)

Tchaikovsky, Peter
[Suite, orchestra, no.3, op.55, G major]. Suite no.3 in G, op.55 / [by] Peter Ilyich Tchaikovsky ; foreword by Gerald Abraham. — London : Eulenburg, 1978. — x,260p ; 8vo.
Miniature score. — Foreword in English and German.
Unpriced
(B79-50170)

MMH — Dances

Yun, Isang
Muak : tänzerische Fantasie für grosses Orchester, 1978 / [von] Isang Yun. — Berlin ; Weisbaden : Bote und Bock, 1979. — 52p ; fol.
Duration 16 min.
£9.60
1.Ti
(B79-51019)

MMHG — Dance suites

Lane, Philip
Suite of Cotswold folkdances / [by] Philip Lane. — London : Edwin Ashdown, 1978. — [2],38p ; 4to.
Duration 13 min.
£5.00
1.Ti
(B79-50171)

MMJ — Miscellaneous works

Argento, Dominick
In praise of music : (seven songs for orchestra) / [by] Dominick Argento. — New York ; [London] : Boosey and Hawkes, 1978. — [6],102p ; 8vo.
Miniature score. — Duration 30 min.
Unpriced
1.Ti
(B79-50172)

Berlioz, Hector
[Les Troyens, part 2. Chasse royale et orage]. Chase royale et orage / [by] Hector Berlioz ; edited by Hugh Macdonald. — London : Bärenreiter, 1978. — [5],34p ; 8vo.
Miniature score.
Unpriced
1.Ti 2.Macdonald, Hugh
(B79-50173)

Beyer, Frank Michael
Diaphonie : für Orchester / von Frank Michael Beyer. — Berlin : Bote und Bock ; [London] : [Schirmer], 1978. — 85p ; fol.
Duration 20 min.
£14.40
1.Ti
(B79-51020)

Birtwistle, Harrison
Silbury air / [by] Harrison Birtwistle. — London : Universal, 1979. — [6],52p ; fol.
For orchestra. — Duration 15 min. — Facsimile of the composer's manuscript.
Unpriced
1.Ti
(B79-51021)

Blake, David
Metamorphoses : for large orchestra / [by] David Blake. — Sevenoaks : Novello, 1979. — [4],67p ; 8vo.
£2.75
1.Ti
(B79-50174)

Brown, Christopher
The sun rising : threnody for orchestra. Op.45 / [by] Christopher Brown. — London : Chester Music, 1979. — 43p ; 4to.
Unpriced
1.Ti
(B79-51022)

Fortner, Wolfgang
Triptychon : für Orchester (1977) / [von] Wolfgang Fortner. — Mainz ; London : Schott, 1978. — 63p ; fol.
Duration 26 min.
£20.00
1.Ti
(B79-50175)

Goehr, Alexander
Metamorphosis : dance / [by] Alexander Goehr. — London : Schott, 1978. — [3],77p ; 8vo.
For orchestra.
Unpriced
1.Ti
(B79-50176)

Gould, Morton
American ballads : settings of familiar tunes ... for orchestra / [by] Morton Gould. — New York ; London : Schirmer.
Duration 5 min.
1 : Star-spangled overture (on 'The star-spangled banner'). — 1978. — 48p ; 4to.
£6.10
1.Ti

(B79-50570)

Gould, Morton
American ballads : settings of familiar tunes ... for orchestra / by Morton Gould. — New York ; London : Schirmer.
Duration 6 1/2 min.
2 : Amber waves (on 'America the beautiful'). — 1978. — 24p ; 4to.
£6.10
1.Ti

(B79-50571)

3 : Jubilo (on 'Year of Jubilo'). — 1978. — 34p ; 4to.
£6.10
1.Ti

(B79-50572)

4 : Memorials (on 'Taps'). — 1978. — 26p ; 4to. —
£6.10
1.Ti

(B79-50573)

5 : Saratoga quickstep (on 'The girl I left behind me'). — 1978. — 42p ; 4to.
£6.10
1.Ti

(B79-50574)

6 : Hymnal (on 'We shall overcome'). — 1978. — 39p ; 4to. —
£6.10
1.Ti

(B79-50575)

Grieg, Edvard
Two elegiac melodies. Op.34 / [by] Edvard Grieg ; foreword by John Horton. — London : Eulenburg, 1978. — vi,12p ; 8vo.
Miniature score.
Unpriced
1.Ti

(B79-50177)

Henze, Hans Werner
Aria de la folía española : für Orchester = for orchestra : (1977) / [von] Hans Werner Henze. — Mainz ; [London] : Schott, 1978. — 100p ; fol.
Duration 20 min.
£19.60
1.Ti

(B79-50576)

Hoddinott, Alun
Landscapes, Op.86 : for orchestra / [by] Alun Hoddinott. — London : Oxford University Press, 1979. — [2],101p ; 8vo.
ISBN 0-19-364492-4 : Unpriced
1.Ti

(B79-50577)

Holliger, Heinz
Atembogen : für Orchester / [von] Heinz Holliger. — Mainz ; London : Schott, 1979. — 61p ; fol.
Study score.
£18.00
1.Ti

(B79-51023)

Holloway, Robin
Scenes from Schumann : seven paraphrases for orchestra, opus 13, / [by] Robin Holloway .. ; a reproduction in facsimile of the composer's autograph manuscript. — London : Boosey and Hawkes, 1979. — [5],121p ; 8vo. — (Hawkes pocket scores ; 947)
Unpriced
1.Ti 2.Sr

(B79-50178)

Kelterborn, Rudolf
Erinnerungen an Orpheus : Musik für Orchester (1977/78) / von Rudolf Kelterborn. — Berlin : Bote and Bock, 1979. — 45p ; 4to.
£11.50
1.Ti

(B79-51024)

Kelterborn, Rudolf
Phantasmen : für grosses Orchester, 1965-1966 / [von] Rudolf Kelterborn. — Kassel ; London : Bärenreiter, 1978. — 43p ; 4to.
Duration 10 min. — Facsimile of the composer's autograph.
£10.89
1.Ti

(B79-50578)

Liszt, Franz
Phantasie über ungarische Volksmelodien = Fantasia on Hungarian folk themes / [von] Franz Liszt ; foreword by Robert Collet. — London : Eulenburg, 1979. — [5],44p ; 8vo.
Miniature score.
£1.20
1.Ti

(B79-50179)

Sculthorpe, Peter
Music for Japan : for orchestra / [by] Peter Sculthorpe. — London : Faber Music, 1979. — [4],27p ; 4to.
Unpriced
1.Ti

(B79-51025)

Wimberger, Gerhard
Motus : für grosses Orchester / [von] Gerhard Wimberger. — Kassel ; London : Bärenreiter, 1978. — 36p ; 4to.
Duration 17 min.
£8.91
1.Ti

(B79-50579)

Wolf-Ferrari, Ermanno
[Il segreto di Susanna. Overture]. Susanna's secret = Il segreto di Susanna = Susannens Geheimnis : overture / [by] Ermanno Wolf-Ferrari. — London : Weinberger, [1979]. — [2],32p ; 8vo.
Miniature score.
Unpriced
1.Ti 2.Ti

(B79-50180)

Yūasa, Jōji
[Time of orchestral time]. Jkesutora no toki no toki = Time of orchestral time / Joji Yuasa. — Tokyo : Zen-on Music ; Mainz ; [London] : Schott, 1977. — 40p ; fol.
Duration 18 1/2 min. — Title in Japanese script.
£12.00
1.Ti 2.Ti

(B79-51026)

MP — WORKS FOR SOLO INSTRUMENT (S) & ORCHESTRA
MPQ — Piano & orchestra
Feldman, Morton
Piano and orchestra / [by] Morton Feldman. — Toronto ; [London] : Universal, 1978. — [4],39p ; 4to.
Duration 21 min.
Unpriced
1.Ti

(B79-50181)

Rands, Bernard
Mésalliance : for piano and orchestra / [by] Bernard Rands. — London : Universal, 1978. — 28p ; fol.
Duration 14 min.
Unpriced
1.Ti

(B79-50182)

MPQF — Piano & orchestra. Concertos
Mozart, Wolfgang Amadeus
[Concerto, piano, no.19, K.459, F major]. Konzert in F für Klavier und Orchester KV459 = Concerto in F major for pianoforte and orchestra K.459 / [von] Wolfgang Amadeus Mozart ; herausgegeben von ... Eva und Paul Badura-Skoda. — Kassel ; London : Bärenreiter, 1978. — xiii,84p ; 8vo.
Miniature score.
£3.96
1.Badura-Skoda, Eva 2.Badura-Skoda, Paul

(B79-50580)

Travis, Roy
[Concerto, piano]. Piano concerto / [by] Roy Travis. — New York ; London : Oxford University Press, 1976. — 85p ; 4to.
Duration 19 min. — Facsimile of the composer's manuscript.
Unpriced

(B79-50581)

MPSF — Violin & orchestra. Concertos
Baur, Jürg
[Concerto, violin, no.2]. 2 Violinkonzert : in Form einer Ballade, für Violine und Orchester, (1978) / [von] Jürg Baur. — Weisbaden ; [London] : Breitkopf und Härtel, 1979. — [2],126p ; 8vo. — (Breitkopf und Härtel Partitur-Bibliothek ; no.5060)
Duration 31 min.
£8.40
1.Ti 2.Zweite Violinkonzert : in Form einer Ballade 3.Sr

(B79-51028)

Schurmann, Gerard
[Concerto, violin]. Concerto for violin and orchestra / [by] Gerard Schurmann. — Sevenoaks : Novello, 1979. — [2],109p ; 4to.
Duration 30 min.
£8.85
1.Ti

(B79-51029)

Schwertsik, Kurt
[Concerto, violin, op.31]. Violinkonzert opus 31 : Romanzen im
Schwarztiten-Ton und in der geblümtem Paradies-Weis / [von]
Kurt Schwertsik. — London : Boosey and Hawkes, 1978. — [4],
82p ; 8vo. — (Hawkes pocket scores ; 943)
Study score. — Duration 20 min.
Unpriced
1.Sr

(B79-50582)

MPSQF — Viola & orchestra. Concertos
Martinu, Bohuslav
Rhapsody - concerto : für Viola und Orchester = pro violu a
orchestr = for viola and orchestra / [von] Bohuslav Martinu. —
Kassel ; London : Bärenreiter, 1978. — [1],52p ; 4to.
Duration 22 min.
£12.54
1.Ti

(B79-50583)

MPSRF — Cello & orchestra. Concertos
Bridge, Frank
Oration : (concerto elegiaco) for solo cello and orchestra / [by]
Frank Bridge ; edited by Paul Hindmarsh. — London : Faber
Music, 1979. — [2],70p ; fol.
Duration: c.28 min.
Unpriced
1.Ti 2.Hindmarsh, Paul

(B79-50584)

Halffter, Cristóbal
[Concerto, cello]. Concierto para violoncello y orquesta / [de]
Cristóbal Halffter. — London : Universal, 1975. — [8],54p.
Reproduction of the composer's manuscript.
Unpriced

(B79-51030)

Matthus, Siegfried
[Concerto, cello (1975)]. Konzert für Violoncello und Orchester /
[von] Siegfried Matthus. — Leipzig : VEB Deutscher Verlag für
Musik ; [London] : [Breitkopf und Härtel], 1978. — 4to.
Score (82p.) & part. — Duration 23 min.
£5.40

(B79-50585)

MPVNSF — Woodwind quartet & orchestra. Concertos
Sutermeister, Heinrich
Quadrifoglio : concerto per quattro fiati ed orchestra / [di]
Heinrich Sutermeister. — Mainz ; London : Schott, 1978. — 92p ;
4to.
£16.80
1.Ti

(B79-50586)

MPVRF — Flute & orchestra. Concertos
Fétis, François Joseph
[Concerto, flute, B minor]. Konzert für Flöte und Orchester in
h-moll / [von] François Joseph Fétis ; herausgegeben von Albrecht
Imbescheid. — Zürich ; [London] : Eulenburg, 1978. — 41p ; 4to.
£3.50
1.Imbescheid, Albrecht

(B79-50587)

Piston, Walter
[Concerto, flute]. Concerto, flute and orchestra / [by] Walter
Piston. — New York ; London : Associated Music, 1978. — [2],
39p ; 4to.
Duration 19 min.
£7.55
1.Ti

(B79-51031)

Romberg, Bernhard
[Concerto, flute, op.30, B minor]. Konzert für Flöte und Orchester
in h-moll, op.30 (17) / [von] Bernhard Romberg ; herausgegeben
von Dieter H. Förster. — Zürich ; [London] : Eulenburg, 1978. —
77p ; 4to.
£4.20
1.Förster, Dieter H

(B79-50588)

MPVTQ — Oboe d'amore & orchestra
Stranz, Ulrich
Déjà vu : für Oboe d'amore und kleines Orchester / [von] Ulrich
Stranz. — Kassel ; London : Bärenreiter, 1978. — [1],48p ; 4to.
£11.22
1.Ti

(B79-50589)

MPVVFL — Clarinet & orchestra. Concertinos
Donizetti, Gaetano
[Concertino, clarinet, B flat major]. Concertino für Klarinette und
Kammerorchester B-dur / [von] Gaetano Donizetti ;
herausgegeben und rekonstruiert von Raymond Meylan. —
Frankfurt : Litolff ; London : Peters, 1979. — 26p ; 4to. —
(Sinfonietta)
Unpriced
1.Meylan, Raymond 2.Sr

(B79-50590)

MPWSF — Trumpet and orchestra
Hummel, Johann Nepomuk
[Concerto, trumpet, E major]. Concerto, E major, for trumpet and
orchestra / [by] Johann Nepomuk Hummel ; edited by Stefan de
Haan. — London : Eulenburg, 1979. — xiv,50p ; 8vo.
Miniature score.
Unpriced
1.Haan, Stefan de

(B79-51032)

MPWVF — Tuba & orchestra. Concertos
Vaughan Williams, Ralph
[Concerto, Tuba]. Concerto for bass tuba and orchestra / [by]
Ralph Vaughan Williams. — London : Oxford University Press,
1979. — 4to.
ISBN 0-19-369454-9 : Unpriced

(B79-50591)

MPX — Percussion instruments & orchestra
Tircuit, Heuwell
Odoru katachi = Dance patterns : for percussion soloist and
chamber orchestra / [by] Heuwell Tircuit. — New York ;
London : Associated Music, 1978. — [4],47p ; 4to.
£5.45
1.Ti

(B79-50592)

MR — WORKS FOR CHAMBER ORCHESTRA
MRE — Symphonies
Mozart, Wolfgang Amadeus
[Symphony, no.14, K.114, A major]. Symphonie A-Dur, KV114 /
herausgegeben von Günter Kehr. — Mainz ; London : Schott,
1979. — 22p ; 4to. — (Concertino ; 101)
£4.80
1.Ti 2.Kehr, Günter 3.Sr

(B79-51033)

MRH/T — Dances. Variations
Mathias, William
Dance variations : for orchestra / [by] William Mathias. —
London : Oxford University Press, 1979. — [2],93p ; 8vo.
Op.72 - A reduced facsimile of the composer's manuscript.
ISBN 0-19-365669-8 : Unpriced
1.Ti

(B79-51034)

MRJ — Miscellaneous works
Bedford, David
Jack of shadows / [by] David Bedford. — London : Universal,
1978. — [8],51p ; obl. 4to.
For instrumental ensemble. — Duration 14 1/2 min.
£8.06
1.Ti

(B79-51035)

Boatwright, Howard
Variations for small orchestra / [by] Howard Boatwright. — New
York ; London : Oxford University Press, 1979. — 55p ; 4to.
Facsimile of the composer's manuscript.
Unpriced
1.Ti

(B79-51036)

MRK/AG — Arrangements. Suites
Cruft, Adrian
[Stilestone suite. Op.62. arr]. Stilestone suite : for chamber
ensemble or wind, brass, percussion op.62a / [by] Adrian Cruft.
— London ((1 The Retreat, S.W.14) : Joad Press, 1976. — 4to.
Score (16p.) & 12 parts.
Unpriced
1.Ti 2.Ti

(B79-50183)

MS — WORKS FOR LIGHT ORCHESTRA
MSHJK — Bossa novas
Levitt, Rod
Mon plaisir : for stage band / [by] Rod Levitt. — New York ;
London : Associated Music, 1978. — 8p ; 4to.
£7.55
1.Ti

(B79-50593)

MT — JAZZ
MT/DZ — Improvisation
Kynaston, Trent P
Jazz improvisation / [by] Trent P. Kynaston and Robert J. Ricci.
— Englewood Cliffs ; Londfon : Prentice-Hall, 1978. — [5],218p ;
4to.
ISBN 0-13-509307-4 : Unpriced
1.Ti 2.Ricci, Robert J

(B79-50184)

MTJ — Miscellaneous works
Levitt, Rod
Babylon : for stage band / [by] Rod Levitt. — New York ;
London : Associated Music, 1978. — 8p ; 4to.
£7.55
1.Ti

(B79-50594)

Levitt, Rod
Mamma's eyes : for stage band / [by] Rod Levitt. — New York ;
London : Schirmer, 1978. — 7p ; 4to.
Unpriced
1.Ti

(B79-50595)

NU — WIND, STRINGS & KEYBOARD
NUNN — Octets
Brown, Earle
Novara / [by] Earle Brown. — London : Universal, 1979. — 4p ;
fol.
For instrumental ensemble. — With directions for performance in English
and German inserted.
Unpriced
1.Ti

(B79-51037)

NUP — Woodwind, strings & keyboard
Rands, Bernard
Scherzi / [by] Bernard Rands. — London : Universal, 1978. — 9
leaves ; fol.
For clarinet/bass clarinet, piano, violin, cello. — Duration 20 min.
Unpriced
1.Ti

(B79-51038)

NUPNP — Woodwind, strings & keyboard. Septets
Bedford, David
A horse, his name was Henry Fencewaver Watkins / [by] David
Bedford. — London : Universal, 1978. — 41p ; obl.4to.
For guitar, flute, clarinet, violin, violoncello, double bass and piano. —
Facsimile of the composer's manuscript.
Unpriced
1.Ti

(B79-50185)

NUPNTF — Woodwind, string & keyboard trio. Concertos
Böhm, I C F
[Concerto, viola d'amore, oboe d'amore & continuo, F major].
Concerto for viola d'amore or viola, oboe d'amore or viola and
basso continuo with cello / by I.C.F. Böhm ; (harpsichord part by
Andrew Pledge) ; edited by Ian White. — Kings Langley ((Little
Margaret, Penmans Green, Chipperfield)) : E.L. White, 1977. —
11p ; fol.
Unpriced
1.White, Ian 2.Pledge, Andrew

(B79-50596)

NURNSF — Flute, strings & keyboard. Concertos
Telemann, Georg Philipp
[Concerto, flute, violins (2) & continuo, G major]. Concerto in
G-dur für Flöte, 2 Violinen und Basso continuo = Concerto in G
major for flute, 2 violins and basso continuo / [von] Georg
Philipp Telemann ; herausgegeben von ... Hermien Teske. —
Zürich : Amadeus ; [London] : [Bärenreiter], 1979. — 4to.
Score ([1],15p.) & 4 parts.
£3.25
1.Teske, Hermien

(B79-50597)

NURNT — Trios
Weber, Carl Maria von, *Freiherr*
[Trio, flute, cello & piano, op.63]. Trio, op.63, for flute, cello (or
viola) and piano / [by] Carl Maria von Weber ... ; edited by Louis
Moyse. — New York ; London : Schirmer, 1979. — 4to. —
(Louis Moyse flute collection)
Score (31p.) & 3 parts.
£6.10
1.Moyse, Louis 2.Sr

(B79-51039)

NUSNSK/LF — Recorders, strings & keyboard. Concertos
Bach, Johann Sebastian
[Brandenburg concerto, flutes (2), violin & string orchestra, no.4,
BWV1049, G major. *arr*]. Brandenburgisches Konzert Nr.4,
G-dur : für 2 Blockflöten (Flöten), Violine, Streicher und
Continuo, BWV1049 / [von] Johann Sebastian Bach ; Ausgabe für
2 Blockflöten (Flöten), Violine und Klavier, Klavierauszug von
Ulrich Haverkampf. — Weisbaden ; [London] : Breitkopf und
Härtel, 1979. — 4to.
Score (36p.) & 3 parts.
£8.40
1.Ti 2.Haverkampf, Ulrich

(B79-51040)

NUSNTE — Recorder, strings & keyboard. Sonatas
Telemann, Georg Philipp
[Sonata, recorder, violin & continuo, F major]. 26 Triosonate in
F-dur für Altblockflöte (Querflöte), Violine (Querflöte, Oboe) und
Basso continuo. Sonata a tre in F major for treble recorder (flute),
violin (flute, oboe) and basso continuo / [von] Georg Philipp
Telemann ; herausgegeben nach der Handschrift (Darmstadt, Mus.
ms.1042/26) und Continuo von Willy Hess. — Zürich :
Amadeus ; [London] : [Breitkopf and Härtel], 1979. — 4to.
Score (7p.) & 3 parts.
£2.80
1.Hess, Willy 2.Sechsundzwanzigste Triosonate in F-dur für Altblockflöte
(Querflöte), Violine (Querflöte, Oboe) und Basso continuo

(B79-51041)

NUVNR — Clarinet, strings & keyboard. Quintets
Feldman, Morton
Three clarinets, cello and piano / [by] Morton Feldman. —
Toronto ; [London] : Universal, 1978. — 4to.
Duration 8 min. — Score ([3],8p.) & 4 parts.
Unpriced
1.Ti

(B79-50186)

NUXSNPE — Trumpet, strings & keyboard. Sonatas
Gabrielli, Domenico
[Sonata, trumpet, string quintet & continuo, D.XI.7, D major].
Sonata D.XI.7 in D for trumpet, strings and basso continuo / [by]
Domenico Gabrielli ; ed. R.P. Block. — London : Musica rara,
1979. — 4to. — (Italian 17th and 18th century sinfonias and
sonatas for trumpet and strings ; 23)
Score ([1],11p.) & 10 parts.
Unpriced
1.Block, Robert Paul 2.Sr

(B79-50598)

NUXSNQE — Trumpets (2), strings & keyboard sextet. Sonatas
Paisible, James
[Sonata, trumpets (2), violins (2), viola & continuo, no.10, D
major]. Sonata 10 in D major for two trumpets (or oboes), strings
and continuo / [by] James Paisible ; edited by Richard Platt. —
London : Oxford University Press, 1978. — 4to. — (Musica da
camera ; 43)
Score ([1],12p.) & part.
ISBN 0-19-366260-4 : Unpriced
1.Platt, Richard 2.Sr

(B79-50187)

NUXSNRE — Trumpet, strings & keyboard quintet. Sonatas
Jacchini, Giuseppe Maria
[Sonata, trumpet, strings & continuo, D XII 6, D major]. Sonata,
D XII 6 for tromba, (trumpet), strings and continuo / [by]
Giuseppe Jacchini ; edited by R.P. Block. — London : Musica
rara, 1978. — 4to. — (Italian 17th & 18th century sinfonias and
sonatas for trumpets and strings ; 30)
Score (8p.) & 7 parts.
Unpriced
1.Block, Robert Paul 2.Sr

(B79-50599)

NUXSNRK/LE — Trumpets, strings & keyboard. Arrangements. Sonatas
Biber, Heinrich Ignaz Franz
[Sonatae tam aris quam aulis servientes. Sonata, trumpets (2) &
string orchestra, no.1, C major. *arr*]. Sonata 1 for 2 trumpets, 2
violins, 2 violas, cello & basso continuo / [by] H.I.F. Biber ; 2
trumpets, 2 violins and piano reduction. — London : Musica rara,
1979. — 4to. — (Music at the Court of Kroměřiž ; 13)
Piano reduction by John Madden. — Score ([1],10p.) & 4 parts.
Unpriced
1.Madden, John 2.Sr

(B79-51042)

NUXSNSE — Trumpet, strings & keyboard quartet. Sonatas
Jacchini, Giuseppe Maria
[Sonata, trumpet, violins(2) & continuo, D XII 5, D major].
Sonata, D XII 5 for tromba, (trumpet), strings and continuo /
[by] Giuseppe Jacchini ; edited by R.P. Block. — London :
Musica rara, 1978. — 4to. — (Italian 17th & 18th century
sinfonias and sonatas for trumpets and strings ; 28)
Score ([1],8p.) & 6 parts. — Described as for '2 trumpets' on cover.
Unpriced
1.Block, Robert Paul 2.Sr

(B79-50600)

NUXSNTK/LE — Trumpet, strings & keyboard. Arrangements. Sonatas
Biber, Heinrich Ignaz Franz
[Sonatae tam aris quam aulis servientes. Sonata, trumpet & string orchestra, no.4, C major. *arr*]. Sonata 4 for trumpet, violin, 2 violas and basso continuo / [by] H.I.F. Biber ; trumpet, violin & piano reduction. — London : Musica rara, 1979. — 4to. — (Music at the Court of Krom'e'ri'z ; 14)
Piano reduction by John Madden.- Score ([1],6p.) & 2 parts.
Unpriced
1.Ti 2.Madden, John 3.Sr

(B79-51043)

Biber, Heinrich Ignaz Franz
[Sonatae tam aris quam aulis servientes. Sonata, trumpet & string orchestra, no.12, C. major. *arr*]. Sonata 12 for 2 trumpets, 2 violins, 2 violas, cello / [by] H.I.F. Biber ; trumpet, violin & piano reduction. — London : Muscia rara, 1979. — 4to. — (Music at the Court of Krom'e'ri'z ; 17)
Reduction by John Madden. — Score (10p.) & 4 parts.
Unpriced
1.Ti 2.Madden, John 3.Sr

(B79-51044)

NUXUNT — Trombone, strings & keyboard. Trios
Riccio, Giovanni Battista
[Divine lodi, lib.3. *Selections*]. 3 canzonas for violin (trumpet), trombone and basso continuo / [by] G.B. Riccio ; [edited by] Glenn P. Smith, continuo realization by Lesie Basset. — London : Musica rara, 1978. — 4to.
Score [1],14p.) & 4 parts.
Unpriced
1.Ti 2.Ti 3.Smith, Glenn P 4.Basset, Lesie

(B79-50188)

NV — WIND & STRINGS
NVPNT — Woodwind & strings. Trios
Pössinger, Alexander
[Trio, flute, viola & horn, op.28, D major]. Trio in D-dur für Flöte, Viola and Horn. Op.28 = Trio in D major for flute, viola and horn / herausgegeben von ... Otto Biba. — Zürich : Amadeus ; [London] : [Bärenreiter], 1979. — 4to.
Score (15p.) & part.
£3.25
1.Biba, Otto

(B79-50601)

NVRNT — Flute & strings. Trios
Matthus, Siegfried
[Trio, flute, viola & harp]. Trio für Flöte, Bratsche und Harfe / [von] Siegfried Matthus. — Leipzig : VEB Deutscher Verlag für Musik ; [London] : [Breitkopf und Härtel], 1978. — 25p ; 4to.
£2.10

(B79-50602)

Musgrave, Thea
Sonata for three : for flute, violin and guitar / [by] Thea Musgrave. — Sevenoaks : Novello, 1979. — [4],12p ; 8vo.
£4.25

(B79-50189)

NVVNR — Clarinet & strings. Quintets
Gál, Hans
[Quintet, clarinet & string quartet, op.107]. Quintet for clarinet and string quartet, op.107 / [by] Hans Gál. — Hamburg ; London : Simrock, 1978. — [2],26p ; 8vo.
Unpriced

(B79-50190)

Gál, Hans
[Quintet, clarinet & string quartet, op.107]. Quintet for clarinet and string quartet, op.107 / [by] Hans Gál. — Hamburg ; London : Simrock, 1978. — 5pt ; 4to.
£5.20

(B79-50191)

NVVNR/T — Clarinet & strings. Quintets. Variations
Spohr, Louis
Fantaisie and variations on a theme of Danzi. Op.81 : for clarinet and string quartet / [by] Louis Spohr. — London : Musica rara, 1979. — 5pt ; 4to.
Unpriced
1.Ti

(B79-51045)

NVWNR — Bassoon & strings. Quintets
Brunetti, Gaetano
[Quintet, bassoon & string quartet, no.4, D major]. Quintet no.4 for bassoon and strings / [by] Gaetano Brunetti ; [edited by] George Zukerman. — London : Musica rara, 1979. — 4to.
Includes Andante con variazoni from Quintet, bassoon & string quartet, no.6. — Score ([1],28p.) & part.
Unpriced
1.Zukerman, George

(B79-50192)

NWNR — Quintets
Lannoy, Eduard von
[Quintet, wind & piano, op.2, E flat major]. Quintett Es-dur für Klavier, Oboe, Klarinette, Horn und Fagctt, Op.2 / [von] Eduard von Lannoy ; herausgegeben von Georg Meerwein. — Zurich ; [London] : Eulenburg, 1977. — 4to.
Score ([2],47p.) & 4 parts.
Unpriced
1.Meerwein, Georg

(B79-50193)

NWNTE — Wind & keyboard. Sonatas
Poglietti, Alessandro
[Sonata, trumpet, bassoon & continuo, C major]. Sonata à 3 for trumpet/oboe/flute/violin, bassoon & basso continuo / [by] A. Poglieti ; [edited by] John Madden. — London : Musica rara, 1979. — 4to. — (Music at the Court of Krom'e'ri'z ; 26)
Score ([1],12p.) & 4 parts.
Unpriced
1.Madden, John 2.Sr

(B79-51046)

NWPNT — Woodwind & keyboard. Trios
Quantz, Johann Joachim
[Sonata, oboe, bassoon & continuo, K.46, G major]. Trio sonata in G. K.46, oboe (or flute, violin, descant recorder), bassoon or violoncello and basso continuo / [by] Johann Joachim Quantz ; edited by David Lasocki. — London : Nova Music, 1979. — 4to.
Score (10p.) & 3 parts.
Unpriced
1.Lasocki, David

(B79-51047)

NWPNTE — Woodwind & keyboard trio. Sonatas
Schickhard, Johann Christian
[Sonata, recorder, oboe & continuo, op.5, no.2, D major]. Sonata D major for flute/recorder, two oboes, viola da gamba/violoncello/bassoon, and basso continuo / [by] Johann Christian Schickhardt ; edited by Barry Cooper. — London : Oxford University Press, 1978. — fol. — (Musica da camera ; 39)
Score (9p.) & 4 parts.
ISBN 0-19-358815-3 : Unpriced
1.Cooper, Barry 2.Sr

(B79-50194)

NWPNTK/DJ — Woodwind & keyboard trio. Arrangements. Motets
Cherubini, Luigi
[Hymnes sacrées. Ave Maria. *arr*]. Ave Maria. Offertorium / [by] Luigi Cherubini ; edited by Robin de Smet for 1. Soprano, B flat clarinet, (or flute) and piano, 2, two B flat clarinets and piano, 3, Flute, B flat clarinet and piano. — London : Fentone Music : Breitkopf and Härtel, 1979. — 4to.
Score (8p.) & 4 parts.
Unpriced
Primary classification KFLE/VVPDJ
1.Ti 2.Ti 3.De Smet, Robin

(B79-51001)

NWXP — BRASS & KEYBOARD
NWXPF — Brass & keyboard. Concertos
Wenzel, Eberhard
'Weihnachtskonzert' : Zyklus zu Advent bis Epiphanians, für Blechbläser und Orgel / von Eberhard Wenzel ; [herausgegeben von] Wilhelm Ehmann. — Kassel ; London : Bärenreiter, 1978. — 4to. — (Musik for Blechbläser und Tasteninstrumente)
Score ([1],27p.) & part ; the parts for brass are printed in score.
£2.31
1.Ti 2.Ehmann, Wilhelm 3.Sr

(B79-50603)

NX — STRINGS & KEYBOARD
NXNS — Quartets
Killmayer, Wilhelm
[Quartet, strings & keyboard]. Quartett für 2 Violinen, Violoncello und Klavier / [von] Wilhelm Killmayer. — Mainz ; London : Schott, 1978. — 4to.
Score (10p.) & 3 parts. — Duration 10 min.
£11.20

(B79-50196)

Leighton, Kenneth
Quartet in one movement. Contrasts and variants : for violin, viola, cello and piano, opus 63 / [by] Kenneth Leighton. — Sevenoaks : Novello, 1978. — 4to.
Score ([3],68p.) & 4 parts. — Duration 20 min.
Unpriced
1.Ti
(B79-50197)

NXNT — Trios
Fauré, Gabriel
[Quartet, strings & keyboard, no.1, op.15]. First piano quartet. Op.15 / [by] Gabriel Faure ; edited by Robert Orledge. — London : Eulenburg, 1979. — vii,83p ; 8vo.
Miniature score.
£2.05
1.Orledge, Robert
(B79-50604)

Fauré, Gabriel
[Quartet, strings & keyboard, no.2, op.45]. Second piano quartet. Op.45 / [by] Gabriel Faure ; edited by Robert Orledge. — London : Eulenburg, 1979. — viii,89p ; 8vo.
Miniature score.
Unpriced
1.Orledge, Robert
(B79-50605)

Fortner, Wolfgang
[Trio, strings & piano, 1978]. Trio, für Violine, Violoncello und Klavier, for violin, cello and piano, (1978) / [von] Wolfgang Fortner. — Mainz ; London : Schott, 1978. — 4to.
Score (36p.) & 2 parts.
£12.00
(B79-50198)

NXNTE — Trios. Symphonies
Schmidt
[Sinfonia, viola d'amore, violin & continuo, D major]. Sinfonia for viola d'amore, violin and basso / by Schmidt ; edited by Ian White. — Kings Langley ((Little Margaret, Penmans Green, Chipperfield)) : E.L. White, 1978. — 4p ; fol.
Unpriced
1.White, Ian
(B79-50606)

NYD — WIND, STRINGS, KEYBOARD & PERCUSSION
NYDPNP/FG — Woodwind, strings, keyboard & percussion septet. With added tape recorder
Harvey, Jonathan
Inner light (1) : for seven players and tape / [by] Jonathan Harvey. — Sevenoaks : Novello, 1979. — [6],109p ; 8vo.
Duration 30 min.
£5.00
1.Ti
(B79-50607)

NYDPNPF — Woodwind, strings, keyboard & percussion septet. Concertos
Holloway, Robin
The rivers of hell. Opus 34 : concertante for seven players / [by] Robin Holloway. — London : Boosey and Hawkes, 1979. — [4], 67p ; 8vo. — (Hawkes pocket scores ; no.945)
Miniature score. — A reproduction in facsimile of the composer's autograph manuscript. — Duration 31 min.
Unpriced
1.Ti 2.Sr
(B79-51048)

NYE — WIND, STRINGS & PERCUSSION
NYE/J — Theatre music
Frazer, Alan
A little theatre music : for flute, clarinet, trumpet, violin, cello and percussion / by Alan Frazer. — London (7 Garrick St., W.C.2) : Middle Eight Music, 1979. — 4to. — (Middle eight ensemble series ; 8)
Score (8p.) & 6 parts.
Unpriced
1.Ti 2.Sr
(B79-50199)

NYENQ — Sextets
Sohal, Naresh
Hexad : for six players / [by] Naresh Sohal. — Sevenoaks : Novello, 1979. — [4],32p ; 8vo.
For flute, horn in F, percussion, violin, cello and double bass.- Duration 17 min.
£2.25
1.Ti
(B79-51049)

NYEPNQ — Woodwind, strings & percussion. Sextets
Davies, Peter Maxwell
Runes from a holy island : for chamber ensemble / [by] Peter Maxwell Davies. — London : Chester Music, 1979. — [2],17p ; 4to.
Unpriced
1.Ti
(B79-51050)

NYEPNQK/AH/AYDL — Woodwind, strings & percussion. Sextets. Arrangements. Collections. Scotland
Renaissance Scottish dances / [by] Peter Maxwell Davies. — London : Boosey and Hawkes, 1979. — fol. — (Exploring music series)
For flute, clarinet, guitar, violin, cello and percussion.
Unpriced
1.Davies, Peter Maxwell 2.Sr
(B79-50200)

NYEPNR/W — Woodwind, strings & percussion. Quintets. Rondos
Mozart, Wolfgang Amadeus
Adagio and rondo for glass harmonica, flute, oboe, viola and cello. K.617 / [by] W.A. Mozart ; edited by Lionel Salter. — London : Eulenburg, 1979. — vii,20p ; 8vo.
Miniature score.
£1.20
1.Ti 2.Salter, Lionel
(B79-51051)

NYF — WIND, KEYBOARD & PERCUSSION
NYFSRK/DW/GJ/AY — Descant recorders, keyboard & percussion. Arrangements. Children's songs. Collections
First nursery suite : four traditional songs / arranged for group music making by Peter Jenkyns. — Sevenoaks : Novello, 1979. — [4],7p ; 4to.
For voices, descant recorders, percussion and piano. — Duration 3 1/2 min. — Contents: 1: Go and tell Aunt Nancy - 2: Pease pudding hot - 3: Au clair de la lune - 4: Lavender's blue.
£0.98
1.Jenkyns, Peter
(B79-50608)

Second nursery suite : three traditional songs / arranged for group music making by Peter Jenkyns. — Sevenoaks : Novello, 1979. — [2],9p ; 4to.
For voices, descant recorders, percussion and piano. — Duration 3 1/2 min. — Contents: 1: O dear, what can the matter be - 2: Dance to your daddy - 3: Polly-wolly-doodle.
£0.98
1.Jenkyns, Peter
(B79-50609)

NYJ — STRINGS & PERCUSSION
NYJNT — Trios
Humel, Gerald
Arabesque : für Gitarre, Violoncello und Schlagzeug = for guitar, violoncello and percussion / [von] Gerald Humel. — Mainz ; London : Schott, 1978. — 4to.
Score (20p.) & 3 parts.
£10.80
1.Ti
(B79-50201)

NYL — KEYBOARD & PERCUSSION
Evans, Colin
Fun with xylophones : four pieces in popular style for group music making / by Colin Evans. — Sevenoaks : Paxton, 1978. — 17p ; 4to.
For percussion, piano and optional guitar.
£1.30
1.Ti
(B79-50202)

PWP — KEYBOARD SOLOS
PWPE — Sonatas
Maichelbek, Franz Anton
Die auf dem Clavier spielende und das Gehör vergnügende Caecilia (1736) : acht Sonaten, für Tasteninstrumente / [von] Franz Anton Maichelbeck ; herausgegeben von Alfred Reichling. — Berlin : Merseburger ; [London] : [Bärenreiter], 1978. — 86p : facsim ; obl.4to.
£5.45
1.Ti 2.Reichling, Alfred
(B79-50610)

PWPJ — Miscellaneous works
Bach, Johann Sebastian
[Keyboard music. *Selections*]. Johann Sebastian Bach 1685-1750 / edited by Bradford G. Thompson. — London [etc.] : East-West Publications, 1979. — 191p ; port ; 4to. — (The classic piano repertoire ; no.2)
Unpriced
1.Thompson, Bradford G 2.Sr
(B79-50611)

Q — PIANO
Q/AC — Tutors
Barratt, Carol
Chester's piano book / written by Carol Barratt; illustrated by
Wendy Hoile. — London : Chester Music.
Number 5. — 1979. — 40p ; 4to. —
Unpriced
1.Ti

(B79-50203)

Pieper, Manfred
Swing und Beat, Schwarz auf weiss = Swing and beat. Black on
white : Anregungen zum Musizieren auf Klavier und
Elektronenorgel = Hints on playing the piano and the electronic
organ / [von] Manfred Pieper ; herausgegeben unter Mitarbeit von
Wieland Ziegenrücker ... — Leipzig : VEB Deutscher Verlag für
Musik ; [London] : [Breitkopf und Härtel], 1978. — 123p ; 4to.
£6.30
Also classified at RPV/AC
1.Ti 2.Ziegenrücker, Wieland

(B79-50612)

Runze, Klaus
[Zwei Hände-zwölf Tasten. *English*]. Two hands-twelve notes /
[by] Klaus Runze. — London : Schott.
Book 1 : A picture-book for young pianists. — 1977. — 65p ; obl. 4to. —
£3.00
1.Ti 2.Ti

(B79-51052)

Book 2 : Playing with music. — 1977. — 51p : obl. 4to. —
£2.50
1.Ti 2.Ti

(B79-51053)

Q/AF — Exercises
Burnam, Edna Mae
A dozen a day : technical exercises for the piano to be done each
day before practicing [sic] / by Edna Mae Burnam. —
Cincinnati : Willis Music ; London : Chappell, 1979. — 24p ; 4to.
Unpriced
1.Ti

(B79-50613)

Q/AL — Examinations
Associated Board of the Royal Schools of Music
Pianoforte examination pieces, 1980. — London : Associated
Board of the Royal Schools of Music.
Grade 1 : Lists A & B. — 1979. — 7p ; 4to. —
£0.50
1.Ti

(B79-51054)

Grade 2 : Lists A & B. — 1979. — 7p ; 4to. —
£0.50
1.Ti

(B79-51055)

Grade 3 : Lists A & B. — 1979. — 11p ; 4to. —
£0.60
1.Ti

(B79-51056)

Grade 4 : Lists A & B. — 1979. — 11p ; 4to. —
£0.60
1.Ti

(B79-51057)

Grade 5 : Lists A & B. — 1979. — 23p ; 4to. —
£0.90
1.Ti

(B79-51058)

Grade 6 : Lists A & B. — 1979. — 23p ; 4to. —
£0.90
1.Ti

(B79-51059)

Grade 7 : Lists A & B. — 1979. — 28p ; 4to. —
£1.10
1.Ti

(B79-51060)

Q/RGD/AC — Figured bass. Tutors
Thorne, Adrian
Classical harmony through figured bass / [by] Adrian Thorne. —
London : Chappell, 1979. — 52p ; 4to.
Unpriced
1.Ti

(B79-51061)

QNU — TWO PIANOS, 4 HANDS
QNUK/AG — Arrangements. Suites
Holst, Gustav
[The planets. Op.32. *arr*]. The planets / [by] Gustav Holst ;
arranged for two pianos by the composer. — London : Curwen
Edition, 1979. — [2],109p. ; 4to.
With a foreword by Imogen Holst.
Unpriced
1.Ti

(B79-51062)

QNUK/L/T — Arrangements. Variations
Lees, Benjamin
[Variations, piano & orchestra. *arr*]. Variations for piano and
orchestra / [by] Benjamin Lees ; piano reduction. — New York ;
[London] : Boosey and Hawkes, 1979. — [2],46p ; 4to.
Duration 16 min.
Unpriced

(B79-50204)

QNV — ONE PIANO, 4 HANDS
Furze, Jessie
[In the days of long ago. *Selections*]. The tin soldiers, and, Lords
and ladies : two simple piano duets from the suite 'In the days of
long ago' / by Jessie Furze. — Wendover : Roberton, [1978]. —
3-11p ; 4to.
£0.50
1.Ti 2.Ti

(B79-50614)

Gruber, Josef
[ABC]. Two at the piano : 50 duets for young pianists / [by] Josef
Gruber ; edited by Fanny Waterman and Marion Harewood. —
London : Faber Music, 1979. — [1],55p ; obl.4to. — (The
Waterman/Harewood piano series)
Unpriced
1.Ti 2.Ti 3.Sr

(B79-50615)

QNVG — Suites
Debussy, Claude
Petite suite / [by] Claude Debussy ; edited by H. Swarsenski. —
2nd ed. — London : Peters, 1979. — [2],34p ; 4to.
Unpriced
1.Ti 2.Swarsenski, H

(B79-50205)

QNVK — Arrangements
Zabrack, Harold
[Scherzo, piano. *arr*]. Scherzo : hommage à Prokofieff / [by]
Harold Zabrack ; arr. piano duet. — [New York] ; [London] :
Boosey and Hawkes, 1979. — 9p ; 4to.
ISBN 0-934286-14-0 : Unpriced
1.Ti 2.Ti

(B79-51063)

QNVK/DP/LF/AY — Arrangements. Christmas carols. Collections
Christmas songs you like : piano duets for elementary level /
arranged by Mark Nevin. — New York ; London : Schroeder and
Gunther, 1978. — [1],25p ; 4to.
£1.75
1.Nevin, Mark

(B79-51064)

QP — PIANO SOLOS
QP/AY — Collections
42 piano classics. — London : EMI, 1979. — 104p ; 4to.
ISBN 0-86175-057-8 : Unpriced
1.Forty-two piano classics

(B79-51065)

[**Anthology** of French piano music. *Selections*]. French piano
music : an anthology / edited by Isidor Philipp. — New York :
Dover ; [London] : [Constable], 1977. — [4],188p ; 4to.
Selections from the two-volume set originally published: Boston : Oliver
Ditson, 1906.
ISBN 0-486-23381-2 : Unpriced
1.Philipp, Isidor

(B79-50616)

Chester's concert pieces / compiled and edited by Carol Barratt. —
London : Chester Music.
Vol.2 : From Purcell to Prokofiev for the younger pianist. — 1979. — [1],
24p ; 4to.
Unpriced
1.Barratt, Carol

(B79-50206)

Leichte Klavierstücke und Sonatinen des 17-20 Jahrhunderts /
herausgegeben von Hans-Georg Schwerdtner. — Mainz ; London :
Schott, 1979. — 67p ; 4to.
Foreword in German and English.
£6.00
1.Schwerdtner, Hans Georg

(B79-50617)

Piano playtime : very first solos and duets / written, selected and
edited by Fanny Waterman and Marion Harewood. — London :
faber Music. — (Waterman/Harewood piano series)
Includes compositions by the compilers.
Book 2. — 1978. — [3],24p ; 4to.
Unpriced
1.Waterman, Fanny 2.Lascelles, Maria Donata, Countess 3.Sr

(B79-50207)

QP/AZ — Collected works of individual composers
Ireland, John
[Piano music]. The collected piano works of John Ireland /
foreword by Geoffrey Bush. — London : Stainer and Bell.
Vol.4. — 1976. — [4],65p ; 4to. —
ISBN 0-85249-396-7 : Unpriced
(B79-50209)

Liszt, Franz
[Piano music]. Klavierwerke = Piano works / [von] Franz Liszt.
— Kassel ; London : Bärenreiter.
[Heft 12] : Einzelne Charakterstücke 2 = Individual character pieces /
herausgegeben von Imre Sulyok, Imre Mezö ... Fingersatz revidiert von
Kurnél Zempléni ... — 1978. — xviii,101p : facsim ; 4to.
£5.94
1.Sulyok, Imre 2.Mezö, Imre 3.Zempléni, Kurnél
(B79-50618)

QP/T — Variations
Schwaen, Kurt
Über allen strahlt die Sonne : Variationen für Klavier über allerlei
Themen / [von] Kurt Schwaen. — Berlin : Verlag Neue Musik ;
[London] : [Breitkopf und Härtel], 1979. — 32p ; 4to.
Unpriced
1.Ti
(B79-50619)

QPE — Sonatas
Beethoven, Ludwig van
[Sonata, piano, G.162, C major]. Piano sonata in C.Wo 051 / [by]
Beethoven ; edited and completed by Ates Orga. — Wendover :
Roberton, 1979. — 26p ; 4to.
£2.50
1.Orga, Ates
(B79-50620)

Benjamin, George
[Sonata, piano]. Piano sonata / [by] George Benjamin. —
London : Faber Music, 1979. — 57p. ; fol.
Unpriced
1.Ti
(B79-51066)

Husa, Karel
[Sonata, piano, no.2]. Sonata no.2 for piano / [by] Karel Husa. —
New York ; London : Associated Music, 1978. — [2],28p ; 4to.
£4.55
(B79-50621)

Johnson, Robert Sherlaw
[Sonata, piano, no.3]. Sonata no.3 for piano / [by] Robert Sherlaw
Johnson. — London : Oxford University Press, 1979. — [2],14p ;
4to.
Duration 12 min.
ISBN 0-19-373004-9 : Unpriced
(B79-51067)

Mozart, Wolfgang Amadeus
[Sonata, piano, no.1, K.279, C major]. Sonata in C / [by]
Mozart ; edited by Stanley Sadie. — London : Associated Board
of the Royal Schools of Music, 1979. — 15p ; 4to.
Unpriced
1.Ti 2.Sadie, Stanley
(B79-51068)

Mozart, Wolfgang Amadeus
[Sonata, piano, no.6, K.284, D major]. Sonata in D, K.284, 205b,
1775 / [by] Mozart ; edited by Stanley Sadie, fingering and notes
on performance by Denis Matthews. — London : Associated
Board of the Royal Schools of Music, 1978. — 32p ; 4to.
Unpriced
1.Sadie, Stanley 2.Matthews, Denis
(B79-50622)

QPE/AZ — Collected works of individual composers
Beethoven, Ludwig van
[Sonatas. Collections]. Sonaten für Klavier zu zwei Händen /
[von] Ludwig van Beethoven ; herausgegeben von Claudio Arrau,
musikwissenschaftliche Revision von Lothar Hoffmann-Erbrecht.
— Frankfurt : Litolff ; New York ; London : Peters.
Sonatas 1-15.
Band 1. — 1973. — 290p ; 4to.
Unpriced
1.Arrau, Claudio 2.Hoffman-Erbrecht, Lothar
(B79-50623)
Band 2. — 1978. — 334p ; 4to.
Unpriced
1.Arrau, Claudio 2.Hoffman-Erbrecht, Lothar
(B79-50624)

Schubert, Franz
[Sonatas, piano]. Complete pianoforte sonatas, including the
unfinished works / [by] Schubert ; edited, annotated and fingered
by Howard Ferguson. — [London] : Associated Board of the
Royal Schools of Music.
Volume 3. — 1979. — 200p ; 4to.
Unpriced
1.Ti 2.Ferguson, Howard
(B79-51069)

QPEM — Sonatinas
Glover, David Carr
[Piano music. *Selections*]. Three sonatinas and a sonata : for piano
solo / [by] David Carr Glover. — New York ; London :
Schroeder and Gunther, 1978. — 24p ; 4to.
£1.75
1.Ti
(B79-50625)

QPG — Suites
Cruft, Adrian
Stilestone suite : for piano, op.62 / [by] Adrian Cruft. — London
((1 The Retreat, S.W.1)) : Joad Press, 1976. — 16p ; 4to.
Unpriced
1.Ti
(B79-50210)

Debussy, Claude
Suite bergamasque / [by] Claude Debussy ; edited by H.
Swarsenski. — London : Peters, 1978. — 29p ; 4to.
For piano.
Unpriced
1.Ti 2.Swarsenski, H
(B79-50211)

Glover, David Carr
The three bears go on a picnic : a piano suite with narration / by
David Carr Gordon. — Revised ed. — New York ; London :
Schroeder and Gunther, 1978. — 11p ; fol.
£1.35
1.Ti
(B79-50626)

QPH — Dances
Jacobson, Maurice
[The music room. Selections]. Sarabande and Rustic ballet ... : two
miniatures for piano solo / [by] Maurice Jacobson. — Wendover :
Roberton, 1978. — 7p ; 4to.
£0.50
1.Ti 2.Ti
(B79-50627)

QPH/H/AL — Dances for dancing. Examinations
Imperial Society of Teachers of Dancing. *Modern Dance Branch*
Original music and alternative music for the Modern Dance Grade
Examinations. — London : Imperial Society of Teachers of
Dancing.
Grades 2 and 3 : including pieces needed for the course of movement for
boys / composed by Catherine Barlow, boys work for grade examinations,
composed by Barry Farnsworth, transcribed and rearranged for solo piano
by Richard Muncey. — 1979. — [1],60p ; 4to.
£3.50
1.Ti 2.Barlow, Catherine 3.Farnsworth, Barry 4.Muncey, Richard
(B79-51070)
Primary and Grade 1 : including pieces needed for the course of movement
for boys / composed by Catherine Barlow, boys work for grade
examinations, composed by Barry Farnsworth, transcribed and rearranged
for solo piano by Richard Muncey. — 1979. — [2],54p ; 4to.
£3.00
1.Ti 2.Barlow, Catherine 3.Farnsworth, Barry 4.Muncey, Richard
(B79-51071)

QPHM — Gavottes
Cosentino, Manuel
Pizzicato : tempo de gavota / de Manuel Cosentino. — São
Paulo : Arapuã ; [London] : [Clifford Essex], 1979. — [3]p ; fol.
For piano.
Unpriced
1.Ti
(B79-51072)

QPHP — Jigs
Parke, Dorothy
Gigue for piano solo / [by] Dorothy Parke. — York : Banks,
1979. — [2]p ; 4to.
Unpriced
1.Ti
(B79-51074)

QPHW — Waltzes
Atkins, Florrie
La pensée petît [sic] valse / by Florrie Atkins. — Havant ((85
Wakefords Way, West Leigh)) : Florrie Atkins, 1979. — s.sh ;
4to.
For piano.
Unpriced
1.Ti
(B79-50628)

QPHW/W — Waltzes. Rondos
Ives, Charles
Waltz-rondo for piano / [by] Charles Ives ; edited by John
Kirkpatrick and Jerrold Cox. — New York ; London : Schirmer,
1978. — iv,15p ; 4to.
£3.65
1.Ti 2.Kirkpatrick, John 3.Cox, Jerrold
(B79-50629)

QPHX — Jazz
Dentato, John
Jazz players library : 10 classic tunes in their original versions and
in completely notated jazz versions / arranged by Johnny 'Dee'
Dentato. — Bryn Mawr ; [London] : Chappell, 1979. — 24p. ;
4to.
For piano.
Unpriced
1.Ti
(B79-51075)

QPHX/AF — Jazz. Exercises
Schmitz, Manfred
Jazz Parnass : Etüden, Stücke und Studien, für Klavier / [von]
Manfred Schmitz. –– Mainz ; London : Schott, 1978. — 104p ;
4to.
£7.20
1.Ti
(B79-50212)

QPHXJ — Ragtime
The **Mississippi** Valley rags : for piano / selected and with a
preface by Max Morath. — New York ; London : Schirmer, 1979.
— 64p ; 4to.
£1.75
1.Morath, Max
(B79-51076)

QPHXJ/AY — Ragtime. Collections
Original ragtime, as recorded by Claude Bolling. — Paris ;
[London] : Chappell, 1979. — 59p ; ill ; 4to.
Unpriced
(B79-51077)

QPJ — Miscellaneous works
Balada, Leonardo
Persistencies : for piano / [by] Leonardo Balada. — New York ;
London : Schirmer, 1978. — 20p ; 4to.
Duration 8 1/2 min.
£4.55
1.Ti
(B79-50630)

Chopin, Frédéric
[Piano music. *Selections*]. Frédéric François Chopin, 1810-1844 /
edited by Bradford G. Thompson. — The Hague ; London :
East-West, 1978. — 190p ; 4to. — (The classic piano repertoire ;
1)
Selections from Chopin's preludes, nocturnes, waltzes, mazurkas, polonaises,
études, etc.
ISBN 0-904499-04-9 : Unpriced
1.Ti 2.Thompson, Bradford G 3.Sr
(B79-50213)

Clark, Harold Ronald
Sketches for young pianists : (Grade 3-4) / [by] Harold R. Clark.
— Peterborough ((42 Glebe Rd)) : Harold R. Clark, 1979. — [6p]
; 4to.
Unpriced
1.Ti
(B79-51078)

Cooper, Joseph
Still more hidden melodies : six improvisations for piano / [by]
Joseph Cooper ; drawings by Bernard Hollowood. — Sevenoaks :
Novello, 1978. — 27p ; 4to.
Unpriced
1.Ti
(B79-50214)

Deroyan, Douglas
[Piano music. *Selections*]. Music by Douglas Deroyan. — London
(37 Buckland Cresc. N.W.3) : Douglas Deroyan, 1979. — [17p] ;
fol.
With one song.
Unpriced
1.Ti
(B79-51079)

Ezell, Helen Ingle
Next week Terry & I ... : 5 easy pieces for the piano / [by] Helen
Ingle Ezell. — New York ; [London] : Oxford University Press,
1979. — 11p ; 4to.
Unpriced
1.Ti
(B79-51080)

Hedges, Anthony
Five concert pieces : for young pianists / [by] Anthony Hedges.
— London : Universal, 1979. — 8p ; 4to.
Unpriced
1.Ti
(B79-51081)

Helyer, Marjorie
Awayday : a holiday album of ten pieces for young pianists / [by]
Marjorie Helyer ... ; illustrations by Dennis Reader. —
Sevenoaks : Novello, 1978. — [2],10p ; 4to.
1.Ti
(B79-50215)

Helyer, Marjorie
Polka dot : ten characteristic pieces for piano, grade 2 / [by]
Marjorie Helyer. — Sevenoaks : Novello, 1978. — [1],16p ; 4to.
£0.91
1.Ti
(B79-50216)

Holloway, Laurie
Pop preludes for piano : easy music in pop style / [by] Laurie
Holloway. — Sevenoaks : Novello, 1979. — [2],14p ; 4to.
£1.15
1.Ti
(B79-50631)

Holstein, Jean Paul
[Rêves éveillés]. Rêves éveillés [et] Rêves endormis : pour piano /
[par] Jean-Paul Holstein. — Paris ; [London] : Chappell, 1979. —
29p ; fol.
Unpriced
1.Ti 2.Ti 3.Rêves endormis
(B79-51082)

Judd, Margaret
Dawn : piano solo / by Margaret Judd. — London : Bosworth
and Co., 1978. — [2]p ; 4to.
Unpriced
1.Ti
(B79-50217)

Kagel, Mauricio
MM51 : ein Stück Filmmusik für Klavier, 1976 / [von] Mauricio
Kagel. — London : Universal, 1978. — 20 leaves ; fol.
Unpriced
1.Ti
(B79-51083)

Kolb, Barbara
Appello : for piano / [by] Barbara Kolb ; edited by Jay Gottlieb
and Diane Walsh. — [New York] ; [London] : Boosey and
Hawkes, 1978. — [6],17p ; 4to.
Duration 14 min.
Unpriced
1.Ti 2.Gottlieb, Jay 3.Walsh, Diane
(B79-50218)

Last, Joan
Gymnastics : piano pieces for beginners / by Joan Last. —
London : Boosey and Hawkes, 1979. — 8p ; fol.
Unpriced
1.Ti
(B79-51084)

Liszt, Franz
[Consolations. G.172]. Consolations / [by] Franz Liszt ; revised by
David Wilde. — [London] : Stainer and Bell, [1979]. — [1],23p ;
4to.
For piano solo. — 'The present edition is a complete revision of Kuhlstrom's
old Augener text' - Preface.
ISBN 0-85249-526-9 : Unpriced
1.Ti 2.Ti 3.Wilde, David
(B79-50632)

Mendelssohn, Felix
[Piano music. *Selections*]. Eine Auswahl aus 'Sechs Kinderstücke'.
Op.72 und 'Lieder ohne Worte' / [von] Felix Mendelssohn
Bartholdy ; herausgegeben von Heinz Walter. — Wiesbaden ;
[London] : [Breitkopf und Härtel], 1979. — 13p ; 4to.
Op.72, no.6 simplified.
£2.10
1.Ti 2.Walter, Heinz
(B79-51085)

Mersson, Boris
Fünf Klavierstücke. Op.23 / [von] Boris Mersson. — Zürich ;
[London] : Eulenburg, 1979. — 19p ; 4to.
£2.80

(B79-50633)

Mills, Frank
Music box dancer : piano solo / by Frank Mills. — London :
Valentine Music, 1974. — [3p] ; 4to.
Unpriced
1.Ti

(B79-51086)

Nevin, Mark
[Piano music. Selections]. Piano favorites : seven select solos for
intermediate grade / [by] Mark Nevin. — New York ; London :
Schroeder and Gunther, 1978. — 15p ; 4to.
£1.35
1.Ti

(B79-50634)

Rautavaara, Einojuhani
Music for upright piano / [by] Einojuhani Rautavaara. — New
York ; London : Schirmer, 1978. — [2],17p ; obl. 4to. —
(Composer's autograph series)
Facsimile of composer's autograph.
£2.40
1.Ti 2.Sr

(B79-50635)

Rautavaara, Einojuhani
Second music for upright piano / [by] Einojuhani Rautavaara. —
New York ; London : Schirmer, 1978. — 6p ; obl. 4to. —
(Composer's autograph series)
Facsimile of composer's autograph.
£1.80
1.Ti 2.Sr

(B79-50636)

Ross, Walter
Six shades of blue : preludes for piano / [by] Walter Ross. —
New York ; [London] : Boosey and Hawkes, 1979. — 19p ; 4to.
Unpriced
1.Ti

(B79-50637)

Scelsi, Giacinto
Five incantations = Cinque incantesimi : for piano / [by]
Giacinto Scelsi. — New York ; London : Schirmer, 1978. — 24p ;
4to. — (Composer's autograph series)
Facsimile of composer's autograph.
£3.05
1.Ti 2.Sr

(B79-50638)

Sergi, Antonio
Desencontro : improviso no.1 / de Antonio Sergi. — São Paulo :
Seresta ; [London] : [Clifford Essex], 1979. — [2p] ; fol.
For piano.
Unpriced
1.Ti

(B79-51087)

Shipley, Edward
La luna / [by] Edward Shipley. — London : Fentone Music :
Breitkopf and Härtel, 1979. — 16p ; 4to.
Piano.
Unpriced
1.Ti

(B79-51088)

Shipley, Edward
La luna : for piano / [by] Edward Shipley. — London : Fentone
Music, 1979. — 16p ; 4to.
£3.00
1.Ti

(B79-51089)

Stevens, Bernard
Ballade no.2 : Op.42 : for piano solo / by Bernard Stevens. —
Wendover : Roberton, 1979. — 12p ; 4to.
£1.50
1.Ti

(B79-51090)

Thomson, Virgil
Man of iron : a portrait of Willy Eisenhart, for piano / [by] Virgil
Thomson. — New York ; London : Schirmer, 1978. — 3p ; fol.
£1.20
1.Ti

(B79-50639)

Van Appledorn, Mary Jeanne
Set of five : for piano / [by] Mary Jeanne van Appledorn. — New
York ; London : Oxford University Press, 1978. — 15p ; 4to.
Duration 8 min.
Unpriced
1.Ti

(B79-50219)

Waldman, Robert
A rag bag : for piano / by Robert Waldman. — New York ;
London : Schirmer, 1977. — 24p ; 4to.
£1.75
1.Ti

(B79-50640)

Walker, Robert E
Twelve O : twelve easy pieces for piano / [by] Robert Walker;
drawings by Victoria Hartuny. — Sevenoaks : Novello, 1979. —
[3],27p ; 4to.
£1.95
1.Ti

(B79-51091)

QPK — Arrangements
Cosma, Vladimir
[David's song. arr]. David's song : theme music from the serial
Kidnapped / by Vladimir Cosma. — London : Warner : Music
Sales, 1978. — 3p ; 4to.
For piano.
£0.60
1.Ti

(B79-51092)

Elgar, Sir Edward, bart
[Selections. arr]. Elgar piano album / arranged by Desmond
Ratcliffe. — Sevenoaks : Novello, 1979. — [3],27p ; 4to.
Unpriced
1.Ratcliffe, Desmond

(B79-50220)

Vieira, Luiz
[Prelúdio pra Ninar Gente Grande. arr]. Prelúdio pra Ninar Gente
Grande / [por] Luiz Vieira ; arranjo e harmonização p/piano solo
de Hector Lagna Fietta. — Rio de Janeiro : Rio Musical ;
[London] : [Essex Music], 1979. — [2p] ; fol.
Unpriced
1.Ti 2.Ti 3.Fietta, Hector Lagna

(B79-51093)

QPK/AAY — Arrangements. Collections
20 piano selections by modern composers. — London : EMI, 1979.
— 84p ; 4to.
Unpriced
1.Twenty piano selections by modern composers

(B79-51094)

Piano cameos. — London : EMI, 1979. — 96p ; 4to.
Arrangements of popular tunes.
Unpriced

(B79-51095)

QPK/AGM — Arrangements. Marches
Granados, Enrique
[2 Marchas militares, no.1. arr]. Marcha militar no.1 / [by] E.
Granados ; arranged for piano solo by Sylvia De'Ath. — London :
Leonard, Gould and Bolttler, 1979. — 4p ; 4to.
£0.40
1.Ti 2.Ti 3.De'Ath, Sylvia 4.Dos marchas militares

(B79-50641)

QPK/AH — Arrangements. Dances
Handel, George Frideric
[Almira. Selections : arr]. Dances from 'Almira' / [by] G.F.
Handel ; arranged by A. Craig Bell for piano solo. — York :
Banks Music, 1978. — 6p ; 4to.
Unpriced
1.Ti 2.Bell, Arnold Craig

(B79-50221)

Madi, Tito
[Selections. arr]. Álbum para piano / [por] Tito Madi ;
harmonizações especialmente arranjadas para piano solo por
Hector Lagna Fietta. — São Paulo : Fermata do Brasil ;
[London] : [Clifford Essex], 1979. — 40p ; fol.
Unpriced
1.Ti 2.Fietta, Hector Lagna

(B79-51096)

QPK/AH/AYDL — Arrangements. Dances. Scotland
The Foss Collection of Scottish dances / [edited by] Robert Donald.
— Dalry : H. Foss, 1978. — [3],32p ; 4to.
For piano. — Some arrangements are by Peter White.
Unpriced
1.Donald, Robert 2.Foss, Hugh

(B79-50222)

QPK/CC — Arrangements. Opera
Menotti, Gian Carlo
[Amahl and the night visitors. Selections : arr]. Amahl and the
night visitors : piano selections / [by] Gian Carlo Menotti ;
illustrations by Kiffi Diamond. — New York ; London :
Schirmer, 1978. — 31p ; 4to.
£3.00
1.Ti 2.Ti

(B79-51097)

QPK/DP/LF/AY — Arrangements. Carols. Christmas. Collections
Carols for piano / arranged by Gillian Earl. — London : Oxford
University Press, 1978. — [3],28p ; fol.
ISBN 0-19-372608-4 : Unpriced
1.Earl, Gillian
(B79-50223)

A **feast** of easy carols / arranged for piano by Carol Barratt ;
illustrated by Wendy Hoile. — London : Chester Music, 1979. —
[1],40p ; 4to.
Unpriced
1.Barratt, Carol
(B79-51098)

Happy Christmas : easy piano [or] organ / arranged by Cecil
Bolton and Jack Moore. — London : EMI, 1978. — 76p ; 4to.
Carols.
Unpriced
Also classified at RK/DP/LF/AY
1.Moore, Jack 2.Bolton, Cecil
(B79-50224)

22ct. gold : for piano solo / editor, Cecil Bolton. — London : EMI,
1979. — 72p ; 4to.
Popular songs.
Unpriced
1.Bolton, Cecil 2.Twenty-two ct. gold
(B79-50642)

Fun piano : for young people of any age / music arrangements, Roy
Slack. — London : EMI, 1979. — 24p ; 4to.
ISBN 0-86175-062-4 : Unpriced
1.Slack, Roy
(B79-51101)

V.I.P. piano solos. — London : Chappell.
Book 2. — 1977. — 96p ; 4to. —
Unpriced
(B79-51102)
Book 3. — 1979. — 96p ; 4to. —
Unpriced
(B79-51103)
Book 4. — 1979. — 95p. ; 4to. —
Unpriced
(B79-51104)

QPK/JR — Arrangements. Films
Coulter, Phil
[The water babies. *Selections: arr*]. The water babies / songs by
Phil Coulter and Bill Martin. — London : Chappell, 1979. — 48p.
; 4to.
Songs from the film.
Unpriced
1.Ti 2.Martin, Bill
(B79-51105)

Fanshawe, David
[Tarka the otter. Theme. *arr*]. Tarka the otter / music by David
Fanshawe. — Ilford : Chappell, 1979. — 5p. ; 4to.
Unpriced
1.Ti 2.Ti
(B79-51106)

Williams, John
[Superman. Theme. *arr*]. Theme from 'Superman' / [by] John
Williams. — London : Warner, 1978. — 5p ; 4to.
Arranged for piano.
Unpriced
1.Ti
(B79-50225)

QPK/JS — Arrangements. Television
Hartley, Richard
Penmarric : from the BBC classic serial / music by Richard
Hartley. — London : EMI, 1979. — 4p. ; 4to.
Piano.
Unpriced
1.Ti
(B79-51107)

QPK/JS/AY — Arrangements. Television. Collections
Hits in vision. — London : Chappell.
Piano solos with two songs.
No.2 : 10 top TV themes. — 1979. — 40p ; 4to.
Unpriced
(B79-51109)

Hits in vision. — London : Chappell.
With two songs.
No.3 : 10 top T.V. themes. — 1979. — 43p. ; 4to.
Unpriced
(B79-51108)

T.V. detectives / edited and compiled by Cecil Bolton. — London :
EMI, 1979. — 48p ; 4to.
Signature tunes from television detective series.
Unpriced
1.Bolton, Cecil
(B79-50643)

QPLRK — Piano & organ. Arrangements
Bach, Johann Sebastian
[Uns ist ein Kind geboren. BWV142. Overture. *arr*]. Overture to
cantata 'For us a Child is born' (Uns ist ein Kind geborn [sic]) :
for organ and piano / by J.S. Bach ; arranged by Louis
Hollingsworth. — Illinois : Sycamore ; New York ; London :
Schirmer (dist.), 1978. — 7p ; 4to.
Two copies.
£1.50
1.Ti 2.Ti 3.Hollingsworth, Louis
(B79-51110)

Debussy, Claude
[Arabesque, no.1]. Ist arabesque : for organ and piano / by
Claude Debussy ; arranged by Louis Hollingsworth. — Sycamore :
Columns Music ; New York ; London : Schirmer (dist.), 1978. —
12p ; 4to.
Two copies.
£1.95
1.Ti 2.Ti 3.Hollingsworth, Louis
(B79-51111)

QPLX — Percussion & piano
Pearn, David
Diversions for percussion and piano / [by] David Pearn. — South
Croydon : Lengnick, 1979. — 4to.
Score (12p.) & part.
Unpriced
1.Ti
(B79-50226)

QRP — HARPSICHORD SOLOS
QRPE — Sonatas
Scarlatti, Domenico
Essercizi (1738) : 30 sonatas for keyboard / [by] Domenico
Scarlatti. — New York ; London : Schirmer, 1979. — [6],122p ;
4to.
Edited by Fernando Valenti.
£7.55
1.Ti 2.Valenti, Fernando
(B79-51112)

Scarlatti, Domenico
[Sonatas, harpsichord. *Selections*]. Sonatas for harpsichord / [by]
Domenico Scarlatti ; revised by Christopher Kite. — [London] :
Stainer and Bell.
Book one. — [1979]. — [2],49p ; 4to.
'... contains the first fifteen of Thomas Dunhill's selection of 29 sonatas first
published by Augener in 1917, in a thoroughly revised performing edition
...' - p.[2].
ISBN 0-85249-513-7 : Unpriced
1.Kite, Christopher James
(B79-50644)

QRPG — Suites
Handel, George Frideric
[Suite, harpsichord, no.6 (1st collection), F sharp minor]. Suite
no.6, F sharp minor / [by] George Frideric Handel ; edited by
James Erber. — London : Peters, 1979. — 16p ; 4to.
Unpriced
1.Erber, James
(B79-50645)

QRPH — Dances
Jones, Kenneth Victor
Serpentine dances : for harpsichord / [by] Kenneth Jones. —
London : Chester Music, 1979. — 21p ; 4to.
Unpriced
1.Ti
(B79-51113)

QRPHT — Passacaglias
Ligeti, György
Passacaglia ungherese : für Cembalo = for harpsichord / [von]
György Ligeti. — Mainz ; London : Schott, 1979. — 7p ; 4to.
£3.70
1.Ti
(B79-51114)

QRPJ — Miscellaneous works
John Blow's anthology : Froberger, Strungk, Fischer, Blow : a
selection of keyboard music (twenty suites, capriccios, ricercars,
toccatas, etc.) copied out by John Blow around 1700 / transcribed
and edited by Thurston Dart ; revised, with an introduction, by
Davitt Moroney. — London : Stainer and Bell, 1978. — 64p ; 4to.
ISBN 0-85249-446-7 : Unpriced
1.Dart, Thurston 2.Moroney, Davitt

(B79-50646)

QRPK/HM — Arrangements. Ballet
Rameau, Jean Philippe
[Les Indes galantes. *arr*]. Les Indes galantes / [by] Jean-Philippe
Rameau ; the composer's transcription for harpsichord, edited by
Graham Sadler. — London : Oxford University Press, 1979. — [6]
,34p ; fol.
ISBN 0-19-373556-3 : Unpriced
1.Ti 2.Ti 3.Sadler, Graham

(B79-51115)

R — ORGAN
R/AY — Collections
Anthologia organi : Orgelmusik aus acht Jahrhunderten /
herausgegeben von Sándor Margittay. — Mainz ; [London] :
Schott.
Band 5 : Die Meister der Sweelinck-Schule. — 1978. — 97p ; obl.4to.
£8.00
1.Margitay, Sándor

(B79-50227)

Band 6 : Frescobaldi und sein Wirkungskreis. — 1978. — 82p ; obl.4to.
£8.00
1.Margittay, Sándor

(B79-50228)

Band 7 : Das italienische Barock. — 1979. — 82p : chart ; obl.4to.
£8.00
1.Margittay, Sándor

(B79-51116)

Band 8 : Französische Orgelmusik von Titelouze bis d'Aquin. — 1979. —
78p. ; obl.4to.
£8.00
1.Margittay, Sándor

(B79-51117)

Gloucester organ album / edited by John Sanders. — Sevenoaks :
Novello, 1979. — 50p ; 4to.
Six compositions by organists of Gloucester Cathedral. — Contents: 1: An
air composed for Holsworthy Church bells, by S.S. Wesley - 2: Allegretto,
by C.H. Lloyd - 3: The chimes of Gloucester Cathedral - 4: Cloister-Garth -
5: Procession from Air, Berceuse and Procession by Herbert Sumsion - 6:
Toccata by John Sanders.
£2.15
1.Sanders, John

(B79-51118)

R/AYC — Collections. Great Britain
The **cathedral** organist, 1977-1978. — London : Cramer, 1979. —
23p ; 4to.
Works by Robert Ashfield, Barry Ferguson and others.
Unpriced

(B79-50229)

R/AYEA — Collections. Germany. East Germany
Pro organo : Zeitgenössische Orgelmusik von Komponisten der
Deutschen Demokratischen Republik / ausgewählt und mit
Geleitwort versehen von Johannes Ernst Köhler. — Leipzig : VEB
Deutscher Verlag für Musik ; [London] : [Breitkopf und Härtel],
1977. — 107p ; obl.4to.
£4.80
1.Köhler, Johannes Ernst

(B79-50647)

R/AYH — Collections. France
Old French organ music / edited by Martin Neary. — London :
Oxford University Press, 1978. — 5,2-43p ; fol.
ISBN 0-19-375616-1 : Unpriced
1.Neary, Martin

(B79-50230)

R/LF — Christmas
Blackmore, George
Christmas at home : carol-medleys for all organs / [by] George
Blackmore. — Sevenoaks : Paxton, 1979. — 32p. ; 4to.
£1.40
1.Ti

(B79-51119)

R/Y — Fugues
Zbinden, Julien François
[Prelude & fugue, organ, op.58]. Prélude et fugue pour grand
orgue, op.58 (1978) / [par] Julien François Zbinden. — Zürich ;
[London] : Eulenburg, 1979. — 11p ; obl.4to. — (Organa
helvetica)
£2.10
1.Sr

(B79-50648)

RDGF — Agnus Dei
Martin, Frank
Agnus Dei : pour orgue = für Orgel / [par] Frank Martin. —
Kassel ; London : Bärenreiter, 1978. — 5p ; obl.fol.
£2.97
1.Ti

(B79-50231)

RG — Suites
Křenek, Ernst
Die vier Winde = Four-winds : suite ; für Orgel, for organ,
1975 / [von] Ernst Křenek. — Kassel ; London : Bärenreiter,
1978. — 18p ; obl.fol.
Duration 11 min.
£6.60
1.Ti

(B79-50232)

RGN — Fanfares
Two flourishes : for organ. — York : Banks, 1979. — 4p ; 4to.
Contents: 1: Heraldic flourish, by Francis Jackson - 2: Flourish for the tuba,
by Peter Melville Smith.
Unpriced
1.Smith, Peter Melville 2.Jackson, Francis

(B79-50233)

RHVS — Tarantellas
Salles, Anita
O monge napolitano : tarantela para órgâo / [de] Anita Salles. —
São Paulo : Fermata do Brasil ; [London] : [Clifford Essex], 1979.
— 6p ; fol.
Unpriced
1.Ti

(B79-51120)

RJ — Miscellaneous works
Albrechtsberger, Johann Georg
[12 neue leichte Präludien. Op.2]. Twelve new easy preludes for
organ / [by] Johann Georg Albrechtsberger ; facsimile edition
with an introduction by John Brock. — London : Oxford
University Press, 1979. — [2],14p ; obl.fol.
Originally published: Leipzig : Kühnel, 1813.
ISBN 0-19-375207-7 : Unpriced
1.Ti 2.Ti 3.Zwölf neue leichte Präludien. Op.2

(B79-51121)

Baur, Jürg
Drei Ricercare über das Thema des Musikalischen Opfers von
Johann Sebastian Bach (1977) : Orgel / [von] Jürg Baur. —
Wiesbaden ; [London] : [Breitkopf and Härtel], 1979. — [3],19p ;
obl. 4to.
£5.40
1.Ti

(B79-51122)

Bennett, Richard Rodney
Alba (1973) / [by] Richard Rodney Bennett. — Sevenoaks :
Novello, 1978. — [4],16p ; obl.4to. — (Novello modern organ
repertory ; no.11)
For organ. — Based on the Tema seriale from Britten's Cantata accademica.
— Duration 7 1/4 min.
£1.45
1.Ti 2.Sr

(B79-50234)

Bridge, Frank
[First book of organ pieces]. Six organ pieces / [by] Frank Bridge.
— London : Boosey and Hawkes, 1979. — 27p. ; obl.fol.
This publication presents Bridge's First book and second book of organ
pieces which were originally published separately.
Unpriced
1.Ti 2.Ti

(B79-51123)

Davies, Peter Maxwell
Three organ voluntaries / [by] Peter Maxwell Davies. — London :
Chester Music, 1979. — 7p ; 4to.
Unpriced
1.Ti

(B79-51124)

Eben, Peter
Laudes : for organ / [by] Peter Eben. — London : United Music,
1979. — 40p ; 4to.
Unpriced
1.Ti

(B79-51125)

Müller, Paul
Fantasia super 'Urbs Turegem, urbs famosa' sive 'Lauda Sion
salvatorem' : fur Orgel ... / [von] Paul Müller. — Zürich : Verlag
der Zentralbibliothek Zurich in Kommission bei Amadeus Verlag ;
[London] : [Bärenreiter], 1979. — 7p ; 4to. — (Schweizerische
Musikbibliothek ; Einzelkomponisten, 79-1)
Unpriced
1.Ti 2.Sr

(B79-50649)

Naumann, Johann Gottlieb
[40 freym Anrerlieder. Anhang]. Two masonic pieces for organ / [by] Johann Gottlieb Naumann ; edited by John Morehen. — New York ; [London] : Oxford University Press, 1979. — 4p ; 4to.
Unpriced
1.Ti 2.Ti 3.Morehen, John 4.Vierzig freym Aurerlieder. Anhang
(B79-50650)

Smith, Peter Melville
Scherzo : for organ (manuals only) / [by] Peter Melville Smith. — York : Banks, 1978. — 4p ; 4to.
Unpriced
1.Ti
(B79-50235)

Veal, Arthur
Prelude, interlude and carillon : (for organ) / by A. Veal. — London : Cramer, 1978. — 12p ; 4to.
Unpriced
1.Ti
(B79-50236)

Wehrle, Heinz
Choral-Toccata, 'O Heiland, reiss die Himmel auf' : Melodie Augsburg 1666 / [von] Heinz Wehrle. — Zürich ; [London] : Eulenburg, 1979. — 10p ; obl.4to. — (Organa helvetica)
£1.85
1.Ti 2.Sr
(B79-50651)

Williamson, Malcolm
The lion of Suffolk : for organ / [by] Malcolm Williamson. — London : Weinberger, 1979. — 12p ; obl.4to.
Unpriced
1.Ti
(B79-50652)

Wills, Arthur
Resurrection : for organ / by Arthur Wills. — London : Weinberger, 1979. — [1],12p ; obl. 4to.
Unpriced
1.Ti
(B79-51126)

Wills, Arthur
[Variations on 'Amazing Grace']. Variations on 'Amazing grace' [and] Toccata : for organ / [by] Arthur Wills. — Sevenoaks : Novello, 1979. — [2],38p ; 4to. — (International series of contemporary organ music ; no.30)
£2.25
1.Ti 2.Ti 3.Toccata, organ 4.Sr
(B79-51127)

RK — Arrangements
Arne, Thomas Augustine
[Comus. Dances. *arr*]. Two dances from 'Comus' / [by] Thomas Arne ; arranged by Terence Greaves for piano solo. — York : Banks, 1979. — 4p ; 4to.
Unpriced
1.Ti 2.Greaves, Terence
(B79-50653)

Handel, George Frideric
[Selections. *arr*]. Handel's greatest hits : all organ / arranged by James Burt. — London : Chappell, 1979. — 38p ; 4to.
Unpriced
1.Ti 2.Burt, James
(B79-50654)

RK/AAY — Arrangements. Collections
A C.H. Trevor organ miscellany. — Sevenoaks : Elkin, 1978. — 27p ; 4to.
Works by Bach, Boyce, Volkmar, Gounod, Franck and Rebikov.
£1.55
1.Trevor, Caleb Henry
(B79-50655)

RK/AHM — Arrangements. Gavottes
Boyce, William
[The shepherd's lottery. Symphony. *arr*]. Gavot, from symphony no.4 / [by] William Boyce ; transcribed for organ by Patrick Williams. — London : Edwin Ashdown, 1978. — 4p ; 4to.
£0.40
1.Ti 2.Williams, Patrick
(B79-50237)

RK/B/FK — Arrangements. Automata
Mozart, Wolfgang Amadeus
[Fantasia, clock-organ, K.608, F minor. *arr*]. Fantasia in F minor for organ (mechanical clock-organ, K.608) / [by] Wolfgang Amadeus Mozart ; edited for organ by Anthony Newman. — New York ; London : Schirmer, 1979. — [4],16p ; 4to. — (Great performer's edition)
£3.65
1.Newman, Anthony 2.Sr
(B79-51128)

RK/DP/LF/AY — Arrangements. Carols. Christmas. Collections
Happy Christmas : easy piano [or] organ / arranged by Cecil Bolton and Jack Moore. — London : EMI, 1978. — 76p ; 4to.
Carols.
Unpriced
Primary classification QPK/DP/LF/AY
1.Moore, Jack 2.Bolton, Cecil
(B79-50224)

RK/DW/GB/AY — Arrangements. Popular songs. Collections
18 ct. gold for all organ / editor, Cecil Bolton. — London : EMI, 1979. — 64p : port ; 4to.
Popular songs arranged.
Unpriced
1.Bolton, Cecil
(B79-51129)

22 ct. gold : for all organ / editor, Cecil Bolton. — London : EMI, 1979. — 76p ; 4to.
Popular songs.
Unpriced
1.Bolton, Cecil 2.Twenty-two ct. gold
(B79-50656)

Organ gold. — London : Chappell.
Organ arrangements of popular songs.
1. — 1977. — 52p ; 4to.
Unpriced
(B79-50238)

2. — 1977. — 56p ; 4to.
Organ arrangements of popular songs.
Unpriced
(B79-50239)

3 / arranged by Bert Brewis. — 1977. — 56p ; 4to.
Organ arrangements of popular songs.
Unpriced
1.Brewis, Bert
(B79-50240)

4 / arranged by Bert Brewis. — 1978. — 48p ; 4to.
Organ arrangements of popular songs.
Unpriced
1.Brewis, Bert
(B79-50241)

5 / arranged by Bert Brewis. — 1979. — 48p ; 4to.
Unpriced
1.Brewis, Bert
(B79-50657)

RK/DW/HKR/JR — Arrangements. Rock songs. Films
Bee Gees
[Saturday night fever. *Selections : arr*]. Saturday night fever : from the original movie soundtrack / words and music by [the group]. — London : Chappell, 1979. — 23p ; 4to.
Unpriced
1.Ti
(B79-50658)

RK/DW/HKR/JR/AY — Arrangements. Rock songs. Films. Collections
[**Grease**. *Selections : arr*]. Grease : organ, original soundtrack songs from the motion picture. — London : Chappell, 1979. — 24p ; 4to.
Unpriced
(B79-50659)

RK/KDD/AY — Arrangements. Weddings. Collections
A **wedding** album / arranged for organ by Philip Lane. — London : Edwin Ashdown, 1978. — 22p ; 4to.
Unpriced
1.Lane, Philip
(B79-50242)

A **wedding** bouquet : organ music for the marriage ceremony. — Sevenoaks : Novello, 1979. — 48p ; 4to.
Unpriced
(B79-51130)

RPV — ELECTRIC ORGANS
RPV/AC — Tutors
Delrieu, Jean Philippe
A vous de jouer : cours d'initiation rapide et progressive à l'argue électronique / [par] Jean-Philippe Delrieu. — Paris ; [London] : Chappell.
Vol.2. — 1979. — 62p. ; 4to. —
Unpriced
1.Ti
(B79-51132)

Enzberg, Hans
Top Music an der Orgel : leicht verständlicher Einfuhrungskurs,
für elektronische Heimorgel in 5 Bänden mit 40 Lektionen / [von]
Hans Enzberg. — Mainz ; London : Schott.
Band 1 : Lektion 1-8. — 1979. — 65p ; 4to. —
£5.60
1.Ti
(B79-50243)

Band 2 : Lektion 9-16. — 1979. — 81p ; 4to. —
£5.60
1.Ti
(B79-50244)

Band 3 : Lektion 17-24. — 1979. — 81p ; 4to. —
£5.60
1.Ti
(B79-50245)

Band 4 : Lektion 25-32. — 1979. — 97p ; 4to. —
£5.60
1.Ti
(B79-50246)

Band 5 : Lektion 33-40. — 1979. — 113p ; 4to. —
£5.60
1.Ti
(B79-50247)

Pieper, Manfred
Swing und Beat, Schwarz auf weiss = Swing and beat. Black on
white : Anregungen zum Musizieren auf Klavier und
Elektronenorgel = Hints on playing the piano and the electronic
organ / [von] Manfred Pieper ; herausgegeben unter Mitarbeit von
Wieland Ziegenrücker ... — Leipzig : VEB Deutscher Verlag für
Musik ; [London] : [Breitkopf und Härtel], 1978. — 123p ; 4to.
£6.30
Primary classification Q/AC
1.Ti 2.Ziegenrücker, Wieland
(B79-50612)

RPVCK/AAY — Chord organ. Arrangements. Collections
Fun organ : arrangements ... for all electronic and 'C' chord organs.
— London : EMI.
Folio no.2 / arranged by Jack Moore. — 1978. — 40p ; 4to.
Unpriced
1.Moore, Jack
(B79-50660)

RPVCK/DP/LF/AY — Chord organ. Arrangements. Carols.
Christmas. Collections
Happy Christmas : chord organ / arranged by Cecil Bolton and
Jack Moore. — London : EMI, 1976. — 48p ; 4to.
Carols.
Unpriced
1.Bolton, Cecil 2.Moore, Jack
(B79-50248)

RPVCK/DW/GB/AY — Chord organ. Arrangements. Popular songs.
Collections
Fun chord organ : for young people of any age / music
arrangements, Cecil Bolton and Jack Moore. — London : EMI,
1979. — 24p ; 4to.
ISBN 0-86175-064-0 : Unpriced
1.Bolton, Cecil 2.Moore, Jack
(B79-51133)

RPVK/AGM/AY — Arrangements. Marches. Collections
Polkas and marches : for all organs / arranged and edited by
Arthur Bayas and Larry Buckner. — Carlstadt : Lewis Music ;
[London] : [Phoenix], 1978. — 72p ; 4to.
'Ashley Publications Inc.' is given as the publisher on the front cover.
Unpriced
Primary classification RPVK/AHVH/AY
(B79-50661)

RPVK/AHVH/AY — Arrangements. Polkas. Collections
Polkas and marches : for all organs / arranged and edited by
Arthur Bayas and Larry Buckner. — Carlstadt : Lewis Music ;
[London] : [Phoenix], 1978. — 72p ; 4to.
'Ashley Publications Inc.' is given as the publisher on the front cover.
Unpriced
Also classified at RPVK/AGM/AY
(B79-50661)

RPVK/DP/LF/AY — Electronic organ. Arrangements. Christmas
carols. Collections
Die Weihnachts-Orgel : Top Music an der Orgel, die schönsten
Weihnachtslieder für elektronische Heimorgel im
Schwierigkeitsgrad 1-5 der Hans Enzberg-Schule. — Mainz ;
[London] : Schott, 1979. — [1],48p : ill ; 4to.
£4.80
1.Enzberg, Hans
(B79-51134)

RS — ACCORDION
RS/AC — Tutors
Beynon, Ivor
The complete piano accordion tutor / by Ivor Beynon. —
London : EMI, 1979. — [1],98p ; 4to.
Unpriced
1.Ti
(B79-50249)

RSPM — UNACCOMPANIED ACCORDION SOLOS
RSPMJ — Miscellaneous works
Abbott, Alan
Black and white toccata : concert accordion / [by] Alain Abbott.
— Waterloo : Waterloo Music ; [Wendover] : [Robertson], 1978.
— 11p ; 4to.
£1.65
1.Ti
(B79-50250)

Abbott, Alan
Le grand âne noir : accordeon de concert / [par] Alain Abbott. —
Waterloo : Waterloo Music ; [Wendover] : [Robertson], 1978. —
3p ; 4to.
£0.90
1.Ti
(B79-50251)

Abbott, Alan
Sad birds = Oiseaux tristes : concert accordion = accordeon de
concert / [by] Alain Annott. — Waterloo : Waterloo Music ;
[Wendover] : [Robertson], 1978. — 4p ; 4to.
£1.05
1.Ti
(B79-50252)

Abbott, Nelly
Ballade et jeu : pour accordeon / [par] Nelly Abbott. —
Waterloo : Waterloo Music ; [Wendover] : [Robertson], 1978. —
3p ; 4to.
Two pieces.
£0.90
1.Ti
(B79-50253)

Apparailly, Yves
The seasons = Les saisons / [by] Yves Apparailly. — Waterloo :
Waterloo Music ; [Wendover] : [Robertson], 1978. — 7p ; 4to.
For accordion.
£1.35
1.Ti
(B79-50254)

Motte, Diether de la
Liebeserklärung für ein verkanntes Instrument : 6 Stücke für
Akkordeon, 1977 / [von] Diether da la Motte ; spieltechnische
Einrichtung und Registrierung von Hugo Noth. — Kassel ;
London : Bärenreiter, 1978. — [4],16p ; fol.
Unpriced
1.Ti 2.Noth, Hugo
(B79-50255)

RSPMK/DP/LF/AY — Arrangements. Christmas carols. Collections
Happy Christmas : accordion. — London : EMI, 1979. — 76p ;
4to.
Unpriced
(B79-51135)

RSPMK/DW/GB/AY — Arrangements. Popular songs. Collections
The **modern** accordionist / by Cecil Bolton and Jack Moore. —
London : EMI, 1979. — 36p ; 4to.
Songs arranged for accordion.
Unpriced
1.Bolton, Cecil 2.Moore, Jack
(B79-50662)

RXM — STRING ORCHESTRA
RXM/HM — Ballet
Lully, Jean Baptiste
Le ballet des muses : for baroque ensemble / [by] Jean Baptiste
Lully : modern edition prepared by Karel Husa. — New York ;
London : Associated Music, 1978. — 4to.
£15.10
1.Ti 2.Husa, Karel
(B79-50663)

RXM/T — Variations
Schwaen, Kurt
Hört ihr den Trommelschlag : Variationen für Streichorchester /
[von] Kurt Schwaen. — Leipzig : VEB Deutscher Verlag ;
[London] : [Breitkopf and Härtel], 1979. — 24p ; 4to.
£2.10
1.Ti
(B79-51136)

RXMF — Concertos
Surinach, Carlos
[Quartet, strings. *arr*]. Concerto for string orchestra / [by] Carlos Surinach ; a transcription of the composer's string quartet reworked for string orchestra. — New York ; London : Associated Music, 1978. — 80p ; 4to.
£9.10
Primary classification RXMK

(B79-50666)

RXMG — Suites
Barsanti, Francesco
[Overture a quattro. Op.4, no.2]. Ouverture, Opus 4, No.2 : für Streicher und Basso continuo = for strings and basso continuo / [von] Francesco Barsanti ; herausgegeben von, edited by, David Johnson. — Mainz ; London : Schott, 1978. — 15p ; 4to. — (Concertino ; 186)
£6.00
1.Ti 2.Johnson, David 3.Sr

(B79-50257)

RXMHJN — Chaconnes
Purcell, Henry
[Chacony, string orchestra, Z.730, G minor]. Chacony for strings / [by] Henry Purcell ; edited by Walter Bergmann. — London : Eulenburg, 1979. — viii,7p. ; 8vo.
Unpriced
1.Ti 2.Bergmann, Walter

(B79-51137)

RXMJ — Miscellaneous works
Corigliano, John
Voyage : for string orchestra / [by] John Corigliano ; a string orchestra version of the choral setting. — New York ; London : Schirmer, 1978. — 6p ; 4to.
Unpriced
1.Ti

(B79-50664)

Gould, Morton
Elegy : for string orchestra / [by] Morton Gould. — New York ; London : Schirmer, 1978. — 4p ; 4to.
Unpriced
1.Ti

(B79-50665)

RXMK — Arrangements
Surinach, Carlos
[Quartet, strings. *arr*]. Concerto for string orchestra / [by] Carlos Surinach ; a transcription of the composer's string quartet reworked for string orchestra. — New York ; London : Associated Music, 1978. — 80p ; 4to.
£9.10
Also classified at RXMF

(B79-50666)

RXMK/AH/AYU — Arrangements. Dances. Collections. Latin America
Alla danza : lateinamerikanische Tänze (Cha-Cha, Tango argentino, Bossa nova) zu vier Stimmen, Stabspiele, Schlagzeug und Klavier, für Orchester, Streichorchester oder Instrumentalenensemble / [von] Friedrich Zehm. — Mainz ; London : Schott, 1978. — 31p ; 4to.
Duration 12 min.
£8.00
Primary classification MK/AH/AYU
1.Zehm, Friedrich

(B79-50566)

RXMP — SOLO INSTRUMENT (S) & STRING ORCHESTRA
RXMPPWF — Keyboard & string orchestra. Concertos
Bach, Carl Philipp Emanuel
[Concerto, keyboard & string orchestra, Wq 9, C minor]. Concerto in C-moll für Cembalo (Klavier) und Streicher = Concerto in C minor for harpsichord (piano) and strings / [von] Carl Philipp Emanuel Bach ; herausgegeben von, edited by, György Balla. — Erstausgabe = First ed. — Kassel : Nagel ; Budapest : Editio Musica ; London : Bärenreiter, 1976. — 79p ; 4to. — (Nagels Musik-Archiv ; 253)
Unpriced
1.Balla, György 2.Sr

(B79-50258)

RXMPQNUF — Pianos (2) & string orchestra. Concertos
Williamson, Malcolm
[Concerto, pianos (2) & string orchestra]. Concerto for two pianos and string orchestra / [by] Malcolm Williamson. — London : Weinberger, 1973 [i.e.1979]. — 72p ; 8vo.
Miniature score.
Unpriced

(B79-50667)

RXMPSF — Violin & string orchestra. Concertos
Vivaldi, Antonio
[Concerto, violin & string orchestra, R.761, C minor, 'Amato bene']. Concerto in C minor 'Amato bene', RV761, for violin and string orchestra / [by] Antonio Vivaldi ; edited by Michael Tilmouth. — London : Oxford University Press, 1979. — fol. — (Musica da camera ; 100)
Score [1],25p. & part.
ISBN 0-19-367972-8 : Unpriced
1.Tilmouth, Michael 2.Sr

(B79-51138)

RXMPVRNUF — Flutes (2) & string orchestra. Concertos
Mieg, Peter
[Concerto, flutes (2) & string orchestra]. Concerto pour deux flûtes et orchestre à cordes, 1974 / [par] Peter Mieg. — Winterthur : Amadeus ; [London] : [Schott], 1977. — 32p ; 4to.
Unpriced

(B79-50259)

RXMPVTF — Oboe & string orchestra. Concertos
Telemann, Georg Philipp
[Concerto, oboe & string orchestra, D major]. Concerto in D for oboe, violins and basso continuo / [by] Georg Philipp Telemann ; [edited by] Anders Wiklund. — London : Musica rara, 1978. — 4to.
Score ([1],18p.) & 5 parts.
Unpriced
1.Wiklund, Anders

(B79-50260)

Telemann, Georg Philipp
[Concerto, oboe & string orchestra, F major]. Concerto in F for solo oboe, violin, strings and basso continuo / [by] Georg Philipp Telemann ; [edited by] Anders Wiklund. — London : Musica rara, 1978. — 4to.
Score ([1]p,16p.) & 7 parts ; the cello part is in duplicate.
Unpriced
1.Wicklund, Anders

(B79-50261)

Vivaldi, Antonio
[Il cimento dell'armonia e dell'inventione. Op.8, Concerto, oboe & string orchestra, P.259, D minor]. Concerto in d minor, RV454 (F.VII/1), P.259, for oboe, strings and basso continuo / [by] Antonio Vivaldi ; [edited by] R.P. Block. — London : Musica rara, 1978. — 4to.
Score ([1],27p.) & 6 parts.
Unpriced
1.Ti 2.Block, Robert Paul

(B79-50668)

Vivaldi, Antonio
[Concerto, oboe & string orchestra, R.455, F major]. Concerto in F, RV.455, (P.306) for oboe, strings and basso continuo / ed. R.P. Block. — London : Musica rara, 1979. — 4to.
Score (19p.) & 6 parts.
Unpriced
1.Block, Robert Paul

(B79-50669)

Vivaldi, Antonio
[Concerto, oboe & string orchestra, R.461, A minor]. Concerto in A minor for oboe, strings and continuo, RV461 (F.VII,no.5) (P.42) / [by] Antonio Vivaldi ; ed. R.P. Block. — London : Musica rara, 1979. — 4to.
Score (18p.) + 6 parts.
Unpriced
1.Block, Robert Paul

(B79-51139)

Vivaldi, Antonio
[Concerto, oboe & string orchestra, R.463, A minor]. Concerto in A minor for oboe, strings and continuo, RV463 (F.VII,no.13) / [by] Antonio Vivaldi ; ed. R.P. Block. — London : Musica rara, 1979. — 4to.
Score ([1],17p.) & 6 parts.
Unpriced
1.Block, Robert Paul

(B79-51140)

RXMPVTFL — Oboe & string orchestra. Concertinos
Tull, Fisher
[Concertino, oboe & string orchestra]. Concertino for oboe and strings / [by] Fisher Tull. — London : Boosey and Hawkes, 1979. — fol. — (Hawkes school series ; no.306)
Score (20p.) & 15 parts, with several copies of various parts.
Unpriced
1.Sr

(B79-51141)

RXMPWSE — Trumpet & string orchestra. Sonatas
Gabrielli, Domenico
[Sonata, trumpet & string orchestra, D. XI, 8, D major]. Sonata
D. XI, 8 in D, for trumpet, strings and basso continuo / [by]
Domenico Gabrielli ; ed. R.P. Block. — London : Musica rara,
1979. — 4to. — (Italian 17th and 18th century sinfonias and
sonatas for trumpets and strings ; 23)
Score ([1],11p.) & 8 parts.
Unpriced
1.Block, Robert Paul 2.Sr
                                                                (B79-50670)

RXMPWSG — Trumpet & string orchestra. Suites
Telemann, Georg Philipp
[Suite, trumpet & string orchestra, D major]. Suite 1 for trumpet,
strings and basso continuo / [by] G.P. Telemann ; ed. R.P. Block.
— London : Musica rara, 1978. — 4to. — (17th and 18th century
sonatas, concerti and overtures for trumpets and orchestra ; no.95)
Score ([1],33p.) & 7 parts, with alternative parts for trumpets in D and B
flat.
Unpriced
1.Block, Robert Paul 2.Sr
                                                                (B79-50262)

RXMPWSNUE — Trumpets (2) & string orchestra. Sonatas
Jacchini, Giuseppe Maria
[Trattenimenti per camera, op.5. Sonata, trumpets (2), strings &
continuo, op.5, no.1, D major]. Sonata, op.5, no.1, for 2 trombe
(trumpets) strins and continuo / [by] Giuseppe Jacchini ; edited
by R.P. Block. — London : Musica rara, 1978. — 4to. — (Italian
17th & 18th century sinfonias and sonatas for trumpets and
strings ; 31)
Score ([1],12p.) & 7 parts.
Unpriced
1.Ti 2.Block, Robert Paul 3.Sr
                                                                (B79-50263)

RXMPWSNUE — Trumpets (2) & string orchestra. Symphonies
Jacchini, Giuseppe Maria
[Trattenimenti per camera. Sinfonia, trumpets (2) & string
orchestra, op.5, no.8, D major]. Sinfonia, op.5 no.8 for 2 trumpets,
strings and basso continuo / [by] Giuseppe Jacchini ; edited by
R.P. Block. — London : Musica rara, 1978. — 4to. — (Italian
17th and 18th century sinfonias and sonatas for trumpets and
strings ; 32)
Score ([1],10p.) & 8 parts.
Unpriced
1.Ti 2.Block, Robert Paul 3.Sr
                                                                (B79-50671)

RXNR — Quintets
Eybler, Joseph von
[Quintet, strings, D major]. Quintet, vln., viola, viola d'amore,
cello, bass / by Joseph Eybler ; source British Museum, edited by
Ian White and Ambrose Miller. — Kings Langley ((Little
Margaret, Penmans Green, Chipperfield)) : E.L. White, 1977. —
5pt ; fol.
Unpriced
1.White, Ian 2.Miller, Ambrose
                                                                (B79-50672)

Gál, Hans
Quintet for 2 violins, 2 violas and violoncello, op.106 / [by] Hans
Gál. — London : Simrock, 1979. — 5pt ; 4to.
Unpriced
1.Ti
                                                                (B79-50264)

Gál, Hans
[Quintet, violins (2), violas (2) & cello]. Quintet for 2 violins, 2
violas and violoncello, op.106 / [by] Hans Gál. — London :
Simrock, 1979. — [1],38p ; 8vo.
Unpriced
                                                                (B79-50265)

Mozart, Wolfgang Amadeus
[Quintet, strings, no.1, K.174, B flat major]. Quintet, B flat major
for 2 violins, 2 violas and cello K.174 / [by] Wolfgang Amadeus
Mozart ; edited by Ronald Woodham. — London : Eulenburg,
1979. — viii,43p ; 8vo.
Miniature score.
£1.55
1.Woodham, Ronald
                                                                (B79-51142)

RXNRK/DJ — Quintets. Arrangements. Motets
Schütz, Heinrich
[Geistliche Chormusik. Die mit Thränen säen. arr]. Fantasia a 5 /
[by] Heinrich Schütz ; transcribed for recorders or strings
(especially viols) by Aaron Williams. — Chesham : Ricordi, 1978.
— 4to.
Score (4p.) & 6 parts, with alternative parts for treble recorder III/violin III
and cello/bass back to back.
Unpriced
Primary classification VSNRK/DJ
1.Ti 2.Ti 3.Williams, Aaron
                                                                (B79-50338)

RXNS — Quartets
Guy, Barry
[Quartet, strings, no.2]. String quartet no.2 / [by] Barry Guy. —
Sevenoaks : Novello, 1979. — [4],40p ; 4to.
Facsimile of the composer's manuscript.
£5.50
                                                                (B79-50266)

Holliger, Heinz
[Quartet, strings, (1973)]. Streichquartett = String quartet :
1973 / [von] Heinz Holliger. — Mainz ; London : Schott, 1979.
— 4pt ; fol.
£39.20
                                                                (B79-50673)

Korngold, Erich Wolfgang
[Quartet, strings, no.3, op.34, D major]. Streichquartett No.3, opus
34, D-Dur : für Violine, Viola und Violoncello / [von] E.W.
Korngold. — Mainz ; London : Schott, 1978. — 4pt ; 4to.
£16.00
                                                                (B79-50267)

Korngold, Erich Wolfgang
[Quartet, strings, no.3, op.34, D major]. Streichquartett No.3, opus
34, D-Dur, für 2 Violinen, Viola und Violoncello = String quartet
no.3, opus 34, D major, for 2 violins, viola and violoncello / [von]
E.W. Korngold. — Mainz ; London : Schott, 1978. — 63p ; 4to.
£14.00
                                                                (B79-50268)

Simpson, Robert
[Quartet, strings, no.7]. Quartet n.7 (1977) / [by] Robert Simpson.
— South Croydon : Lengnick, 1979. — [1],50p ; 8vo.
Unpriced
                                                                (B79-51143)

Standford, Patric
A London suite : for elementary string quartets / by Patrick
Standford. — London (7 Garrick St., W.C.2) : Middle Eight
Music, 1979. — 4to. — (Middle eight ensemble series ; 2)
Score (7p.) & 4 parts.
Unpriced
1.Ti 2.Sr
                                                                (B79-50269)

Terzakis, Dimitri
[Quartet, strings, no.2]. Streichquartett Nr.2 / [von] Dimitri
Terzakis. — Kassel ; [London] : Bärenreiter, 1978. — 16p ; 4to.
£3.96
                                                                (B79-50270)

RXNSK/AHXJ — Quartets. Arrangements. Ragtime
Joplin, Scott
[Ragtime. Selections. *arr*]. String along with Scott : 10 ragtime
pieces / by Scott Joplin, for string quartet with double bass, guitar
and piano ad lib., or string orchestra with guitar and piano ad
lib. ; arranged by Jerry Silverman. — New York ; London :
Schirmer, 1978. — 88p ; 4to.
£7.85
1.Ti 2.Ti
                                                                (B79-50674)

RXNT — Trios
Albrechtsberger, Johann Georg
[Divertimento, violas (2) & double bass]. Divertimento in D-dur
für zwei Violen und Kontrabass = Divertimento in D major for
two violas and double bass / [von] Johann Georg Albrechtsberger
... ; herausgegeben von ... edited by Alexander Weinmann. —
Zürich : Amadeus ; [London] : [Bärenreiter], 1979. — 4to.
Score (8p.) & 3 parts.
Unpriced
1.Weinmann, Alexander
                                                                (B79-50675)

Binkerd, Gordon
[Trio, string instruments]. Trio for strings / [by] Gordon Binkerd.
— New York ; [London] : Boosey and Hawkes, 1979. — 3pt ;
4to.
Unpriced
                                                                (B79-50676)

Binkerd, Gordon
[Trio, string instruments]. Trio for strings / [by] Gordon Binkerd.
— New York ; [London] : Boosey and Hawkes, 1979. — [2],24p ;
8vo. — (Hawkes pocket scores ; 921)
Miniature score.
Unpriced
1.Sr
                                                                (B79-50677)

Finke, Fidelio Fritz
Acht Musiken : für zwei Geigen und Bratsche (1923) / [von]
Fidelio F. Finke. — Berlin : Neue Musik ; [London] : [Breitkopf
and Härtel], 1977[i.e.1979]. — 4to.
Score (14p.) & 3 parts.
£3.60
1.Ti
                                                                (B79-51144)

Standford, Patric
Holiday memories : for elementary string trio (2 violins and cello) / by Patric Standford. — London (7 Garrick St., W.C.2) : Middle Eight Music, 1979. — 4to. — (Middle eight ensemble series ; 1)
Score (4p.) & 3 parts.
Unpriced
1.Ti 2.Sr

(B79-50271)

RXNTK — Trios. Arrangements
Haydn, Joseph
[Divertimentos, baryton, viola & cello, Hob. XI. *Selections : arr*]. Divertimento for violin, viola d'amore and gamba / by Joseph Haydn ; editor, Ian White. ((Little Margaret, Penmans Green, Chipperfield)) : E.L. White, 1977. — 3pt : fol.
First movement unidentified at time of cataloguing.
Unpriced
1.White, Ian

(B79-50678)

S — VIOLIN
S/AC — Tutors
Cohen, Eta
[First year violin method]. Eta Cohen Violinschule. — Sevenoaks : Paxton.
Score for violin & piano (94p.) & violin part (35p.).
1. Band. — 1979. — 4to.
Unpriced
1.Ti 2.Ti

(B79-50272)

S/AF — Exercises
Whiteley, Faith
A first violin book / [by] Faith Whiteley and Walter Bergmann. — London : Oxford University Press, 1979. — 4to & obl.4to.
Teacher's book (43p.), Pupil's book (32p.).
ISBN 0-19-359511-7 : Unpriced
1.Ti 2.Bergmann, Walter

(B79-51145)

SN — VIOLIN ENSEMBLE
Schwaen, Kurt
Spatzenmusik für zwei, drei und mehr Geigen / [von] Kurt Schwaen. — Berlin : Neue Musik ; [London] : [Breitkopf and Härtel], 1979. — 4to.
Score (24p.) & 3 parts.
£3.00
1.Ti

(B79-50679)

SNSPWHP — Violins (3) & keyboard. Gigues
Pachelbel, Johann
[Canon & gigue, violins (3) & continuo, D major]. Canon & gigue for three violins and keyboard (cello continuo ad lib.) / [by] Johann Pachelbel ; edited by Robin de Smet. — London : Fentone Music : Breitkopf and Härtel, 1979. — 4to.
Score (11p.) & 4 parts.
Unpriced
1.Ti 2.Ti 3.De Smet, Robin

(B79-51146)

SNSQK/LE — Violins (3) & piano. Symphonies
Mayr, Simon
[Sinfonia concertante, violins (3). *arr*]. Sinfonia concertante für drei Violinen und Orchester / [von] Simon Mayr ; Ausgabe für drei Violinen und Klavier von Heinrich Creuzburg. — Zum ersten Mal / herausgegeben von Heinrich Bauer. — Frankfurt : Litolff ; London : Peters, 1978. — 4to.
Score (28p.) & 3 parts.
Unpriced
1.Bauer, Heinrich 2.Creuzburg, Heinrich

(B79-50680)

SNTPWE — Violins (2) & continuo. Sonatas
Boyce, William
[Sonata, violins (2) & continuo, no.1, A minor]. Trio sonata, no.1, A minor, for 2 violins and continuo / [by] William Boyce ; edited with a keyboard realisation by Stanley Sadie. — London : Peters, 1979. — 4to.
Score (12p.) & 3 parts.
Unpriced
1.Sadie, Stanley

(B79-51147)

Boyce, William
[Sonata, violins (2) & continuo, no.3, A major]. Trio sonata, no.3, A major, for 2 violins and continuo / [by] William Boyce ; edited with a keyboard realisation by Stanley Sadie. — London : Peters, 1979. — 4to.
Score (12p.) & 3 parts.
Unpriced
1.Sadie, Stanley

(B79-51148)

SNUE — Duets. Sonatas
Boismortier, Joseph Bodin de
[Sonatas, flutes (2), op.2, nos.3, 4]. Two sonatas, Opus 2, Nos. 3 and 4 for two flutes, or oboes, or violins / [by] J.B. de Boismortier ; edited by Gwilym Beechey. — London : Oxford University Press, 1978. — 11p ; fol. — (Musica da camera ; 68)
ISBN 0-19-355578-6 : Unpriced
Primary classification VRNUE
1.Beechey, Gwilym 2.Sr

(B79-50327)

SP — VIOLIN & PIANO
SPE — Sonatas
Arne, Thomas Augustine
[Sonata, violin & continuo, E major]. Sonata in E major for violin and basso continuo / [by] Thomas Augustine Arne ; edited by John A. Parkinson. — London : Oxford University Press, 1978. — fol. — (Musica da camera ; 80)
Duration 6 min. — Score (8p.) & 2 parts.
ISBN 0-19-355216-7 : Unpriced
1.Parkinson, John Alfred 2.Sr

(B79-50273)

Babell, William
[Sonata, violin & continuo, op.posth., pt.1, no.11, G minor]. Sonata 11 in G minor for oboe (or violin) and basso continuo / [by] William Babell ; edited by George Pratt. — London : Oxford University Press, 1978. — 4to. — (Musica da camera ; 52)
Score ([11],13p.) & part.
ISBN 0-19-355226-4 : Unpriced
Also classified at VTPE
1.Pratt, George 2.Sr

(B79-50274)

SPG — Suites
Telemann, Georg Philipp
[Kleine Cammermusic]. Die kleine Kammermusik : sechs Partiten für Blockflöte, Querflöte, Oboe oder Violine und Basso continuo = six partitas for recorder, flute, oboe or violin and basso continuo / [von] Georg Philipp Telemann ; herausgegeben und Continuo-Aussetzung von ... Willy Hess. — Zürich : Amadeus ; [London] : [Eulenburg], 1979. — 4to.
Score ([1],40p.) & 2 parts.
£4.70
Primary classification VSPG
1.Ti 2.Hess, Willy

(B79-50764)

SPHX — Jazz
Jazz fiddle / arr. Antony le Fleming. — London : Chappell, 1979. — 4to.
Arrangements of standards. — Score (60p.) & part.
Unpriced
1.Le Fleming, Antony

(B79-50681)

SPJ — Miscellaneous works
Dalby, Martin
Unicorn : for violin and piano / [by] Martin Dalby. — Sevenoaks : Novello, 1978. — 4to.
Score (12p.) & part.
£2.00
1.Ti

(B79-50275)

Deshaulle, Jacques
Trois pièces facile : première position violon avec accompagnement de piano / [par] Jacques Deshaulle. — Paris ; [London] : Chappell, 1979. — fol.
Score (4p.) & part.
Unpriced
1.Ti

(B79-51149)

Druckman, Jacob
[Duet, violin & piano]. Duo for violin and piano / [by] Jacob Druckman. — London : Boosey and Hawkes, 1978. — 4to.
Duration 12 min. — Score (19p.) & part.
Unpriced

(B79-50276)

Frescobaldi, Girolamo
[Libro della canzoni, no.1. Canzona 2 'La Bernadina']. Canzona (II) 'La Bernadina' per canto solo : für Sopranblockflöte (Flöte, Oboe, Violine) und Generalbass = for descant recorder (flute, oboe, violin) and continuo / [von] Girolamo Frescobaldi ; Continuo-Einrichtung für Gitarre von... Konrad Ragossnig. — [Mainz] ; [London] : [Schott], [1979]. — facsim ; 4to. — (Original musik für Blockflöte ; no.140)
Score (7p.) & part.
£3.20
Primary classification VSRPJ
1.Ti 2.Ti 3.Ragossnig, Konrad 4.Sr

(B79-51242)

Rose, Michael
   Fiddler's ten : easy tunes for violin with piano accompaniment /
   [by] Michael Rose. — Sevenoaks : Novello, 1978. — 4to.
   Score ([2],29p.) & part.
   £1.65
   1.Ti
                                                                    (B79-50277)

SPK — Arrangements
   Copland, Aaron
   [Duet, flute & piano. *arr*]. Duo for violin and piano / [by] Aaron
   Copland ; edited by Robert Mann. — London : Boosey and
   Hawkes, 1979. — fol.
   Score ([2],21p.) & part.
   Unpriced
   1.Ti 2.Ti 3.Mann, Robert
                                                                    (B79-51150)

   Piston, Walter
   [Fantasia, violin & orchestra. *arr*]. Fantasia for violin and
   orchestra / [by] Walter Piston ; for violin and piano ; reduction
   by the composer. — New York ; London : Associated Music,
   1978. — 4to.
   Duration 16 mins. — Score (25p.) & part.
   £4.25
                                                                    (B79-51151)

SPK/AAY — Arrangements. Collections
   Fun music : for violin / arranged by Bert Brewis. — London :
   Chappell.
   Score (28p.) & part.
   [Vol.1]. — 1976. — 4to.
   Unpriced
   1.Brewis, Bert
                                                                    (B79-50278)
   Vol.2. — 1977. — 4to.
   Unpriced
   1.Brewis, Bert
                                                                    (B79-50279)

   Violin fancies / compiled and arranged by C. Paul Herfurth with
   piano accompaniment. — London : Chappell, 1979. — 4to.
   Score (27p.) & part.
   Unpriced
   1.Herfurth, C Paul
                                                                    (B79-51152)

SPK/AGM — Arrangements. Marches
   Weber, Carl Maria von, *Freiherr*
   [6 petites pièces faciles. Op.3. Marcia. *arr*]. March. Op.3, no.5 /
   by Weber ; arranged for violin or viola or cello with piano by
   Watson Forbes. — Wendover : Roberton, 1978. — 4to.
   Score (4p.) & 2 parts: the cello part is printed on the verso of the viola part.
   Unpriced
   1.Ti 2.Six petites pieces faciles. Op.3. Marcia. arr
                                                                    (B79-50280)

SPK/DW/GB/AY — Arrangements. Popular songs. Collections
   Fun violin : for young people of any age / music arrangements, Roy
   Slack. — London : EMI, 1979. — 4to.
   With piano. — Score (24p.) & part.
   ISBN 0-86175-066-7 : Unpriced
   1.Slack, Roy
                                                                    (B79-51153)

SPK/LF — Arrangements. Concertos
   Vivaldi, Antonio
   [Il cimento dell'armonia e dell'inventione. Op.8. Le quattro
   stagione. Autunno.. *arr*]. Four seasons, op.8 (Concerto for violin
   and orchestra) / [by] Antonio Vivaldi. — New York ; London :
   Schirmer. — (Schirmer's library of musical classics ; vol.1929)
   Score (14p.) & part.
   Autumn : for violin and piano / piano reduction by Alojz Srebotnjak ; violin
   part edited by Rok Klopčič. — 1978. — 4to.
   £2.40
   1.Ti 2.Ti 3.Srebotnjak, Alojz 4.Klopčič, Rok 5.Sr
                                                                    (B79-50682)

   Vivaldi, Antonio
   [Il cimento dell'armonia e dell'inventione. Op.8, nos 1-4. *arr*].
   Four seasons, op.8 (Concerto for violin and orchestra / [by]
   Antonio Vivaldi. — New York ; London : Schirmer. —
   (Schirmer's library of musical classics ; vol.1930)
   Score (14p.) & part.
   [Op.8, no.4]. Winter : for violin and piano / piano reduction by Alojz
   Srebotnjak, violin part edited by Rok Klopčič. — 1979. — 4to.
   £2.40
   1.Ti 2.Ti 3.Srebotnjak, Alojz 4.Klopčič, Rok 5.Sr
                                                                    (B79-51154)

SPM — UNACCOMPANIED VIOLIN
SPME — Sonatas
   Stiles, Frank
   [Sonata, violin]. Sonata for solo violin / [by] Frank Stiles. —
   Braintree ((Paigles, Perry Green, Bradwell)) : Anglian Edition,
   1978. — 6p ; 4to. — (Anglian new music series ; 39)
   Unpriced
   1.Sr
                                                                    (B79-50683)

SPMH — Dances
   McGuire, Edward
   Rant : for solo violin / [by] Edward McGuire. — Edinburgh :
   Scotus Music, 1977. — 6p ; 4to.
   Facsimile of the composer's autograph.
   ISBN 0-86100-009-9 : Unpriced
   1.Ti
                                                                    (B79-50684)

SPMK — Arrangements
   Nazareth, Ernesto, *b.1863*
   [Piano music. *Selections : arr*]. Album de violão / [de] Ernesto
   Nazareth ; transcriçoes de Nelson Pilo. — Rio de Janeiro : Arthur
   Napoleão ; [London] : [Essex Music], 1978. — 31p ; fol.
   Unpriced
   1.Pilo, Nelson
                                                                    (B79-50281)

   Vivaldi, Antonio
   [Selections. *arr*]. Vivaldi themes : easy melodies transcribed for
   descant (tenor) recorder (or flute, oboe or violin) with symbols for
   accompaniment on the guitar (ad lib.) / edited by Torallo. —
   Chesham : Ricordi, 1979. — 13p ; obl. 8vo.
   Unpriced
   Primary classification VSRPMK
   1.Ti 2.Torallo
                                                                    (B79-51243)

**SPMK/AH/G/AYT — Arrangements. Folk dances. Collections.
   United States**
   Play old-time country fiddle : seventy-five traditional tunes arranged
   with words and chords including twenty-five square dances with
   complete calls and instructions, plus transposing guides for guitar,
   banjo, piano, bass or mandolin / [compiled by] Jerry Silverman.
   — New York ; London : Oak : Music Sales, 1979. — [10],132p ;
   4to.
   ISBN 0-86001-506-8 : Unpriced
   1.Silverman, Jerry
                                                                    (B79-51155)

SQP — VIOLA & PIANO
SQP/AY — Collections
   Viola. — Berlin : Neue Musik ; [London] : [Breitkopf and Härtel].
   1 : Stücke für Viola und Klavier / herausgegeben von Alfred Lipka. —
   1976. — 4to.
   £2.10
   1.Lipka, Alfred
                                                                    (B79-51156)

SQPK — Arrangements
   Hummel, Johann Nepomuk
   [Potpourri, viola & orchestra, op.94]. Potpourri for viola and
   orchestra, op.94 / [by] J.N. Hummel ; edited with a piano
   reduction by John Madden. — London : Musica rara, 1978. —
   4to.
   Score ([1],48p.) & part.
   Unpriced
   1.Madden, John
                                                                    (B79-50282)

SQPLSR — VIOLA & CELLO
   Danzi, Franz
   Drei Duos für Viola und Violoncello, erstes Buch / [von] Franz
   Danzi ; herausgegeben von, edited by, Ulrich Drüner. — Zurich :
   Amadeus ; [London] : [Schott], 1979. — 2pt ; 4to.
   Unpriced
   1.Ti 2.Drüner, Ulrich
                                                                    (B79-50283)

   Knorr, Ernst Lothar von
   [Duo, viola & cello, (1961)]. Duo für Viola und Violoncello
   (1961) / [von] Ernst Lothar von Knorr. — Zürich : Amadeus ;
   [London] : [Eulenburg], 1978. — 11p ; 4to.
   Two copies.
   £3.70
                                                                    (B79-50685)

SQPLSS — VIOLA & DOUBLE BASS
SQPLSSK/LE — Arrangements. Symphonies
Dittersdorf, Carl Ditters von
[Sinfonia concertante, viola & double bass, Krebs 127, D major. *arr*]. Sinfonia concertante for double bass and viola / [by] Karl Ditters von Dittersdorf ; piano reduction edited by Rodnney Slatford. — London : Yorke Edition, 1978. — 4to.
Score ([7p.],19p) & 2 parts.
Unpriced
1.Slatford, Rodney

(B79-50285)

SQPLTS — VIOLA & GUITAR
SQPLTSK — Arrangements
Marais, Marin
[Pièces de violes, liv. 4. *Selections : arr*]. Cinque antiche danze francesi / [di] Marin Marais ; realizzazione per viola & chitarra di Giovanni Antonioni & Carlo Carfagna. — Ancona : Berben ; [London] : [Breitkopf und Härtel], 1979. — 13p ; fol.
£1.90
1.Ti 2.Ti 3.Antonioni, Giovanni 4.Carfagna, Carlo

(B79-50686)

SQPLX — VIOLA & PERCUSSION
SQPLXE — Sonatas
Sculthorpe, Peter
[Sonata, viola & percussion (1960)]. Sonata for viola and percussion (1960) / [by] Peter Sculthorpe. — London : Faber Music, 1979. — [3],12p ; 4to.
Duration: 12 min.
Unpriced

(B79-50687)

SQPM — UNACCOMPANIED VIOLA
SQPMJ — Miscellaneous works
Davies, Peter Maxwell
The door of the sun : solo viola / [by] Peter Maxwell Davies. — London : Boosey and Hawkes, 1978. — [1].4p ; fol.
Duration 5 1/2 min.
Unpriced
1.Ti

(B79-50286)

Stevens, Bernard
Improvisation. Op.48 : for solo viola / by Bernard Stevens. — Wendover : Roberton, 1979. — 8p ; 4to.
£1.50
1.Ti

(B79-51157)

SQQ — VIOLA D'AMORE
Biber, Heinrich
[Harmonia artificiosa Partia, violas d'amore (2) & continuo, no.7 C minor. *Viola d'amore parts*]. Harmonia artificiosa, partita no. VIII [in fact, 7] : for two violas d'amore and cello, with optional organ or harpsichord / by Heinrich Biber ; edited by Ian White. — Kings Langley ((Little Margaret, Penmans Green, Chipperfield)) : E.L. White, 1978. — 4p ; fol.
The parts, which on the cover are described as 'the score only'.
Unpriced
1.Ti 2.White, Ian

(B79-50688)

SQQPE — Sonatas
Ariosti, Attilio
[Sonatas, viola d'amore & continuo, 'Stockholm']. 'Stockholmer Sonaten' für Viola d'amore (Viola) und Basso continuo = 'Stockholm sonatas' for viola d'amore (viola) and basso continuo / [von] Attilio Ariosti ; herausgegeben von, edited by, Günther Weiss, Continuo-Aussetzung von, continuo-realization by, Theodor Klein. — Kassel ; London : Bärenreiter. — (Hortus musicus ; 223)
2 : Sonatas in ... B flat major ... G minor ... A minor. — 1977. — 4to.
Score (22p.) & 2 parts.
£5.28
1.Ti 2.Weiss, Günther 3.Klein, Theodor 4.Sr

(B79-50287)

SR — CELLO
SR/AC — Tutors
Smith, Doreen
Cello positions / [by] Doreen Smith. — London : Oxford University Press, 1978. — 48p ; fol.
With a leaf of corrigenda inserted.
ISBN 0-19-322346-5 : Unpriced
1.Ti

(B79-51158)

Smith, Doreen
Introduction to the cello / [by] Doreen Smith. — London : Oxford University Press, 1979. — 48p ; fol.
ISBN 0-19-322345-7 : Unpriced
1.Ti

(B79-51159)

SRP — CELLO & PIANO
SRPE — Sonatas
Baker, David
[Sonata, cello & piano]. Sonata for cello and piano / [by] David Baker ; cello part edited by Janos Starker. — New York ; London : Associated Music, 1978. — 4to.
Score (36p.) & part.
£6.10
1.Starker, Janos

(B79-50689)

Telemann, Georg Philipp
[Der getreue Music Meister. Sonata, bassoon & continuo, F minor]. Sonate in f-moll für Fagott oder Violoncello und Basso continuo = Sonata in F minor for bassoon or cello and basso continuo / [von] Georg Philipp Telemann ; herausgegeben von, edited, Winfried Michel. — Winterthur : Amadeus ; [London] : [Schott], 1977. — 4to.
Score ([1],14p.) & 2 parts.
Unpriced
Primary classification VWPE
1.Ti 2.Michel, Winfried

(B79-50363)

SRPJ — Miscellaneous works
Rautavaara, Einojuhani
Music for upright piano and amplified cello / [by] Einojuhani Rautavaara. — New York ; London : Schirmer, 1979. — [4],10p ; fol. — (Composer's autograph series)
Facsimile of composer's autograph.
£3.05
1.Ti 2.Sr

(B79-50690)

Sullivan, *Sir* Arthur Seymour
An idyll : for violoncello and piano / [by] Arthur Sullivan. — London : Leonard, Gould and Bolttler, 1979. — 4to.
Score (4p.) & part.
£0.50
1.Ti

(B79-50691)

SRPK/AAY — Arrangements. Collections
The **romantic** cello / [pieces collected by] Julian Lloyd Webber. — London : Chappell, 1978. — 4to.
Score (36p.) & part.
Unpriced
1.Webber, Julian Lloyd

(B79-50288)

SRPM — UNACCOMPANIED CELLO
SRPMG — Suites
Bach, Johann Sebastian
[Suites, cello, B.W.V. 1007-1012]. Six suites for solo cello / [by] J.S. Bach ; revised by George Pratt. — London : Stainer and Bell, 1979. — [2],57p ; 4to.
'The present edition replaces the earlier Augener edition of 1919, by Percy Such' - Preface.
ISBN 0-85249-562-5 : Unpriced
1.Pratt, George

(B79-50692)

SRPMJ — Miscellaneous works
Buller, John
Scribenery : for solo cello / [by] John Buller. — New York ; London : Schirmer, 1979. — 8p ; fol.
£1.25
1.Ti

(B79-51161)

Rózsa, Miklós
Toccata capricciosa : für Violoncello-Solo. Op.36 / [von] Miklós Rózsa. — Wiesbaden ; [London] : Breitkopf and Härtel, 1979. — [1],6p ; 4to.
£3.30
1.Ti

(B79-51160)

SSN — DOUBLE BASS ENSEMBLE
SSNSG — Quartets. Suites
Brumby, Colin
Suite for four double basses / [by] Colin Brumby. — London : Yorke, 1978. — 4to.
Duration 12 min. — Foreword in English and German. — Score ([2],10p.) & 4 parts.
Unpriced

(B79-50289)

SSP — DOUBLE BASS & PIANO
SSPJ — Miscellaneous works
Dragonetti, Domenico
[Solo, double bass & piano, E minor]. The famous solo in E minor : for double bass and piano / [by] Domenico Dragonetti ; ed. Randall Shannon. — London : Yorke, 1979. — 4to.
Score (16p.) & part.
Unpriced
1.Ti 2.Shannon, Randall

(B79-50290)

Smith-Masters, Anthony
  All mimsy : for double bass and piano / [by] Anthony
  Smith-Masters. — London : Yorke, 1978. — 4to.
  Score (9p.) & part.
  Unpriced
  1.Ti
                                                                          (B79-50291)

SSPK/LF — Arrangements. Concertos
  Dittersdorf, Carl Ditters von
  [Concertos, double bass, Krebs 171, 172. *arr*]. Concertos for
  double bass and orchestra / [by] Karl Ditters von Dittersdorf ;
  piano reduction by Clifford Lee ; edited by Rodney Slatford. —
  London : Yorke, 1978. — 4to.
  Foreword in English and German. — Score ([8],55p.) & part.
  Unpriced
  1.Lee, Clifford 2.Slatford, Rodney
                                                                          (B79-50292)

SSPM — UNACCOMPANIED DOUBLE BASS
SSPMJ — Miscellaneous works
  Antoniou, Theodore
  Two likes for contrabass, 1976 / [by] Theodore Antoniou. —
  Kassel ; London : Bärenreiter, 1978. — 3p ; fol.
  £5.94
  1.Ti
                                                                          (B79-50693)

STN — VIOL CONSORT
STNPR — Viols (6) & organ
  Lawes, William
  [Consort music]. Consort sets in five and six parts / [by] William
  Lawes ; edited by David Pinto. — London : Faber Music, 1979.
  — fol.
  Score (xxiv,157p.) & 7 parts.
  Unpriced
  Primary classification STNQR
  1.Pinto, David
                                                                          (B79-51162)

STNQR — Viols (5) & organ
  Lawes, William
  [Consort music]. Consort sets in five and six parts / [by] William
  Lawes ; edited by David Pinto. — London : Faber Music, 1979.
  — fol..
  Score (xxiv,157p.) & 7 parts.
  Unpriced
  Also classified at STNPR
  1.Pinto, David
                                                                          (B79-51162)

TQ — HARP
TQK/AF — Arrangements. Exercises
  Bartók, Béla
  [Mikrokosmos. *arr*]. Mikrokosmos for harp : 20 intermediate solos
  and ensembles for harps with and without pedals / edited and
  arranged by Marilyn S. Marzuki. — [New York] ; [London] :
  Boosey and Hawkes, 1979. — 35p ; 4to.
  Unpriced
  1.Ti 2.Marzuki, Marilyn S
                                                                          (B79-50694)

TQPM — UNACCOMPANIED HARP
TQPM/T — Variations
  Davies, Oliver
  The popular Cambrian Bacchanalian air, of Gland meddwdod
  mwyn, or 'Good humored and merry' with an introduction and
  variations : for the harp / composed ... by Oliver Davies. —
  Abergavenny : Adlais, 1977. — 11p ; 4to.
  Unpriced
  1.Ti
                                                                          (B79-50293)

  Thomas, John, *b.1826*
  [Welsh melodies. Dafydd y garreg wen]. Dafydd y garreg wen =
  David of the white rock / trefniant. John Thomas. —
  [Abergavenny] : Adlais, 1976. — 8p ; fol. — (Alawon
  traddodiadol Cymreig)
  Unpriced
  1.Ti 2.Ti 3.Sr
                                                                          (B79-50294)

TQPMEM — Sonatinas
  Dussek, Jan Ladislav
  [Sonatina, harp, op.20, no.6, E flat major]. Sonatina in E flat for
  harp / [by] J.L. Dussek ; revised and edited by Jethro Llwyd. —
  Abergavenny : Adlais, 1978. — 7p ; fol.
  Unpriced
  1.Llwyd, Jethro
                                                                          (B79-50295)

TQPMJ — Miscellaneous works
  Glyn, Gareth
  Triban : telyn = harp / [gan] Gareth Glyn. — Y Fenni =
  Abergavenny : Adlais, 1978. — 18p ; fol.
  With separate leaf containing a glossary inserted.
  Unpriced
  1.Ti
                                                                          (B79-50296)

  Rubbra, Edmund
  Transformations : for solo harp, op.141 / [by] Edmund Rubbra ;
  edited and fingered by Ann Griffiths. — South Croydon :
  Lengnick, 1979. — [2],13p ; 4to.
  £1.00
  1.Ti 2.Griffiths, Ann
                                                                          (B79-50695)

TQPMK/AYCC — Arrangements. Collections. Celtic music
  Sounding strings : an album of Celtic music for clarsach pedal harp
  or piano / arranged by Ronald Stevenson. — Wendover : United
  Music, 1979. — 16p ; 4to.
  £1.80
  1.Stevenson, Ronald
                                                                          (B79-50696)

TS — GUITAR
TS/AC — Tutors
  Daniels, Charlie
  How to play rock guitar / [by] Charlie Daniels. — [New York] :
  Warner-Tamerlane ; [London] : [Blossom], 1978. — 32p ; 4to.
  Unpriced
  1.Ti
                                                                          (B79-50297)

  Ferandiere, Fernando
  Arte de tocar la guitarra española por música, (Madrid, 1799) /
  [de] Fernando Ferandiere ; complete facsimile edition with an
  introduction, English translation, and transcription of the music
  by Brian Jeffery. — London : Tecla, 1977. — 99p ; 8vo.
  ISBN 0-8494-0093-7 : Unpriced
  1.Ti 2.Jeffery, Brian
                                                                          (B79-51163)

  Kreidler, Dieter
  Gitarrenschule / [von] Dieter Kreidler. — Mainz ; London :
  Schott.
  Band 2. — 1979. — 128p. ; 4to. —
  £8.50
  1.Ti
                                                                          (B79-51165)

  Lester, Bryan
  The arpeggio = L'arpeggio = Das Arpeggio : essential guitar
  skill = tecnica essenziale per la chitarra = Grundlagen der
  Fertigkeit im Gitarrenspiel / [by] Bryan Lester. — London :
  Ricordi, 1979. — [1],21p ; 4to.
  Unpriced
  1.Ti
                                                                          (B79-51164)

  Noad, Frederick
  First book for the guitar / [by] Frederick Noad ; illustrations by
  Charles Boyer. — New York ; London : Schirmer.
  Part 1. — 1978. — vi,57p : ill ; 4to. —
  £1.75
  1.Ti
                                                                          (B79-51166)
  Part 2. — 1979. — vi,60p : ill ; 4to. —
  £1.75
  1.Ti
                                                                          (B79-51167)

  Pairman, David
  Easy stretch guitar : new method for the complete beginner / by
  David Pairman ... ; with drawings by Keith Stapleton ... —
  London : Galliard, 1978. — [5],73p : ill, music ; 4to.
  With bibliography.
  ISBN 0-85249-447-5 Pbk : £3.00
  1.Ti
                                                                          (B79-50697)

TS/AF — Exercises
  Rossi, Abner
  Trenta melodie : per il corso preparatorio di chitarra classica /
  [di] Abner Rossi. — Ancona ; Milano : Berben ; [London] :
  [Breitkopf und Härtel], 1979. — 27p ; fol.
  £3.30
  1.Ti
                                                                          (B79-50698)

TS/AY — Collections
  Gitarre. — Berlin : Verlag Neue Musik ; [London] : [Breitkopf and
  Härtel].
  4 / herausgegeben von Werner Pauli. — 1977. — 24p ; 8vo.
  £2.10
  1.Pauli, Werner
                                                                          (B79-50699)

Gitarre. — Berlin : Neue Musik ; [London] : [Breitkopf and Härtel].
5 / herausgegeben von Werner Pauli. — 1978. — 24p ; 8vo.
£2.10
1.Pauli, Werner

(B79-51168)

TS/ED — Accompaniment
Shipton, Russ
'Folk guitar styles of today' / by Russ Shipton ; tells you how to pick and strum like Bob Dylan, Cat Stevens, Tom Paxton [et al.] ; included is full accompaniment in tablature and music notation to twenty famous hits ... — London : Oak Publications : Music Sales (dist.), [1974]. — 121p ; 4to.
ISBN 0-86001-077-5 : Unpriced
1.Ti

(B79-50298)

TSN — GUITAR ENSEMBLE
TSNS — Quartets
Hunt, Oliver
Two quartets : for four guitars / by Oliver Hunt. — London : Schott, 1977. — 10p ; obl.4to.
Contents: 1: Canons - 2.: Berceuse.
Unpriced
1.Ti

(B79-50700)

TSNSF/T — Quartets. Concertos. Variations
Brindle, Reginald Smith
Concerto de angelis : for four guitars / by Reginald Smith Brindle. — London : Schott, 1978. — obl.4to.
Unpriced
1.Ti

(B79-50299)

TSNT — Trios
Hunt, Oliver
Ricercare for three guitars / by Oliver Hunt. — London : Schott, 1978. — 7p ; obl.4to.
£0.80
1.Ti

(B79-50300)

TSNTK/AAY — Trios. Arrangements. Collections
Three ways to go : a suite for three guitars / arranged by Tony Mason. — London (7 Garrick St., London W.C.2) : Middle Eight Music, 1979. — 4to. — (Middle eight ensemble series ; 7)
Score (8p.) & 3 parts.
Unpriced
1.Mason, Tony 2.Sr

(B79-50301)

TSNTK/Y — Arrangements. Fugues
Bach, Johann Sebastian
[Das wohltemperierte Clavier. Fugue 14. BWV859. arr]. Fugue 14 ... for three guitars / transcribed by Jeffrey Van. — New York ; London : Associated Music, 1978. — 4to.
Score (5p.) & 3 parts.
£2.75
1.Ti 2.Van, Jeffrey

(B79-50701)

TSNU — Duets
Sor, Fernando
[Duet, guitars, op.55, no.1, D major]. Duo in la maggiore, op.55, n.1 / [di] Fernando Sor ; revisione di Carlo Carfagna. — Ancona : Bèrben ; [London] : [Breitkopf and Härtel], 1979. — 8p ; fol.
£1.70
1.Ti 2.Carfagna, Carlo

(B79-51169)

TSNUG — Duets. Suites
Duarte, John William
Suite française. Op.61 : pour deux guitares / [par] John William Duarte ; diteggiatura di Ako Ito e Henry Dorigny. — Ancona ; Milano : Bèrben ; [London] : [Breitkopf and Härtel], 1979. — 25p ; fol.
£3.30
1.Ti 2.Ito, Ako 3.Dorigny, Henry

(B79-51170)

TSNUK — Duets. Arrangements
Brahms, Johannes
[Sextet, string instruments, op.18, B flat major. Andante. arr]. Theme and variations / [by] Johannes Brahms ; arranged for two guitars by John Williams. — London : Boosey and Hawkes, 1979. — 2pt ; fol. — (John Williams series ; 1)
Unpriced
1.Williams, John 2.Sr

(B79-50702)

Dowland, John
[Lute music. Selections : arr]. Zwei Duette / [von] John Dowland ... ; nach den Tabulaturen übertragen und für Gitarre bearbeitet von ... Dieter Kreidler. — Mainz ; London : Schott, 1979. — 8p ; 4to. — (Gitarren-Archiv ; 463)
£2.20
1.Kreidler, Dieter 2.Sr

(B79-51171)

Mendelssohn, Felix
[Lieder ohne Worte. Selections : arr]. 5 Lieder ohne Worte : für zwei Gitarren = for two guitars / [von] Felix Mendelssohn Bartholdy ; bearbeitet von ... Anton Stingl. — Mainz ; London : Schott, 1979. — 21p ; 4to. — (Gitarren-Archiv ; 461)
£4.00
1.Ti 2.Stingl, Anton 3.Fünf Lieder ohne Worte 4.Sr

(B79-51172)

Purcell, Henry
[A ground in gamut. Z645. arr]. A ground in gamut / [by] Henry Purcell ; arranged for guitar duo by John Gavall. — York : Banks, 1979. — 4p ; 4to.
Unpriced
1.Ti 2.Ti 3.Gavall, John

(B79-50703)

Vivaldi, Antonio
[L'estro armonico. Op.3. Selections : arr]. Two concerto movements / [by] Antonio Vivaldi ; arranged as guitar duos by John Gavall. — York : Banks, 1978. — 4p ; 8vo.
Unpriced
1.Ti 2.Ti 3.Gavall, John

(B79-50302)

TSNUK/AE — Duets. Arrangements. Sonatas
Paganini, Nicolò
[Sonata, guitar & violin, op.39, A major. arr]. Grande sonata in la maggiore / [di] Nicolò Paganini ; libera trascrizione per due chitarre di Luigi Schininá (op.39). — Ancona : Bèrben ; [London] : [Breitkopf and Härtel], 1979. — 29p ; fol.
£3.80
1.Schininá, Luigi

(B79-51173)

TSNUK/AEM — Duets. Arrangements. Sonatinas
Dussek, Jan Ladislav
[Sonatina, piano, op.20, no.1, G major. arr]. Sonatina für zwei Gitarren / [von] Johann Ladislaus Dussek ; herausgegeben von Pavle Polacek ... — Weisbaden ; [London] : Breitkopf und Härtel, 1979. — 8p ; 4to.
£2.55
1.Polacek, Pavle

(B79-51174)

TSNUK/AG — Duets. Arrangements. Suites
Handel, George Frideric
[Suite, harpsichord, C.B. 60, no.19, G minor]. Suite in A minor / [by] G.F. Handel ; arranged [and transcribed] for two guitars by Jennifer Larrad. — London : Oxford University Press, 1979. — 11p ; fol.
ISBN 0-19-356997-3 : Unpriced
1.Larrad, Jennifer

(B79-50303)

TSNUK/AH — Duets. Arrangements. Dances
Debussy, Claude
[Danse bohémienne. arr]. Danse bohémienne : für zwei Gitarren oder Oktavgitarre und Gitarre = for two guitars or octave guitar and guitar = pour deux guitares ou guitare octave et guitare / [von] Claude Debussy ; bearbeitet von ... Wilhelm Bruck/Theodor Ross. — Mainz ; London : Schott, 1979. — 7p ; 4to. — (Gitarren-Archiv ; 460)
The alternative part is printed on pages 6 and 7.
£3.20
1.Ti 2.Ti 3.Bruck, Wilhelm 4.Ross, Theodor 5.Sr

(B79-51175)

TSNUK/W — Duets. Arrangements. Rondos
Hindemith, Paul
[Rondo, guitars (3)]. Rondo für zwei Gitarren, for two guitars / [von] Paul Hindemith ... ; nach der Originalausgabe für drei Gitarren (1925) bearbeitet und eingerichtet von Wilheim Bruck und Theodor Russ = arranged and adapted from the original edition for three guitars (1925) by Wilhelm Bruck and Theodor Russ. — Mainz ; London : Schott, 1978. — 4p ; 4to. — (Gitarren - Archiv ; 457)
£2.00
1.Ross, Theodor 2.Bruck, Wilhelm 3.Sr

(B79-50304)

TSPM — UNACCOMPANIED GUITAR
TSPM/AYK — Collections. Spain
Spanish masters : 19 original easy pieces / collected, edited and
arranged in progressive order by June Yakeley. — Chesham :
Ricordi, 1978. — 12p ; 4to. — (Guitar masters of the century)
Pieces by Sor, Aguado and Huerta.
Unpriced
1.Yakeley, June 2.Sr
(B79-50305)

TSPM/T — Variations
Blyton, Carey
The oceans of the moon : eight variations and a theme, op.75 : for
guitar / [by] Carey Blyton ; revisione e diteggiatura di Angelo
Gilardino. — Ancona ; Milano : Bèrben ; [London] : [Breitkopf
and Härtel], 1979. — 18p ; fol.
Theme taken from 'Lachrymae' by Carey Blyton.
£2.85
1.Ti 2.Gilardino, Angelo
(B79-51176)

TSPME — Sonatas
Hand, Colin
[Sonatina, guitar, no.2. 'Allotropes']. Sonatina no.2 (Allotropes)
for guitar / [by] Colin Hand. — London : Schott, 1979. — [2],
18p ; 4to.
£0.80
(B79-50306)

Santórsola, Güido
[Sonata, guitar, no.4, 'Italiana', 'Sonovidades 1977']. Sonata n.4
(Italiana), ! Sonoridades 1977! : para guitarra / [di] Guido
Santórsola ; diteggiatura di Angelo Gilardino. — Ancona ;
Milano : Bèrben ; [London] : [Breitkopf and Härtel], 1979. —
19p ; fol.
£2.85
1.Ti 2.Gilardino, Angelo
(B79-51177)

TSPMEM — Sonatinas
Platts, Kenneth
[Sonatina, guitar, op.47]. Sonatina for guitar, opus 47 / [by]
Kenneth Platts. — London : Edwin Ashdown, 1979. — 15p ; 4to.
Duration 13 1/2 min.
£3.00
(B79-51178)

TSPMG — Suites
Giuliani, Mauro
[Rossiniana, no.1, op.119]. Rossiniana no.1 : for solo guitar,
op.119 / [by] Mauro Giuliani ; edited and revised by Julian
Bream. — London : Faber Music, 1979. — [16],18p ; 4to. —
(Faber guitar series)
Based on themes from Rossini's operas. — The allegro maestoso march from
the fourth Rossiniana, op.122, has been substituted for the central sections.
Unpriced
1.Ti 2.Bream, Julian 3.Sr
(B79-50704)

Swayne, Giles
[Suite, guitar]. Suite for guitar / [by] Giles Swayne ; edited by
Julian Bream. — Sevenoaks : Novello, 1979. — [3],12p ; 4to.
Duration 13 min.
£1.65
1.Bream, Julian
(B79-50307)

Viozzi, Giulio
Suite variata : per chitarra / [di] Giulio Viozzi ; revisione e
diteggiatura di Angelo Gilardino. — Milano : Bèrben ; [London] :
[Breitkopf and Härtel], 1979. — 15p ; fol.
£2.35
1.Ti
(B79-51179)

TSPMHG — Dances. Suites
Castelnuovo-Tedesco, Mario
Escarraman : a suite of Spanish dances from the XVIth century
(after Cervantes), op.177, for guitar / [by] Mario
Castelnuovo-Tedesco ; revisione e diteggiatura di Angelo
Gilardino. — Ancona ; Milano : Bèrben ; [London] : [Breitkopf
and Härtel], 1979. — 36p ; fol.
£4.70
1.Ti 2.Gilardino, Angelo
(B79-51180)

TSPMHX — Jazz
Dentato, John
Jazz players library : 10 classic tunes in their original versions and
in completely notated jazz versions / arranged by Johnny 'Dee'
Dentato. — Bryn Mawr ; [London] : Chappell, 1979. — 24p. ;
4to.
For unaccompanied flute and unaccompanied guitar.
Unpriced
Primary classification VRPMHX
1.Ti
(B79-51230)

TSPMJ — Miscellaneous works
Brindle, Reginald Smith
Guitarcosmos 1 : progressive pieces for guitar / [by] Reginald
Smith Brindle ; with an introduction by Julian Bream. —
London : Schott, 1979. — [5],43p ; 4to.
£2.50
1.Ti
(B79-51181)

Brindle, Reginald Smith
Guitarcosmos 2 : progressive pieces for guitar / [by] Reginald
Smith Brindle ; with an introduction by Julian Bream. —
London : Schott, 1979. — [4],56p ; 4to.
£2.50
1.Ti
(B79-51182)

Brindle, Reginald Smith
Guitarcosmos 3 : Progressive pieces for guitar / [by] Reginald
Smith Brindle ; with an introduction by Julian Bream. —
London : Schott, 1979. — [5],42p ; 4to.
£2.50
1.Ti
(B79-51183)

Duarte, John William
Within easy reach : 10 easy pieces for guitarists with small hands
= 10 pezzi facili por chitarristi con le mani piccole = 10 leichte
Stücke für Gitarrenspieler mit kleinen Händen / [by] John Duarte.
— Chesham : Ricordi, 1979. — 12p ; 4to.
Op.73.
Unpriced
1.Ti
(B79-51184)

Eastwood, Tom
Romance et plainte : for guitar / [by] Tom Eastwood ;
diteggiatara di Angelo Gilardino. — Ancona ; Milano : Bèrben ;
[London] : [Breitkopf and Härtel], 1979. — 15p ; fol.
£2.35
1.Ti 2.Gilardino, Angelo
(B79-51185)

Legnani, Luigi
[6 capriccetti, che servono di compimento dell' op.250]. Sei
capricci ... per chitarra / [di] Luigi Legnani. — Ancona ; Milano :
Berben, 1979. — 12p ; fol.
£1.70
1.Ti 2.Ti 3.Sei capriccetti, che servono di compimento dell' op.250
(B79-50705)

Nunn, Ruth
Moods for guitar / by Ruth Nunn ; edited by John W. Duarte. —
Sevenoaks : Novello, 1978. — [2],6p ; 4to. — (Teacher series of
guitar publications)
£0.66
1.Ti 2.Duarte, John William 3.Sr
(B79-50308)

Royal, Timothy
Folksong 2 / by Timothy Royal. — Bristol ([16 Oldfield Place,
Hotwells, Bristol BS8 4QJ]) : Shed Music, 1979. — [6]p ; 4to.
For solo guitar.
Unpriced
1.Ti
(B79-50706)

Swayne, Giles
Canto for guitar / [by] Giles Swayne ; edited by Timothy Walker.
— Sevenoaks : Novello, 1979. — 8p ; 4to.
Duration 10 min.
£1.65
1.Ti
(B79-50309)

Wilson, Thomas
Soliloquy : for guitar / [by] Thomas Wilson. — Ancona ; Milano :
Bèrben ; [London] : [Breitkopf and Härtel], 1979. — 13p ; 4to.
£1.90
1.Ti
(B79-51186)

Wilson, Thomas Brendan
Canción : for solo guitar / [by] Thomas Wilson. — Edinburgh :
Scotus ; London : Schirmer, 1977. — [3p.] ; 4to. — (Scotus guitar
series ; no.1)
Unpriced
1.Ti 2.Sr
(B79-50707)

TSPMK — Arrangements

Dalza, Joan Ambrosio
[Intabulatura de laũto. *Selections : arr*]. Two pieces / [by] Joan Ambrosio Dalzo ; transcribed from the lute tablature and edited for classic guitar by Joseph Weidlich. — Washington : DeCamera ; London : Schirmer, 1976. — [1],6p ; 4to.
£1.50
1.Ti 2.Weidlich, Joseph

(B79-51187)

Dlugoraj, Wojciech
[Lute music. *Selections : arr*]. Four pieces / [by] Alberti Dlugoraj ; transcribed and edited for classical guitar by Joseph Weidlich. — Washington : DeCamera ; London : Schirmer, 1976. — [1],6p ; 4to.
£1.50
1.Weidlich, Joseph

(B79-51188)

Mudarra, Alonso
[Tres libros de música en cifra para vihuela. Fantasia no.9. *arr*]. Fantasie no.9 / [by] Alonso Mudarra ; transcribed from the vihuela tablature and edited for classic guitar by Joseph Weidlich. — Washington : DeCamera ; London : Schirmer, 1976. — [1],6p ; 4to.
£1.50
1.Ti 2.Weidlich, Joseph

(B79-51189)

Newsidler, Hans
[Lute music. *Selections : arr*]. Four pieces / [by] Hans Newsidler ; transcribed from the lute tablature and edited for classic guitar by Joseph Weidlich. — Washington : DeCamera ; London : Schirmer, 1976. — [1],8p ; 4to.
£1.50
1.Ti 2.Weidlich, Joseph

(B79-51190)

Ravinale, Irma
Improvvisazione : per chitarra / [di] Irma Ravinale ; diteggiatura di Mario Gangi. — Ancona : Berben ; [London] : [Breitkopf und Härtel], 1979. — 11p ; fol.
£1.70
1.Ti 2.Gangi, Mario

(B79-50708)

Saint-Saëns, Camille
[Le carnival des animaux. Le cygne. *arr*]. Il cigno / [di] Camille Saint-Saens ; trascrizione per chitarra di Miguel Abloniz. — Ancona : Berben ; [London] : [Breitkopf und Härtel], 1979. — [2] p : fol.
£1.10
1.Ti 2.Ti 3.Ablóniz, Miguel

(B79-50709)

Weiss, Sylvius Leopold
[Fantasie, lute, C minor. *arr*]. Fantasie (in C minor) / [by] Sylvius Leopold Weiss ; transcribed from the lute tablature and edited for classic guitar by Joseph Weidlich. — Washington : DeCamera ; London : Schirmer, 1976. — [1],4p ; 4to.
£1.50
1.Weidlich, Joseph

(B79-51191)

TSPMK/AAY — Arrangements. Collections
More guitar pieces : folktunes and Elizabethan pieces / written and arranged by Gerald Garcia and John Whitworth. — Oxford : Holley Music, 1979. — 7p ; 4to.
Unpriced
1.Garcia, Gerald 2.Whitworth, John

(B79-50310)

TSPMK/AE — Arrangements. Sonatas
Scarlatti, Domenico
[Essercizi. *Selections*]. Five sonatas / [by] Domenico Scarlatti ; transcribed and edited for guitar by Eliot Fisk. — Wash. [i.e. Washington] : DeCamera ; London : Schirmer, 1976. — ii,18p ; 4to.
Contents: L.23, 108, 95, 423, 104.
£2.50
1.Fisk, Eliot

(B79-51192)

Scarlatti, Domenico
[Sonatas, harpsichord. *Selections : arr*]. Three sonatas (K.176/L163, K.177/L364,K.208/L238) : guitar solo / [by] Domenico Scarlatti ; edited by John W. Duarte. — Sydney ; [London] : Universal, 1978. — 13p ; 4to.
Unpriced
1.Duarte, John William

(B79-51193)

TSPMK/AG — Arrangements. Suites
Weiss, Sylvius Leopold
[Suite, lute, A major. *arr*]. Suite in A / [von] Silvius Leopold Weiss ... ; aus der Lautentabulatur übertragen und bearbeitet von ... Robert Brojer. — Mainz ; London : Schott, 1979. — 12p : facsims ; 4to. — (Gitarren-Archiv ; 462)
£3.20
1.Brojer, Robert 2.Sr

(B79-51194)

Weiss, Sylvius Leopold
[Suite, lute, D major. *arr*]. Suite in D / [von] Silvius Leopold Weiss ; aus der Lautentabulatur übertragen und neu herausgegeben ... Robert Brojer. — Mainz ; London : Schott, 1979. — [1],16p : facsim ; 4to. — (Gitarren-Archiv ; 458)
£2.60
1.Brojer, Robert 2.Sr

(B79-51195)

TSPMK/AH — Arrangements. Dances
Praetorius, Michael
[Terpsichore. *Selections : arr*]. Four dances ... guitar / [by] Michael Praetorius ; arranged by John Williams. — London : Boosey and Hawkes, 1979. — 3p ; fol. — (The John Williams series ; 2)
Unpriced
1.Ti 2.Williams, John 3.Sr

(B79-50710)

TSPMK/AHS — Arrangements. Musettes
Vogel, Vladimir
[Musette. *arr*]. Musette : für Gitarre solo = for guitar solo / [von] Vladimir Vogel ; eingerichtet von, arranged by, Konrad Ragossnig. — Mainz ; London : Schott, 1978. — 3 ; 4to. — (Gitarren-Archiv)
£2.00
1.Ti 2.Ragossnig, Konrad 3.Sr

(B79-50311)

TSPMK/AHXJ — Arrangements. Ragtime
Joplin, Scott
[Ragtimes. *Selections : arr*]. Ragtimes ... / [von] Scott Joplin ; für Gitarre solo bearbeitet von ... Dieter Kreidler. — Mainz ; London : Schott, 1979. — 7p ; 4to.
Contents: The entertainer - Maple leaf rag - Weeping willow.
£2.60
1.Ti 2.Ti 3.Kreidler, Dieter

(B79-51196)

TSPMK/AYD — Arrangements. Collections. England
Galliards and airs : fünf altenglische Lautenstucke nach Tabulaturen übertragen und für Gitarre bearbeitet von = five old English lute pieces / transcribed from tablatures and arranged for guitar by Dieter Kreidler. — Mainz ; London : Schott, 1979. — 8p ; 4to.
Contents: 1: Greensleeves, arranged by Cutting - 2: Sir John Sounchs Galliard by Dowland - 3: Galliard on Walsingham, by Dowland - 4: Galiarde of Clarkes, by Holborne - 5: Air 'As I went to Walsingham' : anon.
£3.20
1.Kreidler, Dieter

(B79-50711)

TSPMK/B/FK — Arrangements. Musical clocks
Time pieces : a collection of works for musical clocks by Handel and Haydn / arranged for guitar by Alan Lawrence. — London : Fentone Music : Breitkopf und Härtel, 1978. — 24p ; 4to.
Unpriced
1.Lawrence, Alan

(B79-50312)

TSPMK/DP/LF/AY — Arrangements. Carols. Christmas. Collections
Ten traditional English carols / arranged for guitar by Alan Lawrence. — London : Fenone Music, Breitkopf und Härtel, 1978. — 8p ; 4to.
£0.95
1.Lawrence, Alan

(B79-50313)

TSPMK/DW — Arrangements. Songs, etc
Songs from the stage and screen : for 5-string bluegrass banjo / by Bill Knopf. — Bryn Mawr ; [London] : Chappell, 1979. — 48p. ; 4to.
Unpriced
1.Knopf, Bill

(B79-51197)

TSPMK/DW/GB/AY — Arrangements. Popular songs. Collections
22ct. gold : for guitar / editor, Cecil Bolton. — London : EMI, 1979. — 72p ; 4to.
Popular songs.
Unpriced
1.Bolton, Cecil 2.Twenty-two ct. gold

(B79-50712)

TSPMK/DW/HKR/JR — Arrangement. Rock songs. Films
Bee Gees
[Saturday night fever. *Selections : arr*]. Saturday night fever : from the original movie soundtrack / words and music by [the group]. — London : Chappell, 1978. — 32p : ill ; 4to.
Unpriced
1.Ti
(B79-50713)

TSPMK/DW/HKR/JR/AY — Arrangements. Rock songs. Films. Collections
[**Grease**. *Selections : arr*]. Grease : easy guitar, original sound track songs from the motion picture. — London : Chappell, 1978. — 32p ; 4to.
Unpriced
(B79-50714)

TSPMK/T — Arrangements. Variations
Cutting, Francis
[Greensleeves. *arr*]. Greensleeves / [stting by] Francis Cutting ; transcribed from the lute tablature and edited for classic guitar by Joseph Weidlich. — Washington : DeCamera ; London : Schirmer, 1976. — [1],3p ; 4to.
£1.50
1.Ti 2.Ti 3.Weidlich, Joseph
(B79-51198)

Paganini, Nicolò
[Caprice, violin, op.1, no.24, A minor. *arr*]. Caprice no.24 / [by] Niccolo Paganini ; arranged by John Williams. — London : Boosey and Hawkes, 1979. — 7p ; fol. — (The John Williams series ; 3)
Unpriced
1.Williams, John 2.Sr
(B79-50715)

TSPMK/Y — Arrangements. Fugues
Bach, Johann Sebastian
[Sonata, violin, no.1, B.W.V. 1001. Adagio and fugue. *arr*]. Prelude and fugue in A minor / [by] J.S. Bach ; arranged for solo guitar by Hector Quine. — London : Oxford University Press, 1978. — 7p ; fol.
ISBN 0-19-355304-x : Unpriced
1.Quine, Hector
(B79-50314)

TSUPV/AC — Bass electric guitar. Tutors
Canty, Laurence
Electric bass guitar : a complete guide / by Laurence Canty. — London : Chappell, 1978. — 64p ; 4to.
Unpriced
1.Ti
(B79-50716)

TWT — PSALTERY
TWT/AC — Tutors
Jones, Clayton S
Simple gifts for the dulcimer : an instruction manual for beginners, a collection of songs and tunes for dulcimer players / by Clayton S. Jones. — New York : TRO Ludlow Music ; [London] : [Essex Music], 1979. — ix,86p ; 4to.
Unpriced
1.Ti
(B79-50717)

UM — WIND BAND
UM/AY — Collections
A **second** wind band book / arranged by Bram Wiggins. — London : Oxford University Press, 1979. — fol.
Score ([2],60p.) & 45 parts, with several copies of various parts.
ISBN 0-19-369831-5 : Unpriced
1.Wiggins, Bram
(B79-50718)

UMJ — Miscellaneous works
Balent, Andrew
Boogie woogie band / by Andrew Balent. — New York : Warner ; [London] : [Blossom], 1979. — 4to. — (Supersound series for young bands)
Score (7p.) & 50 parts.
Unpriced
1.Ti 2.Sr
(B79-51200)

Balent, Andrew
Let's go band! : for beginning band / [by] Andrew Balent. — New York : Warner ; [London] : [Blossom], 1979. — 4to.
Score (5p.) & 51 parts with several copies of various parts.
Unpriced
1.Ti
(B79-51201)

UMK/AGM — Arrangements. Marches
Meyerbeer, Giacomo
[Le prophète. March. *arr*]. Coronation march. (Le prophète) / [by] Meyerbeer ; arrangements for wind orchestra by Sidney Lawton. — Sevenoaks : Novello, 1979. — 23p ; 4to. — (Windscore ; 10)
£2.00
1.Ti 2.Ti 3.Lawton, Sidney 4.Sr
(B79-50315)

UMK/AH — Arrangements. Dances
Weber, Carl Maria von, *Freiherr*
[12 allemandes pour le piano forte. Op.4. *Selections : arr*]. Five German dances / [by] Weber ; arranged for wind band by Bram Wiggins. — London : Oxford University Press, 1978. — [1],24p ; fol.
Op.4, nos.1-3,6,5.
ISBN 0-19-368668-6 : Unpriced
1.Ti 2.Wiggins, Bram 3.Douze allemandes pour le piano. Op.4. Selections : arr
(B79-50316)

UMK/AHW — Arrangements. Waltzes
Weber, Carl Maria von, *Freiherr*
[Waltzes, piano. *Selections : arr*]. Five waltzes / [by] Carl Maria von Weber ; arranged for wind band by Bram Wiggins. — London : Oxford University Press, 1978. — [2],30p ; fol.
J.185,191,144-6.
ISBN 0-19-368704-6 : Unpriced
1.Wiggins, Bram
(B79-50317)

UMK/DW — Arrangements. Songs, etc
Farrar, John
[Hopelessly devoted to you. *arr*]. Hopelessly devoted to you / words and music by John Farrar; arranged for easy stage band by Bob Lowden. — Bryn Mawr ; [London] : Chappell, 1978. — 4to & obl. 4to.
Unpriced
1.Ti 2.Lowden, Bob
(B79-51202)

Gibb, Barry
[(Our love). Don't throw it all away. *arr*]. (Our love). Don't throw it all away / words and music by Barry Gibb and Blue Weaver; arranged for easy stage band by Jerry Nowak. — Bryn Mawr ; [London] : Stigwood Music, 1979. — 4to & obl. 4to.
Score (8p.) & 17 parts.
Unpriced
1.Ti 2.Weaver, Blue 3.Nowak, Jerry
(B79-51203)

Goodrum, Randy
You needed me / words and music by Randy Goodrum ; arranged for easy stage band by Jeffrey Steinberg. — Bryn Mawr ; [London] : Chappell, 1978. — 4to & obl. 4to.
Score (8p.) & 18 parts.
Unpriced
1.Ti 2.Steinberg, Jeffrey
(B79-51204)

Lehár, Franz
[Der Graf von Luxemburg. *Selections: arr*]. Der Graf von Luxemburg : Melodienfolge / [von] Franz Lehár ; Blasmusik, neues Arrangement, Alfred Hofbauer. — Neue Ausgabe. — Chur ; [London] : Glocken, 1978. — 8vo.
Duration 7 min. — Conductor (8p.) & 51 parts ; various parts are in duplicate.
Unpriced
1.Ti 2.Hofbauer, Alfred
(B79-50318)

Lehár, Franz
[Zigeunerliebe. *Selections: arr*]. Zigeunerliebe : Melodienfolge / [von] Franz Lehár ; Blasmusik, neues Arrangement, Alfred Hofbauer. — Neue Ausgabe. — Chur ; [London] : Glocken, 1978. — 8vo.
Duration 8 1/2 min. — Conductor (11p.) & 51 parts; various parts are in duplicate.
Unpriced
1.Ti 2.Hofbauer, Alfred
(B79-50319)

UMK/T — Arrangements. Variations
Paganini, Nicolò
[Capriccio, violin solo, op.1, no.24, A minor. *arr*]. Paganini caprice 24 : for double woodwind quintet / [transcribed by] Allan Blank. — New York ; London : Associated Music, 1978. — 4to.
Score (12p.) & 10 parts.
£10.60
1.Blank, Allan

(B79-51205)

UMM — MILITARY BAND
UMMG — Suites
D'arville, Jasper
New wings suite : music for band / [by] Jasper D'Arville. — [London] : Boosey and Hawkes, 1979. — fol. — (Q.M.B. edition ; 289)
Score (40p.) + 49 parts, with several copies of various parts.
£22.00
1.Ti 2.Sr

(B79-51206)

UMMGM — Marches
Foster, Bob
Chopbuster march : an outrageous trumpet feature / by Bob Foster. — New York : Warner ; [London] : [Blossom], 1979. — obl.8vo & 8vo. — (BBI marching band series)
Score (12p.) & 115 parts, with several copies of various parts.
Unpriced
1.Ti 2.Sr

(B79-50719)

Littell, Barbara
March for a celebration / by Barbara Littell. — New York : Warner ; [London] : [Blossom], 1979. — 4to. — (Supersound series for young bands)
For military band. — Score (7p.) & 48 parts, with several copies of various parts.
Unpriced
1.Ti 2.Sr

(B79-50720)

UMMGM/KH — Regimental marches
Marshall, D J
Regimental quick march, Worcestershire and Sherwood Foresters Regiment, 'Young May moon' and 'Royal Windsor' / arranged by D.J. Marshall. — London : Boosey and Hawkes, 1979. — 28p ; obl.8vo.
With several copies of various parts.
Unpriced
1.Ti

(B79-50721)

UMMJ — Miscellaneous works
Elms, Albert
Parade of champions / [by] Albert Elms. — London : Boosey and Hawkes, 1979. — 8vo, obl. 8vo.
Conductor & 32 parts, with several copies of various parts.
Unpriced
1.Ti

(B79-51207)

Grundman, Clare
Norwegian rhapsody / [by] Clare Grundman. — New York ; [London] : Boosey and Hawkes, [1979]. — 4to.
For military band. — Score ([2],24p.) and 73 parts. — Duration about 6 min. — 'Based on six old Norse folk melodies' - notes.
Unpriced
1.Ti

(B79-50722)

Littell, Barbara
Strawberry rock / by Barbara Littell. — New York : Warner ; [London] : [Blossom], 1979. — 4to. — (Supersound series for young bands)
For military band. — Score (8p.) & 48 parts, with several copies of various parts.
Unpriced
1.Ti 2.Sr

(B79-50723)

Olivadoti, Joseph
Castle and woods : overture / [by] J. Olivadoti. — Miami : Rubank ; [Sevenoaks] : [Novello], 1979. — 4to. — (Rubank symphonic band library ; no.155)
For military band. — Conductor (11p.) & 43 parts, with several copies of various parts.
Unpriced
1.Ti 2.Sr

(B79-50724)

Tull, Fisher
The final covenent : for symphonic band or wind ensemble / [by] Fisher Tull. — [New York] ; [London] : Boosey and Hawkes, 1979. — 4to. — (Q.M.B. Edition ; 411)
Score (24p.) & 68 parts, with several copies of various parts.
Unpriced
1.Ti 2.Sr

(B79-50725)

Turok, Paul
Songs, dances and studies : for band / [by] Paul Turok. — New York ; London : Schirmer.
Set 1. — 1978. — 12p ; 4to. —
£2.10
1.Ti

(B79-50726)

Set 2. — 1978. — 12p ; 4to. —
£2.10
1.Ti

(B79-50727)

Set 3. — 1978. — 12p ; 4to. —
£2.10
1.Ti

(B79-50728)

UMMK/AGN — Arrangements. Fanfares
Strauss, Richard
[Fanfare der Stadt Wien. *arr*]. Festmusik der Stadt Wien / [by] Richard Strauss ; military band arrangement by Eric Banks. — London : Boosey and Hawkes, 1979. — 4to.
Score (11p.) & 28 parts, various parts are in duplicate.
Unpriced
1.Ti 2.Ti 3.Banks, Eric

(B79-50729)

UMP — SOLO INSTRUMENT (S) & WIND BAND
UMPVUSF — Saxophone (alto) & wind band. Concertos
Husa, Karel
[Concerto, saxophone (alto) & wind band]. Concerto for alto saxophone and concert band / [by] Karel Husa. — New York ; London : Associated Music, 1978. — 70p ; 4to.
£45.30

(B79-50730)

UN — WIND ENSEMBLE
Françaix, Jean
Quasi improvvisando : pour ensemble à vent = für Bläserensemble / [par] Jean Françaix. — Mainz ; London : Schott, 1978. — 10pt ; 4to.
£12.00
1.Ti

(B79-50320)

UNN — Octets
Triebensee, Josef
Menuetto con variazioni in F, on a theme from Mozart's Don Giovanni : for 2 oboes, 2 clarinets, 2 bassoons and 2 horns / [by] Josef Triebensee ; edited by James Brown. — London : Nova Music, 1979. — 4to.
Score ([1],8p.) & 8 parts.
Unpriced
1.Brown, James

(B79-51208)

UNQ — Sextets
Mozart, Wolfgang Amadeus
[Serenade, wind sextet, no.11, K.375, E flat major]. Serenade in E flat. K.375, original version : for two clarinets, two horns, and two bassoons / [by] W.A. Mozart ; edited by Roger Hellyer. — London : Oxford University Press, 1979. — 34p ; 8vo. — (Musica da camera ; no.75)
ISBN 0-19-357939-1 : Unpriced
1.Hellyer, Roger 2.Sr

(B79-51209)

Mozart, Wolfgang Amadeus
[Serenade, wind sextet, no.11, K.375, E flat major. *Original version*]. Serenade in E flat. K.375. Original version : for two clarinets, two horns and two bassoons / [by] W.A. Mozart ; edited by Roger Hellyer. — London : Oxford University Press, 1979. — 6pt ; 4to. — (Musica da camera ; no.75)
ISBN 0-19-357940-5 : Unpriced
1.Hellyer, Roger 2.Sr

(B79-51210)

UNR — Quintets
Kievman, Carson
Sirocco (1975) : for wood-wind quintet (flute, oboe, B flat clarinet, bassoon, F horn) / [by] Carson Kievman. — New York ; London : Associated Music, 1978. — obl. 4to. — (Composer's autograph series)
Facsimile of composer's autograph. — Duration 4 min.
Unpriced
1.Ti 2.Sr

(B79-50731)

Sander, Peter
[Quintet, wind, instruments, no.1]. Wind quintet no.1 / [by] Peter Sander. — Zürich ; [London] : Eulenburg, 1978. — 4to.
Score (32p.) & 5 parts.
Unpriced

(B79-50321)

UNSK/HM — Quartets. Arrangements. Ballet
Delibes, Leo
[Ballet music. *arr*]. Music from the ballet / [by] Delibes ; arranged by Alan Frazer [for] ... woodwind quartets for variable combinations. — London ((7 Garrick St., W.C.2)) : Middle Eight Music, 1979. — 4to. — (Options 4 woodwind ; fol.3)
Score (8p.) & 8 parts. — Contents: 1: Scène from Coppélia - 2: Le berger from 'Sylvia' - 3: Stretto - galop from 'Sylvia'.
Unpriced
1.Ti 2.Frazer, Alan 3.Sr

(B79-50732)

Tchaikovsky, Peter
[Ballet music. *Selections : arr*]. Music from the ballet / [by] Tchaikovsky ; arranged by Alan Frazer, [for] ... woodwind quartet for variable combinations. — London ((7 Garrick St., W.C.2)) : Middle Eight Music, 1979. — 4to. — (Options 4 woodwind ; fol.4)
Score (8p.) & 6 parts. — Contents: 1: Overture from 'The nutcracker' - 2: Little Red Riding Hood and the Wolf from 'The sleeping beauty' - 3: Dance hongroise - czardas from 'Swan Lake'.
Unpriced
1.Ti 2.Frazer, Alan 3.Sr

(B79-50733)

VN — WOODWIND ENSEMBLE
VNT — Trios
Fontyn, Jacqueline
Seven little pieces for woodwind trio / [by] Jacqueline Fontyn. — New York ; London : Schirmer, 1978. — fol.
Score ([2], 12p.) & part.
£4.85
1.Ti

(B79-50734)

Vogel, Vladimir
Terzett für Flöte (Piccolo), Klarinette und Fagott / [von] Vladimir Vogel. — Zürich : Eulenburg, 1978. — 4to.
Score (14p.) & 3 parts.
£4.65
1.Ti

(B79-50735)

VNTF — Trios. Concertos
Pleyel, Ignaz Joseph
[3 trios concertants pour flûte, clarinette et basson, Ben.4705. Trio no.2]. Trio 2 for flute, clarinet and bassoon / [by] Ignace Pleyel ; [edited by] H. Voxman. — London : Musica rara, 1978. — 4to.
Score ([1],12p.) & 3 parts.
Unpriced
1.Ti 2.Voxman, Himie 3.Trois trios concertants pour flûte, clarinette et basson. Ben.4705

(B79-50322)

VNTK/AHXJ — Trios
Two ragtime trios : for 2 clarinets and tenor saxophone (or bass clarinet). — London (7 Garrick St., W.C.2) : Middle Eight Music, 1979. — 4to. — (Middle eight ensemble series ; 3)
Score (8p.) & 3 parts. — Contents: 1: Apple pie rag by Alan Frazer - 2: The fascinator, by James Scott, (arr. Alan Frazer).
Unpriced
1.Frazer, Alan 2.Scott, James 3.Sr

(B79-50323)

VNTK/DW — Trios. Arrangements. Songs, etc
Offenbach, Jacques
[Operetta. *Selections: arr*]. M'sieur Offenbach : a suite for clarinet, alto and tenor saxophones / [by] Jacques Offenbach] ; arr. Alexander Faris. — London (7 Garrick St., W.C.2) : Middle Eight Music, 1979. — 4to. — (Middle eight ensemble series ; 4)
From 'La vie parisienne', 'La chanson de Fortunio' etc. — Score (8p.) & 3 parts.
Unpriced
1.Ti 2.Faris, Alexander 3.Sr

(B79-50324)

VR — FLUTE
VR/AC — Tutors
Wastall, Peter
Learn as you play flute / by Peter Wastall. — London : Boosey and Hawkes, 1979. — 4to.
Tutor (65p.) & piano accompaniments (17p.).
£0.85
1.Ti

(B79-51212)

VR/AF — Exercises
Boehm, Theobald
24 Caprices-Études, opus 26 : für Flöte solo = for solo flute = pour flûte seule / [von] Theobald Boehm. — Reprint der Schott-Originalausgabe von 1852. — Mainz ; London : Schott, 1979. — 39p ; 4to. — (Il flauto traverso ; 117)
£4.00
1.Ti 2.Vierundzwanzig Caprices-Études, opus 26 3.Sr

(B79-51213)

Boehm, Theobald
[Capriccios, flute]. Twenty-four capriccios for solo flute / [by] Theodor Boehm ; editor, Trevor Wye. — London : Chester Music, 1979. — 37p ; 4to. — (Chester woodwind series)
Unpriced
1.Wye, Trevor 2.Sr

(B79-50736)

Drouet, Louis
[Méthode pour la flûte. Exercices de tous genres]. 25 Etüden für Flöte = 25 studies for flute = 25 exercices pour flûte / [von] Louis Drouet ; [revidiert] Nikolaus Delius. — Reprint der Schott-Originalausgabe von 1827. — Mainz ; London : Schott, 1979. — 40p ; 4to. — (Il flauto traverso ; 118)
£4.00
1.Ti 2.Ti 3.Delius, Nikolaus 4.Fünfundzwanzig Etüden für Flöte = Twenty-five studies for flute = Vingtcing exercices pour flûte 5.Sr

(B79-51214)

Pfuhl, Sabine
Das bunte Spielbuch : für die Kindergartenflöte / [von] Sabine Pfuhl. — Mainz ; London : Schott, 1978. — 32p ; obl.4to.
£4.00
1.Ti

(B79-50325)

VR/AY — Collections
World's favorite masterworks for flute / compiled by Jay Arnold. — Carlstadt : Ashley ; [London] : [Phoenix]. — (World's favorite series ; no.111)
Book 2. — 1978. — 128p ; 4to.
Contains studies by Andersen and Hugues, and the first flute parts of works by Pessard and Handel.
Unpriced
1.Arnold, Jay 2.Sr

(B79-50737)

Book 3. — 1978. — 128p ; 4to.
Contains studies by Paganini, Hugues and Andersen, and the first flute parts of works by Tchaikovsky, Doppler and Rimsky Korsakoff.
Unpriced
1.Arnold, Jay 2.Sr

(B79-50738)

World's favorite masterworks for flute / complied [i.e. compiled] by Jay Arnold. — Carlstadt : Ashley ; [London] : [Phoenix]. — (World's favorite series ; no.110)
Book 1. — 1978. — 127p ; 4to.
Contains studies by Andersen and Schade and the first flute parts of works by Tchaikovsky and Rimsky-Korsakoff.
Unpriced
1.Arnold, Jay 2.Sr

(B79-50739)

VRN — FLUTE ENSEMBLE
VRNM — Nonets
Jenni, Donald
Cherry valley : an ensemble for nine flutes / [by] Donald Jenni. — New York ; London : Associated Music, 1978. — 4to.
Score ([1],8p.) & 9 parts.
Unpriced
1.Ti

(B79-51215)

VRNQ — Sextets
Walters, Harold L
Scenes from the west : flute sextet or choir / [by] Harold L.
Walters ... — Miami : Rubank ; [Sevenoaks] : [Novello], 1979. —
4to.
Score (14p.) & 6 parts.
Unpriced
1.Ti

(B79-50740)

VRNT/AY — Trios. Collections
Flute trios / editor, Trevor Wye. — London : Chester Music. —
(Chester woodwind series)
Vol.1. — 1979. — 4to.
Score ([2],25p.) & 2 parts.
Unpriced
1.Wye, Trevor 2.Sr

(B79-51216)

Vol.2. — 1979. — 4to.
Score (28p.) & 2 parts.
Unpriced
1.Wye, Trevor 2.Sr

(B79-51217)

VRNTPWE — Flutes (2) & keyboard. Sonatas
Hotteterre, Jacques Martin
[Sonatas, flutes (2) & continuo, op.3]. Triosonaten für zwei Flöten,
(Flöte und Violine) und Basso continuo, op.3 / [von] Jacques
Martin Hotteterre, 'Le romain' ... ; herausgegeben von Paul M.
Douglas ; Continuo-Aussetzung von James Bailey. — Zürich ;
[London] : Eulenburg.
Score ([2],17p.) & 3 parts.
Nos 1 & 2 : E-moll, D-dur. — 1979. — 4to.
£3.50
1.Douglas, Paul M 2.Bailey, James

(B79-50741)

Hotteterre, Jacques Martin
[Sonatas, flutes (2) & continuo, op.3]. Triosonaten für zwei Flöten
(Flöte und Violine) und Basso continuo, op.3 / [von] Jacques
Martin Hotteterre, 'Le romain' ... ; herausgegeben von Paul M.
Douglas ; Continuo-Aussetzung von James Bailey. — Zürich ;
[London] : Eulenburg.
Score (20p.) & 3 parts.
Nos 3 & 4 : B-moll, E-moll. — 1979. — 4to.
£3.50
1.Douglas, Paul M 2.Bailey, James

(B79-50742)

Nos 5 & 6 : A-dur, G-dur. — 1979. — 4to.
£3.50
1.Douglas, Paul M 2.Bailey, James

(B79-50743)

VRNTQ — Flutes (2) & piano
Doppler, Franz
Souvenir de Prague. Op.24 : for two flutes and piano / [by] Franz
and Carl Doppler. — London : Musica rara, 1979. — 4to.
Score (16p.) & part.
Unpriced
1.Ti 2.Doppler, Carl

(B79-50744)

VRNU/AF — Duets. Exercises
Lyons, Graham
Set two : flute duets for teacher and pupil / written and arranged
by Graham Lyons. — London : Chester Music.
Vol.1. — 1979. — 13p. ; 4to. —
Unpriced
1.Ti

(B79-51219)

Lyons, Graham
Set two : flute duets for teacher and pupil / written and arranged
by Graham Lyons. — London : Chester Music.
Vol.2. — 1979. — 14p. ; 8vo. —
Unpriced
1.Ti

(B79-51218)

VRNUE — Duets. Sonatas
Bach, Wilhelm Friedemann
[Sonatas, flutes (2), nos.1,2]. Zwei Sonaten für zwei Querflöten
allein = Two sonatas for two solo flutes / [von] Wilhelm
Friedemann Bach ; herausgegeben von, edited by, Albert
Rodemann. — Kassel ; London : Bärenreiter, 1978. — 15p ; 4to.
Unpriced
1.Rodemann, Albert

(B79-50326)

Boismortier, Joseph Bodin de
[Sonatas, flutes (2), op.2, nos.3, 4]. Two sonatas, Opus 2, Nos. 3
and 4 for two flutes, or oboes, or violins / [by] J.B. de
Boismortier ; edited by Gwilym Beechey. — London : Oxford
University Press, 1978. — 11p ; fol. — (Musica da camera ; 68)
ISBN 0-19-355578-6 : Unpriced
Also classified at SNUE
1.Beechey, Gwilym 2.Sr

(B79-50327)

Boismortier, Joseph Bodin de
[Sonatas, flutes (2), op.47]. Sechs Sonaten für zwei Querflöten,
op.47 / [von] Joseph Bodin de Boismortier ; herausgegeben von
Frank Nagel. — Zurich ; [London] : Eulenburg, 1977. — [1],30p ;
4to.
Unpriced
1.Ti 2.Nagel, Frank

(B79-50328)

Loeillet, Jean Baptiste
[Sonatas, flutes (2), op.5, bk.2]. Six sonatas, opus 5, book 2 for 2
flutes/oboes/recorders in C without bass (Priestman VI) / [by]
Jean-Baptiste Loeillet de Gant ; edited by R.P. Block. — London :
Musica rara, 1979. — [2],49p ; 4to.
Unpriced
1.Block, Robert Paul

(B79-51220)

VRP — FLUTE & PIANO
VRP/AY — Collections
Blockflöte : Altblockflöte und Klavier, herausgegeben von Wolfram
Hoffmann. — Berlin : Neue Musik ; [London] : [Breitkopf und
Härtel].
Score (27p.) & part. — Contents: 1: Vier Capriccios, Jürgen Wilbrandt. —
2: Tagzeiten, Kurt Schwaen -3: Allegro ... in F, Fritz Geissler.
1. — 1979. — 4to.
£2.10
1.Hoffmann, Wolfram

(B79-50745)

VRP/T — Variations
Czerny, Carl
[Introduction, variations & finale, flute & piano, op.80, C major].
Introduktion, Variationen und Finale für Flöte oder Violine und
Klavier in C-dur. Op.80 / von Carl Czerny ; herausgegeben von
Dieter H. Förster. — Zürich ; [London] : Eulenburg, 1978. —
4to.
Score ([2],28p.) & part.
£3.25
1.Förster, Dieter H

(B79-50746)

VRPE — Sonatas
Berkeley, *Sir* Lennox
[Sonata, flute & piano, op.97]. Sonata for flute and piano. Op.97 /
[by] Lennox Berkeley. — London : Chester Music, 1979. — 4to.
Score ([2],22p.) & part.
Unpriced

(B79-50747)

Hebden, John
[Sonata, flute & continuo, no.1, D major]. Sonata 1 in D major
for flute and basso continuo / [by] John Hebden ; edited by
Jeremy Barlow. — London : Oxford University Press, 1979. —
fol. — (Musica da camera ; no.74)
Score (11p.) & 2 parts.
ISBN 0-19-357021-1 : Unpriced
1.Barlow, Jeremy 2.Sr

(B79-51221)

Platti, Giovanni Benedetto
[Sonata, flute & continuo, op.3, no.3, E minor]. Sonate e-Moll, e
minor, mi mineur, opus III, no.3, für Flöte und Basso continuo,
for flute and basso continuo, pour flûte et basse continue / [von]
Giovanni Platti ; herausgegeben von ... Nikolaus Delius ;
Generalbass ... Gottfried Bach. — Mainz ; London : Schott, 1979.
— 4to. — (Il flauto traverso ; 114)
Score (15p.) & part.
£4.80
1.Delius, Nikolaus 2.Bach, Gottfried 3.Sr

(B79-51222)

Roseingrave, Thomas
[Sonata, flute & continuo, no.2, D major]. Sonata 2 in D major
for flute and basso continuo / [by] Thomas Roseingrave ; edited
by Jeremy Barlow. — London : Oxford University Press, 1978. —
fol. — (Musica da camera ; 54)
Score ([1],9p.) & part.
ISBN 0-19-358643-6 : Unpriced
1.Barlow, Jeremy 2.Sr

(B79-50329)

Schneider, Johann Christian Friedrich
[Sonata, flute & piano, op.33, G major]. Sonate in G-dur für Flöte
und Klavier, op.33 / [von] Joh. Chr. Friedrich Schneider ;
herausgegeben von Bernhard Päuler. — Zurich : Amadeus ;
[London] : [Schott], 1979. — 4to.
Score ([1],36p.) & part.
Unpriced
1.Päuler, Bernhard

(B79-50330)

VRPJ — Miscellaneous works
Geraedts, Jaap
Canzonetta for flute and piano (1947) / [by] Jaap Geraedts. —
Amsterdam : Donemus ; [London] : [Lengnick], [1976]. — fol.
Score (4p.) & part.
Unpriced

(B79-50748)

Kelterborn, Rudolf
Sevenminute - Play : für Flöte und Klavier = for flute and
piano / [von] Rudolf Kelterborn. — Kassel ; London :
Bärenreiter, 1978. — 4to.
Score ([1],16p.) & part.
£4.95
1.Ti
(B79-50749)

Lyell, Margaret
Barcarollina : for flute and piano / [by] Margaret Lyell. —
Wendover : Roberton, 1979. — 4to.
Score (5p.) & part.
£1.00
1.Ti
(B79-51223)

Montanari, Nunzio
24 momenti musicali : per flauto e pianoforte nelle 24 tunalità del
sistema temperato / [di] Nunzio Montanari. — Ancona ; Milano :
Bèrben.
Score (36p.) & part.
1° volume : 1-12. — 1979. — 4to.
Unpriced
1.Ti 2.Ventiquattro momenti musicali
(B79-51224)

VRPK — Arrangements
Couperin, François
[Piéces de clavecin, livre 3, ordre 24,15,16. *Selections : arr*]. Four
duos for flute or oboe and keyboard (harpsichord or piano) / [by]
François Couperin ; arranged from Couperin's 'Troisiéme livre de
piéces de clavecin', 1722, by Howard Ferguson. — London :
Oxford University Press, 1978. — 4to.
Score ([4],20p) & part.
ISBN 0-19-355912-9 : Unpriced
1.Ti 2.Ti 3.Ferguson, Howard
(B79-50331)

Finzi, Gerald
[Bagatelles, clarinet & piano. *arr*]. Five bagatelles / [by] Gerald
Finzi ; arranged for flute and piano by Terence Allbright. —
London : Boosey and Hawkes, 1979. — fol.
Score (21p.) & part.
Unpriced
1.Ti 2.Allbright, Terence
(B79-51225)

VRPK/AAY — Arrangements. Collections
Flute encores / editor, Trevor Wye. — London : Chester Music.
Vol.1. — 1979. — 4to.
Score (40p.) & part. — Works by Tershak, Reichert, Briccialdi, Boehm, J.S.
Bach and Köhler.
Unpriced
1.Wye, Trevor
(B79-50750)

Flute magic / [pieces] arranged by Alan Laken. — London :
Chappell, 1978. — 4to.
Score (59p.) & part.
Unpriced
1.Laken, Alan
(B79-50332)

Fun music : for flute / arranged by Bert Brewis. — London :
Chappell.
Score (28p.) & part.
[Vol.1]. — 1976. — 4to.
Unpriced
1.Brewis, Bert
(B79-50333)
Vol.2. — 1977. — 4to.
Unpriced
1.Brewis, Bert
(B79-50334)

VRPK/AHXJ — Arrangements. Ragtime
Joplin, Scott
[Ragtimes. *Selections : arr*]. Sechs Ragtimes für Flöte oder
Klarinette in B and Klavier / [von] Scott Joplin ; arrangiert und
herausgegeben von Dieter H. Forster. — Zürich ; [London] :
Eulenburg, 1979. — 4to.
Score (24p.) & 2 parts.
£4.20
1.Ti 2.Forster, Dieter H
(B79-50751)

VRPK/DW/GB/AY — Arrangements. Popular songs. Collections
Flute magic / arranged by Alan Laken. — London : Chappell.
Popular songs arranged for flute and piano. — Score (61p.) & part.
2. — 1979. — 4to.
Unpriced
(B79-51226)

Fun flute : for young people of any age / music arrangements, Roy
Slack. — London : EMI, 1979. — 4to.
With piano. — Score (24p.) & part.
ISBN 0-86175-058-6 : Unpriced
1.Slack, Roy
(B79-51227)

VRPK/LF — Arrangements. Concertos
Fétis, François Joseph
[Concerto, flute, B minor. *arr*]. Konzert in h-moll für Flote und
Orchester / [von] François Joseph Fétis ... ; herausgegeben von
Albrecht Imberscheid. — Zürich ; London : Eulenburg, 1978. —
4to.
Score (30p.) & part.
£3.25
1.Imberscheid, Albrecht
(B79-50752)

VRPK/LF — Arrangements, Concertos
Piston, Walter
[Concerto, flute. *arr*]. Concerto for flute and orchestra / [by]
Walter Piston ; for flute and piano ; reduction by the composer.
— New York ; London : Associated Music, 1978. — 4to.
Score ([2],22p.) & part.
£4.25
(B79-51228)

VRPK/LFL — Arrangements. Concertinos
Reissiger, Carl Gottlieb
[Concertino, flute, op.60, D major. *arr*]. Concertino für Flöte und
Orchester in D-dur. op.60 / [von] Carl Gottlieb Reissiger ... ;
herausgegeben von Dieter H. Förster. — Zürich ; London :
Eulenburg, 1978. — 4to.
Score (29p.) & part.
£3.70
1.Förster, Dieter H
(B79-50753)

VRPL/AAY — Arrangements. Collections
The **magic** flute of James Galway. — Sevenoaks : Novello, 1979. —
ill, port ; 4to.
Arrangements by Philip Moll, flute parts edited by James Galway. — Score
([8],64p.) & part. — Works by Handel, Rachmaninoff, Bach, Mendelssohn,
Schumann, Gossec, Chopin, Kreisler, Dvorak, and Briccialdi.
Unpriced
1.Moll, Philip 2.Galway, James
(B79-50754)

VRPLS — FLUTE & VIOLIN
Telemann, Georg Philipp
[Der getreue Music Meister. Duet, flute & viola pomposa. *arr*].
Dueto in G-dur für Flote und Violine = Duet in G major for
flute and violin / [von] Georg Philipp Telemann ; herausgegeben
von ... Hermien Teske. — Zurich : Amadeus ; [London] :
[Bärenreiter], 1979. — [1],7p ; 4to.
£1.85
1.Ti 2.Teske, Hermien
(B79-50755)

VRPLTQ — FLUTE & HARP
Nowka, Dieter
Sept esquisses : pour flûte et harpe / [par] Dieter Nowka. —
Berlin : Verlag Neue Musik ; [London] : [Breitkopf und Härtel],
1977. — 4to. — (Reihe Kammermusik)
Score (20p.) & part.
£2.70
1.Ti 2.Sr
(B79-50756)

VRPLTS — FLUTE & GUITAR
Antioniou, Theodore
Stichomythia : for flute and guitar, 1976 / [by] Theodore
Antioniou. — Kassel ; London : Bärenreiter, 1978. — obl.fol.
Edited by J. Ketcham and P. Segal. — Printed on one side of the leaf only.
£8.58
1.Ti 2.Ketcham, J 3.Segal, P
(B79-50335)

Ben-Tovim, Atarah
Atarah's bandkit / selected and introduced by Atarah Ben-Tovim
and John Harper ; editor, Douglas Boyd ; arrangements, John
Harper. — Sevenoaks : Novello.
Strand D1 : With a friend or two : eight duets for flute and classical guitar,
with companion cassette. — 1979. — 4to.
Contents: 1: Greensleeves, Elizabethan song - 2: Pavana, Venetian dance - 3:
Papageno's song, classical (Mozart) - 4: Atarah's fancy, pop song - 5:
Scarborough fair, contemporary folk - 6: Radetzky march & Viennese march
(Strauss) - 7: Gospel train, rock blues - 8: My bonnie, traditional Scottish
air.
£7.00
1.Ti 2.Harper, John 3.Boyd, Douglas
(B79-50758)

Suter, Robert
Musik für Flöte und Gitarre / [von] Robert Suter. — Zürich ;
[London] : Eulenburg, 1979. — [1],15p ; 4to.
£2.10
1.Ti
(B79-50757)

VRPLX — FLUTE & PERCUSSION
Buller, John
Poor Jenny : for flutes (1 player) and percussion (1 player) / [by]
John Buller. — New York ; London : Schirmer, 1979. — [1],16p ;
fol.
£3.50
1.Ti

(B79-51229)

VRPM — UNACCOMPANIED FLUTE
VRPMHX — Jazz
Dentato, John
Jazz players library : 10 classic tunes in their original versions and
in completely notated jazz versions / arranged by Johnny 'Dee'
Dentato. — Bryn Mawr ; [London] : Chappell, 1979. — 24p. ;
4to.
For unaccompanied flute and unaccompanied guitar.
Unpriced
Also classified at TSPMHX
1.Ti

(B79-51230)

VRPMJ — Miscellaneous works
Camilleri, Charles
Sama'i : for flute solo / [by] Charles Camilleri. -- Wendover :
Basil Ramsey : Roberton, 1979. — 11p ; 4to.
Unpriced
1.Ti

(B79-51231)

Hoffmeister, Franz Anton
Prélude ou exercise pour la flûte seule, op.35, nach dem Erstdruck
... / [von] Franz Anton Hoffmeister ; herausgegeben von Bernhard
Päuler. — Zurich : Amadeus ; [London] : [Schott], 1979. — 4to.
Unpriced
1.Ti 2.Päuler, Bernhard

(B79-50336)

Lusse, Charles de
[L'art de la flûte traversière. *Selections*]. 12 caprices : for solo
flute / [by] Charles de Lusse ; edited by David Lasocki. —
London : Nova Music, 1979. — ii,13p ; 4to.
Unpriced
1.Ti 2.Ti 3.Lasocki, David 4.Twelve caprices

(B79-51232)

VS — RECORDER
VS/AC — Tutors
Tobin, Candida
Wizard's way recorder colouring book / [by] C. Tobin. —
Bishop's Stortford : Helicon Press, 1976. — 35p ; 4to.
Illustrated by Rachel Fenton.
ISBN 0-905684-00-1 : Unpriced
1.Ti

(B79-50337)

VS/AY — Collections
Blockflöte. — Berlin : Neue Musik ; [London] : [Breitkopf and
Härtel].
Score (31p.) & part.
2 : Altblockflöte und Klavier / herausgegeben von Wolfram Hoffmann. —
1979. — 4to.
Unpriced
1.Hoffmann, Wolfram

(B79-51233)

VS/FT — With tape recorder
Dickinson, Peter
Recorder music / [by] Peter Dickinson. — Sevenoaks : Novello,
1979. — [4],12p ; 4to.
For one player and a tape recording, or for two players. — Various kinds of
recorder are called for in the course of the performance. — Duration 13
min.
£1.95
Also classified at VSNU
1.Ti

(B79-51234)

VSN — RECORDER ENSEMBLE
Gabrieli, Andrea
[Madrigali et ricercari a quattro voci. *Selections*]. Five ricercare in
four parts for recorders / [by] A. Gabrieli ; ed. R.P. Block. —
London : Musica rara, 1979. — 4to.
Score ([1],28p.) & 4 parts.
Unpriced
1.Ti 2.Ti 3.Block, Robert Paul

(B79-50759)

VSN/AY — Collections
The **recorder** consort : forty seven pieces for recorder consort /
collected by Steve Rosenberg. — London : Boosey and Hawkes,
1978. — 49p ; 4to.
Unpriced
1.Rosenberg, Steve

(B79-50760)

VSNQ — Sextets
Adler, Samuel
Déjà vu : 5 dance excursions into the past, for 6 recorders / [by]
Samuel Adler. — New York ; London : Schirmer, 1978. — 4to.
Score (12p.) & 6 parts.
£6.10
1.Ti

(B79-50761)

VSNRK/DJ — Quintets. Arrangements. Motets
Schütz, Heinrich
[Geistliche Chormusik. Die mit Thränen säen. *arr*]. Fantasia a 5 /
[by] Heinrich Schütz ; transcribed for recorders or strings
(especially viols) by Aaron Williams. — Chesham : Ricordi, 1978.
— 4to.
Score (4p.) & 6 parts, with alternative parts for treble recorder III/violin III
and cello/bass back to back.
Unpriced
Also classified at RXNRK/DJ
1.Ti 2.Ti 3.Williams, Aaron

(B79-50338)

VSNRQK/AHW — Quintets. Arrangements. Waltzes
Strauss, Johann, *b.1825*
[Wein, Weib und Gesang. Op.333. *arr*]. Wine, women and song /
[by] Johann Strauss ; arranged by Brian Bonsor for descant (div.),
treble (div.) recorders and piano. — New revised ed. — London :
Schott, 1979. — 4to.
Score (8p.) & part.
£0.90
1.Ti 2.Ti 3.Bonsor, Brian

(B79-50762)

VSNS — Quartets
Gabrieli, Andrea
[Madrigali et ricercari a quattro voci. *Selections*]. Five ricercare in
four parts : for brass or recorders / [by] A. Gabrieli. — London :
Musica rara, 1979. — 4to.
Edited by R.P. Block. — Score ([1],28p.) & part.
Unpriced
1.Ti 2.Ti 3.Block, Robert Paul

(B79-51235)

VSNSK/AH/AYH — Quartets. Arrangements. Dances. Collections.
France
Gervaise, Claude
[Danceries, liv.3. *Selections : arr*]. Tanz-Suite ... für
Blockflötenquartett (SATB ; ATTB) oder andere
Melodieinstrumente (Violen oder Flöten), Schlagwerk ad lib. =
Dance suite ... for recorder quartet (SATB ; ATTB) or other
melodic instruments (viols or flutes), percussion instruments ad
lib. / [von] Claude Gervaise ; herausgegeben von ... James Staley.
— Mainz ; London : Schott, 1979. — 19p ; obl. 4to.
Unpriced
1.Ti 2.Ti 3.Staley, James

(B79-51236)

VSNSK/DP/LF/AY — Quartets. Arrangements. Carols. Christmas.
Collections
Carols in consort : Christmas music for two descant, treble, tenor
and optional bass recorders / arranged by Gordon Hitchcock. —
London : EMI, 1978. — 4to.
Score (15p.) & 5 parts.
Unpriced
1.Hitchcock, Gordon

(B79-50339)

VSNTK — Trios. Arrangements
Mozart, Wolfgang Amadeus
[Divertimentos, K. Anh. 229. *Selections: arr*]. Six movements from
the Mozart divertimenti / arranged for recorder trio by Carol
Medway. — London : Cramer, 1978. — [2],15p ; obl.4to.
Unpriced
1.Ti 2.Medway, Carol

(B79-50340)

VSNTK/AH/AY — Trios. Arrangements. Dances. Collections
A tre : Tänze und Stücke alter Meister für 2 Sopran-und 1
Altblockflöte = dances and tunes of old masters for two
soprano - and one alto-recorder / herausgegeben von ... Walter
Keller-Löwy. — Zürich : Pelikan ; [London] : [Bärenreiter], 1978.
— [1],16p ; obl.8vo.
£1.23
1.Keller-Löwy, Walter

(B79-50763)

VSNU — Duets
Dickinson, Peter
Recorder music / [by] Peter Dickinson. — Sevenoaks : Novello,
1979. — [4],12p ; 4to.
For one player and a tape recording, or for two players. — Various kinds of
recorder are called for in the course of the performance. — Duration 13
min.
£1.95
Primary classification VS/FT
1.Ti

(B79-51234)

VSP — RECORDER & PIANO
VSPE — Sonatas
Krug, Reinhold
  Zwota-Sonate, 1974 : Blockflöte und Klavier / [von] Reinhold
  Krug. — Berlin : Neue Musik ; [London] : [Breitkopf and Härtel],
  1977[i.e.1979]. — 4to.
  Score (23p.) & part.
  £3.90
  1.Ti
                                                                   (B79-51237)

VSPG — Suites
Telemann, Georg Philipp
  [Kleine Cammermusic]. Die kleine Kammermusik : sechs Partiten
  für Blockflöte, Querflöte, Oboe oder Violine und Basso continuo
  = six partitas for recorder, flute, oboe or violin and basso
  continuo / [von] Georg Philipp Telemann ; herausgegeben und
  Continuo-Aussetzung von ... Willy Hess. — Zürich : Amadeus ;
  [London] : [Eulenburg], 1979. — 4to.
  Score ([1],40p.) & 2 parts.
  £4.70
  Also classified at SPG
  1.Ti 2.Hess, Willy
                                                                   (B79-50764)

VSPK/AAY — Arrangements. Collections
  Fun music for recorder / arranged by Bert Brewis. — London :
  Chappell.
  Score (28p.) & part.
  [Vol.1]. — 1976. — 4to.
  Unpriced
  1.Brewis, Bert
                                                                   (B79-50341)

  Fun music : for recorder / arranged by Bert Brewis. — London :
  Chappell.
  Score (24p.) & part.
  [Vol.2]. — 1976. — 4to.
  Unpriced
  1.Brewis, Bert
                                                                   (B79-50342)

VSPLTS — RECORDER & GUITAR
VSPLTSK/DW/AY — Arrangements. Songs, etc. Collections
  Starting together : easy duets for recorder and guitar groups /
  arranged by Graham Lyons and Roger Cawkwell. — London :
  Chester Music.
  Vol.1. — 1979. — [2],12p. ; 4to.
  Unpriced
  1.Lyons, Graham 2.Cawkwell, Roger
                                                                   (B79-51238)

  Starting together : easy duets for recorders and guitar groups /
  arranged by Graham Lyons and Roger Cawkwell. — London :
  Chester Music.
  Vol.2. — 1979. — [2],18p. ; 4to.
  Unpriced
  1.Lyons, Graham 2.Cawkwell, Roger
                                                                   (B79-51239)

  Vol.3. — 1974. — [2],17p. ; 4to.
  Unpriced
  1.Lyons, Graham 2.Cawkwell, Roger
                                                                   (B79-51240)

VSPM — UNACCOMPANIED RECORDER
VSPM/AYVU — Collections. Japan
  Eight traditional Japanese pieces / selected and transcribed by
  Gordon Saunders for solo tenor recorder [or] descant recorder [or]
  flute. — Sevenoaks : Novello, 1979. — 12p ; 4to.
  £1.55
  1.Saunders, Gordon
                                                                   (B79-50765)

VSR — DESCANT RECORDER
VSRNUH — Descant recorders. Duets. Dances
Biebl, Franz
  Fröhlicher Reigen = Cheerful round dance : Tänze für zwei
  Sopranblockflöten mit Gitarre ad lib. = dances for two soprano
  recorders with guitarre [sic] ad lib. / komponiert von ... Franz
  Biebl. — Zürich : Pelikan ; [London] : [Bärenreiter], 1978. —
  15p ; 8vo.
  £1.49
  1.Ti
                                                                   (B79-50766)

**VSRNUK/AH/AY — Descant recorder duets. Arrangements. Dances.
  Collections**
  Der Siebensprung : und andere Tänze aus aller Welt, leicht gesetzt
  für zwei Sopranblockflöten = and other dances from all over the
  world, in easy arrangements for two soprano-recorders /
  herausgegeben von ... Walter Keller-Löwy. — Zürich : Pelikan ;
  [London] : [Bärenreiter], 1976. — [1],16p ; obl.8vo.
  £1.47
  1.Keller-Löwy, Walter
                                                                   (B79-50767)

VSRPE — Descant recorder & piano. Sonatas
Castello, Dario
  [Sonate concertate, lib. 2, no.1]. Sonata prima a soprano solo... :
  für Sopranblockflöte (Flöte, Violine) und Generalbass = for
  descant recorder (flute, violin) and continuo / [von] Dario
  Castello ; Continuo-Einrichtung für Gitarre von... Konrad
  Ragossnig. — Mainz ; London : Schott, 1979. — facsim ; 4to. —
  (Originalmusik für Blockflöte ; no.141)
  Score (10p.) + part.
  £3.20
  1.Ti 2.Ragossnig, Konrad 3.Sr
                                                                   (B79-51241)

VSRPJ — Descant recorder & piano. Miscellaneous works
Frescobaldi, Girolamo
  [Libro della canzoni, no.1. Canzona 2 'La Bernadina']. Canzona
  (II) 'La Bernadina' per canto solo : für Sopranblockflöte (Flöte,
  Oboe, Violine) und Generalbass = for descant recorder (flute,
  oboe, violin) and continuo / [von] Girolamo Frescobaldi ;
  Continuo-Einrichtung für Gitarre von... Konrad Ragossnig. —
  [Mainz] ; [London] : [Schott], [1979]. — facsim ; 4to. — (Original
  musik für Blockflöte ; no.140)
  Score (7p.) & part.
  £3.20
  Also classified at SPJ
  1.Ti 2.Ti 3.Ragossnig, Konrad 4.Sr
                                                                   (B79-51242)

VSRPK/AAY — Arrangements. Collections
  Advertising the classics / arranged for descant recorder and piano
  by Roy Slack. — London : Leonard, Gould and Bolttler, 1979. —
  18p ; 4to.
  £0.75
  1.Slack, Roy
                                                                   (B79-50768)

VSRPMK — Unaccompanied descant recorder. Arrangements
Vivaldi, Antonio
  [Selections. *arr*]. Vivaldi themes : easy melodies transcribed for
  descant (tenor) recorder (or flute, oboe or violin) with symbols for
  accompaniment on the guitar (ad lib.) / edited by Torallo. —
  Chesham : Ricordi, 1979. — 13p ; obl. 8vo.
  Unpriced
  Also classified at SPMK
  1.Ti 2.Torallo
                                                                   (B79-51243)

VSS — TREBLE RECORDER
VSSNT — Treble recorder ensembles. Trios
Finger, Gottfried
  [Pastorelle, recorders (treble) (3), G major]. Pastorelle and sonata :
  for three treble recorders / [by] Gottfried Finger ; edited by
  Richard Platt. — London : Oxford University Press, 1978. — fol.
  — (Musica da camera ; 48)
  The sonata mentioned on the title page is the Sonata for three treble
  recorders in F major which is published with the Pastorella. — Score (11p.)
  & two parts.
  ISBN 0-19-363204-7 : Unpriced
  1.Ti 2.Ti 3.Platt, Richard 4.Sonata, recorders (treble) (3), F major 5.Sr
                                                                   (B79-50343)

VSSNTPW/T — Treble recorders (2) & keyboard. Variations
Schickhardt, Johann Christian
  [Sonata, recorders (treble) (2) & continuo, op.6, no.6, D minor,
  'La Folia']. Variations on La folia, op.6, no.6 : for 2 treble
  recorders and basso continuo / [by] J.C. Schickhardt ; edited by
  David Lasocki. — London : Nova Music, 1979. — 4to.
  Score (11p.) & 3 parts.
  Unpriced
  Also classified at VSSNTPWE
  1.Ti 2.Lasocki, David
                                                                   (B79-51244)

VSSNTPWE — Treble recorders (2) & keyboard. Sonatas
Keller, Gottfried
  [Sonata, recorders (treble) (2) & continuo, G major]. Sonata in G,
  2 treble recorders (or flutes), 2 oboes/violins (or flutes) & basso
  continuo / [by] Gottfried Keller ; edited by David Lasocki. —
  London : Nova Music, 1979. — 4to.
  Realisation of basso continuo by John Madden. — Score ([1],7p.) & 5 parts.
  Unpriced
  1.Lasocki, David 2.Madden, John
                                                                   (B79-51246)

Schickhardt, Johann Christian
[Sonata, recorders (treble) (2) & continuo, op.6, no.6, D minor, 'La Folia']. Variations on La folia, op.6, no.6 : for 2 treble recorders and basso continuo / [by] J.C. Schickhardt ; edited by David Lasocki. — London : Nova Music, 1979. — 4to.
Score (11p.) & 3 parts.
Unpriced
Primary classification VSSNTPW/T
1.Ti 2.Lasocki, David

(B79-51244)

VSSNTPWG — Treble recorders (2) & keyboard. Suites
Pez, Johann Christoph
[Second collection of sonatas for two flutes and a bass. *Selections*]. Zwei Suiten für zwei Altblockflöten und Basso continuo / [von] Johann Christoph Petz...; herausgegeben von Hugo Ruf. — Mainz ; London : Schott. — (Original musik für Blockflöte)
Score (19p.) & 3 parts.
Suite 1 : C-Dur = C major. — 1979. — 4to.
£4.00
1.Ti 2.Ti 3.Ruf, Hugo 4.Sr

(B79-51247)

VSSNTPWK/LF — Treble recorders (2) & keyboard. Arrangements. Concertos
Corelli, Arcangelo
[Concerto grosso, op.6, no.3, C major. *arr*]. Trio sonata in d / by A. Corelli ; arr. from concerto grosso in C, op.6, no.3, for 2 treble recorders and basso continuo, arr. J.C. Schickhardt. — London : Nova Music, 1979. — 4to.
Edited by David Lasocki, realisation of the basso continuo by John Madden. — Score ([1]12p.) & 3 parts.
Unpriced
1.Schickhardt, Johann Christian 2.Lasocki, David 3.Madden, John

(B79-51248)

VSSNUE — Treble recorder duets. Sonatas
Loeillet, Jean Baptiste
[Sonatas, recorders (treble) (2)]. Six sonatas for 2 treble recorders (flutes) without bass ... / [by] Jean Baptiste Loeillet ; edited by R.P. Block. — London : Musica rara, 1979. — [2],41p ; 4to.
Unpriced
1.Block, Robert Paul

(B79-51249)

VSSPE — Treble recorder & piano. Sonatas
Dieupart, Francis
[Sonata, recorder (treble) & continuo, no.1, G major]. Sonata no.1 in G for treble (alto) recorder and basso continuo / [by] Francis Dieupart ; edited by Walter Bergmann. — London : Schott, 1979. — 4to.
Score ([4],9p.) & part.
Unpriced
1.Bergmann, Walter

(B79-51251)

Dieupart, Francis
[Sonata, recorder (treble) & continuo, no.6, F major]. Sonata no.6 in F for treble (alto) recorder and basso continuo / [by] Francis Dieupart ; edited by Walter Bergmann. — London : Schott, 1979. — 4to.
Score ([4],14p.) & 2 parts.
Unpriced
1.Bergmann, Walter

(B79-51250)

Finger, Gottfried
[Sonata, recorder (treble) & continuo, op.3, no.2, C minor]. Sonata in C, opus 3, no.2, for treble recorder and basso continuo / by Godfrey Finger ; edited by Arthur Marshall. — London : Nova Music, 1979. — 4to.
Score (10p.) & 2 parts.
Unpriced
1.Marshall, Arthur W

(B79-51252)

Schickhard, Johann Christian
[L'alphabet de la musique : Op.30. Sonatas 4, 7, 16]. 3 Sonaten aus 'L'alphabet de la musique' = 3 sonatas from 'L'alphabet de la musique' : für Altblockflöte und Basso continuo = for alto recorder and basso continuo / [von] Johann Christian Schickhardt ; herausgegeben von ... Richard Erig. — Zürich : Pelikan ; [London] : [Bärenreiter], 1977. — 4to. — (Musica instrumentalis ; Hft.26)
Score (30p.) & 2 parts.
£9.10
1.Ti 2.Ti 3.Erig, Richard 4.Drei 5.Three 6.Sr

(B79-50769)

Schickhard, Johann Christian
L'alphabet de la musique, op.30 : 24 sonatas in all the keys, for treble recorder and basso continuo ... / [by] J.C. Schickhardt. — London : Musica rara.
Edited by Paul J. Everett. — Score ([6],45p.).
Vol.4 : Sonatas 13-16. — 1978. — 4to.
Unpriced
1.Ti 2.Everett, Paul J

(B79-50344)

Vol.5 : Sonatas 17-20. — 1978. — 4to.
Unpriced
1.Ti 2.Everett, Paul J

(B79-50345)

Vol.6 : Sonatas 21-24. — 1978. — 4to.
Unpriced
1.Ti 2.Everett, Paul J

(B79-50346)

Telemann, Georg Philipp
[Der getreue Music Meister. *Selections*]. 4 sonatas for treble recorder and basso continuo / [edited by] R.P. Block. — London : Musica rara, 1979. — 4to.
Score (27p.) & 2 parts.
Unpriced
1.Ti 2.Ti 3.Block, Robert Paul 4.Four sonatas for treble recorder and basso continuo

(B79-50347)

VSSPE/AZ — Treble recorder & piano. Sonatas. Collected works of individual composers
Handel, George Frideric
[Sonatas, recorder (treble) & continuo]. The complete sonatas for treble (alto) recorder and basso continuo = Die gesamten Sonaten für Altblockflöte und basso continuo / [by] G.F. Handel ; edited from all the autograph manuscripts and other contemporary sources by David Lasocki and Walter Bergmann. — London : Faber Music, 1979. — 4to.
Score ([6],79p.) & 2 parts.
Unpriced
1.Ti 2.Lasocki, David 3.Bergmann, Walter

(B79-51253)

VSSPG — Suites
Jacques, Michael
Midsummer suite : for treble recorder or flute and piano / [by] Michael Jacques. — Wendover : Roberton, 1979. — 4to.
Score (12p.) & part.
£1.50
1.Ti

(B79-50770)

VSSPJ — Miscellaneous works
Casken, John
Thymehaze : for alto recorder and piano / [by] John Casken. — London : Schott, 1979. — [3],9p ; 4to. — (Modern recorder series ; no.6)
Unpriced
1.Ti 2.Sr

(B79-51254)

VSSPM/T — Variations
Sterne, Colin
Meadow, hedge, cuckoo : variations for solo alto recorder on John Dowland's ayre 'Away with these self-loving lads' / by Colin Sterne. — New York : Galaxy Music ; [London] : [Galliard], 1978. — 5p ; obl.fol.
Unpriced
1.Ti

(B79-50348)

VSX — PIPES
VSY/AY — Bamboo pipes. Collections
Pipers' Guild
In memoriam : Margaret James : a treasury of bamboo pipe music. — [Tonbridge Wells?] : Pipers' Guild, 1979. — 39p ; 4to.
Unpriced
1.Ti

(B79-51255)

VTN — OBOE ENSEMBLE
VTNT/AY — Trios. Collections
Oboe trios / editor, James Brown. — London : Chester.
Score ([1],24p.) & 2 parts.
Vol.1. — 1979. — 4to.
Unpriced
1.Brown, James

(B79-50349)

VTNTPWE — Oboes (2) & keyboard. Sonatas
Finger, Gottfried
[Sonata, oboes (2) & continuo, B flat major]. Sonata in B flat for 2 oboes/violins (or recorders in C) and basso continuo / [by] Godfrey Finger ; edited by Peter Holman. — London : Nova Music, 1979. — 4to.
Score ([1],8p.) & 3 parts.
Unpriced
1.Holman, Peter

(B79-51256)

VTNTPWEM — Oboes (2) & keyboard. Sonatinas
Pezel, Johann
[Bicinia variorum instrumentorum. *Selections*]. Six sonatinas, nos 1, 2, 3, 7, 9, 11 for 2 oboes/violins/recorders in C and basso continuo / [by] Johann Pezel ; edited by Fazi Dov. — London : Nova Music, 1979. — 4to.
Score (13p.) & 3 parts.
Unpriced
1.Ti 2.Dov, Fazi

(B79-51257)

VTNU — Duets
Gordon, Christopher
Twelve oboe duets / [by] Christopher Gordon and Elizabeth London. — London (265 Magdalen Road, SW18 3NZ) : Janus Music, 1979. — [2],11p ; 4to.
Unpriced
1.London, Elizabeth

(B79-50771)

VTP — OBOE & PIANO
VTP/T — Variations
Brown, James
Rossini and Chopin variations for oboe and piano / edited and arranged by James Brown. — London : Lordship Publications, 1979. — 4to.
Contents: 1: Variations for oboe and piano by Gioacchino Rossini - 2: Variations on a theme by Rossini by Frédéric Chopin.
Unpriced
1.Ti 2.Rossini, Gioacchino Antonio 3.Chopin, Frédéric

(B79-51258)

VTPE — Sonatas
Babell, William
[Sonata, violin & continuo, op.posth., pt.1, no.11, G minor]. Sonata 11 in G minor for oboe (or violin) and basso continuo / [by] William Babell ; edited by George Pratt. — London : Oxford University Press, 1978. — 4to. — (Musica da camera ; 52)
Score ([11],13p.) & part.
ISBN 0-19-355226-4 : Unpriced
Primary classification SPE
1.Pratt, George 2.Sr

(B79-50274)

Handel, George Frideric
[Sonatas, oboe & continuo]. The three authentic sonatas : oboe & basso continuo in F, opus 1, no.5, B flat, 'Fitzwilliam', C [minor], opus 1, no.8 / [by] Handel ; edited by David Lasocki. — London : Nova Music, 1979. — 4to.
Score (v,19p.) & 2 parts.
Unpriced
1.Ti 2.Lasocki, David

(B79-51259)

Schickhardt, Johann Christian
[Sonata, oboe & continuo, op.2, no.5, G minor]. Sonata in g, op.2, no.5 for oboe or violin and basso continuo / [by] J.C. Schickhardt ; edited by David Lasocki. — London : Nova Music, 1979. — 4to.
Score ([1],12p.) & 2 parts. — Continuo realised by John Madden.
Unpriced
1.Lasocki, David 2.Madden, John

(B79-51260)

Stiles, Frank
[Sonata, oboe & piano]. Sonata for oboe and piano / [by] Frank Stiles. — Braintree ((Paigles, Perry Green, Bradwell)) : Anglian Edition, 1977. — fol. — (Anglian new music series ; 40)
Score (20p.) & part.
Unpriced
1.Sr

(B79-50772)

VTPEM — Sonatinas
Richardson, Alan
[Sonatina, oboes (2)]. Sonatina for 2 oboes / [by] Alan Richardson. — London : Nova Music, 1979. — 7p ; 4to.
Unpriced

(B79-51261)

VTPG — Suites
Kelly, Bryan
Partita : for oboe and piano / [by] Bryan Kelly. — London : Chester Music, 1979. — 4to.
Score (20p.) & part.
Unpriced
1.Ti

(B79-50773)

VTPJ — Miscellaneous works
Butterworth, Neil
Kettlebury hill : for oboe and piano (or strings) / [by] Neil Butterworth. — York : Banks, 1978. — 4to.
Score (7p.) & part.
Unpriced
1.Ti

(B79-50350)

Kalliwoda, Jan Václav
Morceau de salon. Op.228 : for oboe and piano / [by] J.W. Kalliwoda ; edited by Robin Canter. — London : Nova Music, 1979. — 4to.
Op.288 on cover. — Score ([1],14p.) & part.
Unpriced
1.Ti 2.Canter, Robin

(B79-51262)

VTPK/LF — Arrangements. Concertos
Telemann, Georg Philipp
[Concerto, oboe & string orchestra, D major. *arr*]. Concerto in D for oboe, violins and basso continuo / [by] Georg Philipp Telemann ; [edited by] Anders Wiklund. — London : Musica rara, 1978. — 4to.
Score ([1],15p.) & part.
Unpriced
1.Wicklund, Anders

(B79-50351)

Telemann, Georg Philipp
[Concerto, oboe & string orchestra, F major. *arr*]. Concerto in F for solo oboe, violin, strings and basso continuo / [by] Georg Philipp Telemann ; [edited by] Anders Wiklund. — London : Musica rara, 1978. — 4to.
Score ([1],8p.) & part.
Unpriced
1.Wicklund, Anders

(B79-50352)

Vivaldi, Antonio
[Il cimento dell'armonia e dell'inventione. Op.8 Concerto, oboe & string orchestra, P.259, D minor. *arr*]. Concerto in F, RV454, (F.VII/1), P.259 for oboe, strings and basso continuo / [by] Antonio Vivaldi ; [edited] as an oboe and piano reduction by R.P. Block. — London : Musica rara, 1978. — 4to.
Score ([1],14p.) & part.
Unpriced
1.Ti 2.Block, Robert Paul

(B79-50774)

Vivaldi, Antonio
[Concerto, oboe & string orchestra, R.455, F major. *arr*]. Concerto in F, RV.455, (P.306) for oboe, strings and basso continuo / [by] Antonio Vivaldi ; oboe and piano reduction ed. R.P. Block. — London : Musica rara, 1979. — 4to.
Score (16p.) & part.
Unpriced
1.Block, Robert Paul

(B79-50775)

Vivaldi, Antonio
[Concerto, oboe & string orchestra, R.461, A minor. *arr*]. Concerto in A minor for oboe, strings and continuo, RV461 (F.VII,no.5) (P.42) / [by] Antonio Vivaldi ; ed. [as] oboe and piano reduction, R.P. Block. — London : Musica Rara, 1979. — 4to.
Score (14p.) & parts.
Unpriced
1.Block, Robert Paul

(B79-51263)

Vivaldi, Antonio
[Concerto, oboe & string orchestra, R.463, A minor. *arr*]. Concerto in A minor for oboe, strings and continuo, RV463 (F.VII,no.13) / [by] Antonio Vivaldi ; ed. [as] oboe and piano reduction, R.P. Block. — London : Musica rara, 1979. — 4to.
Score ([1],14p.) & part.
Unpriced
1.Block, Robert Paul

(B79-51264)

VTPK/LFL — Arrangements. Concertinos
Tull, Fisher
[Concertino, oboe & string orchestra. *arr*]. Concertino for oboe and strings / [by] Fisher Tull ; reduction for oboe and piano. — London : Boosey and Hawkes, 1979. — fol.
Score (ii,3-16p.) & part. — Duration 81/2 min.
Unpriced

(B79-51265)

VTPLVV — OBOE & CLARINET
VTPLVVEM — Oboe & clarinet. Sonatinas
Gordon, Christopher
[Sonatina, oboe & clarinet]. Sonatina for oboe and clarinet (or flute and clarinet) / [by] Christopher Gordon. — London : Janus Music, 1979. — [2],5p ; 4to.
Unpriced

(B79-50353)

VUN — SAXOPHONE ENSEMBLE
VUNS — Quartets
Harvey, Paul
The Harfleur song : for saxophone quartet / [by] Paul Harvey. — Sevenoaks : Novello, 1979. — 8p ; 8vo.
Duration 2 min.
£0.80
1.Ti

(B79-51266)

VUPM — UNACCOMPANIED SAXOPHONE
VUPMHX — Saxophone. Jazz
Front line sax solos / transcribed by John Robert Brown and Bill Charleson. — London : Chappell, 1979. — 67p ; 4to.
With accompaniment guide (47p.).
Unpriced
1.Brown, John Robert 2.Charleson, Bill

(B79-50776)

VUS — ALTO SAXOPHONE
VUSPH — Alto saxophone & piano. Dances
Tull, Fisher
Sarabande and gigue : E-flat alto saxophone and piano / [by] Fisher Tull. — New York ; [London] : Boosey and Hawkes, 1979. — 4to.
Score (11p.) & part.
Unpriced
1.Ti

(B79-50777)

VUSPK/AAY — Alto saxophone & piano. Arrangements. Collections
Saxophone solos : E flat alto with piano accompaniment / editor, Paul Harvey. — London : Chester Music.
Score (24p.) & parts.
Vol.1. — 1977. — 4to.
Unpriced
1.Harvey, Paul

(B79-50354)

Vol.2. — 1977. — 4to.
Unpriced
1.Harvey, Paul

(B79-50355)

VUSPK/LF — Alto-saxophone & piano. Arrangements. Concertos
Schibler, Armin
[Fantasy concertante, alto saxophone & orchestra. *arr*].
Konzertante Fantasie für Alt–saxophon und kleines Orchester / [von] Armin Schibler ; Ausgabe für Alt-Saxophon und Klavier. — Zürich ; [London] : Eulenburg, 1979. — 4to.
Facsimile of the composer's autograph.
£4.60

(B79-50778)

VUSPMHX — Unaccompanied alto saxophone. Jazz
Dentato, John
Jazz players library : 10 classic tunes in their original versions and in completely notated jazz versions / arranged by Johnny 'Dee' Dentato. — Bryn Mawr ; [London] : Chappell, 1979. — 24p ; 4to.
For unaccompanied alto saxophone.
Unpriced
1.Ti

(B79-51268)

VUTPK/AAY — Arrangements. Collections
Saxophone solos : B flat tenor with piano accompaniment / editor, Paul Harvey. — London : Chester Music. — (Chester woodwind series)
Score ([2],24p.) & part.
Vol.1. — 1979. — 4to.
Unpriced
1.Harvey, Paul 2.Sr

(B79-51269)

Vol.2. — 1979. — 4to.
Unpriced
1.Harvey, Paul 2.Sr

(B79-51270)

VUTPMHX — Unaccompanied tenor saxophone. Jazz
Dentato, John
Jazz players library : 10 classic tunes in their original versions and in completely notated jazz versions / arranged by Johnny 'Dee' Dentato. — Bryn Mawr ; [London] : Chappell, 1979. — 24p ; 4to.
For unaccompanied tenor saxophone.
Unpriced
Also classified at VVPMHX
1.Ti

(B79-51271)

VV — CLARINET
VV/AC — Tutors
Thurston, Frederick J
The clarinet : a comprehensive method for the Boehm clarinet / by Frederick J. Thurston and Alan Frank ; with an historical sketch by F.G. Rendall. — 3rd ed. (revised and enlarged). — London : Boosey and Hawkes, 1979. — 167p ; ill ; 4to.
Prepared under the direction of Alan Frank and Thea King.
Unpriced
1.Ti 2.Frank, Alan 3.King, Thea

(B79-51272)

Wastall, Peter
Learn as you play clarinet / by Peter Wastall. — London : Boosey and Hawkes, 1979. — 64p ; 4to.
Unpriced
1.Ti

(B79-51273)

VVK/AAY — Arrangements. Collections
Transposition à vue / réalisation Jean Michel Bardez. — Paris ; [London] : Chappell.
1er recueil : Pièces ou fragments pour clarinette en si bémol à chanter, ou à jouer avec d'autres instruments-non transpositeurs-en lisant en clé d'ut 4e. — 1979. — 26p ; obl.4to.
Unpriced
1.Bardez, Jean Michel

(B79-51274)

VVN — CLARINET ENSEMBLE
VVNK — Arrangements
Erbach, Christian
Canzona. (La paglia) / [by] Christian Erbach ; arranged by Carl Anderson, for clarinet choir, 3 B-flat clarinets, E-flat alto clarinet, B-flat bass clarinet, E-flat contrabass clarinet. — New York ; London : Schirmer, 1978. — 4to. — (Early German music for clarinet choir)
Score (5p.) & 6 parts.
Unpriced
1.Ti 2.Anderson, Carl 3.Sr

(B79-50779)

Scheidt, Samuel
[Paduana, galliarda. *arr*]. Canzon super intradam aechiopicam / [by] Samuel Scheidt ; arranged by Carl Anderson, for clarinet choir, 3 B-flat clarinets, E-flat alto clarinet, B-flat bass clarinet, E-flat contrabass clarinet. — New York ; London : Schirmer, 1978. — 4to. — (Early German music for clarinet choir)
Score (12p.) & 6 parts.
£7.55
1.Ti 2.Anderson, Carl 3.Sr

(B79-50780)

VVNK/AE — Arrangements. Sonatas
Graupner, Christoph
Sonata in G major / [by] Christoph Graupner ; arranged by Carl Anderson, for clarinet choir, 2 B-flat clarinets, E-flat alto clarinet, B-flat bass clarinet, E-flat contrabass clarinet. — New York ; London : Schirmer, 1978. — 4to. — (Early German music for clarinet choir)
Score (18p.) & 5 parts.
£9.10
1.Anderson, Carl 2.Sr

(B79-50781)

VVNSK — Quartets. Arrangements
Weber, Carl Maria von, *Freiherr*
[Fughettas, piano, op.1. *arr*]. Six fughettas. Op.1 / [by] Carl Maria von Weber ; arranged by John Horton for four B flat clarinets. — London : Schott, 1979. — [2],6p. ; 4to.
Unpriced
1.Ti 2.Horton, John

(B79-51275)

VVNTQK — Clarinets(2) & piano. Arrangements
Albéniz, Isaac
[España. Op.165. *Selections : arr*]. Two pieces from España / [by] Isaac Albéniz ; arranged for two clarinets and piano by Alan Frank. — London : Oxford University Press, 1979. — 4to.
Score (15p.) & 2 parts.
ISBN 0-19-355137-3 : Unpriced
1.Ti 2.Ti 3.Frank, Alan

(B79-50782)

VVNTQK/DJ — Clarinets (2) & piano. Arrangements. Motets
Cherubini, Luigi
[Hymnes sacrées. Ave Maria. *arr*]. Ave Maria. Offertorium / [by] Luigi Cherubini ; edited by Robin de Smet for 1. Soprano, B flat clarinet, (or flute) and piano, 2, two B flat clarinets and piano, 3, Flute, B flat clarinet and piano. — London : Fentone Music : Breitkopf and Härtel, 1979. — 4to.
Score (8p.) & 4 parts.
Unpriced
Primary classification KFLE/VVPDJ
1.Ti 2.Ti 3.De Smet, Robin

(B79-51001)

VVNU — Duets
Boufil, Jacques Jules
[Duo, clarinets, op.2, no.1, C major]. Grand duo, op.2, no.1 : for
two clarinets / [by] Jacques Boufil ; edited by Pamela Weston. —
London : Fentone Music, 1979. — 20p ; 4to.
£1.80
1.Weston, Pamela

(B79-50783)

Yost, Michel
[Duets, clarinets, op.5, nos.1-3]. Six duos. Op.5, nos.1-3 for 2
clarinets / [by] Michel Yost. — London : Musica rara, 1979. —
2pt ; 4to.
Unpriced
1.Ti 2.Ti

(B79-51276)

VVNU/AF — Duets. Exercises
Lyons, Graham
Set two : clarinet duets for teacher and pupil / written and
arranged by Graham Lyons. — London : Chester Music.
Vol.1. — 1974. — 4to. —
Unpriced
1.Ti

(B79-51277)

Vol.1. — 1979. — 4to. —
Unpriced
1.Ti

(B79-51278)

VVNUK/AAY — Duets. Arrangements. Collections
Thirty easy classical duets : for unaccompanied clarinets / arranged
by Alan Frank and Watson Forbes. — London : Oxford
University Press, 1978. — [1],26p ; fol.
ISBN 0-19-356566-8 : Unpriced
1.Frank, Alan 2.Forbes, Watson

(B79-50356)

VVP — CLARINET & PIANO
VVPJ — Miscellaneous works
Oberthür, Charles
[Cadeaux de noces. Op.65. Le désir]. 'Le désir' : for clarinet and
piano / [by] Carl Oberthuer ; edited by Colin Bradbury. —
London : Chester Music, 1979. — 4to. — (Chester woodwind
series)
Score ([2],5p.) & part.
Unpriced
1.Ti 2.Ti 3.Bradbury, Colin 4.Sr

(B79-51279)

Pert, Morris
Luminos. Op.16a : for basset horn (or clarinet B flat) and piano /
[by] Morris Pert. — London : Weinberger, 1978. — 4to.
Duration 15 min. — Score (15p.) & part.
Unpriced
Primary classification VVXPJ
1.Ti

(B79-50361)

Stanford, *Sir* Charles Villiers
[Intermezzos, clarinet & piano, op.13]. Three intermezzi, op.13 :
for clarinet and piano / [by] Charles Villiers Stanford ; edited by
Colin Bradbury. — London : Chester Music, 1979. — 4to. —
(Chester woodwind series)
Score ([2],15p.) + part.
Unpriced
1.Sr

(B79-51280)

VVPK/AAY — Arrangements. Collections
Clarinet series / [arranged by] Jack Brymer. — London :
Weinberger.
For clarinet and piano. — Score ([2],10p.) & part.
Easy book 2. — 1979. — 4to.
Unpriced
1.Brymer, Jack

(B79-51281)

Moderate book 2. — 1979. — 4to.
Unpriced
1.Brymer, Jack

(B79-51282)

Fun music : for clarinet / arranged by Bert Brewis. — London :
Chappell.
Score (28p.) & part.
[Vol.1]. — 1976. — 4to.
Unpriced
1.Brewis, Bert

(B79-50357)

Vol.2. — 1977. — 4to.
Unpriced
1.Brewis, Bert

(B79-50358)

VVPK/AE — Arrangements. Sonatas
Beethoven, Ludwig van
[Sonata, piano duet, op.6, D major. *arr*]. Sonata in D major, op.6,
for clarinet and piano / [by] Ludwig van Beethoven ; transcribed
by Michael Webster. — New York ; London : Schirmer, 1978. —
4to. — (Schirmer's library of musical classics ; vol.1926)
Score (16p.) & part.
£3.05
1.Webster, Michael 2.Sr

(B79-50784)

VVPK/AHP — Arrangements. Jigs
Humphries, J S
[Sonata, violins (2), op.1, no.12, G major. Gigue. *arr*]. Jig / [by]
J.S. Humphries ; arranged by Richard Graves. — York : Banks,
1979. — 4to.
Score (4p.) & part.
Unpriced
1.Graves, Richard

(B79-50785)

VVPK/DW/GB/AY — Arrangements. Popular songs. Collections
Fun clarinet : for young people of any age / music arrangements,
Roy Slack. — London : EMI, 1979. — 4to.
With piano. — Score (24p.) & part.
ISBN 0-86175-060-8 : Unpriced
1.Slack, Roy

(B79-51283)

VVPK/LFL — Arrangements. Concertinos
Donizetti, Gaetano
[Concertino, clarinet, B flat major. *arr*]. Concertino für Klarinette
und Kammerorchester. B-dur / [von] Gaetano Donizetti ;
herausgegeben und rekonstruiert von Raymond Meylan, Ausgabe
für Klarinette und Klavier vom Komponisten. — Frankfurt :
Litolff ; London : Peters, 1979. — 4to.
Score (12p.) & part.
Unpriced
1.Meylan, Raymond

(B79-50786)

VVPLVW — CLARINET & BASSOON
Tausch, Franz
[Duos, clarinet & bassoon, op.21]. Three duos for clarinet and
bassoon. Op.21 / [by] J. [sic] Tausch ; [edited by] H. Voxman. —
London : Musica rara, 1979. — 2pt ; 4to.
Unpriced
1.Ti 2.Voxman, Himie

(B79-51285)

VVPM — UNACCOMPANIED CLARINET
VVPMG — Suites
Harvey, Paul
Pets : a suite of 8 pieces for unaccompanied clarinet / by Paul
Harvey. — Chesham : Ricordi, 1979. — 13p ; 4to.
Unpriced
1.Ti

(B79-51286)

VVPMHX — Jazz
Dentato, John
Jazz players library : 10 classic tunes in their original versions and
in completely notated jazz versions / arranged by Johnny 'Dee'
Dentato. — Bryn Mawr ; [London] : Chappell, 1979. — 24p ; 4to.
For unaccompanied tenor saxophone.
Unpriced
Primary classification VUTPMHX
1.Ti

(B79-51271)

VVPMJ — Miscellaneous works
Bennett, Richard Rodney
Scena III : clarinet solo / [by] Richard Rodney Bennett. —
Sevenoaks : Novello, 1979. — 11p ; 4to.
£2.60
1.Ti

(B79-51287)

Davies, Peter Maxwell
The seven brightness : solo B flat clarinet / [by] Peter Maxwell
Davies. — London : Boosey and Hawkes, 1978. — [1],4p ; fol.
Duration 3 1/2 min.
Unpriced
1.Ti
(B79-50359)

Feld, Jindřich
Suite rhapsodica : for clarinet solo, 1976 / by Jindřich Feld. —
New York ; London : Schirmer, 1978. — 7p ; 4to.
£1.80
1.Ti
(B79-51288)

Harvey, Paul
Clarinet à la carte : a menu for unaccompanied clarinet / [by]
Paul Harvey. — Chesham : Ricordi, 1979. — [1],12p ; 4to.
Unpriced
1.Ti
(B79-51289)

VVPMK/AAY — Arrangements. Collections
17 classical solos : for unaccompanied clarinet / edited by Pamela
Weston. — London : Fentone Music : Breitkopf and Härtel, 1979.
— 28p ; 4to.
£1.85
1.Weston, Pamela 2.Seventeen classical solos
(B79-51290)

VVPMK/DP/LF/AY — Arrangements. Carols. Christmas.
Collections
Happy Christmas : B flat clarinet / arranged by Cecil Bolton and
Jack Moore. — London : EMI, 1978. — 44p ; 4to.
Carols.
Unpriced
1.Bolton, Cecil 2.Moore, Jack
(B79-50360)

VVX — BASSET HORN
VVXPJ — Basset horn & piano. Miscellaneous works
Pert, Morris
Luminos. Op.16a : for basset horn (or clarinet B flat) and piano /
[by] Morris Pert. — London : Weinberger, 1978. — 4to.
Duration 15 min. — Score (15p.) & part.
Unpriced
Also classified at VVPJ
1.Ti
(B79-50361)

VWN — BASSOON ENSEMBLE
VWNTPW — Two bassoons & keyboard
Schiffelholz, Johann Paul
[Trio, bassoons & continuo, G major]. Trio in G for 2 bassoons
and basso continuo / [by] (Johann Paul?) Schiffelholz ; edited by
H. Voxman, continuo realisation by R. Block. — London :
Musica rara, 1978. — 4to.
Attributed to Johann Paul Schiffelholz. — Score ([1],24p.) & 3 parts.
Unpriced
1.Block, Robert Paul 2.Voxman, Himie
(B79-50362)

VWP — BASSOON & PIANO
VWP/AY — Collections
First book of bassoon solos / by Lyndon Hilling and Walter
Bergmann. — London : Faber Music, 1979. — 4to.
Score ([4],25p.) & part.
Unpriced
1.Hilling, Lyndon 2.Bergmann, Walter
(B79-50787)

VWPE — Sonatas
Telemann, Georg Philipp
[Der getreue Music Meister. Sonata, bassoon & continuo, F
minor]. Sonate in f-moll für Fagott oder Violoncello und Basso
continuo = Sonata in F minor for bassoon or cello and basso
continuo / [von] Georg Philipp Telemann ; herausgegeben von,
edited, Winfried Michel. — Winterthur : Amadeus ; [London] :
[Schott], 1977. — 4to.
Score ([1],14p.) & 2 parts.
Unpriced
Also classified at SRPE
1.Ti 2.Michel, Winfried
(B79-50363)

VWPK — Arrangements
Hess, Willy
[Quintet, contrabassoon & string quartet, op.63]. Quintet für
Kontrafagott oder Fagott und Streichquartett op.63 / [von] Willy
Hess ; Original-Quintett-Fassung und Ausgabe für Kontrafagott
oder Fagott und Klavier vom Komponisten. — Zurich :
Amadeus ; [London] : [Schott], 1979. — 4to.
Score (15p.) & part.
Unpriced
(B79-50364)

VY — BAGPIPES
VY/AYDL — Collections. Scotland
Duncan Johnstone collection of pipe tunes. — Glasgow : Duncan
Johnston Piping School.
Vol.1. — 1978. — [5],43p ; 4to.
Unpriced
1.Johnstone, Duncan
(B79-50365)

W — BRASS WIND INSTRUMENTS
W/AC — Tutors
Riddgeon, John
Brass for beginners : bass clef, trombone, euphonium and
baritone / [by] John Ridgeon. — London : Boosey and Hawkes,
1979. — [6],53p : ill,port ; 4to.
Unpriced
1.Ti
(B79-51292)

WM — BRASS BAND
WM/AY — Collections
Johnson, Stuart
Second intermediate band book / [by] Stuart Johnson. —
Watford : R. Smith, 1979. — 68p ; 4to.
Unpriced
1.Ti
(B79-50788)

The **Salvation** Army Brass Band Journal (Festival series). —
London : Salvationist Publishing and Supplies.
Nos.392-395 : Swiss rhapsody for flugel horn (or cornet) by Leslie Condon.
Variations on Laudate Dominum by Edward Gregson. Endless song : moto
perpetuo, by Michael Kenyon. Near the cross : meditation by Dudley
Bright. — 1978. — [1],85p ; obl.8vo. —
Unpriced
(B79-50366)

Nos.396-398 : The call to arms : selection, by James Curnow. Logos : tone
poem by Ray Steadman-Allen. Home on the range : euphonium solo, by
Erik Leidzén. — 1979. — [1],85p ; obl. 8vo. —
Unpriced
(B79-51293)

Nos.399-402 : Songs of childhood: suite, by David Catherwood. Variations
and fugue on 'Rachie' (a young person's guide to the brass band) by Michael
Kenyon. The sound of the gospel: festival march, by Robert Redhead.
Golden slippers: cornet solo, by Norman Bearcroft. — 1979. — [1],85p. ;
obl.8vo. —
Unpriced
(B79-51294)

The **Salvation** Army Brass Band Journal (General series). —
London : Salvationist Publishing and Supplies.
Nos. 1709-1712 : Kilmarnock Temple - march / by James Anderson. The
everlasting arms : selection, by Ray Steadman-Allen. What is life? Flugel
horn solo, by Gluck, arr. Brian Bowen. The Easter message ; selection by
Leslie Condon. — 1978. — [1],49p ; obl.4to. —
Unpriced
(B79-50367)

Nos. 1713-1716 : Brooklands, march by Dudley Bright. Sing along with the
band, by Norman Bearcroft. I love to sing : song setting, by Leslie Condon.
Theodora : hymn tune arrangement by David Jones. Become aware of Him :
song setting by Robert Redhead. — 1979. — [1],49p ; obl.4to. —
Unpriced
(B79-50789)

The **Salvation** Army Brass Band Journal (Triumph series). —
London : Salvation Army Brass Band Journal.
Nos. 829-832 : Brazilian jubilee : march, by Leslie Condon. Christ is the
answer : air varié, by Erik Silfverberg. Jesus is real to me : trombone solo by
Noel Jones, and, Prayer of childhood : cornet solo, by Leslie Condon.
Where joy and duty meet : march, by Derek Jordan. — 1979. — [1],37p :
obl.8vo. —
Unpriced
(B79-50790)

The **Salvation** Army Brass Band Journal, (Triumph series). —
London : Salvationist Publishing and Supplies.
Nos 833-836 : It's new : march, by John Larsson. A call to action : tone
poem, by Ray Steadman-Allen. The manger scene : carol setting, by Leslie
Condon. Coming to the King : meditation, by David Wells. — 1979. — [1],
57p ; obl. 8vo. —
Unpriced
(B79-51295)

The **Salvation** Army Brass Band Journal (Triumph series). —
London : Salvationist Publishing and Supplies.
Nos.825-828 : God's children, [by] William Himes. My heavenly home:
selection [by] A.H. Jakeway. By the light of that star: carol setting [by] John
Larsson, arr. Roy Steadman-Allen. Life's dedication: selection [by]
Christopher Cole. — 1978. — [1],41p ; obl.8vo. —
Unpriced

(B79-50368)

The **Salvation** Army Brass Band Journal (Unity series). —
London : Salvationist Publishing and Supplies.
Nos.81-88 : Alice Springs : march by Allen Pengilly. Sleaford : march by
Neville McFarlane. Harvest home, fantasy by Ralph Pearce. Mannheim :
hymn tune arrangement by Michael Kirk. Trumpet tune, by Purcell, arr.
Ray Steadman-Allen. It happened to me : selection songs by John Gowans
and John Larsson arr. Ray Steadman-Allen. Three Czech carols, by G. John
Swansbury. Chorus time no.1 : selection, choruses by Sidney E. Cox. Christ
for all : selection by Erik Silfverberg. — 1979. — [1],33p ; obl. 8vo. —
Unpriced

(B79-51296)

WMFL — Concertinos
Lane, Philip
Concertino / [by] Philip Lane. — Watford : R. Smith, 1979. —
42p ; obl.4to.
For brass band.
Unpriced
1.Ti

(B79-51297)

WMG — Suites
Ehmann, Wilhelm
Leichte Choral-Partiten : für Bläser / herausgegeben von Wilhelm
Ehmann. — Kassel ; [London] : Bärenreiter, 1978. — 48p ; 4to.
£3.96
1.Ti

(B79-50369)

Slack, Roy
Alacita : a suite for brass band / [by] Roy Slack. — London :
Peters, 1978. — 28p ; obl.4to.
Unpriced
1.Ti

(B79-50370)

WMGM — Marches
Spurgin, Anthony
The Duke of York'&s patrol / by Anthony Spurgin. — London :
Studio Music, 1978. — 8vo.
Duration 3 min. — Conductor & 25 parts, with several copies of various
parts.
Unpriced
1.Ti

(B79-50371)

WMGN — Fanfares
Hodkinson, Sydney
Two fanfares for a festival : for brass, timpani, and percussion /
[by] Sydney Hodkinson. — New York ; London : Associated
Music, 1978. — 4to.
Score (13p.) & 10 parts.
£7.25
1.Ti

(B79-50791)

WMHNG — Hornpipes. Suites
Cruft, Adrian
Traditional hornpipe suite : for brass band / [by] Adrian Cruft ;
arranged Peter A. Summer. — London ((1 The Retreat, S.W.14)) :
Joad Press, 1977. — fol.
Conductor (8p.) & 17 parts.
Unpriced
1.Ti

(B79-50372)

WMJ — Miscellaneous works
Catelinet, Philip
Three sketches for brass band / [by] Philip Catelinet. —
Sevenoaks : Paxton, 1979. — 32p ; obl. 4to.
Unpriced
1.Ti

(B79-51298)

Huber, Paul
Symphonic music / [by] Paul Huber. — Watford : R. Smith,
1979. — 38p ; obl. 4to.
For brass band.
Unpriced
1.Ti

(B79-51299)

Lear, Hogarth
Mr. Lear's carnival : for brass band / [by] W. Hogarth Lear. —
London : Chester Music, 1979. — 4to. — (Just brass ; no.14 BB)
Score (33p.) & 25 parts, with several copies of various parts.
Unpriced
1.Ti 2.Sr

(B79-51300)

Meacham, Frank W
The American patrol / [by] Frank W. Meacham ; arranged by S.
Smith-Masters. — London : Studio Music, 1979. — 8vo.
Conductor & parts.
Unpriced
1.Ti 2.Smith-Masters, Stanley

(B79-50373)

Newsome, Roy
Dead man's cave / by Roy Newsome. — London : Studio Music,
1978. — 8vo.
For brass band. — Very freely based on 'Down among the dead men'. —
Conductor & 25 parts, with several copies of various parts.
Unpriced
1.Ti

(B79-50374)

Tate, Phyllis
Illustrations : for brass band / by Phyllis Tate. — Sevenoaks :
Novello, 1978. — [6],50p ; 4to. — (Novello brass band series)
Unpriced
1.Ti 2.Sr

(B79-50375)

WMK — Arrangements
Berlioz, Hector
[Béatrice et Bénédict. Overture. arr]. Overture Beatrice and
Benedict / arranged for brass band by Keith Wilkinson. —
Watford : R. Smith, 1979. — 45p. ; obl.4to.
Unpriced
1.Ti 2.Ti 3.Wilkinson, Keith

(B79-51301)

Mozart, Wolfgang Amadeus
[Concerto, piano, no.21, K.467, C major. Andante. arr]. The
Elvira Madigan theme ... / [by] Mozart ; arranged by Godfrey
Richards. — London : Studio Music, 1978. — 8vo.
Short score (2p.) & 25 parts, with several copies of various parts.
Unpriced
1.Ti 2.Richards, Godfrey

(B79-50376)

Mussorgsky, Modest
[Pictures at an exhibition. arr]. Pictures at an exhibition / [by]
Mussorgsky ; arranged for brass ensemble by Elgar Howarth. —
London : Chester Music, 1979. — [2],162p ; 4to. — (Just brass ;
no.36)
Unpriced
1.Ti 2.Howarth, Elgar 3.Sr

(B79-51302)

Myers, Stanley
[Cavatina. arr]. Cavatina / [by] Stanley Myers ; arranged by
Derek Broadbent. — London : EMI, 1979. — 8vo.
For brass band - Conductor & 24 parts.
Unpriced
1.Ti 2.Broadbent, Derek

(B79-50792)

Siebert, Edrich
The good old songs : (Selection no.1) / arranged by Edrich
Siebert. — London : Studio Music, 1978. — 8vo.
For brass band. — Conductor & 25 parts, with several copies of various
parts.
Unpriced
1.Ti 2.Siebert, Edrich

(B79-50377)

WMK/AGM — Arrangements. Marches
Walton, Sir William
[Orb and sceptre. arr]. Orb and sceptre / [by] William Walton ;
arranged for brass band by Eric Ball. — London : Oxford
University Press, 1979. — 41p ; 4to.
Duration 8 1/2 min.
ISBN 0-19-368537-x : Unpriced
1.Ti 2.Ball, Eric

(B79-51303)

WMK/AHLF — Arrangements. Galops
Hertel, Peter Ludwig
[Flick and Flock's Abenteuer. Feuerwehr Galopp. arr]. The
firemen's galop / [by] P. Hertel ; arranged by Edrich Siebert. —
London : Harmer Music : Studio Music, 1978. — 8vo.
For brass band. — Conductor & 24 parts, with several copies of various
parts.
Unpriced
1.Ti 2.Ti 3.Siebert, Edrich

(B79-50378)

WMK/DW — Arrangements, Songs, etc
Livingston, Jerry
[Casper the friendly ghost. *arr*]. Casper the friendly ghost / music by Jerry Livingston ; arranged by Leonard Rush. — New York : Warner ; [London] : [Blossom], 1978. — 4to. — (Supersound series for young bands)
Score (6p.) & 50 parts.
Unpriced
1.Ti 2.Rush, Leonard 3.Sr

(B79-50379)

Richards, Godfrey
Simple gifts : the traditional melody on which 'Lord of the dance' is based / traditional, arranged by Godfrey Richards. — London : Studio Music, 1979. — 8vo.
Conductor & 25 parts.
Unpriced
1.Ti

(B79-50380)

Scott, Alicia Anne, *Lady John Scott*
[Annie Laurie. *arr*]. Annie Laurie / [melody by Lady John Scott] ; arranged by Roy Newsome. — London : Studio Music, 1978. — 8vo.
For brass band. — Conductor & 25 parts, with several copies of various parts.
Unpriced
1.Ti 2.Ti 3.Newsome, Roy

(B79-50381)

Siebert, Edrich
The good old songs : selections no.2 / arranged by Edrich Siebert. — London : Studio Music, 1979. — 8vo.
Conductor & 24 parts, with several copies of various parts.
Unpriced
1.Ti

(B79-50382)

WMK/HM — Arrangements. Ballet
Tchaikovsky, Peter
[Sleeping beauty. Op.66. Panorama. *arr*]. Panorama ... / [by] Tchaikovsky ; arr. Geoffrey Brand. — Watford : R. Smith, 1979. — 4to.
Conductor & 25 parts, with several copies of various parts.
Unpriced
1.Ti 2.Ti 3.Brand, Geoffrey

(B79-50383)

WMP — SOLO INSTRUMENT (S) & BRASS BAND
WMPWTT — Tenor horn & brass band
Woods, Stanley
Little blue boy : for tenor horn and brass band / [by] Stanley Woods. — London : Chester Music, 1979. — 4to. — (Just brass ; no.15 BB)
Conductor & 22 parts with various parts in duplicate.
Unpriced
1.Ti 2.Sr

(B79-51305)

WMPWTTFL — Tenor horn & brass band. Concertinos
Wood, Gareth
[Concertino, horn (tenor) & brass band]. Concertino for tenor horn and brass band / [by] Gareth Wood. — Watford : R. Smith, 1979. — 27p ; obl. 4to.
Facsimile of the composer's autograph.
Unpriced

(B79-51306)

WMPWW — Euphonium & brass band
Sparke, Philip
Fantasy for euphonium and brass band / by Philip Sparke. — Watford : R. Smith, 1979. — 29p ; obl.4to.
Unpriced
1.Ti

(B79-50384)

WN — BRASS ENSEMBLE
WNH/AYH — Dances. Collections. France
Old French dances / arranged for brass ensemble by Peter Reeve. — London : Chester Music, 1979. — 4to. — (Just brass ; no.34)
Score (18p.) & 16 parts.
Unpriced
1.Reeve, Peter 2.Sr

(B79-51307)

WNK — Arrangements
Aston, Hugh
[A hornpype. *arr*]. A hornpype / [by] Hugh Aston ; arranged for brass ensemble by Elgar Howarth. — Sevenoaks : Novello, 1979. — 9p. ; 8vo.
Duration 4 min.
£1.55
1.Ti 2.Howarth, Elgar

(B79-51308)

WNQ — Sextets
Bläsermusik alter Meister : für zwei Trompeten und drei Posaunen / herausgegeben von Horst Wetzlar. — Berlin : Merseburger ; [London] : [Bärenreiter], 1978. — 19p ; 8vo.
£1.32
1.Wetzlar, Horst

(B79-50793)

WNR — Quintets
Antoniou, Theodore
'The DO quintet' : for two trumpets, horn, trombone, tuba, 1978 / [by] Theodore Antoniou. — Kassel ; London : Bärenreiter, 1978. — 4p ; obl.fol.
£5.94
1.Ti

(B79-50385)

Blank, Allan
An American medley : for brass quintet, flute(s) and percussion / [by] Allan Blank. — New York ; London : Associated Music, 1978. — 4to.
£10.60
1.Ti

(B79-51309)

Horovitz, Joseph
Folk song fantasy : for brass quintet / [by] Joseph Horovitz. — London : J. & W. Chester, 1979. — 4to. — (Just brass ; no.33)
Score ([1],6p.) & 6 parts, with an alternative part for E flat bass.
Unpriced
1.Ti 2.Sr

(B79-50386)

WNR/T — Variations
Howarth, Elgar
[Variations, brass quintet]. Variations for brass quintet / [by] Elgar Howarth. — Sevenoaks : Novello, 1979. — [3],15p ; 8vo.
£1.95

(B79-50794)

WNRK/DP/LF/AY — Quintets. Arrangements. Christmas carols. Collections
'Twas the brass before Christmas : five garlands for brass quintet, for 2 trumpets, horn, trombone and tuba / arranged by David Baldwin. — New York ; London : Schirmer.
Garland 1. — 1978. — 4to.
Score (12p.) & 5 parts). — Contents: 1: O come all ye faithful, quintet - 2: Silent night, trio - 3: We wish you a merry Christmas.
£2.50
1.Baldwin, David

(B79-51310)

Garland 2. — 1978. — 4to.
Score (16p.) & 5 parts). — Contents: 1: Joy to the world, quintet - 2: Deck the halls, trio - 3: God rest ye, quintet - 4: Good King Wenceslas, quintet.
£2.50
1.Baldwin, David

(B79-51314)

Garland 3. — 1978. — 4to.
Score (8p.) & 5 parts). — Contents: 1: Away in a manger; trio - 2: March of the kings; duet - 3: Angels we have heard on high; quintet.
£2.50
1.Baldwin, David

(B79-51311)

Garland 4. — 1978. — 4to.
Score (12p.) & 5 parts). — Contents: 1: O come, O come Immanuel; duet - 2: We three kings; trio - 3: Medley : Hark, the herald angels sing, O Christmas tree, the first noel; quintet.
£2.50
1.Baldwin, David

(B79-51312)

Garland 5. — 1978. — 4to.
Score (12p.) & 5 parts). — Contents: 1: Jingle bells; quintet.
£2.50
1.Baldwin, David

(B79-51313)

WNS — Quartets
Clarke, Keith Robert
Cadences : for brass quartet / [by] Keith Robert Clarke. — Sevenoaks : Novello, 1979. — [2],14p ; 8vo.
£1.95
1.Ti

(B79-50795)

Mason, Tony
The night sky : for elementary brass quartet (2 trumpets, 2 trombones) / by Tony Mason. — London (7 Garrick St., W.C.2) : Middle Eight Music, 1979. — 4to. — (Middle eight ensemble series ; 5)
Score (8p.) & 4 parts.
Unpriced
1.Ti 2.Sr

(B79-50387)

Premru, Raymond
[Quartet, trumpets (2), horn & trombone]. Quartet for two trumpets, horn and trombone / [by] Raymond Premru. — London : Chester Music, 1979. — 4to. — (Just brass ; no.35)
Score ([2],11p.) & 4 parts.
Unpriced
1.Sr

(B79-50796)

Saunders, Neil
Fantasia for brass quartet : for 2 trumpets and 2 trombones / [by] Neil Saunders. — Wendover : Roberton, 1979. — 4to.
Score (8p.) & 4 parts. — Duration 5 min.
£3.00
1.Ti

(B79-51315)

Schwertsik, Kurt
Kleine Blasmusik. Op.32 : five short movements for two trumpets and two trombones / [by] Kurt Schwertsik. — London : Boosey and Hawkes, 1978. — fol. — (Exploring music series : Ensemble series)
Score (8p.) & 4 parts.
Unpriced
1.Ti 2.Sr

(B79-50388)

WNSK/AAY — Quartets. Arrangements. Collections
Three Renaissance quartets / arranged for brass by Terence B. Ravenor. — London : Oxford University Press, 1978. — fol.
Piano reduction (2p.) & 8 parts. — Contents: 1: Passamezzo antico by Nicolaus Ammerbach - 2: Ballet du roy pour sonner après - 3: Canzona, by Heinrich Isaac.
ISBN 0-19-358490-5 : Unpriced
1.Ravenor, Terence B

(B79-50389)

WNSK/DW/G/AYB — Quartets. Arrangements. Folk songs.
Collections. Europe
Bläsersätze nach europäischen Volksliedern = Wind pieces from European folksongs : für vier Blechbläser, 2 Trompeten, (Flügelhörner, Horn ad lib., 2 Stimme), 2 Posaunen (Tenorhorn, Bariton, ad lib Tuba) = for four brass instruments, 2 trumpets, (flugelhorns, horn ad lib. 2nd part) 2 trombones (baritone euphonium, ad lib. tuba) / bearbeitet von, arranged by, Richard Zettler. — Mainz ; London : Schott, 1978. — 15p ; 4to.
£3.40
1.Zettler, Richard

(B79-50390)

WR — CORNET
WR/AC — Tutors
Wastall, Peter
Learn as you play trumpet & cornet / by Peter Wastall. — London : Boosey and Hawkes, 1979. — 64p ; 4to. — (Learn as you play)
Unpriced
Primary classification WS/AC
1.Ti 2.Sr

(B79-51316)

WS — TRUMPET
WS/AC — Tutors
Trompetenétuden II = Trumpet studies II = Etudy pro trubku II / herausgegeben von ... Hans-Joachim Krumpfer. — Leipzig : Deutscher Verlag für Musik ; [London] : [Breitkopf und Härtel], 1979. — 135p ; 4to.
Unpriced
1.Krumpfer, Hans Joachim

(B79-50797)

Wastall, Peter
Learn as you play trumpet & cornet / by Peter Wastall. — London : Boosey and Hawkes, 1979. — 64p ; 4to. — (Learn as you play)
Unpriced
Also classified at WR/AC
1.Ti 2.Sr

(B79-51316)

WSN — TRUMPET ENSEMBLE
Gabrieli, Andrea
[Madrigali et ricercari a quattro voci. *Selections*]. Five ricercare in four parts for brass / [by] A. Gabrieli ; ed. R.P. Block. — London : Musica rara, 1979. — 4to.
Score ([1],28p.) & 6 parts.
Unpriced
1.Ti 2.Ti 3.Block, Robert Paul

(B79-50798)

WSNTQK/AE — Trumpets (2) & piano. Arrangements. Symphonies
Jacchini, Giuseppe Maria
[Trattenimenti per camera. Sinfonia, trumpets (2) & string orchestra, op.5, no.8, D major. *arr*]. Sinfonia, op.5 no.8 for 2 trumpets, strings and basso continuo / [by] Giuseppe Jacchini ; edited [as a trumpet and piano reduction] by R.P. Block. — London : Musica rara, 1978. — 4to. — (Italian 17th and 18th century sinfonias and sonatas for trumpets and strings ; 32)
Score ([1],7p.) & 2 parts.
Unpriced
1.Ti 2.Block, Robert Paul 3.Sr

(B79-50799)

WSNTQK/DW — Trumpets (2) & piano. Arrangements. Songs, etc
Cruft, Adrian
[The Eatanswill election. The Eatanswill candidates. *arr*]. The Eatanswill candidates / [by] Adrian Cruft ; arranged for two B flat trumpets (or cornets) and piano. — London ((1 The Retreat, S.W.14)) : Joad Press, 1978. — 4to. — (The Eatanswill series)
Score (11p.) & part ; the parts for trumpets are printed in score - Duration 3 1/2 min.
Unpriced
1.Ti 2.Ti 3.Sr

(B79-50391)

WSNTQK/LE — Trumpets (2) & piano. Arrangements. Sonatas
Jacchini, Giuseppe Maria
[Trattenimenti per camera, op.5. Sonata, trumpets (2), strings & continuo, op.5, no.1, D major. *arr*]. Sonata, op.5, no.1, for 2 trombe (trumpets), strings and continuo / [by] Giuseppe Jacchini ; edited by R.P. Block. — London : Musica rara, 1978. — 4to. — (Italian 17th and 18th century sinfonias and sonatas for trumpets and strings ; 31)
Score ([1],8p.) & 2 parts.
Unpriced
1.Ti 2.Block, Robert Paul 3.Sr

(B79-50392)

WSP — TRUMPET & PIANO
WSP/AY — Collections
Baroque music for trumpet : including music by Albinoni, Charpentier, Keller, Molter, Telemann, Torelli / edited and annotated by Peter Wastall. — London : Boosey and Hawkes, 1979. — fol. — (Exploring music series)
Score ([1],13p.) & part.
£1.65
Also classified at WSPM/AY
1.Wastall, Peter 2.Sr

(B79-50393)

WSPJ — Miscellaneous works
Snell, Howard
3 pastiches : trumpet & piano / [by] Howard Snell. — Wallington (22 Woodcote Ave.) : Dunster Music, 1978. — [12p.] ; 4to.
Unpriced
1.Ti 2.Three pastiches

(B79-51317)

WSPK — Arrangements
Debussy, Claude
[Piano music. *Selections: arr*]. Four pieces / by Claude Debussy ; arranged by Howard Snell. — Wallington ((22 Woodcote Ave.)) : Dunster Music, 1974. — 18p. ; 4to.
Unpriced

(B79-51318)

WSPK/AAY — Arrangements. Collections
Fun music : for trumpet / arranged by Bert Brewis. — London : Chappell.
Score (28p.) & part.
[Vol.1]. — 1976. — 4to.
Unpriced
1.Brewis, Bert

(B79-50394)

Fun music : for trumpets / arranged by Bert Brewis. — London : Chappell.
Score (24p.) & part.
[Vol.2]. — 1977. — 4to.
Unpriced
1.Brewis, Bert

(B79-50395)

WSPK/AE — Arrangements. Sonatas
Gabrielli, Domenico
[Sonata, trumpet, string quintet & continuo, D.XI.7, D major. *arr*]. Sonata D.XI.7 in D for trumpet, strings and basso continuo / [by] Domenico Gabrielli ; [trumpet and piano reduction by] R.P. Block. — London : Musica rara, 1979. — 4to. — (Italian 17th and 18th century sinfonias and sonatas for trumpets and strings ; 23)
Score ([1],7p.) & part.
Unpriced
1.Block, Robert Paul 2.Sr

(B79-50800)

Jacchini, Giuseppe Maria
[Sonata, trumpet, strings & continuo, D XII 5, D major. *arr].*
Sonata, D XII 5 for tromba, (trumpet), strings and continuo /
[by] Giuseppe Jacchini ; edited [as a trumpet and piano reduction]
by R.P. Block. — London : Musica rara, 1978. — 4to. — (Italian
17th & 18th century sinfonias and sonatas for trumpets and
strings ; 30)
Score (6p.) & 2 parts. — Described as for '2 trumpets' on cover.
Unpriced
1.Block, Robert Paul 2.Sr

(B79-50801)

Jacchini, Giuseppe Maria
[Sonata, trumpet, violins (2) & continuo, D XII 5, D major. *arr].*
Sonata, D XII 5 for tromba, (trumpet), strings and continuo /
[by] Giuseppe Jacchini ; edited [as a trumpet and piano reduction]
by R.P. Block. — London : Musica rara, 1978. — 4to. — (Italian
17th & 18th century sinfonias and sonatas for trumpets and
strings ; 28)
Score ([1],7p.) & 2 parts. — Described as for '2 trumpets' on cover.
Unpriced
1.Block, Robert Paul 2.Sr

(B79-50802)

WSPK/AG — Arrangements. Suites
Telemann, Georg Philipp
[Suite, trumpet & string orchestra, D major. *arr].* Suite 1 for
trumpet, strings and basso continuo / [by] G.P. Telemann ; ed. [as
a trumpet and piano reduction by] R.P. Block. — London :
Musica rara, 1978. — 4to. — (17th and 18th century sonatas,
concerti and overtures for trumpets and orchestra ; no.95)
Score ([1],20p.) & part, with alternative parts for trumpets in D and B flat.
Unpriced
1.Block, Robert Paul 2.Sr

(B79-50396)

WSPK/DW — Arrangements. Songs, etc
Cruft, Adrian
[The Eatanswill election. The Anti-Buffs song. *arr].* The Anti-buffs
song : arranged for B flat trumpet (or cornet) and piano / [by]
Adrian Cruft. — London ((1 The Retreat, S.W.14)) : Joad Press,
1979. — 4to. — (The Eatanswill series)
Score (4p.) & part.
Unpriced
1.Ti 2.Ti 3.Sr

(B79-50397)

WSPK/LE — Arrangements. Sonatas
Gabrielli, Domenico
[Sonata, trumpet & string orchestra, D. XI, 8, D major. *arr].*
Sonata D. XI, 8 in D for trumpet, strings and basso continuo /
[by] Domenico Gabrielli ; ed. [as a reduction for trumpet and
piano] R.P. Block. — London : Musica rara, 1979. — 4to. —
(Italian 17th and 18th century sinfonias and sonatas for trumpets
and strings ; 23)
Score ([1],8p.) & 2 parts, with alternative parts in B flat and C (or rather
D).
Unpriced
1.Block, Robert Paul 2.Sr

(B79-50803)

WSPLR
Krebs, Johann Ludwig
[Chorale preludes, trumpet & organ]. Die sechs Choralvorspiele
für Trompete und Orgel = The six chorale preludes for trumpet
and organ / [von] Johann Ludwig Krebs ; [edited by] Edward H.
Tarr. — Hamburg ; London : Simrock, 1978. — obl.4to.
Score (43p.) & part.
Unpriced
1.Ti 2.Ti 3.Tarr, Edward H

(B79-50398)

Schibler, Armin
Rezitativ und Ostinato : für Trompete und Orgel / [von] Armin
Schibler. — Zürich ; [London] : Eulenburg, 1979. — obl.4to &
4to. — (Organa helvetica)
Score (15p.) & 2 parts.
Unpriced
1.Ti 2.Sr

(B79-50804)

Vejvanovský, Pavel Josef
[Balletti pro tabula. *Selections : arr].* Suite in B-Dur für Trompete
und Orgel, 1670 / [von] Pavel Josef Vejvanovský ; herausgegeben
und eingerichtet von Horst Wetzlar. — Berlin : Merseburger ;
[London] : [Bärenreiter], 1977. — 4to. — (Bläser & Orgel ; 5)
Score (20p.) & part.
Unpriced
1.Ti 2.Wetzlar, Horst 3.Sr

(B79-50806)

Zipp, Friedrich
Fünf Choralvorspiele : für Trompete und Orgel, 1975 / [von]
Friedrich Zipp ; herausgegeben von Horst Wetzlar. — Berlin :
Merseburger ; [London] : [Bärenreiter], 1978. — 4to. — (Bläser &
Orgel ; Hft.3)
£4.46
1.Ti 2.Wetzlar, Horst 3.Sr

(B79-50805)

WSPM — UNACCOMPANIED TRUMPET
WSPM/AY — Collections
Baroque music for trumpet : including music by Albinoni,
Charpentier, Keller, Molter, Telemann, Torelli / edited and
annotated by Peter Wastall. — London : Boosey and Hawkes,
1979. — fol. — (Exploring music series)
Score ([1],13p.) & part.
£1.65
Primary classification WSP/AY
1.Wastall, Peter 2.Sr

(B79-50393)

WSPMEM — Sonatinas
Henze, Hans Werner
[Sonatina, trumpet]. Sonatina for solo trumpet / [by] Hans
Werner Henze. — Wallington (22 Woodcote Ave.) : Dunster
Music, 1976. — [5p] ; fol..
Unpriced

(B79-51319)

WSPMHX — Jazz
Dentato, John
Jazz players library : 10 classic tunes in their original versions and
in completely notated jazz versions / arranged by Johnny 'Dee'
Dentato. — Bryn Mawr ; [London] : Chappell, 1979. — 24p. ;
4to.
For unaccompanied trumpet.
Unpriced
1.Ti

(B79-51320)

WSPMK/DP/LF/AY — Arrangements. Carols. Christmas.
Collections
Happy Christmas : B flat trumpet / arranged by Cecil Bolton and
Jack Moore. — London : EMI, 1978. — 44p ; 4to.
Carols.
Unpriced
1.Bolton, Cecil 2.Moore Jack

(B79-50399)

WTN — HORN ENSEMBLE
WTNM — Nonets
Fröhlich, Johannes Frederik
[March and hunting piece. Op.40. *arr].* Nonet for... horns / [by]
Johannes Frederik Fröhlich... ; edited by Richard Merewether. —
London ((116 Long Acre, W.C.2)) : Paxman, 1979. — 9pt. ; 4to.
£4.00
1.Ti 2.Merewether, Richard

(B79-51321)

WTP — HORN & PIANO
WTP/T — Variations
Rossini, Gioacchino Antonio
[Prélude, thème et variations pour cor]. Prelude, theme and
variations for French horn and piano / [by] Gioacchino Rossini ;
edited by Barry Tuckwell. — New York ; London : Schirmer,
1979. — 4to.
Score ([2],17p.) & part.
£3.65
1.Ti 2.Tuckwell, Barry

(B79-51322)

WTPK/DW — Arrangements. Songs, etc
Cruft, Adrian
[The Eatanswill election. The last voter's song. *arr].* The last
voter's song / [by] Adrian Cruft ; arranged for horn and piano. —
London ((1 The Retreat, S.W.14)) : Joad Press, 1978. — 4to. —
(The Eatanswill series)
Score (4p.) & part - Duration 2 min.
Unpriced
1.Ti 2.Ti 3.Sr

(B79-50400)

WTPM — UNACCOMPANIED HORN
WTPMG — Suites
Halstead, Anthony
[Suite, horn]. Suite for solo horn / [by] Anthony Halstead. —
Wallington (22 Woodcote Ave) : Dunster Music, 1978. — [6p.] ;
fol.
Unpriced

(B79-51323)

WUN — TROMBONE ENSEMBLE
WUNRHX — Quintets. Jazz
Jahn, Thomas
    Ten dance studies in jazz idiom : for trombone quintet / [by]
    Thomas Jahn. — New York ; London : Schirmer, 1978. — 4to.
    Score (26p.) & 5 parts.
    £8.50
    1.Ti
                                                                    (B79-50807)

WUNTRE — Trombones (2) & organ. Sonatas
Vejvanovský, Pavel Josef
    Sonata la posta : für drei Posaunen und Orgel, 1667 / [von] Pavel
    Josef Vejvanovský ; herausgegeben und eingerichtet von Horst
    Wetzlar. — Berlin : Merseburger ; [London] : [Bärenreiter], 1977.
    — 4to. — (Bläser & Orgel ; Hft.6)
    Score (8p.) & 3 parts.
    £2.97
    1.Ti 2.Wetzlar, Horst 3.Sr
                                                                    (B79-50808)

WUP — TROMBONE & PIANO
WUPJ — Miscellaneous works
Nash, Harold
    Four solo pieces : for trombone (in bass and treble clefs) / by
    Harold Nash. — London : Paterson, 1979. — 4to.
    With piano. — Score (5p.) & part.
    Unpriced
    1.Ti
                                                                    (B79-51324)

WUPM — UNACCOMPANIED TROMBONE
WUPME — Sonatas
Diethelm, Caspar
    [Sonata, trombone, op.128]. Sonate für Posaune solo, op.128,
    1975 / [von] Caspar Diethelm. — Zürich : Amadeus ; [London] :
    [Eulenburg], 1979. — 8p ; 4to.
    £0.28
                                                                    (B79-50809)

WUPMJ — Miscellaneous works
Beliebte Volkslieder : für Posaune mit 2. Stimme ad lib. / bearbeitet
    von Richard Zettler. — Mainz ; London : Schott, 1978. — 39p ;
    obl. 8vo.
    £2.40
    1.Zettler, Richard
                                                                    (B79-50401)

WVN — TUBA ENSEMBLE
WVNS — Quartets
Kochan, Günter
    Sieben Miniaturen (1977) : für vier Tuben / [von] Günter Kochan.
    — Berlin : Neue Musik ; [London] : [Breitkopf und Härtel], 1978.
    — 4to. — (Reihe Kammermusik)
    Score (19p.) & parts.
    £4.20
    1.Ti 2.Sr
                                                                    (B79-50810)

WVPLX — TUBA & PERCUSSION
WVPLXF — Oboe & percussion. Concertos
Kievman, Carson
    [Concerto, bassoon & percussion ensemble]. Concerto for bassoon
    and percussion ensemble (fire alarm system) / by Carson
    Kievman. — New York ; London : Associated Music, 1978. —
    9pt ; 4to. — (Composer's autograph series)
    Facsimile of composer's autograph.
    £2.75
    1.Sr
                                                                    (B79-50811)

XM — PERCUSSION BAND
XMK/AAY — Arrangements. Collections
The rhythm band book / [compiled] by Ruth Etkin ; illustrated by
    Bunny Cappiello ; with photographs by David Cohen. — New
    York : Sterling ; London : Oak Tree Press, 1979. — 96p ; obl.8vo.
    Unpriced
    1.Etkin, Ruth
                                                                    (B79-50402)

XN — PERCUSSION ENSEMBLE
XNS — Quartets
Beament, Peter
    The Oregon trail : a suite for percussion ensemble / by Peter
    Beament. — London (7 Garrick St., W.C.2) : Middle Eight Music,
    1979. — 4to. — (Middle eight ensemble series ; no.6)
    Score (8p.) & 4 parts.
    Unpriced
    1.Ti 2.Sr
                                                                    (B79-50403)

XNT/AF — Trios. Exercises
Fink, Siegfried
    Krenzpunkte : zwei Studien für Schlagzengtrio / [von] Siegfried
    Fink. — Mainz ; London : Schott, 1979. — 8p ; 4to. — (A
    battere ; 26)
    Foreword in German and English.
    £3.20
    1.Ti 2.Sr
                                                                    (B79-50812)

XPLPV — Percussion & electronic instrument
Antioniou, Theodore
    Parastasis I : for percussion and tape = für Schlagzeug und
    Tonband / [von] Theodore Antoniou. — Kassel ; London :
    Bärenreiter, 1978. — 4ff ; obl.fol.
    Printed on one side of the leaf only, with two copies of f.1.
    £7.92
    1.Ti
                                                                    (B79-50404)

XS — BELLS
XSQK/AAY — Handbells. Arrangements. Collections
Music for handbells : Module AIIN for 1 1/2 octaves : Hymns and
    things / [compiled] by D.A. and P. Bedford. — Chudleigh ((57a
    Fore St.)) : Handbell Ringers of Great Britain, 1979. — 70p ; 4to.
    Numeric notation.
    ISBN 0-904289-03-6 : Unpriced
    1.Bedford, D A 2.Bedford, P
                                                                    (B79-50813)

Composer and Title Index

Vol.5: Sonatas 17-20. (Schickhard, Johann Christian). *Musica rara. Unpriced* VSSPE (B79-50345)
Vol.6: Sonatas 21-24. (Schickhard, Johann Christian). *Musica rara. Unpriced* VSSPE (B79-50346)
Amahl and the night visitors : piano selections. (Menotti, Gian Carlo). *Schirmer. £3.00* QPK/CC (B79-51097)
Amahl and the night visitors. *Selections : arr.* Amahl and the night visitors : piano selections. (Menotti, Gian Carlo). *Schirmer. £3.00* QPK/CC (B79-51097)
Aman, David. The golden bond : a spectacular revue. (Barrow, Kenneth). *2 Cromwell Place, SW7 2JG : National Union of Townswomen's Guilds.* Pbk. *£1.50* BAPACP (B79-27787)
American ballads : settings of familiar tunes ... for orchestra
1: Star-spangled overture (on 'The star-spangled banner'). (Gould, Morton). *Schirmer. £6.10* MMJ (B79-50570)
2: Amber waves (on 'America the beautiful'). (Gould, Morton). *Schirmer. £6.10* MMJ (B79-50571)
3: Jubilo (on 'Year of Jubilo'). (Gould, Morton). *Schirmer. £6.10* MMJ (B79-50572)
4: Memorials (on 'Taps'). (Gould, Morton). *Schirmer. £6.10* MMJ (B79-50573)
5: Saratoga quickstep (on 'The girl I left behind me'). (Gould, Morton). *Schirmer. £6.10* MMJ (B79-50574)
6: Hymnal (on 'We shall overcome'). (Gould, Morton). *Schirmer. £6.10* MMJ (B79-50575)
American medley : for brass quintet, flute(s) and percussion. (Blank, Allan). *Associated Music. £10.60* WNR (B79-51309)
American music : a panorama. (Kingman, Daniel). *Schirmer : Collier Macmillan.* Pbk. *£7.45* A(YT/X) (B79-25329) ISBN 0-02-871260-9
American patrol. (Meacham, Frank W). *Studio Music. Unpriced* WMJ (B79-50373)
Amid nature. Op.63. A song went to my heart. So many songs = Es zog manch Lied : for four-part chorus of mixed voices a cappella. (Dvořák, Antonín). *Schirmer. £0.35* EZDW (B79-50890)
Amid nature. Op.63. Birch tree by the verdant slope. Birch tree on green hill = Birke am grünen Bergeshang : for four-part chorus of mixed voices a cappella. (Dvořák, Antonín). *Schirmer. £0.45* EZDW (B79-50891)
Amid nature. Op.63. Golden fields. Golden meadows = Goldne Fluren : for four-part chorus of mixed voices a cappella. (Dvořák, Antonín). *Schirmer. £0.35* EZDW (B79-50892)
Amid nature. Op.63. This is in truth a day of joy. A summer day = Ein Sommertag : for four-part chorus of mixed voices a cappella. (Dvořák, Antonín). *Schirmer. £0.45* EZDW (B79-50893)
Ammon, Blasius.
Sacrae cantiones. Parvulus filius. Parvulus filius : for 6 voices. *72 Brewery Rd, N.7 : Mapa mundi. Unpriced* EZDJ/LF (B79-50074)
Sacrae cantiones. Tenebrae factae sunt. Tenebrae factae sunt : for 4 voices. *72 Brewery Rd, N.7 : Mapa mundi. Unpriced* EZDJ/LK (B79-50083)
Amour des trois oranges. Opus 33 : opéra en 4 actes et 10 tableaux avec un prologue d'après Carlo Gozzi. (Prokofiev, Sergei). *Boosey and Hawkes. Unpriced* CQC (B79-50822)
Amsel : für Sopranstimme und Oboe. (Gerster, Ottmar). *Neue Musik : Breitkopf und Härtel. £1.20* KFLE/VTDW (B79-50551)
Anatomy of the piano. (Shead, Herbert A). *The Gresham Press, Old Woking, Surrey : Unwin Brothers Ltd.* Pbk. *£8.50* AQ/B (B79-15560) ISBN 0-905418-20-4
Ancestor worship : four poems of Emyr Humphreys, for baritone and piano. (Hoddinott, Alun). *Oxford University Press. Unpriced* KGNDW (B79-51009) ISBN 0-19-345433-5
Anchieta, Juan de. Salve Regina. *72 Brewery Rd, N.7 : Mapa mundi. Unpriced* GEZDJ (B79-50110)
Anderson, Carl.
Canzona. (La paglia). (Erbach, Christian). *Schirmer. Unpriced* VVNK (B79-50779)
Paduana, galliarda. *arr.* Canzon super intradam aechiopicam. (Scheidt, Samuel). *Schirmer. £7.55* VVNK (B79-50780)
Sonata in G major. (Graupner, Christoph). *Schirmer. £9.10* VVNK/AE (B79-50781)
Andersson, Benny. Chiquitita. *arr.* Chiquitita. *Chappell. Unpriced* KDW/GB (B79-50530)
Anderton, Craig.
Electronic projects for musicians. *Guitar Player Productions; 25 East St., Farnham, Surrey : Distributed by Omnibus Book Service.* Pbk. *£5.95* APV (B79-09656) ISBN 0-89122-011-9
Home recording for musicians. *Guitar Player Books; 25 East St., Farnham, Surrey : Distributed by Omnibus Book Service.* Pbk. *£7.95* A/FG (B79-12532) ISBN 0-89122-019-4
Andrews, J Austin. Introduction to music fundamentals : a programmed textbook for the elementary classroom teacher. 4th ed. *Prentice-Hall.* Sp. *£8.00* A/M(VG) (B79-00564) ISBN 0-13-489575-4
Ange. Guet-apens. *arr.* Guet-apens. *Chappell. Unpriced* KDW/HKR (B79-50981)
Anglian new music series.
Stiles, Frank. Sonata, oboe & piano. Sonata for oboe and piano. *(Paigles, Perry Green, Bradwell) : Anglian Edition. Unpriced* VTPE (B79-50772)
Stiles, Frank. Sonata, violin. Sonata for solo violin. *(Paigles, Perry Green, Bradwell) : Anglian Edition. Unpriced* SPME (B79-50683)
Angus-Butterworth, Lionel Milner. Sir Alex K. Butterworth, LL.B. (1854-1946) and Captain G.S.K. Butterworth, M.C.,B.A. (1885-1916). *Old Hall Hotel, Buxton, Derbyshire : The author.* Sd. *£0.50* BBVT(N) (B79-27781)
Annals of opera, 1597-1940. (Loewenburg, Alfred). 3rd ed., revised and corrected. *J. Calder. £30.00* AC/E(X25344) (B79-02988) ISBN 0-7145-3657-1
Annie Laurie. (Scott, Alicia Anne, *Lady John Scott*). *Studio Music. Unpriced* WMK/DW (B79-50381)
Annie Laurie. *arr.* Annie Laurie. (Scott, Alicia Anne, *Lady John Scott*). *Studio Music. Unpriced* WMK/DW (B79-50381)
Another op'nin', another show : for S.A. cambiata, B. or S.A.T.B. with piano. (Porter, Cole). *Chappell. Unpriced* DW (B79-50852)
Anthems from Addington
1: O sing unto the Lord a new song, by Peter Aston. God is gone up, by Anthony Hedges. Think on these things, by Arthur Wills. Daughters of Zion, by Francis Jackson. Thou art Peter, by Tony Hewitt-Jones. *Royal School of Church Music. Unpriced* DK/AY (B79-50440)
Anthologia organi : Orgelmusik aus acht Jahrhunderten
Band 5: Die Meister der Sweelinck-Schule. *Schott. £8.00* R/AY (B79-50227)
Band 6: Frescobaldi und sein Wirkungskreis. *Schott. £8.00* R/AY (B79-50228)
Band 7: Das italienische Barock. *Schott. £8.00* R/AY (B79-51116)
Band 8: Französische Orgelmusik von Titelouze bis d'Aquin. *Schott. £8.00* R/AY (B79-51117)
Anthology of French piano music. *Selections.* French piano music : an anthology. *Dover : Constable. Unpriced* QP/AY (B79-50616) ISBN 0-486-23381-2
Anti-buffs song : arranged for B flat trumpet (or cornet) and piano. (Cruft, Adrian). *(1 The Retreat, S.W.14) : Joad Press. Unpriced* WSPK/DW (B79-50397)
Antioniou, Theodore.
Parastasis I : for percussion and tape = für Schlagzeug und Tonband. *Bärenreiter. £7.92* XPLPV (B79-50404)
Stichomythia : for flute and guitar, 1976. *Bärenreiter. £8.58* VRPLTS (B79-50335)
Antonioni, Giovanni. Pièces de violes, liv. 4. *Selections : arr.* Cinque antiche danze francesi. (Marais, Marin). *Berben Breitkopf und Härtel. £1.90* SQPLTSK (B79-50686)
Antoniou, Theodore.
'The DO quintet' : for two trumpets, horn, trombone, tuba, 1978. *Bärenreiter. £5.94* WNR (B79-50385)
Two likes for contrabass, 1976. *Bärenreiter. £5.94* SSPMJ (B79-50693)
Apparailly, Yves. The seasons = Les saisons. *Waterloo Music : Roberton. £1.35* RSPMJ (B79-50254)
Appello : for piano. (Kolb, Barbara). *Boosey and Hawkes. Unpriced* QPJ (B79-50218)
Appledorn, Mary Jeanne van. *See* Van Appledorn, Mary Jeanne.
Appleford, Patrick. Living Lord : eighty hymns for the eighties. *Weinberger. Unpriced* DM/AY (B79-50838)
Arabesque : für Gitarre, Violoncello und Schlagzeug = for guitar, violoncello and percussion. (Humel, Gerald). *Schott. £10.80* NYJNT (B79-50201)
Arabesque, no.1. Ist arabesque : for organ and piano. (Debussy, Claude). *Columns Music : Schirmer (dist.). £1.95* QPLRK (B79-51111)
Arch, Gwen. The spinning wheel : S.S.A.A. (with divisi). *Oxford University Press. Unpriced* FDW (B79-50909) ISBN 0-19-342599-8
Ardley, Neil.
Musical instruments. *Macmillan. £0.95* AL/B (B79-50008) ISBN 0-333-24465-6
Musical instruments. *Macmillan.* Pbk. *£0.50* AL/B (B79-22637) ISBN 0-333-26156-9
Argento, Dominick.
In praise of music : (seven songs for orchestra). *Boosey and Hawkes. Unpriced* MMJ (B79-50172)
Miss Havisham's fire : opera in two acts. (Olon-Scrymgeour, John). *Boosey and Hawkes.* Sd. *£1.00* BARGAC (B79-26551)
A thanksgiving to God, for his house. *Boosey and Hawkes. Unpriced* EZDH (B79-50875)
The voyage of Edgar Allan Poe. *Vocal score.* The voyage of Edgar Allan Poe : opera in two acts. *Boosey and Hawkes. Unpriced* CC (B79-50413)
Aria de la folía española : für Orchester = for orchestra : (1977). (Henze, Hans Werner). *Schott. £19.60* MMJ (B79-50576)
Arien : für hohe Singstimme, Blockflöten, Fagott und Basso continuo. (Schürmann, Georg Caspar). Erstausgabe. *Bärenreiter. £6.60* KFTE/NWPNSDW (B79-50557)
Ariosti, Attilio. Sonatas, viola d'amore & continuo, 'Stockholm'. 'Stockholmer Sonaten' für Viola d'amore (Viola) und Basso continuo = 'Stockholm sonatas' for viola d'amore (viola) and basso continuo
2: Sonatas in ... B flat major ... G minor ... A minor. *Bärenreiter. £5.28* SQQPE (B79-50287)
Armatrading, Joan. To the limit. *arr.* To the limit. *Chappell. Unpriced* KDW/HKR (B79-50539)
Arne, Thomas Augustine.
Comus. Dances. *arr.* Two dances from 'Comus'. *Banks. Unpriced* RK (B79-50653)
Sonata, violin & continuo, E major. Sonata in E major for violin and basso continuo. *Oxford University Press. Unpriced* SPE (B79-50273) ISBN 0-19-355216-7
Twelve songs : for high voice
Book 1. *Stainer and Bell. Unpriced* KFTDW (B79-50552) ISBN 0-85249-461-0
Book 2. *Stainer and Bell. Unpriced* KFTDW (B79-50553) ISBN 0-85249-462-9
Arnold, Jay.
World's favorite masterworks for flute
Book 1. *Ashley : Phoenix. Unpriced* VR/AY (B79-50739)
Book 2. *Ashley : Phoenix. Unpriced* VR/AY (B79-50737)
Book 3. *Ashley : Phoenix. Unpriced* VR/AY (B79-50738)
Arpeggio = L'arpeggio = Das Arpeggio : essential guitar skill = tecnica essenziale per la chitarra = Grundlagen der Fertigkeit im Gitarrenspiel. (Lester, Bryan). *Ricordi. Unpriced* TS/AC (B79-51164)
Arrau, Claudio.
Sonaten für Klavier zu zwei Händen
Band 1. (Beethoven, Ludwig van). *Litolff : Peters. Unpriced* QPE/AZ (B79-50623)
Band 2. (Beethoven, Ludwig van). *Litolff : Peters. Unpriced* QPE/AZ (B79-50624)
Art de la flûte traversière. *Selections.* 12 caprices : for solo flute. (Lusse, Charles de). *Nova Music. Unpriced* VRPMJ (B79-51232)
Art of listening : developing musical perception. (Bamberger, Jeanne Shapiro). 4th ed. *Harper and Row.* Pbk. *£8.15* A/C (B79-28895) ISBN 0-06-040943-6
Art of singing : a compendium of thoughts on singing published between 1777 and 1927. (Monahan, Brent Jeffrey). *Scarecrow Press : Distributed by Bailey and Swinfen. £9.35* AK/E(VC/XFYS201) (B79-08929) ISBN 0-8108-1155-3
Art of the conductor. Robinson, Paul. Solti. *Macdonald and Jane's. £5.95* A/EC(P) (B79-24592) ISBN 0-354-04288-2
Arte de tocar la guitarra española por música, (Madrid, 1799). (Ferandiere, Fernando). *Tecla. Unpriced* TS/AC (B79-51163) ISBN 0-8494-0093-7
Arts foundation course : arts and society in an age of industrialization. Middleton, Richard. From Liszt to music hall. *Open University Press.* Pbk. *Unpriced* A(XFY101) (B79-36911) ISBN 0-335-05423-4
Arts foundation course. Hendrie, Gerald. Introduction to music. *Open University Press.* Pbk. *Unpriced* A (B79-16836) ISBN 0-335-05414-5
As the clouds with longing wander : Wie die Wolke : for three-part chorus of women's voices with piano accompaniment. (Brahms, Johannes). *Schirmer. £0.35* FDW (B79-50493)
Ascendens Christus : motet for the Ascension of our Lord, for 4 voices. (Handl, Jacob). *72 Brewery Rd, N.7 : Mapa mundi. Unpriced* EZDJ/LM (B79-50085)
Ashdown unison songs.
Barsham, Eve. Come give your hearts to joy this day. *Ashdown. Unpriced* JFDP/LF (B79-50936)
Hudson, Hazel. Go go Gabriel : unison with optional descant. *Ashdown. Unpriced* JFDP/LF (B79-50937)
Olive, Vivienne. Children's songs. *Edwin Ashdown. Unpriced* JFDW/GJ (B79-50519)
Ashdown vocal duets.
Benger, Richard. Requiescat : S.S. and piano. *Edwin Ashdown. £0.20* FLDW (B79-50919)
Hudson, Hazel. Will you be my partner? : a quodlibet. *Edwin Ashdown. £0.25* FDW (B79-50911)
Aslan lion books. Doney, Malcolm. Summer in the city : rock music and way of life. *Lion Publishing.* Pbk. *£1.25* AKDW/HKR(X) (B79-04538) ISBN 0-85648-085-1
Asriel, Andre. Jiddische Volkslieder : Liebeslieder, für Singstimme mit Klavier oder Gitarre. *Verlag Neue Musik : Breitkopf und Härtel. £3.60* KDW/G/AYEU (B79-50529)
Associated Board of the Royal Schools of Music.
Pianoforte examination pieces, 1980
Grade 1: Lists A & B. *Associated Board of the Royal Schools of Music. £0.50* Q/AL (B79-51054)
Grade 2: Lists A & B. *Associated Board of the Royal Schools of Music. £0.50* Q/AL (B79-51055)
Grade 3: Lists A & B. *Associated Board of the Royal Schools of Music. £0.60* Q/AL (B79-51056)
Grade 4: Lists A & B. *Associated Board of the Royal Schools of Music. £0.60* Q/AL (B79-51057)
Grade 5: Lists A & B. *Associated Board of the Royal Schools of Music. £0.90* Q/AL (B79-51058)
Grade 6: Lists A & B. *Associated Board of the Royal Schools of Music. £0.90* Q/AL (B79-51059)
Grade 7: Lists A & B. *Associated Board of the Royal Schools of Music. £1.10* Q/AL (B79-51060)
Association of Paediatric Chartered Physiotherapists. Music to help disabled children to move. (Kennard, Daphne). *A.P.C.P. Publications, 25 Goff's Park Rd, Southgate, Crawley, W. Sussex RH11 8AX : Association of Paediatric Chartered Physiotherapists.* Sd. *£0.50* A(VMX) (B79-13819)
Astell, Betty.
Aladdin. *Evans. Unpriced* CPP (B79-50018) ISBN 0-237-75044-9
Cinderella. */Evans. Unpriced* CPP (B79-50019) ISBN 0-237-75045-7
Dick Whittington. *Evans. Unpriced* CPP (B79-50020) ISBN 0-237-75046-5
Mother goose. *Evans. Unpriced* CPP (B79-50021) ISBN 0-237-75042-2
Queen of hearts. *Evans. Unpriced* CPP (B79-50022) ISBN 0-237-75047-3
The sleeping beauty. *Evans. Unpriced* CPP (B79-50023) ISBN 0-237-75043-0
Aston, Hugh. A hornpype. *arr.* A hornpype. *Novello. £1.55* WNK (B79-51308)
Atarah's bandkit. The elastic band. *Novello. Score, £5.00, Parts, Unpriced* LNK/AAY (B79-50160)
Atarah's bandkit
Strand D1: With a friend or two : eight duets for flute and classical guitar, with companion cassette. (Ben-Tovim, Atarah). *Novello. £7.00* VRPLTSK/AAY (B79-50758)
Atembogen : für Orchester. (Holliger, Heinz). *Schott. £18.00* MMJ (B79-51023)
Ath, Sylvia de'. *See* De'Ath, Sylvia.

Atkins, Florrie. La pensée petît sic valse. *(85 Wakefords Way, West Leigh) : Florrie Atkins. Unpriced* QPHW (B79-50628)
Atkins, John G. A country day : a festival piece. *EMI. Unpriced* JFE/NYFSDX (B79-50945)
Atkinson, René. Ma bonny lad : five traditional songs from Northumbria. *Roberton. £1.50* KDW/G/AYDJJ (B79-50963)
Aubade : song cycle for speaker, SATB and piano (or harp). (Ferguson, Barry). *Novello. Unpriced* DW (B79-50033)
Auckland, Bessie H. Joyful songs. *Oliver and Boyd. Unpriced* JFE/LDM/GJ (B79-50521) ISBN 0-05-003260-7
Audel, Stéphane. My friends and myself : conversations with Francis Poulenc. *Dobson. £4.95* BPO (B78-39780) ISBN 0-234-77251-4
Auden, Wysten Hugh. Paul Bunyan. Op.17. *Vocal score.* Paul Bunyan : an operetta in two acts and a prologue, op.17. (Britten, Benjamin, *Baron Britten*). *Faber Music. Unpriced* CF (B79-50014)
Auf dem Clavier spielende und das Gehör vergnügeude Caecilia (1736) : acht Sonaten, für Tasteninstrumente. (Maichelbek, Franz Anton). *Merseburger : Bärenreiter. £5.45* PWPE (B79-50610)
Australian composition in the twentieth century. *Oxford University Press. £18.50* A/D(M/YX/XM76) (B79-33552) ISBN 0-19-550522-0
Australian hymn book. With one voice : a hymn book for all the churches with Catholic supplement. *Collins. Unpriced* DM/AY (B79-50443)
Australian hymn book. *Melody part.* With one voice : a hymn book for all the churches, with Catholic supplements. *Collins. Unpriced* JADM (B79-50929) ISBN 0-00-599636-8
Auswahl aus 'Sechs Kinderstücke'. Op.72 und 'Lieder ohne Worte'. (Mendelssohn, Felix). *Breitkopf und Härtel. £2.10* QPJ (B79-51085)
Avantgarde, Jazz, Pop : Tenderzen zwischen Tonalität und Atonalität : neun Vorragstexte. *Schott.* Pbk. *£7.20* A/PF (B79-11128)
Ave Maria : for 8 voices. (Lobo, Alfonso). *72 Brewery Rd, N.7 : Mapa mundi. Unpriced* EZDJ (B79-50063)
Ave Maria. Offertorium. (Cherubini, Luigi). *Fentone Music : Breitkopf and Härtel. Unpriced* KFLE/VVPDJ (B79-51001)

Ave regina coelorum : Compline and votive antiphon for the season from Christmas to the Purification. (Lobo, Alfonso). *72 Brewery Rd, N.7 : Mapa mundi. Unpriced* EZDGKR/LF (B79-50057)
Away, delights : for men's chorus a cappella. (Diemer, Emma Lou). *Broude : Breitkopf and Härtel. £0.42* GEZDW (B79-50924)
Away in a manger. *arr.* Away in a manger. (Kirkpatrick, William Jerome). *36 Ranelagh Gdns W.6 : Cathedral Music. Unpriced* EZDP/LF (B79-50095)
Awayday : a holiday album of ten pieces for young pianists. (Helyer, Marjorie). *Novello. Unpriced* QPJ (B79-50215)
Ayres Netto, Marianinha. Sem dizer nada : canto e piano. *Fermata do Brasil : Clifford Essex. Unpriced* KDW (B79-50955)
Aznavour, Charles. Yesterday when I was young. *W.H. Allen. £5.95* AKDW/GB/E(P) (B79-36914) ISBN 0-491-02446-0
B-side the seaside. Seaside woman. *arr.* Seaside woman. (McCartney, Paul). *MPL Communications. Unpriced* KDW/GB (B79-50968)
Babell, William. Sonata, violin & continuo, op.posth., pt.1, no.11, G minor. Sonata 11 in G minor for oboe (or violin) and basso continuo. *Oxford University Press. Unpriced* SPE (B79-50274) ISBN 0-19-355226-4
Babylon : for stage band. (Levitt, Rod). *Associated Music. £7.55* MTJ (B79-50594)
Bach, Carl Philipp Emanuel. Concerto, keyboard & string orchestra, Wq 9, C minor. Concerto in C-moll für Cembalo (Klavier) und Streicher = Concerto in C minor for harpsichord (piano) and strings. Erstausgabe = First ed. *Nagel : Editio Musica : Bärenreiter. Unpriced* RXMPPWF (B79-50258)
Bach, Gottfried.
Operas. *Selections.* Arien : für hohe Singstimme, Blockflöten, Fagott und Basso continuo. (Schürmann, Georg Caspar). Erstausgabe. *Bärenreiter. £6.60* KFTE/NWPNSDW (B79-50557)
Sonata, flute & continuo, op.3, no.3, E minor. Sonate e-Moll, e minor, mi mineur, opus III, no.3, für Flöte und Basso continuo, for flute and basso continuo, pour flûte et basse continue. (Platti, Giovanni Benedetto). *Schott. £4.80* VRPE (B79-51222)
Bach, Johann Christian. Magnificat, D major, (1758). Magnificat. *Editio musica : Eulenburg. Unpriced* EMDGKK (B79-50044)
Bach, Johann Sebastian.
Brandenburg concerto, flutes (2), violin & string orchestra, no.4, BWV1049, G major. *arr.* Brandenburgisches Konzert Nr.4, G-dur : für 2 Blockflöten (Flöten), Violine, Streicher und Continuo, BWV1049. *Breitkopf und Härtel. £8.40* NUSNSK/LF (B79-51040)
Johann Sebastian Bach 1685-1750. *East-West Publications. Unpriced* PWPJ (B79-50611)
Sonata, violin, no.1, B.W.V. 1001. Adagio and fugue. *arr.* Prelude and fugue in A minor. *Oxford University Press. Unpriced* TSPMK/Y (B79-50314) ISBN 0-19-355304-x
Suites, cello, B.W.V. 1007-1012. Six suites for solo cello. *Stainer and Bell. Unpriced* SRPMG (B79-50692) ISBN 0-85249-562-5
Uns ist ein Kind geboren. BWV142. Overture. *arr.* Overture to cantata 'For us a Child is born' (Uns ist ein Kind geborn sic) : for organ and piano. *Sycamore : Schirmer (dist.). £1.50* QPLRK (B79-51110)
Das wohltemperierte Clavier. Fugue 14. BWV859. *arr.* Fugue 14 ... for three guitars. *Associated Music. £2.75* TSNTK/Y (B79-50701)
Bach, Wilhelm Friedemann.
Ach, dass du den Himmel zerrissest. *Vocal score.* Ach, dass du den Himmel zerrissest = Oh! you who doth rend heav'n asunder : festo nativit Christi, Weihnachtskantate von, Christmas cantata. *Belwin Mills. £2.25* DE/LF (B79-50421)
Erzittert und fallet. *Vocal score.* Erzittert und fallet = Oh, tremble and falter : Kantate zum Ostersonntag von, Easter cantata. *Belwin-Mills. £2.25* DE/LL (B79-50423)

Sonatas, flutes (2), nos.1,2. Zwei Sonaten für zwei Querflöten allein = Two sonatas for two solo flutes. *Bärenreiter. Unpriced* VRNUE (B79-50326)
Wie schön leuchtet der Morgenstern. *Vocal score.* Wie schon leuchtet der Morgenstern = How fair the morning star doth glow : Kantate Dom. II. p. Epiph. *Belwin-Mills. £2.25* DE/LFP (B79-50422)
Bacharach, Alfred Louis. The musical companion. Revised ed. *Pan Books.* Pbk. *£2.95* A (B79-50002) ISBN 0-330-25670-x
Bach's passions. (Steinitz, Paul). *Elek. £5.95* BBCADD/LK (B79-14916) ISBN 0-236-40132-7
Back to earth. (Stevens, Cat). *Ashtar : EMI. Unpriced* KDW/HKR (B79-50988)
Back to earth. *arr.* Back to earth. (Stevens, Cat). *Ashtar EMI. Unpriced* KDW/HKR (B79-50988)
Back to the egg. (McCartney, Paul). *MPL Communications. Unpriced* KDW/GB (B79-50966)
Back to the egg. Baby's request. *arr.* Back to the egg. Getting closer. *arr.* Getting closer and Baby's request. (McCartney, Paul). *MPL Communications. Unpriced* KDW/GB (B79-50967)
Back to the egg. Getting closer. *arr.* Getting closer and Baby's request. (McCartney, Paul). *MPL Communications. Unpriced* KDW/GB (B79-50967)
Backless. *arr.* Backless. (Clapton, Eric). *Chappell. Unpriced* KDW/HKR (B79-50983)
Backstage rock : behind the scenes with the bands. (Gorman, Clem). *Pan Books.* Pbk. *£0.90* AKDW/HKR/E(P/YC) (B79-50007) ISBN 0-330-25583-5
Badarak, Mary Lynn. Psalm 100 : (anthem), for four-part chorus of mixed voices with organ and 2 trumpets accompaniment. *Schirmer. Unpriced* EWSNTPLRDR (B79-50870)
Badura-Skoda, Eva. Concerto, piano, no.19, K.459, F major. Konzert in F für Klavier und Orchester KV459 = Concerto in F major for pianoforte and orchestra K.459. (Mozart, Wolfgang Amadeus). *Bärenreiter. £3.96* MPQF (B79-50580)
Badura-Skoda, Paul. Concerto, piano, no.19, K.459, F major. Konzert in F für Klavier und Orchester KV459 = Concerto in F major for pianoforte and orchestra K.459. (Mozart, Wolfgang Amadeus). *Bärenreiter. £3.96* MPQF (B79-50580)
Bailey, James.
Sonatas, flutes (2) & continuo, op.3. Triosonaten für zwei Flöten, (Flöte und Violine) und Basso continuo, op.3 Nos 1 & 2 : E-moll, D-dur. (Hotteterre, Jacques Martin). *Eulenburg. £3.50* VRNTPWE (B79-50741)
Sonatas, flutes (2) & continuo, op.3. Triosonaten für zwei Flöten (Flöte und Violine) und Basso continuo, op.3 Nos 3 & 4 : B-moll, E-moll. (Hotteterre, Jacques Martin). *Eulenburg. £3.50* VRNTPWE (B79-50742)
Sonatas, flutes (2) & continuo, op.3. Triosonaten für zwei Flöten (Flöte und Violine) und Basso continuo, op.3 Nos 5 & 6 : A-dur, G-dur. (Hotteterre, Jacques Martin). *Eulenburg. £3.50* VRNTPWE (B79-50743)
Baker, David. Sonata, cello & piano. Sonata for cello and piano. *Associated Music. £6.10* SRPE (B79-50689)
Baker, Richard, *b.1925.* Richard Baker's music guide. *David and Charles. £3.95 : CIP rev.* A/C (B79-12528) ISBN 0-7153-7782-5
Baker, Theodore.
Baker's biographical dictionary of musicians. 6th ed. *Schirmer Books : Collier Macmillan. £55.00* A(M/C) (B79-17757) ISBN 0-02-870240-9
Schirmer pronouncing pocket manual of musical terms. 4th ed. *Schirmer : Collier Macmillan.* Pbk. *£1.45* A(C) (B79-04535) ISBN 0-02-870250-6
Balada, Leonardo. Persistencies : for piano. *Schirmer. £4.55* QPJ (B79-50630)
Balázs, Béla. Kékszakállú herceg vara. *Adaptations.* Prince Bluebeard's castle : a libretto / adapted from the Hungarian of Béla Balázs ; and, The splendid stags : a Bartók companion. (Ország·Land, Thomas). *Top Floor, 64 Highgate High St., N6 5HX : The author.* Sd. *£2.10* BBGAC (B79-30800) ISBN 0-906057-07-8
Baldwin, David.
'Twas the brass before Christmas : five garlands for brass quintet, for 2 trumpets, horn, trombone and tuba
Garland 1. *Schirmer. £2.50* WNRK/DP/LF/AY (B79-51310)
Garland 2. *Schirmer. £2.50* WNRK/DP/LF/AY (B79-51314)
Garland 3. *Schirmer. £2.50* WNRK/DP/LF/AY (B79-51311)
Garland 4. *Schirmer. £2.50* WNRK/DP/LF/AY (B79-51312)
Garland 5. *Schirmer. £2.50* WNRK/DP/LF/AY (B79-51313)
Balent, Andrew.
Boogie woogie band. *Warner : Blossom. Unpriced* UMJ (B79-51200)
Let's go band! : for beginning band. *Warner : Blossom. Unpriced* UMJ (B79-51201)
Popeye the sailor. I'm Popeye the sailorman. *arr.* I'm Popeye the sailor man : for two-part chorus and piano. (Lerner, Samuel). *Warner : Blossom. Unpriced* FDW/JR (B79-50106)
Ball, Eric. Orb and sceptre. *arr.* Orb and sceptre. (Walton, *Sir* William). *Oxford University Press. Unpriced* WMK/AGM (B79-51303) ISBN 0-19-368537-x
Balla, György. Concerto, keyboard & string orchestra, Wq 9, C minor. Concerto in C-moll für Cembalo (Klavier) und Streicher = Concerto in C minor for harpsichord (piano) and strings. (Bach, Carl Philipp Emanuel). Erstausgabe = First ed. *Nagel : Editio Musica : Bärenreiter. Unpriced* RXMPPWF (B79-50258)
Ballad 3 : for soprano and tape. (Rands, Bernard). *Universal. Unpriced* KFLEZDW (B79-51003)
Ballad history of England : from 1588 to the present day. *Batsford. £6.50* AKDW/K/G(YD) (B79-11132) ISBN 0-7134-0968-1
Ballade et jeu : pour accordeon. (Abbott, Nelly). *Waterloo Music : Roberton. £0.90* RSPMJ (B79-50253)
Ballade no.2 : Op.42 : for piano solo. (Stevens, Bernard). *Roberton. £1.50* QPJ (B79-51090)
Ballata dall'esilio : per voce e chitarra. (Castelnuovo-Tedesco, Mario). *Bèrben : Breitkopf and Härtel. £1.70* KE/TSDW (B79-50992)
Ballet des muses : for baroque ensemble. (Lully, Jean Baptiste). *Associated Music. £15.10* RXM/HM (B79-50663)
Balletti pro tabula. *Selections : arr.* Suite in B-Dur für Trompete und Orgel, 1670. (Vejvanovský, Pavel Josef). *Merseburger : Bärenreiter. Unpriced* WSPLRK/AE (B79-50806)
Balmont, Konstantin Dmitrievich. The bells : Opus 35 : poem for soprano, tenor and baritone soli, chorus and orchestra. (Rachmaninoff, Sergei). *Boosey and Hawkes. Unpriced* EMDX (B79-50455)
Bamberger, Jeanne Shapiro. The art of listening : developing musical perception. 4th ed. *Harper and Row.* Pbk. *£8.15* A/C (B79-28895) ISBN 0-06-040943-6
Banks, Eric. Fanfare der Stadt Wien. *arr.* Festmusik der Stadt Wien. (Strauss, Richard). *Boosey and Hawkes. Unpriced* UMMK/AGN (B79-50729)
Banner, Martin. Motecta, Sancta Maria. Sancta Maria, and, Ecce sacerdos magnus : for four part chorus of mixed voices unaccompanied. (Victoria, Tomás Luis de). *Roberton. £0.28* EZDJ (B79-50469)
Barcarollina : for flute and piano. (Lyell, Margaret). *Roberton. £1.00* VRPJ (B79-51223)
Barclay James Harvest. Gone to earth. *Selections: arr.* Music from two hit albums, Gone to earth and XII. *Chappell. Unpriced* KDW/HKR (B79-50982)
Bardez, Jean Michel. Transposition à vue
1er recueil: Pièces ou fragments pour clarinette en si bémol à chanter, ou à jouer avec d'autres instruments-non transpositeurs-en lisant en clé d'ut 4e. *Chappell. Unpriced* VVK/AAY (B79-51274)
Bärenreiter - Chorreihe. Burkhard, Willy. Fünf Gesänge für gemischten Chor nach Gedichten von Richard Dehmel, Opus 26. *Bärenreiter. £1.16* EZDW (B79-50477)
Barker, Kathleen. Early music hall in Bristol. *74 Bell Barn Rd, Stoke Bishop, Bristol BS9 2DG : Historical Association, Bristol Branch.* Sd. *£0.60* A/JV(YDHDB) (B79-23405)
Barkley, John Monteith. Handbook to 'The church hymnary'. 3rd ed. *Oxford University Press. £3.50* ADM/LSF (B79-31512) ISBN 0-19-146811-8
Barlow, Catherine.
Original music and alternative music for the Modern Dance Grade Examinations
Grades 2 and 3: including pieces needed for the course of movement for boys. (Imperial Society of Teachers of Dancing. *Modern Dance Branch*). *Imperial Society of Teachers of Dancing. £3.50* QPH/H/AL (B79-51070)
Primary and Grade 1: including pieces needed for the course of movement for boys. (Imperial Society of Teachers of Dancing. *Modern Dance Branch*). *Imperial Society of Teachers of Dancing. £3.00* QPH/H/AL (B79-51071)
Barlow, Jeremy.
Sonata, flute & continuo, no.1, D major. Sonata 1 in D major for flute and basso continuo. (Hebden, John). *Oxford University Press. Unpriced* VRPE (B79-51221) ISBN 0-19-357021-1
Sonata, flute & continuo, no.2, D major. Sonata 2 in D major for flute and basso continuo. (Roseingrave, Thomas). *Oxford University Press. Unpriced* VRPE (B79-50329) ISBN 0-19-358643-6
Baroque music for trumpet : including music by Albinoni, Charpentier, Keller, Molter, Telemann, Torelli. *Boosey and Hawkes. £1.65* WSP/AY (B79-50393)
Barratt, Carol.
Chester's concert pieces
Vol.2: From Purcell to Prokofiev for the younger pianist. *Chester Music. Unpriced* QP/AY (B79-50206)
Chester's piano book
Number 5. *Chester Music. Unpriced* Q/AC (B79-50203)
A feast of easy carols. *Chester Music. Unpriced* QPK/DP/LF/AY (B79-51098)
Barrel organ : the story of the mechanical organ and its repair. (Ord-Hume, Arthur Wolfgang Julius Gerald). *Allen and Unwin. £18.50* A/FK (B79-01356) ISBN 0-04-789005-3
Barrow, Kenneth. The golden bond : a spectacular revue. *2 Cromwell Place, SW7 2JG : National Union of Townswomen's Guilds.* Pbk. *£1.50* BAPACP

(B79-27787)

Barsanti, Francesco. Overture a quattro. Op.4, no.2. Ouverture, Opus 4, No.2 : für Streicher und Basso continuo = for strings and basso continuo. *Schott. £6.00* RXMG (B79-50257)

Barsham, Eve. Come give your hearts to joy this day. *Ashdown. Unpriced* JFDP/LF (B79-50936)

Bartók, Béla.

Mikrokosmos. *arr.* Mikrokosmos for harp : 20 intermediate solos and ensembles for harps with and without pedals. *Boosey and Hawkes. Unpriced* TQK/AF (B79-50694)

Prince Bluebeard's castle : a libretto / adapted from the Hungarian of Béla Balázs ; and, The splendid stags : a Bartók companion. (Ország-Land, Thomas). *Top Floor, 64 Highgate High St., N6 5HX : The author.* Sd. *£2.10* BBGAC (B79-30800) ISBN 0-906057-07-8

Basement Writers. Living in the city : a songbook. (Swift, Dave). *59 Watney St., E.1 : Basement Writers.* Sd. *£0.15* KE/TSDW (B79-50545)

Bass for music education. (Swanwick, Keith). *NFER.* Pbk. *£4.75* A(V) (B79-32714) ISBN 0-85633-180-5

Basset, Lesie. Divine lodi, lib.3. *Selections.* 3 canzonas for violin (trumpet), trombone and basso continuo. (Riccio, Giovanni Battista). *Musica rara. Unpriced* NUXUNT (B79-50188)

Bastien, James W. How to teach piano successfully. 2nd ed. *General Words and Music etc.; 20 Earlham St., WC2H 9LN : Distributed by Breitkopf and Hartel (London) Ltd.* Pbk. *£7.90* AQ/E(VC) (B79-25333) ISBN 0-8497-6109-3

Bauer, Heinrich. Sinfonia concertante, violins (3). *arr.* Sinfonia concertante für drei Violinen und Orchester. (Mayr, Simon). Zum ersten Mal. *Litolff : Peters. Unpriced* SNSQK/LE (B79-50680)

Bauld, Alison. One pearl : a monody for soprano and string quartet. *Novello. £4.25* KFLE/RXNSDX (B79-50152)

Baur, Jürg.

Concerto, violin, no.2. 2 Violinkonzert : in Form einer Ballade, für Violine und Orchester, (1978). *Breitkopf und Härtel. £8.40* MPSF (B79-51028)

Drei Ricercare über das Thema des Musikalischen Opfers von Johann Sebastian Bach (1977) : Orgel. *Breitkopf and Härtel. £5.40* RJ (B79-51122)

Bausteine für Musikerziehung und Musikpflege.

Bresgen, Cesar. Tiertanzburlesken. *Vocal score.* Tiertanzburlesken. *Schott. Unpriced* FDW (B79-50103)

Hofbauer, Kurt. Praxis der chorischen Stimmbildung. *Schott.* Pbk. *£6.00* AD/E (B79-11133)

Nobis, Herbert. Hören und Singen : ein Solfège-Übungsbuch zur Gehörbildung. *Schott. £5.60* CB/AF (B79-50816)

Baxter, Kate. Pompaleerie jig. (Thompson, Diana). *E.J. Arnold.* Sd. *£1.30* A(VG/GR) (B79-04968) ISBN 0-560-00319-6

BBC. *See* British Broadcasting Corporation.

BBC music guides. *See* British Broadcasting Corporation. BBC music guides.

BBC TV's Nationwide carols : winners 1978. *Chappell. Unpriced* KDP/LF/AY (B79-50953)

BBI marching band series. Foster, Bob. Chopbuster march : an outrageous trumpet feature. *Warner : Blossom. Unpriced* UMMGM (B79-50719)

Beach Boys. Pet sound plus : 24 greatest hits ... *Chappell. Unpriced* KDW/HKR (B79-50540)

Beadell, Robert. I saw water flowing = Vidi aquam : anthem for Eastertide for four-part chorus of mixed voices a cappella. *Schirmer. Unpriced* EZDH/LL (B79-50881)

Beament, Peter. The Oregon trail : a suite for percussion ensemble. *7 Garrick St., W.C.2 : Middle Eight Music. Unpriced* XNS (B79-50403)

Beat, Janet. Let God arise. *Vocal score.* Let God arise : anthem for soprano and tenor soli, SATB and orchestra. (Handel, George Frideric). *Novello. £1.65* DK (B79-50027)

Beatles forever. (Schaffner, Nicholas). *McGraw-Hill.* Pbk. *£4.95* AKDW/GB/E(P) (B79-20268) ISBN 0-07-055087-5

Beatles in their own words. (Beatles, The). *Omnibus Press.* Pbk. *£2.50* AKDW/GB/E(P) (B79-26552) ISBN 0-86001-540-8

Beatles, The. Beatles in their own words. *Omnibus Press.* Pbk. *£2.50* AKDW/GB/E(P) (B79-26552) ISBN 0-86001-540-8

Béatrice et Bénédict. Overture. *arr.* Overture Beatrice and Benedict. (Berlioz, Hector). *R. Smith. Unpriced* WMK (B79-51301)

Beckerley, Lewis. Thou madest all things well : anthem for unison voices and organ. (Kidd, J Michael). *Weinberger. Unpriced* JFDH (B79-50935)

Bedford, D A. Music for handbells : Module AIIN for 1 1/2 octaves : Hymns and things. *(57a Fore St.) : Handbell Ringers of Great Britain. Unpriced* XSQK/AAY (B79-50813) ISBN 0-904289-03-6

Bedford, David.

An easy decision : soprano voice & piano. *Universal. Unpriced* KFLDW (B79-50997)

A horse, his name was Henry Fencewaver Watkins. *Universal. Unpriced* NUPNP (B79-50185)

Jack of shadows. *Universal. £8.06* MRJ (B79-51035)

Some stars above magnitude 2.9 : soprano voice and piano. *Universal. Unpriced* KFLDW (B79-50149)

Bedford, P. Music for handbells : Module AIIN for 1 1/2 octaves : Hymns and things. *(57a Fore St.) : Handbell Ringers of Great Britain. Unpriced* XSQK/AAY (B79-50813) ISBN 0-904289-03-6

Bee Gees.

Saturday night fever. *Selections : arr.* Saturday night fever : from the original movie soundtrack. *Chappell. Unpriced* RK/DW/HKR/JR (B79-50658)

Saturday night fever. *Selections : arr.* Saturday night fever : from the original movie soundtrack. *Chappell. Unpriced* TSPMK/DW/HKR/JR (B79-50713)

Spirits having flown. *Chappell. Unpriced* KDW/HKR (B79-50541)

Bee Gees, *Group.* Bee Gees : the authorized biography. *Octopus Books.* Pbk. *£2.99* AKDW/GB/E(P) (B79-20269) ISBN 0-7064-1091-2

Bee Gees. (Pryce, Larry). *Panther.* Pbk. *£0.80* AKDW/GB/E(P) (B79-10478) ISBN 0-586-04854-5

Beecham, *Sir* Thomas, *bart.* A mingled chime : leaves from an autobiography. *Hutchinson. £5.95 : CIP rev.* A/EC(P) (B79-08131) ISBN 0-09-138430-3

Beechey, Gwilym. Sonatas, flutes (2), op.2, nos.3, 4. Two sonatas, Opus 2, Nos. 3 and 4 for two flutes, or oboes, or violins. (Boismortier, Joseph Bodin de). *Oxford University Press. Unpriced* VRNUE (B79-50327) ISBN 0-19-355578-6

Beeson, Jack.

A Creole mystery. *Vocal score.* A Creole mystery : a short story for medium voice and string quartet. *Boosey and Hawkes. Unpriced* KFVDX (B79-50560)

The day's no rounder than its angles are. *arr.* The day's no rounder than its angles are : three songs for medium voice and string quartet. *Boosey and Hawkes. Unpriced* KFVDW (B79-50558)

Senex. *Boosey and Hawkes. Unpriced* KGNDW (B79-50562)

Beethoven, Ludwig van.

Sonata, piano duet, op.6, D major. *arr.* Sonata in D major, op.6, for clarinet and piano. *Schirmer. £3.05* VVPK/AE (B79-50784)

Sonata, piano, G.162, C major. Piano sonata in C.Wo 051. *Roberton. £2.50* QPE (B79-50620)

Sonaten für Klavier zu zwei Händen

Band 1. *Litolff : Peters. Unpriced* QPE/AZ (B79-50623)

Band 2. *Litolff : Peters. Unpriced* QPE/AZ (B79-50624)

Beethoven, Ludwig von. Two Beethoven sketchbooks : a description with musical extracts. (Nottebohm, Gustav). *Gollancz. £4.95* BBJ(QVB) (B79-14912) ISBN 0-575-02583-2

Beethoven and his world. (Kendall, Alan, *b.1939*). *Ward Lock. £2.95 : CIP rev.* BBJ(N) (B79-30252) ISBN 0-7063-5867-8

Beethoven, Sibelius and the 'profound logic'. (Pike, Lionel). *Athlone Press. £12.95 : CIP entry* BBJAMME (B78-37102) ISBN 0-485-11178-0

Beethoven's Missa solemnis. (Fiske, Roger). *Elek. £5.95* BBJADG (B79-14016) ISBN 0-236-40146-7

Beggs, Barbara Cass-. *See* Cass-Beggs, Barbara.

Belfield papers. Angus-Butterworth, Lionel Milner. Sir Alex K. Butterworth, LL.B. (1854-1946) and Captain G.S.K. Butterworth, M.C.,B.A. (1885-1916). *Old Hall Hotel, Buxton, Derbyshire : The author.* Sd. *£0.50* BBVT(N) (B79-27781)

Beliebte Volkslieder : für Posaune mit 2. Stimme ad lib. *Schott. £2.40* WUPMJ (B79-50401)

Bell, Arnold Craig. Almira. *Selections : arr.* Dances from 'Almira'. (Handel, George Frideric). *Banks Music. Unpriced* QPK/AH (B79-50221)

Bells, clocks & ringers. (Smith, William Joseph Thomas). *Boreham Vicarage, Chelmsford CM3 3EG : The author.* Pbk. *£0.50* AXSR(YDDEBO) (B79-31934)

Belshazzar's feast : for baritone solo, mixed choir, and orchestra. (Walton, *Sir* William). Limited ed. *Oxford University Press. £60.00* EMDD (B79-50041) ISBN 0-19-338463-9

Ben-Tovim, Atarah.

Atarah's bandkit

Strand D1: With a friend or two : eight duets for flute and classical guitar, with companion cassette. *Novello. £7.00* VRPLTSK/AAY (B79-50758)

The elastic band. *Novello. Score, £5.00, Parts, Unpriced* LNK/AAY (B79-50160)

Benger, Richard.

Fare well. *Edwin Ashdown. £0.20* FDW (B79-50101)

Music : for S.S.C. *Edwin Ashdown. £0.25* FDW (B79-50102)

Requiescat : S.S. and piano. *Edwin Ashdown. £0.20* FLDW (B79-50919)

Benjamin, George. Sonata, piano. Piano sonata. *Faber Music. Unpriced* QPE (B79-51066)

Benjamin, Thomas.

The craft of modal counterpoint : a practical approach. *Schirmer Books : Collier Macmillan.* Pbk. *£7.45* A/RM (B79-30799) ISBN 0-02-870480-0

Techniques and materials of tonal music : with an introduction to twentieth-century techniques. 2nd ed. *Houghton Mifflin. £9.75* A/R (B79-18563) ISBN 0-395-27066-9

Benjamin Britten, 1913-1976 : pictures from a life : a pictorial biography. *Faber. £15.00 : CIP rev.* BBU(EM) (B78-29832) ISBN 0-571-11261-7

Bennet, John. Madrigals to foure voices (1599). *Stainer and Bell. Unpriced* EZDU (B79-50473) ISBN 0-85249-456-4

Bennett, Richard Rodney.

Alba (1973). *Novello. £1.45* RJ (B79-50234)

Concerto, orchestra. *Novello. £4.85* MMF (B79-50169)

Just friends, in print : Marian Montgomery with Richard Rodney Bennett in words, music and pictures. *Novello. £2.95* KDW/GB/AY (B79-50536)

Scena III : clarinet solo. *Novello. £2.60* VVPMJ (B79-51287)

Benson, Kathleen. Scott Joplin. (Haskins, James). *Robson Books. £4.50 : CIP entry* BJRP(N) (B78-38608) ISBN 0-86051-058-1

Bent, Margaret. Fifteenth-century liturgical music 2: Four anonymous masses. *Stainer and Bell. Unpriced* EZDFF/AYD (B79-50873) ISBN 0-85249-544-7

Berger, Edward. The jazz text. (Nanry, Charles). *D. Van Nostrand.* Pbk. *£6.70* AMT (B79-21878) ISBN 0-442-25908-5

Berger, Jean. The fruit of the vine : for full chorus of mixed voices a cappella. *Schirmer. Unpriced* EZDX (B79-50905)

Bergethon, Bjornar.

Musical growth in the elementary school. 3rd ed. *Holt, Rinehart and Winston.* Pbk. *£9.25* A(VG) (B79-07190)

Musical growth in the elementary school. 4th ed. *Holt, Rinehart and Winston.* Sp. *£8.50* A(VK) (B79-10207) ISBN 0-03-020856-4

Bergmann, Walter.

Chacony, string orchestra, Z.730, G minor. Chacony for strings. (Purcell, Henry). *Eulenberg. Unpriced* RXMHJN (B79-51137)

The complete sonatas for treble (alto) recorder and basso continuo = Die gesamten Sonaten für Altblockflöte und basso continuo. (Handel, George Frideric). *Faber Music. Unpriced* VSSPE/AZ (B79-51253)

First book of bassoon solos. *Faber Music. Unpriced* VWP/AY (B79-50787)

A first violin book. (Whiteley, Faith). *Oxford University Press. Unpriced* S/AF (B79-51145) ISBN 0-19-359511-7

Sonata, recorder (treble) & continuo, no.1, G major. Sonata no.1 in G for treble (alto) recorder and basso continuo. (Dieupart, Francis). *Schott. Unpriced* VSSPE (B79-51251)

Sonata, recorder (treble) & continuo, no.6, F major. Sonata no.6 in F for treble (alto) recorder and basso continuo. (Dieupart, Francis). *Schott. Unpriced* VSSPE (B79-51250)

Berkeley, *Sir* Lennox. Sonata, flute & piano, op.97. Sonata for flute and piano. Op.97. *Chester Music. Unpriced* VRPE (B79-50747)

Berkeley, Michael. 3 Christmas carols : for unison voices and piano. *Schirmer. Unpriced* JFDP/LF (B79-50126)

Berliner, Paul. The soul of Mbira : music and traditions of the Shona people of Zimbabwe. *University of California Press. £12.00* BZNM (B79-19448) ISBN 0-520-03315-9

Berlioz, Hector.

Béatrice et Bénédict. Overture. *arr.* Overture Beatrice and Benedict. *R. Smith. Unpriced* WMK (B79-51301)

Te Deum. Op.22. *Vocal score.* Te Deum. Op.22. *Bärenreiter. £3.96* DGKHB (B79-50425)

Les Troyens, part 2. Chasse royale et orage. Chase royale et orage. *Bärenreiter. Unpriced* MMJ (B79-50173)

Bernards and Babani Press radio and electronics books. Berry, M K. Electronic music and creative tape recording. *Babani.* Pbk. *£1.25* APV (B79-32721) ISBN 0-900162-72-4

Bernstein, Leonard. Symphony no.3, 'Kaddish'. Yit'ga dal. *arr.* Canon in five parts ... : for boys chorus with piano accompaniment. *Amberson : Schirmer (dist.). £0.35* DH (B79-50831)

Berry, M K. Electronic music and creative tape recording. *Babani.* Pbk. *£1.25* APV (B79-32721) ISBN 0-900162-72-4

Berry, Mary. Cantors : a collection of Gregorian chants. *Cambridge University Press. Unpriced* JEZDTD (B79-50933) ISBN 0-521-22149-8

Best of popular music

Vol.1: A-L. *Chappell. Unpriced* KDW/GB/AY (B79-50969)

Vol.2: M-Z. *Chappell. Unpriced* KDW/GB/AY (B79-50970)

Betjeman, *Sir* John. Senex. (Beeson, Jack). *Boosey and Hawkes. Unpriced* KGNDW (B79-50562)

Bettina, *b.1903.* The sorcerer's apprentice, and other stories. (Hosier, John). *Oxford University Press.* Pbk. *£1.50* ABN (B79-50005) ISBN 0-19-314922-2

Bevan, Maurice. The King shall rejoice. (Tomkins, John). *36 Ranelagh Gdns, W.6 : Cathedral Music. Unpriced* DK (B79-50028)

Beware of the soldier. Songs of innocence. Little lamb. *arr.* Little lamb : for unison treble choir with piano, four hands accompaniment. (Smith, Gregg). *Schirmer. £0.35* JFLDW (B79-50948)

Beyer, Frank Michael. Diaphonie : für Orchester. *Bote und Bock : Schirmer. £14.40* MMJ (B79-51020)

Beynon, Ivor. The complete piano accordion tutor. *EMI. Unpriced* RS/AC (B79-50249)

Biba, Otto. Trio, flute, viola & horn, op.28, D major. Trio in D-dur für Flöte, Viola and Horn. Op.28 = Trio in D major for flute, viola and horn. (Pössinger, Alexander). *Amadeus : Bärenreiter. £3.25* NVPNT (B79-50601)

Biber, Heinrich. Harmonia artificiosa Partia, violas d'amore (2) & continuo, no.7 C minor. *Viola d'amore parts.* Harmonia artificiosa, partita no. VIII in fact, 7 : for two violas d'amore and cello, with optional organ or harpsichord. *(Little Margaret, Penmans Green, Chipperfield) : E.L. White. Unpriced* SQQ (B79-50688)

Biber, Heinrich Ignaz Franz.

Sonatae tam aris quam aulis servientes. Sonata, trumpet & string orchestra, no.4, C major. *arr.* Sonata 4 for trumpet, violin, 2 violas and basso continuo. *Musica rara. Unpriced* NUXSNTK/LE (B79-51043)

Sonatae tam aris quam aulis servientes. Sonata, trumpet & string orchestra, no.12, C. major. *arr.* Sonata 12 for 2 trumpets, 2 violins, 2 violas, cello. *Muscia rara. Unpriced* NUXSNTK/LE (B79-51044)

Sonatae tam aris quam aulis servientes. Sonata, trumpets (2) & string orchestra, no.1, C major. *arr.* Sonata 1 for 2 trumpets, 2 violins, 2 violas, cello & basso continuo. *Musica rara. Unpriced* NUXSNRK/LE (B79-51042)

Bibliographie des Musikschriftums
1972. *Schott.* *£30.00* A(T) (B79-30467)
Bicinia variorum instrumentorum. *Selections.* Six sonatinas, nos 1, 2, 3, 7, 9, 11 for 2 oboes/violins/recorders in C and basso continuo. (Pezel, Johann). *Nova Music.* *Unpriced* VTNTPWEM (B79-51257)
Biebl, Franz. Fröhlicher Reigen = Cheerful round dance : Tänze für zwei Sopranblockflöten mit Gitarre ad lib. = dances for two soprano recorders with guitarre sic ad lib. *Pelikan : Bärenreiter.* *£1.49* VSRNUH (B79-50766)
'Big Al' : a new musical based on the life and times of the infamous Chicago gangster Al Capone. (Gardiner, John). *6 Friday Furlong, Hitchin, Herts. SG5 2ND Gardiner-Parr Musicals.* Pbk. *£1.50* BPDRACM (B79-31928)
Big red fake book : giant hits of the 50's, 60's and 70's. *Screen Gems-EMI Music : EMI.* *Unpriced* KDW/GB/AY (B79-50535)
Binkerd, Gordon.
Es ist ein Ros entsprungen. Op. 122, no.8. *arr.* Es ist ein Ros entsprungen = Now blooms a rose so tender. (Brahms, Johannes). *Boosey and Hawkes.* *Unpriced* EZDW (B79-50888)
On the king's highway. *Chorus score.* On the king's highway : for children's chorus and chamber orchestra. *Boosey and Hawkes.* *Unpriced* FADW (B79-50488)
Promises like pie-crust : SATB. *Boosey and Hawkes.* *Unpriced* EZDW (B79-50098)
Scherzi armonici. *arr.* Two Salieri canons. (Salieri, Antonio). *Boosey and Hawkes.* *Unpriced* GE/XTBDW/X (B79-50108)
Sorrow hath a double voice : for solo high voice, unison male or female chorus and harp. *Boosey and Hawkes.* *Unpriced* ETQDW (B79-50047)
Trio, string instruments. Trio for strings. *Boosey and Hawkes.* *Unpriced* RXNT (B79-50676)
Trio, string instruments. Trio for strings. *Boosey and Hawkes.* *Unpriced* RXNT (B79-50677)
Binns, David, *b.1941.* The McJazz manuscripts : a collection of the writings of Sandy Brown. (Brown, Sandy). *Faber.* *£6.95 : CIP rev.* AMT(P) (B79-10483) ISBN 0-571-11319-2
Biographical dictionary of musicians. Baker's biographical dictionary of musicians. (Baker, Theodore). 6th ed. *Schirmer Books : Collier Macmillan.* *£55.00* A(M/C) (B79-17757) ISBN 0-02-870240-9
Birch tree on green hill = Birke am grünen Bergeshang : for four-part chorus of mixed voices a cappella. (Dvořák, Antonín). *Schirmer.* *£0.45* EZDW (B79-50891)
Bird, Wendy. Sing a song
1. Teacher's book. *Nelson : ILEA Learning Materials Service.* Sp. *£2.75* A/GR(VG) (B79-07467) ISBN 0-17-413002-3
Birthday hansel. Op.92. *Selections : arr.* Four Burns songs : for high voice and piano. (Britten, Benjamin, *Baron Britten*). *Faber Music.* *Unpriced* KFTDW (B79-50153)
Birtwistle, Harrison. Silbury air. *Universal.* *Unpriced* MMJ (B79-51021)
Bishop, Elizabeth. A mirror on which to dwell : six poems of Elizabeth Bishop, for soprano and chamber orchestra. (Carter, Elliott). *Associated Music.* *£24.20* KFLE/MDW (B79-50550)

Black and white toccata : concert accordion. (Abbott, Alan). *Waterloo Music : Roberton.* *£1.65* RSPMJ (B79-50250)
Black dwarf
1- ; 1978-. *7 Ivywell Rd, Bristol BS9 1NX : 'Black dwarf'.* Sd. *£0.23* AKDW/HKR(B) (B79-01354)
Black rose : a rock legend. (Thin Lizzy). *Chappell.* *Unpriced* KDW/HKR (B79-50991)
Blackford, Andy. Disco dancing tonight : clubs, dances, fashion, music. *Octopus Books.* Pbk. *£1.50* A/FF/ER (B79-16105) ISBN 0-7064-1019-x
Blackley, Karen Ray.
Blues on the run. *arr.* Blues on the run : for SATB chorus and piano with optional bass and drums. (Blackley, Terry J). *Warner : Blossom.* *Unpriced* DW (B79-50845)
Circles. *arr.* Circles : for SATB chorus and piano with optional bass and drums. (Blackley, Terry J). *Warner Blossom.* *Unpriced* DW (B79-50846)
Empty arms. *arr.* Empty arms : for SATB chorus and piano with optional bass and drums. (Blackley, Terry J). *Warner : Blossom.* *Unpriced* DW (B79-50847)
Blackley, Terry J.
Blues on the run. *arr.* Blues on the run : for SATB chorus and piano with optional bass and drums. *Warner Blossom.* *Unpriced* DW (B79-50845)
Circles. *arr.* Circles : for SATB chorus and piano with optional bass and drums. *Warner : Blossom.* *Unpriced* DW (B79-50846)
Empty arms. *arr.* Empty arms : for SATB chorus and piano with optional bass and drums. *Warner : Blossom.* *Unpriced* DW (B79-50847)
Blackmore, George. Christmas at home : carol-medleys for all organs. *Paxton.* *£1.40* R/LF (B79-51119)
Blake, David.

Metamorphoses : for large orchestra. *Novello.* *£2.75* MMJ (B79-50174)
Blake, William. Beware of the soldier. Songs of innocence. Little lamb. *arr.* Little lamb : for unison treble choir with piano, four hands accompaniment. (Smith, Gregg). *Schirmer.* *£0.35* JFLDW (B79-50948)
Blake, William. Five Blake songs : for high voice and piano. (Chapple, Brian). *Chester Music.* *Unpriced* KFTDW (B79-50154)
Blank, Allan.
An American medley : for brass quintet, flute(s) and percussion. *Associated Music.* *£10.60* WNR (B79-51309)

Capriccio, violin solo, op.1, no.24, A minor. *arr.* Paganini caprice 24 : for double woodwind quintet. (Paganini, Nicolò). *Associated Music.* *£10.60* UMK/T (B79-51205)

Bläser & Orgel.
Vejvanovský, Pavel Josef. Balletti pro tabula. *Selections : arr.* Suite in B-Dur für Trompete und Orgel, 1670. *Merseburger : Bärenreiter.* *Unpriced* WSPLRK/AE (B79-50806)
Vejvanovský, Pavel Josef. Sonata la posta : für drei Posaunen und Orgel, 1667. *Merseburger : Bärenreiter.* *£2.97* WUNTRE (B79-50808)
Zipp, Friedrich. Fünf Choralvorspiele : für Trompete und Orgel, 1975. *Merseburger : Bärenreiter.* *£4.46* WSPLR (B79-50805)
Bläsermusik alter Meister : für zwei Trompeten und drei Posaunen. *Merseburger : Bärenreiter.* *£1.32* WNQ (B79-50793)
Bläsersätze nach europäischen Volksliedern = Wind pieces from European folksongs : für vier Blechbläser, 2 Trompeten, (Flügelhörner, Horn ad lib., 2 Stimme), 2 Posaunen (Tenorhorn, Bariton, ad lib Tuba) = for four brass instruments, 2 trumpets, (flugelhorns, horn ad lib. 2nd part) 2 trombones (baritone euphonium, ad lib. tuba). *Schott.* *£3.40* WNSK/DW/G/AYB (B79-50390)
Blatchly, Mark. Magnificat and Nunc dimittis. *36 Ranelagh Gdns, W.6 : Cathedral Music.* *Unpriced* FLDGPP (B79-50107)
Blaug, Mark. Why are Covent Garden seat prices so high? *Royal Opera House Covent Garden, WC2 7QA : Royal Opera House Covent Garden Ltd.* Sd. *Unpriced* AC/E(YC/QB/K) (B79-04908)
Bless the Lord, O my soul : for two-part chorus of women's voices with glockenspiel and triangle accompaniment. (Wienhorst, Richard). *Associated Music.* *£0.30* FE/XTPLXTQWDK (B79-50498)
Block, Robert Paul.
Il cimento dell'armonia e dell'inventione. Op.8, Concerto, oboe & string orchestra, P.259, D minor. Concerto in d minor, RV454 (F.VII/1), P.259, for oboe, strings and basso continuo. (Vivaldi, Antonio). *Musica rara.* *Unpriced* RXMPVTF (B79-50668)
Il cimento dell'armonia e dell'inventione. Op.8 Concerto, oboe & string orchestra, P.259, D minor. *arr.* Concerto in d minor, RV454, (F.VII/1), P.259 for oboe, strings and basso continuo. (Vivaldi, Antonio). *Musica rara.* *Unpriced* VTPK/LF (B79-50774)
Concerto, oboe & string orchestra, R.455, F major. Concerto in F, RV.455, (P.306) for oboe, strings and basso continuo. (Vivaldi, Antonio). *Musica rara.* *Unpriced* RXMPVTF (B79-50669)
Concerto, oboe & string orchestra, R.455, F major. *arr.* Concerto in F, RV.455, (P.306) for oboe, strings and basso continuo. (Vivaldi, Antonio). *Musica rara.* *Unpriced* VTPK/LF (B79-50775)
Concerto, oboe & string orchestra, R.461, A minor. Concerto in A minor for oboe, strings and continuo, RV461 (F.VII,no.5) (P.42). (Vivaldi, Antonio). *Musica rara.* *Unpriced* RXMPVTF (B79-51139)
Concerto, oboe & string orchestra, R.461, A minor. *arr.* Concerto in A minor for oboe, strings and continuo, RV461 (F.VII,no.5) (P.42). (Vivaldi, Antonio). *Musica Rara.* *Unpriced* VTPK/LF (B79-51263)
Concerto, oboe & string orchestra, R.463, A minor. Concerto in A minor for oboe, strings and continuo, RV463 (F.VII,no.13). (Vivaldi, Antonio). *Musica rara.* *Unpriced* RXMPVTF (B79-51140)
Concerto, oboe & string orchestra, R.463, A minor. *arr.* Concerto in A minor for oboe, strings and continuo, RV463 (F.VII,no.13). (Vivaldi, Antonio). *Musica rara.* *Unpriced* VTPK/LF (B79-51264)
Der getreue Music Meister. *Selections.* 4 sonatas for treble recorder and basso continuo. (Telemann, Georg Philipp). *Musica rara.* *Unpriced* VSSPE (B79-50347)
Madrigali et ricercari a quattro voci. *Selections.* Five ricercare in four parts for brass. (Gabrieli, Andrea). *Musica rara.* *Unpriced* WSN (B79-50798)
Madrigali et ricercari a quattro voci. *Selections.* Five ricercare in four parts : for brass or recorders. (Gabrieli, Andrea). *Musica rara.* *Unpriced* VSNS (B79-51235)
Madrigali et ricercari a quattro voci. *Selections.* Five ricercare in four parts for recorders. (Gabrieli, Andrea). *Musica rara.* *Unpriced* VSN (B79-50759)
Sonata, trumpet & string orchestra, D. XI, 8, D major. Sonata D. XI, 8 in D, for trumpet, strings and basso continuo. (Gabrielli, Domenico). *Musica rara.* *Unpriced* RXMPWSE (B79-50670)
Sonata, trumpet & string orchestra, D. XI, 8, D major. *arr.* Sonata D. XI, 8 in D for trumpet, strings and basso continuo. (Gabrielli, Domenico). *Musica rara.* *Unpriced* WSPK/LE (B79-50803)
Sonata, trumpet, string quintet & continuo, D.XI.7, D major. Sonata D.XI.7 in D for trumpet, strings and basso continuo. (Gabrielli, Domenico). *Musica rara.* *Unpriced* NUXSNPE (B79-50598)
Sonata, trumpet, string quintet & continuo, D.XI.7, D major. *arr.* Sonata D.XI.7 in D for trumpet, strings and basso continuo. (Gabrielli, Domenico). *Musica rara.* *Unpriced* WSPK/AE (B79-50800)
Sonata, trumpet, strings & continuo, D XII 5, D major. *arr.* Sonata, D XII 5 for tromba, (trumpet), strings and continuo. (Jacchini, Giuseppe Maria). *Musica rara.* *Unpriced* WSPK/AE (B79-50801)
Sonata, trumpet, strings & continuo, D XII 6, D major. Sonata, D XII 6 for tromba, (trumpet), strings and continuo. (Jacchini, Giuseppe Maria). *Musica rara.* *Unpriced* NUXSNRE (B79-50599)
Sonata, trumpet, violins (2) & continuo, D XII 5, D major. *arr.* Sonata, D XII 5 for tromba, (trumpet), strings and continuo. (Jacchini, Giuseppe Maria). *Musica rara.* *Unpriced* WSPK/AE (B79-50802)
Sonata, trumpet, violins(2) & continuo, D XII 5, D major. Sonata, D XII 5 for tromba, (trumpet), strings and continuo. (Jacchini, Giuseppe Maria). *Musica rara.* *Unpriced* NUXSNSE (B79-50600)
Sonatas, flutes (2), op.5, bk.2. Six sonatas, opus 5, book 2 for 2 flutes/oboes/recorders in C without bass (Priestman VI). (Loeillet, Jean Baptiste). *Musica rara.* *Unpriced* VRNUE (B79-51220)
Sonatas, recorders (treble) (2). Six sonatas for 2 treble recorders (flutes) without bass ... (Loeillet, Jean Baptiste). *Musica rara.* *Unpriced* VSSNUE (B79-51249)
Suite, trumpet & string orchestra, D major. Suite 1 for trumpet, strings and basso continuo. (Telemann, Georg Philipp). *Musica rara.* *Unpriced* RXMPWSG (B79-50262)
Suite, trumpet & string orchestra, D major. *arr.* Suite 1 for trumpet, strings and basso continuo. (Telemann, Georg Philipp). *Musica rara.* *Unpriced* WSPK/AG (B79-50396)
Trattenimenti per camera, op.5. Sonata, trumpets (2), strings & continuo, op.5, no.1, D major. Sonata, op.5, no.1, for 2 trombe (trumpets) strins and continuo. (Jacchini, Giuseppe Maria). *Musica rara.* *Unpriced* RXMPWSNUE (B79-50263)
Trattenimenti per camera, op.5. Sonata, trumpets (2), strings & continuo, op.5, no.1, D major. *arr.* Sonata, op.5, no.1, for 2 trombe (trumpets), strings and continuo. (Jacchini, Giuseppe Maria). *Musica rara.* *Unpriced* WSNTQK/LE (B79-50392)
Trattenimenti per camera. Sinfonia, trumpets (2) & string orchestra, op.5, no.8, D major. Sinfonia, op.5 no.8 for 2 trumpets, strings and basso continuo. (Jacchini, Giuseppe Maria). *Musica rara.* *Unpriced* RXMPWSNUE (B79-50671)
Trattenimenti per camera. Sinfonia, trumpets (2) & string orchestra, op.5, no.8, D major. *arr.* Sinfonia, op.5 no.8 for 2 trumpets, strings and basso continuo. (Jacchini, Giuseppe Maria). *Musica rara.* *Unpriced* WSNTQK/AE (B79-50799)
Trio, bassoons & continuo, G major. Trio in G for 2 bassoons and basso continuo. (Schiffelholz, Johann Paul). *Musica rara.* *Unpriced* VWNTPW (B79-50362)
Blockbuster. (Chinn, Nicky). *Chappell.* *Unpriced* KDW/GB (B79-50531)
Blockflöte : Altblockflöte und Klavier, herausgegeben von Wolfram Hoffmann
1. *Neue Musik : Breitkopf und Härtel.* *£2.10* VRP/AY (B79-50745)
Blockflöte
2: Altblockflöte und Klavier. *Neue Musik : Breitkopf and Härtel.* *Unpriced* VS/AY (B79-51233)
Bloody tourists. *arr.* Bloody tourists. (Ten CC). *Chappell.* *Unpriced* KDW/GB (B79-50532)
Blow, John. Ten songs for high voice. *Stainer and Bell.* *Unpriced* KFTDW (B79-51004) ISBN 0-85249-547-1
'Blue Amberol' cylinders : a catalogue. (Carter, Sydney Horace). *19 Glendale Rd, Bournemouth BH6 4JA : 'Talking machine review'.* Sd. *£4.00* A/FE(QB/WT) (B79-05450) ISBN 0-902338-30-7
Blues on the run. *arr.* Blues on the run : for SATB chorus and piano with optional bass and drums. (Blackley, Terry J). *Warner : Blossom.* *Unpriced* DW (B79-50845)
Blues on the run : for SATB chorus and piano with optional bass and drums. (Blackley, Terry J). *Warner : Blossom.* *Unpriced* DW (B79-50845)
Blume, Friedrich. Classic and Romantic music : a comprehensive survey. *Faber.* Pbk. *£2.50 : CIP rev.* A(XFYK151) (B79-05246) ISBN 0-571-11354-0
Blyton, Carey. The oceans of the moon : eight variations and a theme, op.75 : for guitar. *Bèrben : Breitkopf and Härtel.* *£2.85* TSPM/T (B79-51176)
Boardman, Eunice.
Musical growth in the elementary school. (Bergethon, Bjornar). 3rd ed. *Holt, Rinehart and Winston.* Pbk. *£9.25* A(VG) (B79-07190)
Musical growth in the elementary school. (Bergethon, Bjornar). 4th ed. *Holt, Rinehart and Winston.* Sp. *£8.50* A(VK) (B79-10207) ISBN 0-03-020856-4
Boating. Grannies to sell. Grannies to sell, and, Boating. (Fraser, Shena). *Roberton.* *£0.20* JFDW (B79-50518)
Boatwright, Howard. Variations for small orchestra. *Oxford University Press.* *Unpriced* MRJ (B79-51036)
Bodleian Library. William Boyce, 1711-1779 : a bicentenary exhibition. *Broad St., Oxford OX1 3BG : The Library.* Sd. *£0.15* BBS(WJ) (B79-26827) ISBN 0-900177-69-1
Boehm, Theobald.
24 Caprices-Études, opus 26 : für Flöte solo = for solo flute = pour flûte seule. Reprint der Schott-Originalausgabe von 1852. *Schott.* *£4.00* VR/AF (B79-51213)
Capriccios, flute. Twenty-four capriccios for solo flute. *Chester Music.* *Unpriced* VR/AF (B79-50736)
Boethius. Consolatio philosophiae. *Vocal score.* Consolatio philosophiae : scène dramatique voix haute et orchestre in memoriam Ernest Ansermet (1977). (Sutermeister, Heinrich). *Schott.* *£10.80* KFTDX (B79-50155)
Böhler, Friedel W. Musae Sioniae Tl.3. Allein Gott in der Höh sei Ehr. Allein Gott in der Höh sei Ehr : Choralbearbeitung für zwei vierstimmige Chöre. (Praetorius, Michael). *Bärenreiter.* *£1.16* EZDH (B79-50462)
Böhm, I C F. Concerto, viola d'amore, oboe d'amore & continuo, F major. Concerto for viola d'amore or viola,

oboe d'amore or viola and basso continuo with cello. *(Little Margaret, Penmans Green, Chipperfield) : E.L. White. Unpriced* NUPNTF (B79-50596)
Boismortier, Joseph Bodin de.
Sonatas, flutes (2), op.2, nos.3, 4. Two sonatas, Opus 2, Nos. 3 and 4 for two flutes, or oboes, or violins. *Oxford University Press. Unpriced* VRNUE (B79-50327) ISBN 0-19-355578-6
Sonatas, flutes (2), op.47. Sechs Sonaten für zwei Querflöten, op.47. *Eulenburg. Unpriced* VRNUE (B79-50328)
Bolton, Cecil.
18 ct. gold for all organ. *EMI. Unpriced* RK/DW/GB/AY (B79-51129)
22 ct. gold : for all organ. *EMI. Unpriced* RK/DW/GB/AY (B79-50656)
22ct. gold : for guitar. *EMI. Unpriced* TSPMK/DW/GB/AY (B79-50712)
22ct. gold : for piano solo. *EMI. Unpriced* QPK/DW/GB/AY (B79-50642)
Fats Waller. (Waller, Thomas). *EMI. Unpriced* KDW/GB (B79-50138)
Fun chord organ : for young people of any age. *EMI. Unpriced* RPVCK/DW/GB/AY (B79-51133) ISBN 0-86175-064-0

Happy Christmas : B flat clarinet. *EMI. Unpriced* VVPMK/DP/LF/AY (B79-50360)
Happy Christmas : B flat trumpet. *EMI. Unpriced* WSPMK/DP/LF/AY (B79-50399)
Happy Christmas : chord organ. *EMI. Unpriced* RPVCK/DP/LF/AY (B79-50248)
Happy Christmas : easy piano or organ. *EMI. Unpriced* QPK/DP/LF/AY (B79-50224)
I'll be seeing you ... : featuring the songs, the artists and the memories of the Second World War. *EMI. Unpriced* KDW/GB/AY(XNU7) (B79-50977) ISBN 0-86175-042-x
Lionheart. *arr.* Lionheart. (Bush, Kate). *EMI. Unpriced* KDW/GB (B79-50135)
The modern accordionist. *EMI. Unpriced* RSPMK/DW/GB/AY (B79-50662)
Singalongamax. *EMI. Unpriced* KDW/GB/AY (B79-50976) ISBN 0-86175-043-8
T.V. detectives. *EMI. Unpriced* QPK/JS/AY (B79-50643)

The works of Harry Warren. (Warren, Harry). *EMI. Unpriced* KDW/JR (B79-50145)
Bombs away, dream babies. (Stewart, John). *Chappell. Unpriced* KDW/HKR (B79-50989)
Bombs away, dream babies. *arr.* Bombs away, dream babies. (Stewart, John). *Chappell. Unpriced* KDW/HKR (B79-50989)
Bonsor, Brian. Wein, Weib und Gesang. Op.333. *arr.* Wine, women and song. (Strauss, Johann, *b.1825*). New revised ed. *Schott. £0.90* VSNRQK/AHW (B79-50762)
Boogie wonderland. (Willis, Allee). *Rondor : Chappell. Unpriced* KDW/GB (B79-50534)
Boogie woogie band. (Balent, Andrew). *Warner : Blossom. Unpriced* UMJ (B79-51200)

Boreham histories. Smith, William Joseph Thomas. Bells, clocks & ringers. *Boreham Vicarage, Chelmsford CM3 3EG : The author.* Pbk. *£0.50* AXSR(YDDEBO) (B79-31934)
Borri, Giovanni Battista. Domine Deus, rex coelestis. Quattro pezzi sacri. Laudi alla vergine Maria. Laudi alla vergine Maria = Prayer to the Virgin Mary : for four-part chorus of female voices. (Verdi, Giuseppe). *Roberton. £0.32* FEZDH (B79-50916)
Boufil, Jacques Jules. Duo, clarinets, op.2, no.1, C major. Grand duo, op.2, no.1 : for two clarinets. *Fentone Music. £1.80* VVNU (B79-50783)
Bouis, Antonina W. Testimony. (Shostakovich, Dmitriĭ Dmitrievich). *H. Hamilton. £7.95 : CIP entry* BSGR(N) (B79-25857) ISBN 0-241-10321-5
Boult, *Sir* Adrian. Music and friends : seven decades of letters to Adrian Boult from Elgar, Vaughan Williams, Holst, Bruno Walter, Yehudi Menuhin and other friends. *H. Hamilton. £6.95 : CIP rev.* A/EC(P) (B79-08128) ISBN 0-241-10178-6
Bouquet of Czech folk songs. B72. The betrayed shepherd. The abducted shepherd = Der entführte Hirt : for four-part chorus of men's voices a cappella. (Dvořák, Antonín). *Schirmer. £0.35* GEZDW (B79-50925)
Bouquet of Czech folk songs. B72. The sweetheart's resolve. If you should go away = Wenn du fortgehst : for four-part chorus of men's voices a cappella. (Dvořák, Antonín). *Schirmer. £0.35* GEZDW (B79-50926)
Bow down thine ear. I will thank thee, O Lord. I will thank thee, O Lord. (Purcell, Daniel). *36 Ranelagh Gdns W.6 : Cathedral Music. Unpriced* EZDH (B79-50058)
Bowman, Bonnie. Sleeping innocence : a lullaby, for mixed chorus and piano. (Townsend, Douglas). *Broude Breitkopf and Härtel. £0.42* DW (B79-50451)
'Boy looked at Johnny' : the obituary of rock and roll. (Burchill, Julie). *Pluto Press.* Pbk. *£1.25* AKDW/HKR/E(M) (B79-02984) ISBN 0-86104-030-9
Boyce, William.
The shepherd's lottery. Symphony. *arr.* Gavot, from symphony no.4. *Edwin Ashdown. £0.40* RK/AHM (B79-50237)
Sonata, violins (2) & continuo, no.1, A minor. Trio sonata, no.1, A minor, for 2 violins and continuo. *Peters. Unpriced* SNTPWE (B79-51147)
Sonata, violins (2) & continuo, no.3, A major. Trio sonata, no.3, A major, for 2 violins and continuo. *Peters. Unpriced* SNTPWE (B79-51148)
Ten songs for high voice. *Stainer and Bell. Unpriced* KFTDW (B79-50554) ISBN 0-85249-493-9
Boyd, Douglas.
Atarah's bandkit
Strand D1: With a friend or two : eight duets for flute and classical guitar, with companion cassette. (Ben-Tovim, Atarah). *Novello. £7.00* VRPLTSK/AAY (B79-50758)
The elastic band. *Novello. Score, £5.00, Parts, Unpriced* LNK/AAY (B79-50160)
Boyd, Jack. Quattro pezzi sacri. Laudi alla vergine Maria. Laudi alla vergine Maria = Prayer to the Virgin Mary : for four-part chorus of female voices. (Verdi, Giuseppe). *Roberton. £0.32* FEZDH (B79-50916)
Boyle, Hugh. Intervals, scales and temperaments ... (Lloyd, Llewelyn Southworth). New ed. *Macdonald and Jane's. £9.95* A/B (B79-50003) ISBN 0-354-04229-7
BPI. *See* British Phonographic Industry.
BPI year book : a review of the British record and tape industry
1977 : Centenary ed. : one hundred years of recorded sound. (British Phonographic Industry). *33 Thurloe Pl., SW7 2HQ : BPI.* Pbk. *£2.95* A/FD(BC) (B79-19927) ISBN 0-906154-00-6
1978. (British Phonographic Industry). *33 Thurloe Place, SW7 2HQ : BPI.* Pbk. *£2.95* A/FP(BC) (B79-19928) ISBN 0-906154-01-4
BPI year book : a survey of the British record and tape industries
1976. (British Phonographic Industry). *350 Kilburn High Rd, N.W.6 : Parkway Publications Ltd.* Pbk. *£2.50* A/GB/FD(YC/BC) (B79-19926)
Bradbury, Colin. Cadeaux de noces. Op.65. Le désir. 'Le désir' : for clarinet and piano. (Oberthür, Charles). *Chester Music. Unpriced* VVPJ (B79-51279)
Brahms, Johannes.
Es ist ein Ros entsprungen. Op. 122, no.8. *arr.* Es ist ein Ros entsprungen = Now blooms a rose so tender. *Boosey and Hawkes. Unpriced* EZDW (B79-50888)
Komm'bald. Op.97, no.5. *arr.* Come soon = Komm bald : for three-part chorus of women's voices with piano accompaniment. *Schirmer. £0.35* FDW (B79-50492)
Schicksalslied = Song of destiny. Op.54. *Eulenberg. Unpriced* EMDX (B79-50867)
Sextet, string instruments, op.18, B flat major. Andante. *arr.* Theme and variations. *Boosey and Hawkes. Unpriced* TSNUK (B79-50702)
Wie die Wolke. Op.6, no.5. *arr.* As the clouds with longing wander : Wie die Wolke : for three-part chorus of women's voices with piano accompaniment. *Schirmer. £0.35* FDW (B79-50493)
Brand, Geoffrey.

Sleeping beauty. Op.66. Panorama. *arr.* Panorama ... (Tchaikovsky, Peter). *R. Smith. Unpriced* WMK/HM (B79-50383)
Brandenburg concerto, flutes (2), violin & string orchestra, no.4, BWV1049, G major. *arr.* Brandenburgisches Konzert Nr.4, G-dur : für 2 Blockflöten (Flöten), Violine, Streicher und Continuo, BWV1049. (Bach, Johann Sebastian). *Breitkopf und Härtel. £8.40* NUSNSK/LF (B79-51040)
Brass band. (Taylor, Arthur Richard). *Hart-Davis MacGibbon. £10.00* AWM(X) (B79-06709) ISBN 0-246-11082-1
Brass for beginners : bass clef, trombone, euphonium and baritone. (Riddgeon, John). *Boosey and Hawkes. Unpriced* W/AC (B79-51292)
Bray, Trevor. Introduction to music. (Hendrie, Gerald). *Open University Press.* Pbk. *Unpriced* A (B79-16836) ISBN 0-335-05414-5
Bream, Julian.
Rossiniana, no.1, op.119. Rossiniana no.1 : for solo guitar, op.119. (Giuliani, Mauro). *Faber Music. Unpriced* TSPMG (B79-50704)
Suite, guitar. Suite for guitar. (Swayne, Giles). *Novello. £1.65* TSPMG (B79-50307)
Breitkopf und Härtel Partitur-Bibliothek. Baur, Jürg. Concerto, violin, no.2. 2 Violinkonzert : in Form einer Ballade, für Violine und Orchester, (1978). *Breitkopf und Härtel. £8.40* MPSF (B79-51028)
Bresgen, Cesar. Tiertanzburlesken. *Vocal score.* Tiertanzburlesken. *Schott. Unpriced* FDW (B79-50103)
Brewis, Bert.
Fun music : for clarinet
Vol.1. *Chappell. Unpriced* VVPK/AAY (B79-50357)
Vol.2. *Chappell. Unpriced* VVPK/AAY (B79-50358)
Fun music : for flute
Vol.1. *Chappell. Unpriced* VRPK/AAY (B79-50333)
Vol.2. *Chappell. Unpriced* VRPK/AAY (B79-50334)
Fun music for recorder
Vol.1. *Chappell. Unpriced* VSPK/AAY (B79-50341)
Fun music : for recorder
Vol.2. *Chappell. Unpriced* VSPK/AAY (B79-50342)
Fun music : for trumpet
Vol.1. *Chappell. Unpriced* WSPK/AAY (B79-50394)
Fun music : for trumpets
Vol.2. *Chappell. Unpriced* WSPK/AAY (B79-50395)
Fun music : for violin
Vol.1. *Chappell. Unpriced* SPK/AAY (B79-50278)
Vol.2. *Chappell. Unpriced* SPK/AAY (B79-50279)
Organ gold
3. *Chappell. Unpriced* RK/DW/GB/AY (B79-50240)
4. *Chappell. Unpriced* RK/DW/GB/AY (B79-50241)
5. *Chappell. Unpriced* RK/DW/GB/AY (B79-50657)
Yip-i-addy-i-ay yip-i-addy-i-ay. *Melody part.* Yip-i-addy-i-ay yip-i-addy-i-ay : songs for junior and middle school with optional parts for recorder and percussion. *Chappell. Unpriced* JFDADW/AY (B79-50934)
Brian (Havergal) Society. *See* Havergal Brian Society.
Bridge, Frank.
First book of organ pieces. Six organ pieces. *Boosey and Hawkes. Unpriced* RJ (B79-51123)
Oration : (concerto elegiaco) for solo cello and orchestra. *Faber Music. Unpriced* MPSRF (B79-50584)
Brindle, Reginald Smith.
Concerto de angelis : for four guitars. *Schott. Unpriced* TSNSF/T (B79-50299)
Guitarcosmos 1 : progressive pieces for guitar. *Schott. £2.50* TSPMJ (B79-51181)
Guitarcosmos 2 : progressive pieces for guitar. *Schott. £2.50* TSPMJ (B79-51182)
Guitarcosmos 3 : Progressive pieces for guitar. *Schott. £2.50* TSPMJ (B79-51183)
Brinkmann, Reinhold.
Avantgarde, Jazz, Pop : Tenderzen zwischen Tonalität und Atonalität : neun Vorragstexte. *Schott.* Pbk. *£7.20* A/PF (B79-11128)
Die neue Musik und die Tradition : sieben Kongressbeiträge und eine analytische Studie. (Neue Musik und die Tradition *(Conference), Darmstadt, 1978*). *Schott.* Pbk. *£10.80* A(XPK19) (B79-11940)
Bristol and District Organists' Association : a brief history. (Lawrance, F W J). *57 Burnham Drive, Bleadon Hill, Weston-super-Mare, Avon BS24 9LF : The author.* Sd. *£1.00* AR(QB/DFEB/X) (B79-27792)
British Broadcasting Corporation. BBC music guides.
Hogwood, Christopher. The trio sonata. *British Broadcasting Corporation.* Pbk. *£2.50* ANXNSE (B79-33556) ISBN 0-563-17095-6
Warrack, John. Tchaikovsky ballet music. *British Broadcasting Corporation.* Pbk. *£1.40* BTDAM/HM (B79-31929) ISBN 0-563-12860-7
British Broadcasting Corporation. Catalogue of music broadcast on Radio 3. *For earlier editions of this annual see* British Broadcasting Corporation. Catalogue of music broadcast on Radio 3 and Radio 4.
British Broadcasting Corporation. Catalogue of music broadcast on Radio 3
1975. *B.B.C.* Pbk. *£4.50* A/JT(XQQ) (B79-29149) ISBN 0-563-17372-6
British Broadcasting Corporation. Catalogue of music broadcast on Radio 3 and Radio 4. *For later editions of this annual see* British Broadcasting Corporation. Catalogue of music broadcast on Radio 3.
British Country Music Association. Yearbook
1979. *PO Box 2, Newton Abbot, Devon TQ12 4HT : The Association.* Pbk. *Unpriced* AKDW/GC(BC) (B79-34987)
British Federation of Music Festivals. Year book
1979. *106 Gloucester Place, W1H 3DB : The Federation.* Sd. *£1.50* A(YC/WE/Q/BC) (B79-18561)
British hymn writers and composers : a check-list, giving their dates & places of birth & death. (Hayden, Andrew J). 1st ed. reprinted. *c/o Addington Palace, Croydon CR9 5AD : Hymn Society of Great Britain and Ireland.* Pbk. *£3.00* ADM/D(M/WT) (B79-15556)
British Phonographic Industry.
BPI year book : a review of the British record and tape industry
1977 : Centenary ed. : one hundred years of recorded sound. *33 Thurloe Pl., SW7 2HQ : BPI.* Pbk. *£2.95* A/FD(BC) (B79-19927) ISBN 0-906154-00-6
1978. *33 Thurloe Place, SW7 2HQ : BPI.* Pbk. *£2.95* A/FP(BC) (B79-19928) ISBN 0-906154-01-4
BPI year book : a survey of the British record and tape industries
1976. *350 Kilburn High Rd, N.W.6 : Parkway Publications Ltd.* Pbk. *£2.50* A/GB/FD(YC/BC) (B79-19926)
British record company & music industry index. *Hamilton House, Nelson Close, Staverton, Totnes, Devon TQ9 6PG : R.S. Productions.* Sd. *£1.00* A/FD(QB/WT) (B79-35264)
Britten, Benjamin, *Baron Britten.*
A birthday hansel. Op.92. *Selections : arr.* Four Burns songs : for high voice and piano. *Faber Music. Unpriced* KFTDW (B79-50153)
On receiving the first Aspen Award : a speech. *Faber.* Sd. *£0.80 : CIP rev.* A (B78-09111) ISBN 0-571-10023-6
Paul Bunyan. Op.17. *Vocal score.* Paul Bunyan : an operetta in two acts and a prologue, op.17. *Faber Music. Unpriced* CF (B79-50014)
Broadbent, Derek. Cavatina. *arr.* Cavatina. (Myers, Stanley). *EMI. Unpriced* WMK (B79-50792)
Broadway Joe. *arr.* She was an acrobat's daughter, an English music hall song : for four-part chorus of mixed voices with piano accompaniment. (Ruby, Harry). *Roberton. Unpriced* DW (B79-50450)
Broadway showcase choral series.
Gershwin, George. Porgy and Bess. Summertime. *arr.* Summertime : S.A.C.(T.) B. with piano. *Chappell. Unpriced* DW (B79-50849)
Loewe, Frederick. Paint your wagon. They call the wind Maria. *arr.* They call the wind Maria : S.A.C.(T.) B. with piano. *Chappell. Unpriced* DW (B79-50850)
Porter, Cole. Kiss me, Kate. Another op'nin', another show. *arr.* Another op'nin', another show : for S.A. cambiata, B. or S.A.T.B. with piano. *Chappell. Unpriced* DW (B79-50852)
Rodgers, Richard. The King and I. Getting to know you. *arr.* Getting to know you : for S.A. cambiata, B. or S.A.T.B. *Williamson. Unpriced* DW (B79-50855)

Rodgers, Richard. Oklahoma!. Oh, what a beautiful mornin'. *arr.* Oh, what a beautiful mornin' : S.A.C.(T)B. with piano. *Williamson Music. Unpriced* DW (B79-50856)
Rodgers, Richard. The sound of music. Climb ev'ry mountain. *arr.* Climb ev'ry mountain : for S.A. cambiata, B. or S.A.T.B. with piano. *Williamson Music. Unpriced* DW (B79-50857)
Rodgers, Richard. State fair. Its a grand night for singing. *arr.* Its a grand night for singing : S.A.C.(T).B, with piano. *Williamson. Unpriced* DW (B79-50858)
Styne, Jule. Gypsy. Everything's coming up roses. *arr.* Everything's coming up roses : for S.A. cambiata, B. or S.A.T.B, with piano. *Williamson. Unpriced* DW (B79-50859)
Brofsky, Howard. The art of listening : developing musical perception. (Bamberger, Jeanne Shapiro). 4th ed. *Harper and Row.* Pbk. *£8.15* A/C (B79-28895) ISBN 0-06-040943-6
Brojer, Robert.
Suite, lute, A major. *arr.* Suite in A. (Weiss, Sylvius Leopold). *Schott. £3.20* TSPMK/AG (B79-51194)
Suite, lute, D major. *arr.* Suite in D. (Weiss, Sylvius Leopold). *Schott. £2.60* TSPMK/AG (B79-51195)
Brosnac, Donald. The electric guitar : its history and construction. *Omnibus Press.* Pbk. *£3.50* ATSPV/B(X) (B79-33557) ISBN 0-86001-491-6
Brother Ray : Ray Charles' own story. (Charles, Ray). *Macdonald and Jane's. £5.95* AMT(P) (B79-21877) ISBN 0-354-04393-5
Brown, Ashley. Play drums today. *Hamlyn. £3.50* AXQ/E (B79-24596) ISBN 0-600-37199-9
Brown, Christopher.
Even such is time : for mixed chorus. *J. and W. Chester. Unpriced* EZDW (B79-50476)
The sun rising : threnody for orchestra. Op.45. *Chester Music. Unpriced* MMJ (B79-51022)
Brown, David, *b.1929.* Tchaikovsky : a biographical and critical study
Vol.1: The early years (1840-1874). *Gollancz. £8.50* BTD(N) (B79-05248) ISBN 0-575-02454-2
Brown, Earle. Novara. *Universal. Unpriced* NUNN (B79-51037)
Brown, Gerald Edgar. Five nativity carols : for unison voices, piano and simple percussion. *7 Garrick St. W.C.2 : Middle Eight Music. Unpriced* JFE/NYLDP/LF (B79-50946)
Brown, James.
Menuetto con variazioni in F, on a theme from Mozart's Don Giovanni : for 2 oboes, 2 clarinets, 2 bassoons and 2 horns. (Triebensee, Josef). *Nova Music. Unpriced* UNN (B79-51208)
Oboe trios
Vol.1. *Chester. Unpriced* VTNT/AY (B79-50349)
Rossini and Chopin variations for oboe and piano. *Lordship Publications. Unpriced* VTP/T (B79-51258)
Brown, John Robert. Front line sax solos. *Chappell. Unpriced* VUPMHX (B79-50776)
Brown, Mark.
Gather your rosebuds. (Lawes, William). *Pro Cantione Antiqua : Breitkopf und Härtel. Unpriced* GEZDU (B79-50505)
Partsongs
Vol.1: for unaccompained i.e. unaccompanied male voices (A(A)T(T)B(B)). *(Lyndhurst, Denton Rd, Ben Rhydding) : Pro Cantione Antiqua : Breitkopf and Härtel. £2.40* GEZDW (B79-50508)
The Play of Daniel : a 13th century liturgical drama from Beauvais Cathedral. *(Lyndhurst, Denton Rd, Ben Rhydding) : Pro Cantione Antiqua : Breitkopf und Härtel. £2.95* CQM/L (B79-50417)
Brown, Sandy. The McJazz manuscripts : a collection of the writings of Sandy Brown. *Faber. £6.95 : CIP rev.* AMT(P) (B79-10483) ISBN 0-571-11319-2
Brown University choral series.
Tepper, Albert. 4 American settings. Song of Thyrsis. Song of Thyrsis : S.A.T.B. & piano. *Boosey and Hawkes. £0.35* DW (B79-50860)
Tepper, Albert. The sycophantic fox and the gullible raven : S.A.T.B. & piano. *Boosey and Hawkes. £0.90* DW (B79-50861)
Bruck, Wilhelm.
Danse bohémienne. *arr.* Danse bohémienne : für zwei Gitarren oder Oktavgitarre und Gitarre = for two guitars or octave guitar and guitar = pour deux guitares ou guitare octave et guitare. (Debussy, Claude). *Schott. £3.20* TSNUK/AH (B79-51175)
Rondo, guitars (3). Rondo für zwei Gitarren, for two guitars. (Hindemith, Paul). *Schott. £2.00* TSNUK/W (B79-50304)
Bruckner, Mahler, Schoenberg. (Newlin, Dika). Revised ed.. *Boyars : Distributed by Calder and Boyars. £9.95* BBUE (B79-05247) ISBN 0-7145-2658-4
Brumby, Colin. Suite for four double basses. *Yorke. Unpricd* SSNSG (B79-50289)
Brumel, Antoine. Laudate Dominum de caelis : for 4 voices. *72 Brewery Rd, N.7 : Mapa mundi. Unpriced* EZDR (B79-50097)
Brunetti, Gaetano. Quintet, bassoon & string quartet, no.4, D major. Quintet no.4 for bassoon and strings. *Musica rara. Unpriced* NVWNR (B79-50192)

Brymer, Jack.
Clarinet series
Easy book 2. *Weinberger. Unpriced* VVPK/AAY (B79-51281)
Moderate book 2. *Weinberger. Unpriced* VVPK/AAY (B79-51282)
Buchan, Norman. The Scottish folksinger : 118 modern and traditional folksongs. New ed. *Collins. Unpriced* JE/TSDW/G/AYDL (B79-50119) ISBN 0-00-411125-7
Buckley, Joss. Gunslinger. *Vocal score.* Gunslinger. *Chappell. Unpriced* CM (B79-50820)
Bucknell University. *Music Department.* The Harold E. Cook collection of musical instruments. *Bucknell University Press : Associated University Press. £5.75* AL(YTGLB/WJ) (B79-02987) ISBN 0-8387-1574-5
Buhé, Klaus. Irische Lieder und Balladen. *Schott. £4.00* KE/TSDW/K/G/AYDM (B79-50995)

Building a chamber music collection : a descriptive guide to published scores. (Forsyth, Ella Marie). *Scarecrow Press : Distributed by Bailey and Swinfen. £6.30* AN(T) (B79-32195) ISBN 0-8108-1215-0
Building a library. *Oxford University Press.* Pbk. *£2.95 : CIP entry* A/FD (B79-25861) ISBN 0-19-311324-4
Bullard, Alan. Praise the Lord out of heaven : S.A.T.B. *Banks. Unpriced* DK (B79-50438)
Bullard, Terance. Sweet Scottish isle. *arr.* Sweet Scottish isle. (Mullen, Brian). *(16 Mendip Rd) : Autumn Publications. Unpriced* KDW (B79-50959)
Buller, John.
Poor Jenny : for flutes (1 player) and percussion (1 player). *Schirmer. £3.50* VRPLX (B79-51229)
Scribenery : for solo cello. *Schirmer. £1.25* SRPMJ (B79-51161)
Burbidge, Peter. The Wagner companion. *Faber. £12.50 : CIP rev.* BWC (B78-40353) ISBN 0-571-10471-1
Burchill, Julie. 'The boy looked at Johnny' : the obituary of rock and roll. *Pluto Press.* Pbk. *£1.25* AKDW/HKR/E(M) (B79-02984) ISBN 0-86104-030-9
Burghauser, Jarmil. Sinfonietta. (Janáček, Leoš). *Eulenburg. £2.50* MMEM (B79-50168)
Burgon, Geoffrey.
The fall of Lucifer. *Vocal score.* The fall of Lucifer : for countertenor, tenor and bass soloists, chamber choir and instrumental ensemble. *Chester Music. Unpriced* CM/L (B79-50015)
Magnificat and Nunc dimittis. *Chester Music. Unpriced* FDGPP (B79-50907)
Sisters in song : a collection of new songs from the women's liberation movement. *Onlywomen Press. Unpriced* KDGPR (B79-50951)
Veni spiritus. *Vocal score.* Veni spiritus : for soprano and baritone soloists, chorus and orchestra. *Chester Music. Unpriced* EMDGKADD/LN (B79-50042)
Burkhard, Willy. Fünf Gesänge für gemischten Chor nach Gedichten von Richard Dehmel, Opus 26. *Bärenreiter. £1.16* EZDW (B79-50477)
Burlinson, Nigel. Roots, rock and reggae. *Chappell. Unpriced* KDW/HKR/AY (B79-50543)
Burnam, Edna Mae. A dozen a day : technical exercises for the piano to be done each day before practicing sic. *Willis Music : Chappell. Unpriced* Q/AF (B79-50613)
Burnham, Howard. Grones dictionary of music, or, A golden treasury of musical rubbish, or, Misleading lives of the great composers. *Windmill Farm, Ampleforth, Yorkshire : Emerson Edition.* Pbk. *£2.95* A/D(M/YB) (B79-04539) ISBN 0-9506209-0-4
Burns, Robert.
A birthday hansel. Op.92. *Selections : arr.* Four Burns songs : for high voice and piano. (Britten, Benjamin, *Baron Britten*). *Faber Music. Unpriced* KFTDW (B79-50153)
The de'il's awa wi'th' exiseman : for four-part chorus of mixed voices with piano accompaniment. (Rhein, Robert). *Schirner. £0.35* DW (B79-50854)
Ae fond kiss : for four-part chorus of mixed voices with baritone solo a cappella. (Rhein, Robert). *Schirmer. £0.35* EZDW (B79-50901)
The merry muses of Caledonia. The secret cabinet of Robert Burns : merry muses of Caledonia. New ed.. *P. Harris. £3.50* AKDW/K/G/KDX (B79-36915) ISBN 0-904505-84-7
Bursík, Josef. Dobry den. What a day : Dobry den : a choral cycle, for two-part chorus of young voices with piano accompaniment or a cappella. (Laburda, Jiří). *Schirmer. £2.10* FDW (B79-50495)
Burt, James. Handel's greatest hits : all organ. (Handel, George Frideric). *Chappell. Unpriced* RK (B79-50654)
Bush, Geoffrey.
English lyrics. *selections.* Seven songs for high voice. (Parry, *Sir* Charles Hubert, *bart*). *Stainer and Bell. Unpriced* KFTDW (B79-51006)
Musica Britannica : a national collection of music
Vol.43: English songs, 1800-1860. *Stainer and Bell. Unpriced* C/AYD (B79-50814) ISBN 0-85249-439-4
Six songs for medium voice. (Stanford, *Sir* Charles Villiers). *Stainer and Bell. Unpriced* KFVDW (B79-51008) ISBN 0-85249-526-9
Songs. *Selections.* Eight songs for high voice and piano. *Novello. £2.40* KFTDW (B79-51005)
Bush, Kate. Lionheart. *arr.* Lionheart. *EMI. Unpriced* KDW/GB (B79-50135)
Butterfield, Arthur. Play guitar today. *Hamlyn. £3.50* ATS/E (B79-22642) ISBN 0-600-37200-6
Butterfield, Graham.
Play guitar today. (Butterfield, Arthur). *Hamlyn. £3.50* ATS/E (B79-22642) ISBN 0-600-37200-6
Play rock guitar today. *Hamlyn. £3.50* ATSPV/E (B79-24594) ISBN 0-600-37202-2
Butterworth, Lionel Milner Angus-. *See* Angus-Butterworth, Lionel Milner.
Butterworth, Neil.
Haydn. *Midas Books. £6.50 : CIP entry* BHE(N) (B78-05400) ISBN 0-85936-030-x
Kettlebury hill : for oboe and piano (or strings). *Banks. Unpriced* VTPJ (B79-50350)
Selva morale e spirituale. Ut queant laxis. *arr.* Hymn to Saint John the Baptist. Ut queant laxis. (Monteverdi, Claudio). *36 Ranelagh Gdns W.6 : Cathedral Music. Unpriced* JNFLEE/SNTPWDJ (B79-50130)
Butterworth, Richard. Grones dictionary of music, or, A golden treasury of musical rubbish, or, Misleading lives of the great composers. (Burnham, Howard). *Windmill Farm, Ampleforth, Yorkshire : Emerson Edition.* Pbk. *£2.95* A/D(M/YB) (B79-04539) ISBN 0-9506209-0-4
By the roadside : six songs to poems by Walt Whitman, for soprano and piano. (Schonthal, Ruth). *Oxford University Press. Unpriced* KFLDW (B79-50150)
Byrd, William. Gradualia, lib. 2. Alleluia, ascendit Deus. Alleluia, our Lord is risen : for mixed chorus SSATB. *Broude : Breitkopf und Härtel. £0.42* EZDJ/LM (B79-50470)
Bythier, Jürgen. Love of three oranges. L'amour des trois oranges. Opus 33 : opéra en 4 actes et 10 tableaux avec un prologue d'après Carlo Gozzi. (Prokofiev, Sergei). *Boosey and Hawkes. Unpriced* CQC (B79-50822)
C. John Taylor's islands of beauty : ballad in English and Gaelic. (Taylor, Cecil John). *Isle of Seil, Oban, Argyll, Scotland : Highland Arts Studios. Unpriced* KDW (B79-50527)
Cable, Paul. Bob Dylan : his unreleased works. *P.O. Box 1, W.C.2 : Scorpion Publications Ltd/Dark Star. Unpriced* AKDW/GB/FD(P/WT) (B79-18867) ISBN 0-905906-17-9
Cadeaux de noces. Op.65. Le désir. 'Le désir' : for clarinet and piano. (Oberthür, Charles). *Chester Music. Unpriced* VVPJ (B79-51279)
Cadences : for brass quartet. (Clarke, Keith Robert). *Novello. £1.95* WNS (B79-50795)
Caldara, Antonio. Regini coeli laetare = Freu dich, Maria, Himmelsköningin : für vierstimmigen gemischten Chor und Basso continuo = for four-part mixed chorus and basso continuo. *Bärenreiter. £2.97* DJ (B79-50436)
Callaway, Frank. Australian composition in the twentieth century. *Oxford University Press. £18.50* A/D(M/YX/XM76) (B79-33552) ISBN 0-19-550522-0
Cambridge studies in music. Le Huray, Peter. Music and the Reformation in England, 1549-1660. *Cambridge University Press. £19.50* AD/LD(YD/XDXJ112) (B79-16102) ISBN 0-521-21958-2
Cambridge University. *See* University of Cambridge.
Cambridge University Guild of Change Ringers. The Cambridge University Guild of Change Ringers, 1879-1979 : a centenary history. (Cook, William T). *c/o B.D. Threlfall, 106 High St., Bottisham, Cambridge, Cambs. : C.U.G.C.R.* Sd. *Unpriced* AXSR/E(QB/X) (B79-30802)
Cambridge University Guild of Change Ringers, 1879-1979 : a centenary history. (Cook, William T). *c/o B.D. Threlfall, 106 High St., Bottisham, Cambridge, Cambs. : C.U.G.C.R.* Sd. *Unpriced* AXSR/E(QB/X) (B79-30802)

Camilleri, Charles. Sama'i : for flute solo. *Basil Ramsey : Roberton. Unpriced* VRPMJ (B79-51231)
Campbell, Sidney Schofield. Praise to God in the highest. *arr.* Praise to God in the highest : Russian melody. *Oxford University Press. Unpriced* FDH/LF (B79-50490) ISBN 0-19-351126-6
Canción : for solo guitar. (Wilson, Thomas Brendan). *Scotus : Schirmer. Unpriced* TSPMJ (B79-50707)
Canon & gigue for three violins and keyboard (cello continuo ad lib.). (Pachelbel, Johann). *Fentone Music : Breitkopf and Härtel. Unpriced* SNSPWHP (B79-51146)

Canon & gigue, violins (3) & continuo, D major. Canon & gigue for three violins and keyboard (cello continuo ad lib.). (Pachelbel, Johann). *Fentone Music : Breitkopf and Härtel. Unpriced* SNSPWHP (B79-51146)
Canon in five parts ... : for boys chorus with piano accompaniment. (Bernstein, Leonard). *Amberson : Schirmer (dist.). £0.35* DH (B79-50831)
Cantata, op.20 on German folksong texts : for mezzo-soprano solo, chorus and chamber orchestra. (Spinner, Leopold). *Boosey and Hawkes. Unpriced* EMDX (B79-50045)
Canter, Robin. Morceau de salon. Op.228 : for oboe and piano. (Kalliwoda, Jan Václav). *Nova Music. Unpriced* VTPJ (B79-51262)
Cantiones sacrae, octonis vocibus. Tu es Petrus. Tu es Petrus : for 8 voices. (Philips, Peter). *Mapa mundi. Unpriced* EZDJ (B79-50065)
Canto for guitar. (Swayne, Giles). *Novello. £1.65* TSPMJ (B79-50309)
Cantors : a collection of Gregorian chants. *Cambridge University Press. Unpriced* JEZDTD (B79-50933) ISBN 0-521-22149-8
Canty, Laurence. Electric bass guitar : a complete guide. *Chappell. Unpriced* TSUPV/AC (B79-50716)
Canu'r bobol. (Williams, Huw). *Gwasg Gee. £4.00* ADW(YDK) (B79-04543)
Canzon super intradam aechiopicam. (Scheidt, Samuel). *Schirmer. £7.55* VVNK (B79-50780)
Canzona (II) 'La Bernadina' per canto solo : für Sopranblockflüte (Flüte, Oboe, Violine) und Generalbass = for descant recorder (flute, oboe, violin) and continuo. (Frescobaldi, Girolamo). *Schott. £3.20* VSRPJ (B79-51242)
Canzona. (La paglia). (Erbach, Christian). *Schirmer.*

Unpriced VVNK (B79-50779)
Canzonetti ... libro quarto a quattro voci. Partiro si. Partirò sì = Parting is pain : for four-part chorus of mixed voices a cappella. (Vecchi, Horatio). *Schirmer. £0.35* EZDU (B79-50475)
Caralcanti, Guido. Ballata dall'esilio : per voce e chitarra. (Castelnuovo-Tedesco, Mario). *Bèrben : Breitkopf and Härtel. £1.70* KE/TSDW (B79-50992)
Carfagna, Carlo.
Duet, guitars, op.55, no.1, D major. Duo in la maggiore, op.55, n.1. (Sor, Fernando). *Bèrben : Breitkopf and Härtel. £1.70* TSNU (B79-51169)
Pièces de violes, liv. 4. *Selections : arr.* Cinque antiche danze francesi. (Marais, Marin). *Berben : Breitkopf und Härtel. £1.90* SQPLTSK (B79-50686)
Carmichael, Hoagy. The old music master : 23 great songs. *Chappell. Unpriced* KDW/GB (B79-50965)
Carnival des animaux. Le cygne. *arr.* Il cigno. (Saint-Saëns, Camille). *Berben : Breitkopf und Härtel. £1.10* TSPMK (B79-50709)
Carols for choirs
3: Fifty carols ; edited and arranged by David Willcocks and John Rutter. *Oxford University Press. Unpriced* DP/LF/AY (B79-50031) ISBN 0-19-353570-x
Carols for piano. *Oxford University Press. Unpriced* QPK/DP/LF/AY (B79-50223) ISBN 0-19-372608-4
Carols in concert : six carols for SATB with divisions and organ or piano. *Novello. Unpriced* DP/LF/AY (B79-50843)
Carols in consort : Christmas music for two descant, treble, tenor and optional bass recorders. *EMI. Unpriced* VSNSK/DP/LF/AY (B79-50339)
Carpenter, Roger. Goodnight to Flamboro' : the life and music of William Baines. *22 Pheasants Way, Rickmansworth, Herts. : Triad Press.* Pbk. *£6.95 : CIP rev.* BBCN (B77-21345) ISBN 0-902070-22-3
Carroll, Joseph Robert.
Komm'bald. Op.97, no.5. *arr.* Come soon = Komm bald : for three-part chorus of women's voices with piano accompaniment. (Brahms, Johannes). *Schirmer. £0.35* FDW (B79-50492)
Wie die Wolke. Op.6, no.5. *arr.* As the clouds with longing wander : Wie die Wolke : for three-part chorus of women's voices with piano accompaniment. (Brahms, Johannes). *Schirmer. £0.35* FDW (B79-50493)
Carroll, Lewis.
Songs for Alice : Alice in Wonderland and Through the looking glass. (Harper, Don). *Adam & Charles Black. Unpriced* JFDW (B79-50127) ISBN 0-7136-1879-5
Vintage Alice : fantascene on a mad tea-party. (Del Tredici, David). *Boosey and Hawkes. Unpriced* KFLE/MDX (B79-51000)
Carryl, Guy Wetmore. The sycophantic fox and the gullible raven : S.A.T.B. & piano. (Tepper, Albert). *Boosey and Hawkes. £0.90* DW (B79-50861)
Carter, Andrew.
De Virgin Mary : West Indian traditional carol. S.A.T.B. unacc. *Banks. Unpriced* EZDP/LF (B79-50884)
The twelve days of Christmas : English traditional carol, S.A.T.B. unacc. *Banks. Unpriced* EZDW/LF (B79-50904)
Carter, Elliott. A mirror on which to dwell : six poems of Elizabeth Bishop, for soprano and chamber orchestra. *Associated Music. £24.20* KFLE/MDW (B79-50550)
Carter, Sydney. 9 carols or ballads. Lord of the dance. *arr.* Lord of the dance. *Galliard. Unpriced* ELDM (B79-50453)
Carter, Sydney Horace. 'Blue Amberol' cylinders : a catalogue. *19 Glendale Rd, Bournemouth BH6 4JA : 'Talking machine review'.* Sd. *£4.00* A/FE(QB/WT) (B79-05450) ISBN 0-902338-30-7
Cartwright, Kenneth. Harvest jazz : a cantata for schools. *Boosey and Hawkes. Unpriced* FDE/LP (B79-50489)
Cary, Tristram. Two nativity songs. *Oxford University Press. Unpriced* EZDP/LF (B79-50885) ISBN 0-19-343536-5
Casey, Warren.
Grease. *arr.* Grease : original soundtrack songs from the motion picture. *Warner : Blossom. Unpriced* KDW/JR (B79-50143)
Grease. *arr.* Grease : original soundtrack songs from the motion picture. *Chappell. Unpriced* KDW/JR (B79-50144)
Cashmore, Donald. Carols in concert : six carols for SATB with divisions and organ or piano. *Novello. Unpriced* DP/LF/AY (B79-50843)
Casken, John. Thymehaze : for alto recorder and piano. *Schott. Unpriced* VSSPJ (B79-51254)
Casper the friendly ghost. *arr.* Casper the friendly ghost. (Livingston, Jerry). *Warner : Blossom. Unpriced* WMK/DW (B79-50379)
Cass-Beggs, Barbara. Your baby needs music. *Ward Lock. £4.95* A(Z) (B79-50405) ISBN 0-7063-5900-3
Castello, Dario. Sonate concertate, lib. 2, no.1. Sonata prima a soprano solo... : für Sopranblockflöte (Flöte, Violine) und Generalbass = for descant recorder (flute, violin) and continuo. *Schott. £3.20* VSRPE (B79-51241)
Castelnuovo-Tedesco, Mario.
Ballata dall'esilio : per voce e chitarra. *Bèrben : Breitkopf and Härtel. £1.70* KE/TSDW (B79-50992)
Escarraman : a suite of Spanish dances from the XVIth century (after Cervantes), op.177, for guitar. *Bèrben Breitkopf and Härtel. £4.70* TSPMHG (B79-51180)
Castle and woods : overture. (Olivadoti, Joseph). *Rubank Novello. Unpriced* UMMJ (B79-50724)
Catalogue of music broadcast on Radio 3
1975. (British Broadcasting Corporation). *B.B.C.* Pbk. *£4.50* A/JT(XQQ) (B79-29149) ISBN 0-563-17372-6
Catalogue of music broadcast on Radio 3 and Radio 4. Catalogue of music broadcast on Radio 3
1975. (British Broadcasting Corporation). *B.B.C.* Pbk. *£4.50* A/JT(XQQ) (B79-29149) ISBN 0-563-17372-6
Catalogus musicus.
Wiener Stadt- und Landesbibliothek. Verzeichnis der Schubert-Handschriften in der Musiksammlung der Wiener Stadt- und Landesbibliothek. *17 Bucklersbury, Hutchin, Herts. SG5 1BB : Bärenreiter for the International Association of Music Libraries and the International Musicological Society.* Pbk. *£28.05* BSF(TE) (B79-10755)
Wiener Stadt- und Landesbibliothek. Verzeichnis der Schubert-Handschriften in der Musiksammlung der Wiener Stadt- und Landesbibliothek. *17 Bucklersbury, Hutchin, Herts. SG5 1BB : Bärenreiter for the International Association of Music Libraries and the International Musicological Society.* Pbk. *£28.05* BMS(TC) (B79-10755)
Catelinet, Philip. Three sketches for brass band. *Paxton. Unpriced* WMJ (B79-51298)
Cathedral organist, 1977-1978. *Cramer. Unpriced* R/AYC (B79-50229)
Causley, Charles. Round the town : five Charles Causley poems. (Hurd, Michael). *Novello. £0.74* JFDW (B79-50128)
Cavatina. *arr.* Cavatina. (Myers, Stanley). *EMI. Unpriced* WMK (B79-50792)
Cawkwell, Roger.
Starting together : easy duets for recorder and guitar groups
Vol.1. *Chester Music. Unpriced* VSPLTSK/DW/AY (B79-51238)
Starting together : easy duets for recorders and guitar groups
Vol.2. *Chester Music. Unpriced* VSPLTSK/DW/AY (B79-51239)
Vol.3. *Chester Music. Unpriced* VSPLTSK/DW/AY (B79-51240)
Cello positions. (Smith, Doreen). *Oxford University Press. Unpriced* SR/AC (B79-51158) ISBN 0-19-322346-5
C.H. Trevor organ miscellany. *Elkin. £1.55* RK/AAY (B79-50655)
Chacony for strings. (Purcell, Henry). *Eulenberg. Unpriced* RXMHJN (B79-51137)
Chamberlain, Ronald. Herod and the rooster : a legend for all seasons, a dramatic cantata. *(125 Waxwell Lane) : The Grail. Unpriced* DE/LF (B79-50827) ISBN 0-901829-51-x
Chambre, Tim. Rockmaster
1978. *13 Stanton Rd, Regents Park, Southampton, Hants. : Rockmaster.* Sd. *Unpriced* AKDW/HKR/FD(WT) (B79-35642)
Chapman, Mike. Blockbuster. (Chinn, Nicky). *Chappell. Unpriced* KDW/GB (B79-50531)
Chapple, Brian. Five Blake songs : for high voice and piano. *Chester Music. Unpriced* KFTDW (B79-50154)
Chapple, Sue. Sing a song
1. Teacher's book. *Nelson : ILEA Learning Materials Service.* Sp. *£2.75* A/GR(VG) (B79-07467) ISBN 0-17-413002-3
Charles, Ray. Brother Ray : Ray Charles' own story. *Macdonald and Jane's. £5.95* AMT(P) (B79-21877) ISBN 0-354-04393-5
Charleson, Bill. Front line sax solos. *Chappell. Unpriced* VUPMHX (B79-50776)
Charlton. Take my life : tune, Charlton, words, Frances Ridley Havergal and Come, Holy Ghost : tune, Pentecost, words, Bishop J. Cosin, based on 'Veni creator spiritus'. (Wilson, Alan J). *Weinberger. Unpriced* DM (B79-50442)
Chase, Madeline. Gently the breeze blows : two-part. (Ross, Colin). *Banks. Unpriced* FDW (B79-50496)
Cherry valley : an ensemble for nine flutes. (Jenni, Donald). *Associated Music. Unpriced* VRNM (B79-51215)
Cherubini, Luigi.
Hymnes sacrées. Ave Maria. *arr.* Ave Maria. Offertorium. *Fentone Music : Breitkopf and Härtel. Unpriced* KFLE/VVPDJ (B79-51001)

Chester book of motets : sacred renaissance motets, with Latin texts
7: Motets for 3 voices. *Chester Music. Unpriced* EZDJ/AY (B79-50882)
Chester woodwind series.
Boehm, Theobald. Capriccios, flute. Twenty-four capriccios for solo flute. *Chester Music. Unpriced* VR/AF (B79-50736)
Flute trios
Vol.1. *Chester Music. Unpriced* VRNT/AY (B79-51216)
Flute trios
Vol.2. *Chester Music. Unpriced* VRNT/AY (B79-51217)
Oberthür, Charles. Cadeaux de noces. Op.65. Le désir. 'Le désir' : for clarinet and piano. *Chester Music. Unpriced* VVPJ (B79-51279)
Saxophone solos : B flat tenor with piano accompaniment
Vol.1. *Chester Music. Unpriced* VUTPK/AAY (B79-51269)
Saxophone solos : B flat tenor with piano accompaniment
Vol.2. *Chester Music. Unpriced* VUTPK/AAY (B79-51270)
Stanford, *Sir* Charles Villiers. Intermezzos, clarinet & piano, op.13. Three intermezzi, op.13 : for clarinet and piano. *Chester Music. Unpriced* VVPJ (B79-51280)
Chester's concert pieces
Vol.2: From Purcell to Prokofiev for the younger pianist. *Chester Music. Unpriced* QP/AY (B79-50206)
Chester's piano book
Number 5. (Barratt, Carol). *Chester Music. Unpriced* Q/AC (B79-50203)
Chesterton, Frances. How far is it to Bethlehem? Pa mor bell yur Bethlehem? : unison voices and piano. (Hughes-Jones, Llifon). *Roberton. £0.20* JFDP/LF (B79-50517)
Chicago. *See* Watkins, Maurine Dallas.
Children's crusade. The children's crusade : a morality play for the young, for four-part chorus of mixed voices, three soloists, narrator, piano and guitar accompaniment. (Lebowsky, Stanley). *Schirmer. £5.15* CN/L (B79-50416)
Children's crusade : a morality play for the young, for four-part chorus of mixed voices, three soloists, narrator, piano and guitar accompaniment. (Lebowsky, Stanley). *Schirmer. £5.15* CN/L (B79-50416)
Children's songs. (Olive, Vivienne). *Edwin Ashdown. Unpriced* JFDW/GJ (B79-50519)
Chilton, John. Jazz. *Teach Yourself Books.* Pbk. *£1.95 : CIP rev.* AMT(X) (B79-15559) ISBN 0-340-23847-x
Chinn, Nicky. Blockbuster. *Chappell. Unpriced* KDW/GB (B79-50531)
Chiquitita. (Andersson, Benny). *Chappell. Unpriced* KDW/GB (B79-50530)
Chiquitita. *arr.* Chiquitita. (Andersson, Benny). *Chappell. Unpriced* KDW/GB (B79-50530)
Choir schools. (Choir Schools Association). *c/o The Honorary Secretary, Cathedral Choir School, Whitcliffe La., Ripon, N. Yorkshire HG4 2LA : The Association. Unpriced* AD(VF/YC/WT) (B79-19102)
Choir Schools Association. Choir schools. *c/o The Honorary Secretary, Cathedral Choir School, Whitcliffe La., Ripon, N. Yorkshire HG4 2LA : The Association. Unpriced* AD(VF/YC/WT) (B79-19102)
Choose your instrument : a beginner's guide to making music. *Gollancz. £2.95* AL/E (B79-08927) ISBN 0-575-02495-x
Chopbuster march : an outrageous trumpet feature. (Foster, Bob). *Warner : Blossom. Unpriced* UMMGM (B79-50719)
Chopin, Frédéric.
Frédéric François Chopin, 1810-1844. *East-West. Unpriced* QPJ (B79-50213) ISBN 0-904499-04-9
Rossini and Chopin variations for oboe and piano. (Brown, James). *Lordship Publications. Unpriced* VTP/T (B79-51258)
Chor-Archiv.
Caldara, Antonio. Regini coeli laetare = Freu dich, Maria, Himmelsköningin : für vierstimmigen gemischten Chor und Basso continuo = for four-part mixed chorus and basso continuo. *Bärenreiter. £2.97* DJ (B79-50436)
Haydn, Joseph. Sechs englische Psalmen. Hob. XXIII Anhang, Nachtrag. Sechs Psalmen = Six psalms : für dreistimmigen gemischten Chor = for three-part mixed chorus, Hob. XXIII Anhang, Nachtrag. *Bärenreiter. £2.31* EZDR (B79-50471)
Choral-Toccata, 'O Heiland, reiss die Himmel auf' : Melodie Augsburg 1666. (Wehrle, Heinz). *Eulenburg. £1.85* RJ (B79-50651)
Choralbearbeitung in der protestantischen Figuralmusik zwischen Praetorius und Bach. (Krummacher, Friedhelm). *17 Bucklesbury, Hitchin, Herts. SG51 BB : Bärenreiter.* Pbk. *Unpriced* ADGTCW(YE/XE151) (B79-17763)
Chorale preludes, trumpet & organ. Die sechs Choralvorspiele für Trompete und Orgel = The six chorale preludes for trumpet and organ. (Krebs, Johann Ludwig). *Simrock. Unpriced* WSPLR (B79-50398)
Chorbajian, John. My gift : for four-part chorus of men's voices a cappella. *Schirmer. £0.35* GEZDP/LF (B79-50923)
Chormusik für Kinder
Heft 3: Passion, Ostern, Pfingsten. *Bärenreiter. £3.96* DP/AY (B79-50445)
Christmas at home : carol-medleys for all organs. (Blackmore, George). *Paxton. £1.40* R/LF (B79-51119)
Christmas carol kit
Set 1. *Middle Eight Music. Unpriced* MK/DP/LF/AY (B79-51013)
Set 2. *Middle Eight Music. Unpriced* MK/DP/LF/AY (B79-51014)
Christmas carols. *Helison Press. Unpriced* LK/DP/LF/AY (B79-50157) ISBN 0-905684-04-4
Christmas carols for young children : for piano, guitar and recorder. *East West : Breitkopf and Härtel. £1.50* JFE/NUSNTDP/LF/AY (B79-50943)
Christmas songs you like : piano duets for elementary level. *Schroeder and Gunther. £1.75* QNVK/DP/LF/AY (B79-51064)
Christmas vespers : antiphons, psalms and hymns for soloists, double choir, instruments and organ continuo. (Monteverdi, Claudio). *Novello. £3.50* DJ/LF (B79-50437)
Christopher, Tray. The Son has risen : mixed chorus and organ. (Earnest, David). *Broude : Breitkopf und Härtel. £0.45* DH/LL (B79-50434)
Christopherson, Peter. Wings tour USA. (Powell, Aubrey). *High St., Limpsfield, Surrey RH8 0DY : Paper Tiger.* Pbk. *£3.25* AKDW/GB/E(P/EM/XRF) (B79-05872) ISBN 0-905895-10-x
Christus. *Selections : arr.* There shall a star from Jacob come forth : three excerpts from Christus. (Mendelssohn, Felix). *Addington Press. Unpriced* DH/LF (B79-50834)
Church hymnary. Handbook to 'The church hymnary'. 3rd ed. *Oxford University Press. £3.50* ADM/LSF (B79-31512) ISBN 0-19-146811-8
Cigno. (Saint-Saëns, Camille). *Berben : Breitkopf und Härtel. £1.10* TSPMK (B79-50709)
Cimento dell'armonia e dell'inventione. Op.8, Concerto, oboe & string orchestra, P.259, D minor. Concerto in d minor,

RV454 (F.VII/1), P.259, for oboe, strings and basso continuo. (Vivaldi, Antonio). *Musica rara. Unpriced* RXMPVTF (B79-50668)

Cimento dell'armonia e dell'inventione. Op.8 Concerto, oboe & string orchestra, P.259, D minor. *arr.* Concerto in d minor, RV454, (F.VII/1), P.259 for oboe, strings and basso continuo. (Vivaldi, Antonio). *Musica rara. Unpriced* VTPK/LF (B79-50774)

Cimento dell'armonia e dell'inventione. Op.8. Le quattro stagione. Autunno.. *arr.* Four seasons, op.8 (Concerto for violin and orchestra)
Autumn : for violin and piano. (Vivaldi, Antonio). *Schirmer. £2.40* SPK/LF (B79-50682)

Cimento dell'armonia e dell'inventione. Op.8, nos 1-4. *arr.* Four seasons, op.8. (Concerto for violin and orchestra
Op.8, no.4: Winter : for violin and piano. (Vivaldi, Antonio). *Schirmer. £2.40* SPK/LF (B79-51154)

Cinderella. (Astell, Betty). */Evans. Unpriced* CPP (B79-50019) ISBN 0-237-75045-7

Cinque antiche danze francesi. (Marais, Marin). *Berben Breitkopf und Härtel. £1.90* SQPLTSK (B79-50686)

Ciranda do bom barqueiro : cantiga da infância. (Meira, Augusto). *Sonata : Clifford Essex. Unpriced* KDW (B79-50958)

Circles. *arr.* Circles : for SATB chorus and piano with optional bass and drums. (Blackley, Terry J). *Warner Blossom. Unpriced* DW (B79-50846)

Circles : for SATB chorus and piano with optional bass and drums. (Blackley, Terry J). *Warner : Blossom. Unpriced* DW (B79-50846)

Claire, Vivian. David Bowie! *Flash Books; 78 Newman St., W.1 : Distributed by Books Sales Ltd.* Pbk. *£1.95* AKDW/HKR/E(P) (B79-11131) ISBN 0-8256-3911-5

Clamabat autem mulier. (Escobar, Pedro de). *72 Brewery Rd, N.7 : Mapa mundi. Unpriced* GEZDJ (B79-50111)

Clapham, John, *b.1908.* Dvořák. *David and Charles. £8.95 : CIP entry* BDX(N) (B79-22636) ISBN 0-7153-7790-6

Clapton, Eric. Backless. *arr.* Backless. *Chappell. Unpriced* KDW/HKR (B79-50983)

Clarinet : a comprehensive method for the Boehm clarinet. (Thurston, Frederick J). 3rd ed. (revised and enlarged). *Boosey and Hawkes. Unpriced* VV/AC (B79-51272)

Clarinet à la carte : a menu for unaccompanied clarinet. (Harvey, Paul). *Ricordi. Unpriced* VVPMJ (B79-51289)

Clarinet series
Easy book 2. *Weinberger. Unpriced* VVPK/AAY (B79-51281)
Moderate book 2. *Weinberger. Unpriced* VVPK/AAY (B79-51282)

Clark, Harold Ronald. Sketches for young pianists : (Grade 3-4). *(42 Glebe Rd) : Harold R. Clark. Unpriced* QPJ (B79-51078)

Clarke, Keith Robert. Cadences : for brass quartet. *Novello. £1.95* WNS (B79-50795)

Classic and Romantic music : a comprehensive survey. (Blume, Friedrich). *Faber.* Pbk. *£2.50 : CIP rev.* A(XFYK151) (B79-05246) ISBN 0-571-11354-0

Classic piano repertoire.
Bach, Johann Sebastian. Johann Sebastian Bach 1685-1750. *East-West Publications. Unpriced* PWPJ (B79-50611)
Chopin, Frédéric. Frédéric François Chopin, 1810-1844. *East-West. Unpriced* QPJ (B79-50213) ISBN 0-904499-04-9

Classical composers and recordings. The 'Gramophone' guide to classical composers and recordings. (Salter, Lionel). *Salamander Books. £6.95* A/D(M/FD) (B79-00562) ISBN 0-86101-025-6

Classical harmony through figured bass. (Thorne, Adrian). *Chappell. Unpriced* Q/RGD/AC (B79-51061)

Clements, John. Weepin' Mary : negro spiritual, S.A.T.B. unaccompanied. *EMI. Unpriced* EZDW/LC (B79-50487)

Climb ev'ry mountain : for S.A. cambiata, B. or S.A.T.B. with piano. (Rodgers, Richard). *Williamson Music. Unpriced* DW (B79-50857)

Cohen, Eta. First year violin method. Eta Cohen Violinschule
1. Band. *Paxton. Unpriced* S/AC (B79-50272)

Cole, Bill. John Coltrane. *Schirmer : Collier Macmillan.* Pbk. *£3.25* AMT(P) (B79-12531) ISBN 0-02-870500-9

Coleman, T. Brian. Partners in praise. *Stainer & Bell : Chester House Publications for the Methodist Church Division of Education and Youth. £5.50* DM/LSJ/AY (B79-50444)

Colin, Sid. Al Bowlly. *Elm Tree Books. £5.95 : CIP entry* AKDW/GB/E(P) (B78-37099) ISBN 0-241-10057-7

Collection rock et folk Chappell. Melusine. *Chappell. Unpriced* KDW/G/AYH (B79-50964)

Colloque sentimental = A sentimental conversation : cycle for medium voice and piano. (Matthews, Colin). *Faber Music. Unpriced* KFVDW (B79-51007)

Colour and play books.
Christmas carols. *Helison Press. Unpriced* LK/DP/LF/AY (B79-50157) ISBN 0-905684-04-4
Folksong book 1. *Helicon Press. Unpriced* LK/DW/G/AY (B79-50158) ISBN 0-905684-01-x
Nursery rhymes. *Helicon Press. Unpriced* LK/DW/GK/AY (B79-50159) ISBN 0-905684-03-6

Combined Sound of living waters - Fresh sounds. *Hodder and Stoughton. £6.95* DM/AY (B79-50029) ISBN 0-340-23262-5

Come give your hearts to joy this day. (Barsham, Eve). *Ashdown. Unpriced* JFDP/LF (B79-50936)

Come, Holy Ghost. Charlton. Take my life : tune, Charlton, words, Frances Ridley Havergal and Come, Holy Ghost : tune, Pentecost, words, Bishop J. Cosin, based on 'Veni creator spiritus'. (Wilson, Alan J). *Weinberger. Unpriced* DM (B79-50442)

Come soon = Komm bald : for three-part chorus of women's voices with piano accompaniment. (Brahms, Johannes). *Schirmer. £0.35* FDW (B79-50492)

Come to me, your gentle shepherd. (Gentle shepherd) : theme song. (McDonough, Edward J). *TRO : Essex Music. Unpriced* KDH (B79-50952)

Comic songs of Ireland. *Mercier Press. Unpriced* JE/TSDW/AYDM (B79-50510) ISBN 0-85342-529-9

Communiqué. *arr.* Communiqué. (Dire Straits). *Chappell. Unpriced* KDW/HKR (B79-50984)

Communities Consultative Council. *Anglican Office Book Committee.* Ferial antiphons on Venite, Benedictus and Magnificat with simple tones. *Communities Consultative Council. Unpriced* JEZDGNPE (B79-50932)

Community orchestra : a handbook for conductors, managers and boards. (Van Horn, James). *Greenwood Press. £11.75* AM/E(QB) (B79-33555) ISBN 0-313-20562-0

Complete piano accordion tutor. (Beynon, Ivor). *EMI. Unpriced* RS/AC (B79-50249)

Complete sing for Jesus : songs for children. (Murcott, Peter). *(23 Park Rd) : Moorley's Bible and Bookshop. £1.00* JFDM/GJ (B79-50515) ISBN 0-86071-055-6

Complete sonatas for treble (alto) recorder and basso continuo = Die gesamten Sonaten für Altblockflöte und basso continuo. (Handel, George Frideric). *Faber Music. Unpriced* VSSPE/AZ (B79-51253)

Composers and the nature of music education. (Lawrence, Ian). *Scolar Press. £10.00* A(VC/Z) (B79-00558) ISBN 0-85967-401-0

Composers and their world.
McLeish, Kenneth. Brahms. *Heinemann. £2.50* BBT(N) (B79-27782) ISBN 0-434-95128-5
McLeish, Kenneth. Schubert. *Heinemann. £2.50* BSF(N) (B79-26550) ISBN 0-434-95127-7

Composer's autograph series.
Kievman, Carson. Concerto, bassoon & percussion ensemble. Concerto for bassoon and percussion ensemble (fire alarm system). *Associated Music. £2.75* WVPLXF (B79-50811)
Kievman, Carson. Sirocco (1975) : for wood-wind quintet (flute, oboe, B flat clarinet, bassoon, F horn). *Associated Music. Unpriced* UNR (B79-50731)
Rautavaara, Einojuhani. Music for upright piano. *Schirmer. £2.40* QPJ (B79-50635)
Rautavaara, Einojuhani. Music for upright piano and amplified cello. *Schirmer. £3.05* SRPJ (B79-50690)
Rautavaara, Einojuhani. Second music for upright piano. *Schirmer. £1.80* QPJ (B79-50636)
Scelsi, Giacinto. Five incantations = Cinque incantesimi : for piano. *Schirmer. £3.05* QPJ (B79-50638)

Composers of Wales. Jones, Richard Elfyn. David Wynne. *University of Wales Press for the Welsh Arts Council.* Pbk. *£1.50 : CIP rev.* BWY (B79-09705) ISBN 0-7083-0714-0

Comus. Dances. *arr.* Two dances from 'Comus'. (Arne, Thomas Augustine). *Banks. Unpriced* RK (B79-50653)

Concertino.
Barsanti, Francesco. Overture a quattro. Op.4, no.2. Ouverture, Opus 4, No.2 : für Streicher und Basso continuo = for strings and basso continuo. *Schott. £6.00* RXMG (B79-50257)
Maasz, Gerhard. Wir sind die Musikanten : eine kleine Instrumentenschau für Orchester, Chor ad lib. (2 gl. Stimmen) und Sprecher ad lib. *Schott. £6.00* MJ (B79-50161)
Mozart, Wolfgang Amadeus. Symphony, no.14, K.114, A major. Symphonie A-Dur, KV114. *Schott. £4.80* MRE (B79-51033)

Concertino. (Lane, Philip). *R. Smith. Unpriced* WMFL (B79-51297)

Concerto de angelis : for four guitars. (Brindle, Reginald Smith). *Schott. Unpriced* TSNSF/T (B79-50299)

Concerto, flute and orchestra. (Piston, Walter). *Associated Music. £7.55* MPVRF (B79-51031)

Concerto for violin and orchestra. (Schurmann, Gerard). *Novello. £8.85* MPSF (B79-51029)

Concerto, orchestra. (Bennett, Richard Rodney). *Novello. £4.85* MMF (B79-50169)

Concerto vocale. Martin, Frank. Dédicace de Pierre de Ronsard : 1945 : pour ténor et piano = für Tenor und Klavier. *Bärenreiter. £2.64* KGHDW (B79-50561)

Concise Oxford dictionary of opera. (Rosenthal, Harold). 2nd ed. *Oxford University Press. £6.95* AC(C) (B79-23401) ISBN 0-19-311318-x

Conductors on conducting. *Macdonald and Jane's. £6.95* A/EC (B79-32716) ISBN 0-354-04416-8

Cone, Edward T. Roger Sessions on music : collected essays. (Sessions, Roger Huntington). *Princeton University Press. £14.10* A (B79-14909) ISBN 0-691-09126-9

Congreve, William. Musica Britannica : a national collection of music
Vol.42: The judgement of Paris. *Stainer and Bell. Unpriced* C/AYD (B79-50009)

Connolly, Justin. Poems of Wallace Stevens I : for soprano and seven players, opus 9. *Novello. £3.00* KFLE/NYENPDW (B79-50151)

Consolatio philosophiae : scène dramatique voix haute et orchestre in memoriam Ernest Ansermet (1977). (Sutermeister, Heinrich). *Schott. £10.80* KFTDX (B79-50155)

Consolatio philosophiae. *Vocal score.* Consolatio philosophiae : scène dramatique voix haute et orchestre in memoriam Ernest Ansermet (1977). (Sutermeister, Heinrich). *Schott. £10.80* KFTDX (B79-50155)

Consolations. (Liszt, Franz). *Stainer and Bell. Unpriced* QPJ (B79-50632) ISBN 0-85249-526-9

Consolations. G.172. Consolations. (Liszt, Franz). *Stainer and Bell. Unpriced* QPJ (B79-50632) ISBN 0-85249-526-9

Contemplation upon flowers : 3 songs for soprano and orchestra. (Hoddinott, Alun). *Oxford University Press. Unpriced* KFLDW (B79-50998) ISBN 0-19-346719-4

Contemplation upon flowers. Op.90. *Vocal score.* A contemplation upon flowers : 3 songs for soprano and orchestra. (Hoddinott, Alun). *Oxford University Press. Unpriced* KFLDW (B79-50998) ISBN 0-19-346719-4

Contemporary choral series.
Brown, Christopher. Even such is time : for mixed chorus. *J. and W. Chester. Unpriced* EZDW (B79-50476)
Maconchy, Elizabeth. Four miniatures for unaccompanied chorus SATB. *Chester Music. Unpriced* EZDW (B79-50479)

Contemporary church music series. Burgon, Geoffrey. Magnificat and Nunc dimittis. *Chester Music. Unpriced* FDGPP (B79-50907)

Contemporary music education. (Mark, Michael L). *Schirmer Books : Collier Macmillan. £11.25* A(VC/YT) (B79-19443) ISBN 0-02-871640-x

Cook, Harold E. The Harold E. Cook collection of musical instruments. (Bucknell University. *Music Department*). *Bucknell University Press : Associated University Press. £5.75* AL(YTGLB/WJ) (B79-02987) ISBN 0-8387-1574-5

Cook, William T. The Cambridge University Guild of Change Ringers, 1879-1979 : a centenary history. *c/o B.D. Threlfall, 106 High St., Bottisham, Cambridge, Cambs. : C.U.G.C.R.* Sd. *Unpriced* AXSR/E(QB/X) (B79-30802)

Cooke, Deryck. I saw the world end : a study of Wagner's 'Ring'. *Oxford University Press. £6.50* BWCAC (B79-15554) ISBN 0-19-315318-1

Coombs, John. Johann Sebastian Bach : life, times, influence. *17 Bucklersbury, Hitchin, Herts. SG5 1BB : Bärenreiter. £21.12* BBC(N) (B79-11127)

Cooper, Barry. Sonata, recorder, oboe & continuo, op.5, no.2, D major. Sonata D major for flute/recorder, two oboes, viola da gamba/violoncello/bassoon, and basso continuo. (Schickhard, Johann Christian). *Oxford University Press. Unpriced* NWPNTE (B79-50194) ISBN 0-19-358815-3

Cooper, Joseph. Still more hidden melodies : six improvisations for piano. *Novello. Unpriced* QPJ (B79-50214)

Cope, Dawn. Christmas carols for young children : for piano, guitar and recorder. *East West : Breitkopf and Härtel. £1.50* JFE/NUSNTDP/LF/AY (B79-50943)

Cope, Peter. Christmas carols for young children : for piano, guitar and recorder. *East West : Breitkopf and Härtel. £1.50* JFE/NUSNTDP/LF/AY (B79-50943)

Copeland, Fanny S. The bells : Opus 35 : poem for soprano, tenor and baritone soli, chorus and orchestra. (Rachmaninoff, Sergei). *Boosey and Hawkes. Unpriced* EMDX (B79-50455)

Copland, Aaron.
Duet, flute & piano. *arr.* Duo for violin and piano. *Boosey and Hawkes. Unpriced* SPK (B79-51150)
Four motets
No.1: Help us, O Lord .. *Boosey and Hawkes. Unpriced* EZDJ (B79-50464)
No.2: Thou, O Jehovah .. *Boosey and Hawkes. Unpriced* EZDJ (B79-50465)
No.3: Have mercy on us, O my Lord .. *Boosey and Hawkes. Unpriced* EZDJ (B79-50466)
No.4: Sing ye praises to our King .. *Boosey and Hawkes. Unpriced* EZDJ (B79-50467)

Corelli, Arcangelo. Concerto grosso, op.6, no.3, C major. *arr.* Trio sonata in d. *Nova Music. Unpriced* VSSNTPWK/LF (B79-51248)

Corigliano, John. Voyage : for string orchestra. *Schirmer. Unpriced* RXMJ (B79-50664)

Cormier, Robert de. *See* De Cormier, Robert.

Coronation march. (Le prophète). (Meyerbeer, Giacomo). *Novello. £2.00* UMK/AGM (B79-50315)

Coryell, Julie. Jazz-rock fusion : the people - the music. *Boyars : Distributed by Calder and Boyars. £12.00* AKDW/HKRJ (B79-32718) ISBN 0-7145-2667-3

Cosentino, Manuel. Pizzicato : tempo de gavota. *Arapuã Clifford Essex. Unpriced* QPHM (B79-51072)

Cosma, Vladimir. David's song. *arr.* David's song : theme music from the serial Kidnapped. *Warner : Music Sales. £0.60* QPK (B79-51092)

Cotton, Reynell. Hambledon's cricket glory
Vol.6: The Hambledon cricket song. (Knight, Ronald David). 2nd (revised) ed. *40 Abbotsbury Rd, Weymouth, Dorset DT4 0AE : The author.* Pbk. *£0.50* BCMTADW (B79-29607) ISBN 0-903769-06-9

Coulter, Phil. The water babies. *Selections: arr.* The water babies. *Chappell. Unpriced* QPK/JR (B79-51105)

Country crossroads : 15 dynamic hits. *Chappell. Unpriced* KDW/GC/AY (B79-50980)

Country day : a festival piece. (Atkins, John G). *EMI. Unpriced* JFE/NYFSDX (B79-50945)

Country instruments. Makin' your own country instruments. (De Paule, Andy). *Van Nostrand Reinhold.* Pbk. *£4.45* AL/BC (B79-32720) ISBN 0-442-26117-9

Country people
No.1- ; 1979-. *IPC Magazines.* Sd. *£0.80* A/GC(B) (B79-27777)

Couperin, François. Piéces de clavecin, livre 3, ordre 24,15,16. *Selections : arr.* Four duos for flute or oboe and keyboard (harpsichord or piano). *Oxford University Press. Unpriced* VRPK (B79-50331) ISBN 0-19-355912-9

Coward, *Sir* Noël. There will always be ... *Chappell.*

Unpriced KDW (B79-50525)
Cowgill, Samuel C. The peacemakers gospel songs and choruses. *(Elim Pentecostal Church, Wakefield Rd) : S.C. Cowgill. Unpriced* JE/TSDM (B79-50509)
Cowgill, V J. The peacemakers gospel songs and choruses. (Cowgill, Samuel C). *(Elim Pentecostal Church, Wakefield Rd) : S.C. Cowgill. Unpriced* JE/TSDM (B79-50509)
Cox, Jerrold. Waltz-rondo for piano. (Ives, Charles). *Schirmer. £3.65* QPHW/W (B79-50629)
Craft, Robert. Stravinsky in pictures and documents. (Stravinsky, Vera). *Hutchinson. £16.00* BSV(N) (B79-15553) ISBN 0-09-138000-6
Craft of modal counterpoint : a practical approach. (Benjamin, Thomas). *Schirmer Books : Collier Macmillan.* Pbk. *£7.45* A/RM (B79-30799) ISBN 0-02-870480-0
Craig, Warren. Sweet and lowdown : America's popular song writers. *Scarecrow Press : Distributed by Bailey and Swinfen. £18.75* AKDW/GB(YT/WT) (B79-11129) ISBN 0-8108-1089-1
Crane, Richard. Gunslinger. *Vocal score.* Gunslinger. (Buckley, Joss). *Chappell. Unpriced* CM (B79-50820)
Credo quod redemptor mens vivit : pro defunctis, for 4 voices. (Lobo, Alfonso). *Mapa mundi. Unpriced* EZDJ/KDN (B79-50068)
Creole mystery : a short story for medium voice and string quartet. (Beeson, Jack). *Boosey and Hawkes. Unpriced* KFVDX (B79-50560)
Creole mystery. *Vocal score.* A Creole mystery : a short story for medium voice and string quartet. (Beeson, Jack). *Boosey and Hawkes. Unpriced* KFVDX (B79-50560)
Creuzburg, Heinrich. Sinfonia concertante, violins (3). *arr.* Sinfonia concertante für drei Violinen und Orchester. (Mayr, Simon). Zum ersten Mal. *Litolff : Peters. Unpriced* SNSQK/LE (B79-50680)
Cristo, Pedro de. Quaeramus cum pastoribus : for 4 voices. *72 Brewery Rd, N.7 : Mapa mundi. Unpriced* EZDJ/LF (B79-50075)
Critics' choice top 200 albums. (Gambaccini, Paul). *Omnibus Press; 78 Newman St., W1P 3LA : Distributed by Book Sales Limited.* Pbk. *£2.25* A/HKR/FD(WT) (B79-09962) ISBN 0-86001-494-0
Croft, William. Te Deum. *Vocal score.* Te Deum : for soloists, chorus, and orchestra. *Oxford University Press. Unpriced* DGNQ (B79-50429) ISBN 0-19-335585-x
Crompton, Louis. The great composers : reviews and bombardments. (Shaw, Bernard). *University of California Press. £17.15* A (B79-00561) ISBN 0-520-03253-5
Crucifixion : a meditation on the Sacred Passion of the Holy Redeemer. (Stainer, *Sir* John). *Novello. £1.55* FDE/LK (B79-50100)
Crucifixion. *arr.* The crucifixion : a meditation on the Sacred Passion of the Holy Redeemer. (Stainer, *Sir* John). *Novello. £1.55* FDE/LK (B79-50100)
Cruft, Adrian.
The Eatanswill election. The Anti-Buffs song. *arr.* The Anti-buffs song : arranged for B flat trumpet (or cornet) and piano. *(1 The Retreat, S.W.14) : Joad Press. Unpriced* WSPK/DW (B79-50397)
The Eatanswill election. The Eatanswill candidates. *arr.* The Eatanswill candidates. *(1 The Retreat, S.W.14) : Joad Press. Unpriced* WSNTQK/DW (B79-50391)
The Eatanswill election. The last voter's song. *arr.* The last voter's song. *(1 The Retreat, S.W.14) : Joad Press. Unpriced* WTPK/DW (B79-50400)
Stilestone suite : for piano, op.62. *(1 The Retreat, S.W.1) : Joad Press. Unpriced* QPG (B79-50210)
Stilestone suite. Op.62. *arr.* Stilestone suite : for chamber ensemble or wind, brass, percussion op.62a. *(1 The Retreat, S.W.14) : Joad Press. Unpriced* MRK/AG (B79-50183)
Traditional hornpipe suite : for brass band. *(1 The Retreat, S.W.14) : Joad Press. Unpriced* WMHNG (B79-50372)
CUGCR. *See* Cambridge University Guild of Change Ringers.
Culshaw, John. Wagner : the man and his music. *Hutchinson. £5.95 : CIP rev.* BWC(N) (B78-37864) ISBN 0-09-136210-5
Curtis, Jess. Christmas carols for young children : for piano, guitar and recorder. *East West : Breitkopf und Härtel. £1.50* JFE/NUSNTDP/LF/AY (B79-50943)
Cutting, Francis. Greensleeves. *arr.* Greensleeves. *DeCamera : Schirmer. £1.50* TSPMK/T (B79-51198)
Cyngor Celfyddydau Cymru. *See* Welsh Arts Council.
Czerny, Carl. Introduction, variations & finale, flute & piano, op.80, C major. Introduktion, Variationen und Finale für Flöte oder Violine und Klavier in C-dur. Op.80. *Eulenburg. £3.25* VRP/T (B79-50746)
D., A F. Praise to God in the highest. *arr.* Praise to God in the highest : Russian melody. (Campbell, Sidney Schofield). *Oxford University Press. Unpriced* FDH/LF (B79-50490) ISBN 0-19-351126-6
Da Gagliano, Marco. *See* Gagliano, Marco da.
Dafydd y garreg wen = David of the white rock. (Thomas, John, *b.1826*). *Adlais. Unpriced* TQPM/T (B79-50294)
Dahlhaus, Carl.
Die Idee der absoluten Musik. *12 Bucklesbury, Hitchin, Herts. SG5 1BB : Bärenreiter-Verlag etc.* Pbk. *£2.31* A(YB/XG151) (B79-17758)
Richard Wagner's music dramas. *Cambridge University Press. £7.50* BWCAC (B79-33553) ISBN 0-521-22397-0
Schönberg und andere : gesammelte Aufsätze zur neuen Musik. *Schott.* Pbk. *£14.00* A(D/XM78) (B79-08129)
Dainton, Marie Cleeve. 10 'swingalong' songs : for the primaries. *Regina Music. Unpriced* JFDW/GJ (B79-50129)
Dalby, Martin. Unicorn : for violin and piano. *Novello. £2.00* SPJ (B79-50275)
Dallmann, Wolfgang. Songs and dances of death. *arr.* Lieder und Tänze des Todes. (Mussorgsky, Modest). *Breitkopf und Härtel. £8.40* KDW (B79-50960)
Dalza, Joan Ambrosio. Intabulatura de lauto. *Selections : arr.* Two pieces. *DeCamera : Schirmer. £1.50* TSPMK (B79-51187)
Dampflok-Story : ein Kinder - Musical : für Sprecher, 1-3 stg. Kinderchor und Begleitinstrumente auf Text von James Krüss. (Hess, Reimund). *Schott. £10.00* CQN (B79-50418)
Dance variations : for orchestra. (Mathias, William). *Oxford University Press. Unpriced* MRH/T (B79-51034) ISBN 0-19-365669-8
Danceries, liv.3. *Selections : arr.* Tanz-Suite ... für Blockflötenquartett (SATB ; ATTB) oder andere Melodieinstrumente (Violen oder Flöten), Schlagwerk ad lib. = Dance suite ... for recorder quartet (SATB ; ATTB) or other melodic instruments (viols or flutes), percussion instruments ad lib. (Gervaise, Claude). *Schott. Unpriced* VSNSK/AH/AYH (B79-51236)
Daniels, Charlie. How to play rock guitar. *Warner-Tamerlane : Blossom. Unpriced* TS/AC (B79-50297)
Danks, Harry. The viola d'amore. 2nd ed. *7 Summit Gardens, Halesowen, West Midlands B63 4SP : Stephen Bonner. Unpriced* ASQQ/B (B79-09707)
Dann, Allan. How to succeed in the music business. *Wise Publications; 78 Newman St., W1P 3LA : Distributed by Music Sales Limited.* Pbk. *£2.50* A/GB (B79-10119) ISBN 0-86001-454-1
Danse bohémienne. *arr.* Danse bohémienne : für zwei Gitarren oder Oktavgitarre und Gitarre = for two guitars or octave guitar and guitar = pour deux guitares ou guitare octave et guitare. (Debussy, Claude). *Schott. £3.20* TSNUK/AH (B79-51175)
Danse bohémienne : für zwei Gitarren oder Oktavgitarre und Gitarre = for two guitars or octave guitar and guitar = pour deux guitares ou guitare octave et guitare. (Debussy, Claude). *Schott. £3.20* TSNUK/AH (B79-51175)
Danzi, Franz. Drei Duos für Viola und Violoncello, erstes Buch. *Amadeus : Schott. Unpriced* SQPLSR (B79-50283)
Darmstädter Beiträge zur neuen Musik. Internationale Ferienkurse für Neue Musik, *29, Darmstadt, 1978.* Ferienkurse '78. *Schott.* Pbk. *£9.60* A(XR9) (B79-14011)
Dart, Thurston. John Blow's anthology : Froberger, Strungk, Fischer, Blow : a selection of keyboard music (twenty suites, capriccios, ricercars, toccatas, etc.) copied out by John Blow around 1700. *Stainer and Bell. Unpriced* QRPJ (B79-50646) ISBN 0-85249-446-7
D'arville, Jasper. New wings suite : music for band. *Boosey and Hawkes. £22.00* UMMG (B79-51206)
Das bunte Spielbuch : für die Kindergartenflöte. (Pfuhl, Sabine). *Schott. £4.00* VR/AF (B79-50325)
Dauthendey, Max. Die Amsel : für Sopranstimme und Oboe. (Gerster, Ottmar). *Neue Musik : Breitkopf und Härtel. £1.20* KFLE/VTDW (B79-50551)
David's song. *arr.* David's song : theme music from the serial Kidnapped. (Cosma, Vladimir). *Warner : Music Sales. £0.60* QPK (B79-51092)
Davies, Bryan. Hava nagila : Israeli folk song. *Roberton. £0.32* GDW (B79-50920)
Davies, Oliver. The popular Cambrian Bacchanalian air, of Gland meddwdod mwyn, or 'Good humored and merry' with an introduction and variations : for the harp. *Adlais. Unpriced* TQPM/T (B79-50293)
Davies, Peter Maxwell.
The door of the sun : solo viola. *Boosey and Hawkes. Unpriced* SQPMJ (B79-50286)
Renaissance Scottish dances. *Boosey and Hawkes. Unpriced* NYEPNQK/AH/AYDL (B79-50200)
Runes from a holy island : for chamber ensemble. *Chester Music. Unpriced* NYEPNQ (B79-51050)
The seven brightness : solo B flat clarinet. *Boosey and Hawkes. Unpriced* VVPMJ (B79-50359)
Three organ voluntaries. *Chester Music. Unpriced* RJ (B79-51124)
The two fiddlers. *Vocal score.* The two fiddlers = Die beiden Musikanten : opera in two acts = Oper in zwei Akten. *Boosey and Hawkes. Unpriced* CN (B79-50016)
Davis, Stephen. Reggae bloodlines : in search of the music and culture of Jamaica. *Heinemann Educational.* Pbk. *£4.95* AKDW/GBSR (B79-31926) ISBN 0-435-98190-0
Davison, Nigel.
The Mass Euge bone : for 6 voices. (Tye, Christopher). *72 Brewery Rd, N.7 : Mapa mundi. Unpriced* EZDG (B79-50051)
Missa cum iucunditate : for 4 and 5 voices. (La Rue, Pierre de). *72 Brewery Rd, N.7 : Mapa mundi. Unpriced* GEZDG (B79-50109)
Missa Pange lingua : for voices. (Josquin des Prés). *Chester Music. Unpriced* EZDG (B79-50874)
Dawn : piano solo. (Judd, Margaret). *Bosworth and Co. Unpriced* QPJ (B79-50217)
Day after day, they all say 'sing' : Tutto lo di mi dici : for eight-part chorus of mixed voices a cappella. (Lasso, Orlando di). *Schirmer. £0.45* EZDU (B79-50474)
Day the animals sang : a musical for children. (Walker, Sue). *Mayhew-McCrimmon. Unpriced* CN/LF (B79-50821) ISBN 0-85597-202-5
Day's no rounder than its angles are. *arr.* The day's no rounder than its angles are : three songs for medium voice and string quartet. (Beeson, Jack). *Boosey and Hawkes. Unpriced* KFVDW (B79-50558)
De Anchieta, Juan. *See* Anchieta, Juan de.
De Boismortier, Joseph Bodin. *See* Boismortier, Joseph Bodin de.
De Boismortier, Joseph Bodin. *See* Boismortier, Joseph Bodin de.
De Cormier, Robert.
The Erie Canal, and, Great grandad : American folk songs, for two-part chorus of equal voices and piano. *Roberton. £0.28* FDW (B79-50494)
Frankie and Johnny : for four-part chorus of mixed voices with soprano, alto, baritone and tenor solos a cappella. *Roberton. £0.28* EZDW (B79-50478)
De Cristo, Pedro. *See* Cristo, Pedro de.
De Escobar, Pedro. *See* Escobar, Pedro de.
De Falla, Manuel. *See* Falla, Manuel de.
De Haan, Stefan. *See* Haan, Stefan de.
De la Halle, Adam. *See* Adam de la Halle.
De la Mare, Walter.
Fare well. (Benger, Richard). *Edwin Ashdown. £0.20* FDW (B79-50101)
Music : for S.S.C. (Benger, Richard). *Edwin Ashdown. £0.25* FDW (B79-50102)
De la Motte, Diether. *See* Motte, Diether de la.
De Lusse, Charles. *See* Lusse, Charles de.
De Paule, Andy. Makin' your own country instruments. *Van Nostrand Reinhold.* Pbk. *£4.45* AL/BC (B79-32720) ISBN 0-442-26117-9
De Peñalosa, Francisco. *See* Peñalosa, Francisco de.
De Rivafrencha, Martin. *See* Martin de Rivafrencha.
De Ronsard, Pierre. *See* Ronsard, Pierre de.
De Silva, Andreas. *See* Silva, Andreas de.
De Smet, Robin.
Canon & gigue, violins (3) & continuo, D major. Canon & gigue for three violins and keyboard (cello continuo ad lib.). (Pachelbel, Johann). *Fentone Music : Breitkopf and Härtel. Unpriced* SNSPWHP (B79-51146)
Hymnes sacrées. Ave Maria. *arr.* Ave Maria. Offertorium. (Cherubini, Luigi). *Fentone Music : Breitkopf and Härtel. Unpriced* KFLE/VVPDJ (B79-51001)
De Victoria, Tomás Luis. *See*
Victoria, Tomás Luis.
Victoria, Tomás Luis de.
De Virgin Mary : West Indian traditional carol. S.A.T.B. unacc. (Carter, Andrew). *Banks. Unpriced* EZDP/LF (B79-50884)
De Vivanco, Sebastian. *See* Vivanco, Sebastian de.
Dead man's cave. (Newsome, Roy). *Studio Music. Unpriced* WMJ (B79-50374)
Dearnley, Christopher.
Bow down thine ear. I will thank thee, O Lord. I will thank thee, O Lord. (Purcell, Daniel). *36 Ranelagh Gdns W.6 : Cathedral Music. Unpriced* EZDH (B79-50058)
The isles of the sea : anthem for unaccompanied choir ... *36 Ranelagh Gdns W.6 : Cathedral Music. Unpriced* EZDK (B79-50092)
De'Ath, Sylvia. 2 Marchas militares, no.1. *arr.* Marcha militar no.1. (Granados, Enrique). *Leonard, Gould and Bolttler. £0.40* QPK/AGM (B79-50641)
Deatsman, Gerald. The pianist's resource guide : piano music in print and literature on the pianistic art 1978-79. *Pallma Music; 20 Earlham St., WC2H 9LN Distributed by Breitkopf and Härtel (London) Ltd.* Pbk. *£32.50* AQ (TC) (B79-24852) ISBN 0-8497-7800-x
Debussy, Claude.
Arabesque, no.1. Ist arabesque : for organ and piano. *Columns Music : Schirmer (dist.). £1.95* QPLRK (B79-51111)
Danse bohémienne. *arr.* Danse bohémienne : für zwei Gitarren oder Oktavgitarre und Gitarre = for two guitars or octave guitar and guitar = pour deux guitares ou guitare octave et guitare. *Schott. £3.20* TSNUK/AH (B79-51175)
Four pieces. *(22 Woodcote Ave.) : Dunster Music. Unpriced* WSPK (B79-51318)
Petite suite. 2nd ed. *Peters. Unpriced* QNVG (B79-50205)
Suite bergamasque. *Peters. Unpriced* QPG (B79-50211)
Debussy and Wagner. (Holloway, Robin). *48 Great Marlborough St., W1V 2BN : Ernst Eulenburg Ltd. £5.50* BDJ(Z) (B79-35970) ISBN 0-903873-25-7
Dédicace de Pierre de Ronsard : 1945 : pour ténor et piano = für Tenor und Klavier. (Martin, Frank). *Bärenreiter. £2.64* KGHDW (B79-50561)
Dehmel, Richard. Fünf Gesänge für gemischten Chor nach Gedichten von Richard Dehmel, Opus 26. (Burkhard, Willy). *Bärenreiter. £1.16* EZDW (B79-50477)
De'il's awa wi'th' exiseman : for four-part chorus of mixed voices with piano accompaniment. (Rhein, Robert). *Schirmer. £0.35* DW (B79-50854)
Déjà vu : 5 dance excursions into the past, for 6 recorders. (Adler, Samuel). *Schirmer. £6.10* VSNQ (B79-50761)
Déjà vu : für Oboe d'amore und kleines Orchester. (Stranz, Ulrich). *Bärenreiter. £11.22* MPVTQ (B79-50589)
Del Tredici, David. Vintage Alice : fantascene on a mad tea-party. *Boosey and Hawkes. Unpriced* KFLE/MDX (B79-51000)
Delibes, Leo. Music from the ballet. *(7 Garrick St., W.C.2) : Middle Eight Music. Unpriced* UNSK/HM (B79-50732)
Delius, Frederick.
Hassan : the incidental music to the play by James Elroy Flecker. *Boosey and Hawkes. Unpriced* EM/JM (B79-50040)
The magic fountain. *Vocal score.* The magic fountain : lyric drama in 3 acts. *Delius Trust, Boosey and Hawkes. Unpriced* CC (B79-50010)

Delius, Nikolaus.
Méthode pour la flûte. Exercices de tous genres. 25 Etüden für Flöte = 25 studies for flute = 25 exercices pour flûte. (Drouet, Louis). Reprint der Schott-Originalausgabe von 1827. *Schott. £4.00* VR/AF (B79-51214)
Operas. *Selections.* Arien : für hohe Singstimme, Blockflöten, Fagott und Basso continuo. (Schürmann, Georg Caspar). Erstausgabe. *Bärenreiter. £6.60* KFTE/NWPNSDW (B79-50557)
Sonata, flute & continuo, op.3, no.3, E minor. Sonate e-Moll, e minor, mi mineur, opus III, no.3, für Flöte und Basso continuo, for flute and basso continuo, pour flûte et basse continue. (Platti, Giovanni Benedetto). *Schott. £4.80* VRPE (B79-51222)
Delrieu, Jean Philippe. A vous de jouer : cours d'initiation rapide et progressive à l'argue électronique
Vol.2. *Chappell. Unpriced* RPV/AC (B79-51132)
Dentato, John.
Jazz players library : 10 classic tunes in their original versions and in completely notated jazz versions. *Chappell. Unpriced* QPHX (B79-51075)
Jazz players library : 10 classic tunes in their original versions and in completely notated jazz versions. *Chappell. Unpriced* VRPMHX (B79-51230)
Jazz players library : 10 classic tunes in their original versions and in completely notated jazz versions. *Chappell. Unpriced* VUSPMHX (B79-51268)
Jazz players library : 10 classic tunes in their original versions and in completely notated jazz versions. *Chappell. Unpriced* VUTPMHX (B79-51271)
Jazz players library : 10 classic tunes in their original versions and in completely notated jazz versions. *Chappell. Unpriced* WSPMHX (B79-51320)
Deroyan, Douglas. Music by Douglas Deroyan. *37 Buckland Cresc. N.W.3 : Douglas Deroyan. Unpriced* QPJ (B79-51079)
Desch, Rudolf. Putze dich mit meinem Tüchlein : Kastilianisches Volkslied aus Avila (Spanien). *Schott. £0.48* GEZDW (B79-50507)
Desencontro : improviso no.1. (Sergi, Antonio). *Seresta Clifford Essex. Unpriced* QPJ (B79-51087)
Deshaulle, Jacques. Trois pièces facile : première position violon avec accompagnement de piano. *Chappell. Unpriced* SPJ (B79-51149)
'Désir' : for clarinet and piano. (Oberthür, Charles). *Chester Music. Unpriced* VVPJ (B79-51279)
Di Lasso, Orlando. *See* Lasso, Orlando di.
Di lasso, Orlando. *See* Lasso, Orlndo di.
Diamond, Eileen.
Find a bin : a song/mime for children. *Chappell, in association with Keep Britain Tidy. Unpriced* JFDW/JN (B79-50941)
The toyshop : a song/mime for all children. *Chappell. Unpriced* JFDW/JN (B79-50520)
Diaphonie : für Orchester. (Beyer, Frank Michael). *Bote und Bock : Schirmer. £14.40* MMJ (B79-51020)
Dick Whittington. (Astell, Betty). *Evans. Unpriced* CPP (B79-50020) ISBN 0-237-75046-5
Dickinson, Emily. Indian summer : for mixed chorus and piano. (Ferris, William). *Oxford University Press. Unpriced* DW (B79-50848)
Dickinson, Peter. Recorder music. *Novello. £1.95* VS/FT (B79-51234)
Diddly, diddly, dumpty : finger plays, face games, action rhymes, fun songs, for nursery and infant schools. (Staton, Kathleen). *EMI. Unpriced* JFEZDW/GR (B79-50524)
Diemer, Emma Lou.
Away, delights : for men's chorus a cappella. *Broude Breitkopf and Härtel. £0.42* GEZDW (B79-50924)
Tell me, dearest, what is love? : for mixed chorus a cappella. *Broude : Breitkopf and Härtel. £0.42* EZDW (B79-50889)
Weep no more : for women's chorus a cappella. *Broude Breitkopf and Härtel. £0.42* FEZDW (B79-50917)
Diethelm, Caspar. Sonata, trombone, op.128. Sonate für Posaune solo, op.128, 1975. *Amadeus : Eulenburg. £0.28* WUPME (B79-50809)
Dieupart, Francis.
Sonata, recorder (treble) & continuo, no.1, G major. Sonata no.1 in G for treble (alto) recorder and basso continuo. *Schott. Unpriced* VSSPE (B79-51251)
Sonata, recorder (treble) & continuo, no.6, F major. Sonata no.6 in F for treble (alto) recorder and basso continuo. *Schott. Unpriced* VSSPE (B79-51250)
DiGaetani, John Louis. Penetrating Wagner's Ring : an anthology. *Fairleigh Dickinson University Press : Associated University Presses. £12.00* BWCAC (B79-14015) ISBN 0-8386-1795-6
Dinn, Freda. The observer's book of music. 4th ed. *F. Warne. £1.25* A (B79-50001) ISBN 0-7232-1581-2
Dire Straits. Communiqué. *arr.* Communiqué. *Chappell. Unpriced* KDW/HKR (B79-50984)
Disabled Living Foundation. Access to music for the physically handicapped schoolchild and school leaver : report on 3-year project, 1973-1976. (Kennard, Daphne J). *346 Kensington High St., W14 8NS : Disabled Living Foundation.* Sp. *£2.00* A(VMX) (B79-33201) ISBN 0-901908-31-2
Disco dancing tonight : clubs, dances, fashion, music. (Blackford, Andy). *Octopus Books.* Pbk. *£1.50* A/FF/ER (B79-16105) ISBN 0-7064-1019-x
Discowords
Vol.1, no.1- ; 1978-. *Dormbourne Limited : Distributed by Wells Gardner Darton.* Sd. *£0.20* AKDW/GB/E(M/DE) (B79-00580)
Dittersdorf, Carl Ditters von.
Concertos, double bass, Krebs 171, 172. *arr.* Concertos for double bass and orchestra. *Yorke. Unpriced* SSPK/LF (B79-50292)
Sinfonia concertante, viola & double bass, Krebs 127, D major. *arr.* Sinfonia concertante for double bass and viola. *Yorke Edition. Unpriced* SQPLSSK/LE (B79-50285)
Diversions for percussion and piano. (Pearn, David). *Lengnick. Unpriced* QPLX (B79-50226)
Divertimentos, K. Anh. 229. *Selections: arr.* Six movements from the Mozart divertimenti. (Mozart, Wolfgang Amadeus). *Cramer. Unpriced* VSNTK (B79-50340)
Divine lodi, lib.3. *Selections.* 3 canzonas for violin (trumpet), trombone and basso continuo. (Riccio, Giovanni Battista). *Musica rara. Unpriced* NUXUNT (B79-50188)
Dixit Dominus. *Vocal score.* Dixit Dominus : Psalm 110, for two sopranos, alto, tenor and bass soli, SSATB, strings and continuo. (Handel, George Frideric). *Novello. £2.25* DR (B79-50448)
Dlugoraj, Wojciech. Four pieces. *DeCamera : Schirmer. £1.50* TSPMK (B79-51188)
'DO quintet' : for two trumpets, horn, trombone, tuba, 1978. (Antoniou, Theodore). *Bärenreiter. £5.94* WNR (B79-50385)
Dobry den. What a day : Dobry den : a choral cycle, for two-part chorus of young voices with piano accompaniment or a cappella. (Laburda, Jiří). *Schirmer. £2.10* FDW (B79-50495)
Doce canciones = Twelve songs : with guitar accompaniment ... (Moretti, Federico). *Tecla. Unpriced* KE/TSDW (B79-50993) ISBN 0-8494-0140-2
Doce canciones. Op.24. Doce canciones = Twelve songs : with guitar accompaniment ... (Moretti, Federico). *Tecla. Unpriced* KE/TSDW (B79-50993) ISBN 0-8494-0140-2
Dollase, Rainer. Das Jazzpublikum : zur Sozialpsychologie einer kulturellen Minderheit. *Schott.* Pbk. *£9.60* AMT(Z) (B79-10482)
Dolly. (Nash, Alanna). *Panther.* Pbk. *£1.25* AKDW/GC/E(P) (B79-33546) ISBN 0-586-05051-5
Domine, ne in furore tuo arguas me. Oh my Lord, let not your blinding fury - My heart = Domine, ne in furore - Cor meum : for four-part chorus of men's voices a cappella. (Josquin des Prés). *Schirmer. £0.75* GEZDJ (B79-50504)
Dömling, Wolfgang. Johann Sebastian Bach : life, times, influence. *17 Bucklersbury, Hitchin, Herts. SG5 1BB : Bärenreiter. £21.12* BBC(N) (B79-11127)
Don Williams : piano/vocal. *Chappel. Unpriced* KDW/GC/AY (B79-50979)
Donald, Robert. The Foss Collection of Scottish dances. *H. Foss. Unpriced* QPK/AH/AYDL (B79-50222)
Doney, Malcolm. Summer in the city : rock music and way of life. *Lion Publishing.* Pbk. *£1.25* AKDW/HKR(X) (B79-04538) ISBN 0-85648-085-1
Donizetti, Gaetano.
Concertino, clarinet, B flat major. Concertino für Klarinette und Kammerorchester B-dur. *Litolff : Peters. Unpriced* MPVVFL (B79-50590)
Concertino, clarinet, B flat major. *arr.* Concertino für Klarinette und Kammerorchester. B-dur. *Litolff : Peters. Unpriced* VVPK/LFL (B79-50786)
Donne, John. Hear us, O hear us, Lord : anthem for S.A.T.B. and organ. (Hoiby, Lee). *Broude : Breitkopf und Härtel. £0.55* DH (B79-50431)
Door of the sun : solo viola. (Davies, Peter Maxwell). *Boosey and Hawkes. Unpriced* SQPMJ (B79-50286)
Doppler, Carl. Souvenir de Prague. Op.24 : for two flutes and piano. (Doppler, Franz). *Musica rara. Unpriced* VRNTQ (B79-50744)
Doppler, Franz. Souvenir de Prague. Op.24 : for two flutes and piano. *Musica rara. Unpriced* VRNTQ (B79-50744)
Dorigny, Henry. Suite française. Op.61 : pour deux guitares. (Duarte, John William). *Bèrben : Breitkopf und Härtel. £3.30* TSNUG (B79-51170)
Dorking and Leith Hill District Preservation Society. *Local History Group.* Vaughan Williams in Dorking : a collection of personal reminiscences of the composer Dr Ralph Vaughan Williams, O.M. *c/o C. Newbery, 'Wrencot', Partridge La., Newdigate, Dorking, Surrey : The Group.* Sd. *£0.80* BVD(YDCHD/P (B79-21875)
Dos marchas militares. 2 Marchas militares, no.1. *arr.* Marcha militar no.1. (Granados, Enrique). *Leonard, Gould and Bolttler. £0.40* QPK/AGM (B79-50641)
Double platinum. (Kiss). *Almo : EMI. Unpriced* KDW/HKR (B79-50140)
Douglas, Paul M.
Sonatas, flutes (2) & continuo, op.3. Triosonaten für zwei Flöten, (Flöte und Violine) und Basso continuo, op.3
Nos 1 & 2 : E-moll, D-dur. (Hotteterre, Jacques Martin). *Eulenburg. £3.50* VRNTPWE (B79-50741)
Sonatas, flutes (2) & continuo, op.3. Triosonaten für zwei Flöten (Flöte und Violine) und Basso continuo, op.3
Nos 3 & 4 : B-moll, E-moll. (Hotteterre, Jacques Martin). *Eulenburg. £3.50* VRNTPWE (B79-50742)
Sonatas, flutes (2) & continuo, op.3. Triosonaten für zwei Flöten (Flöte und Violine) und Basso continuo, op.3
Nos 5 & 6 : A-dur, G-dur. (Hotteterre, Jacques Martin). *Eulenburg. £3.50* VRNTPWE (B79-50743)
Douze allemandes pour le piano. Op.4. *Selections : arr.* 12 allemandes pour le piano forte. Op.4. *Selections : arr.* Five German dances. (Weber, Carl Maria von, *Freiherr*). *Oxford University Press. Unpriced* UMK/AH (B79-50316) ISBN 0-19-368668-6
Dov, Fazi. Bicinia variorum instrumentorum. *Selections.* Six sonatinas, nos 1, 2, 3, 7, 9, 11 for 2 oboes/violins/recorders in C and basso continuo. (Pezel, Johann). *Nova Music. Unpriced* VTNTPWEM (B79-51257)
Dowland, John. Zwei Duette. *Schott. £2.20* TSNUK (B79-51171)
Dozen a day : technical exercises for the piano to be done each day before practicing sic. (Burnam, Edna Mae). *Willis Music : Chappell. Unpriced* Q/AF (B79-50613)
Drage, Charles Lovell. An unpublished religious song-book of mid-eighteenth century Russia. (Akademiia nauk SSSR. *Biblioteka. MSS. (33.3.5)). c/o C.L. Drage, 94 Inverness Terrace, W.2 : The editors.* Pbk. *£2.00* AKDH/LSC(YM/XFX31) (B79-37420)
Dragonetti, Domenico. Solo, double bass & piano, E minor. The famous solo in E minor : for double bass and piano. *Yorke. Unpriced* SSPJ (B79-50290)
Drei. L'alphabet de la musique : Op.30. Sonatas 4, 7, 16. 3 Sonaten aus 'L'alphabet de la musique' = 3 sonatas from 'L'alphabet de la musique' : für Altblockflöte und Basso continuo = for alto recorder and basso continuo. (Schickhard, Johann Christian). *Pelikan : Bärenreiter. £9.10* VSSPE (B79-50769)
Drei Duos für Viola und Violoncello, erstes Buch. (Danzi, Franz). *Amadeus : Schott. Unpriced* SQPLSR (B79-50283)
Drei Nestroy-Collagen : für gemischten Chor und zwei Klaviere. (Zimmermann, Heinz Werner). *Bärenreiter. £13.20* DW (B79-50038)
Drei Ricercare über das Thema des Musikalischen Opfers von Johann Sebastian Bach (1977) : Orgel. (Baur, Jürg). *Breitkopf and Härtel. £5.40* RJ (B79-51122)
Drouet, Louis. Méthode pour la flûte. Exercices de tous genres. 25 Etüden für Flöte = 25 studies for flute = 25 exercices pour flûte. Reprint der Schott-Originalausgabe von 1827. *Schott. £4.00* VR/AF (B79-51214)
Druckman, Jacob. Duet, violin & piano. Duo for violin and piano. *Boosey and Hawkes. Unpriced* SPJ (B79-50276)
Drüner, Ulrich. Drei Duos für Viola und Violoncello, erstes Buch. (Danzi, Franz). *Amadeus : Schott. Unpriced* SQPLSR (B79-50283)
Duarte, John William.
Moods for guitar. (Nunn, Ruth). *Novello. £0.66* TSPMJ (B79-50308)
Sonatas, harpsichord. *Selections : arr.* Three sonatas (K.176/L163, K.177/L364,K.208/L238) : guitar solo. (Scarlatti, Domenico). *Universal. Unpriced* TSPMK/AE (B79-51193)
Suite française. Op.61 : pour deux guitares. *Bèrben Breitkopf and Härtel. £3.30* TSNUG (B79-51170)
Within easy reach : 10 easy pieces for guitarists with small hands = 10 pezzi facili por chitarristi con le mani piccole = 10 leichte Stücke für Gitarrenspieler mit kleinen Händen. *Ricordi. Unpriced* TSPMJ (B79-51184)
Duet, flute & piano. *arr.* Duo for violin and piano. (Copland, Aaron). *Boosey and Hawkes. Unpriced* SPK (B79-51150)
Duets, clarinets, op.5, nos.1-3. Six duos. Op.5, nos.1-3 for 2 clarinets. (Yost, Michel). *Musica rara. Unpriced* VVNU (B79-51276)
Duke of York'&s patrol. (Spurgin, Anthony). *Studio Music. Unpriced* WMGM (B79-50371)
Duncan Johnstone collection of pipe tunes
Vol.1. *Duncan Johnston Piping School. Unpriced* VY/AYDL (B79-50365)
Dunhill, Thomas Frederick. Sonatas for harpsichord
Book one. (Scarlatti, Domenico). *Stainer and Bell. Unpriced* QRPE (B79-50644) ISBN 0-85249-513-7
Dunn, Bernard. A waltz dream : operetta in three acts. *10 Rathbone St., W1P 2BJ : Josef Weinberger.* Pbk. *£1.25* BSOTACF (B79-06705)
Duo for violin and piano. (Copland, Aaron). *Boosey and Hawkes. Unpriced* SPK (B79-51150)
Duo in la maggiore, op.55, n.1. (Sor, Fernando). *Bèrben Breitkopf and Härtel. £1.70* TSNU (B79-51169)
Duo seraphim. (Guerrero, Francisco). *Mapa mundi. Unpriced* EZDJ (B79-50062)
Dussek, Jan Ladislav.
Sonatina, harp, op.20, no.6, E flat major. Sonatina in E flat for harp. *Adlais. Unpriced* TQPMEM (B79-50295)
Sonatina, piano, op.20, no.1, G major. *arr.* Sonatina für zwei Gitarren. *Breitkopf und Härtel. £2.55* TSNUK/AEM (B79-51174)
Dvořák, Antonín.
Amid nature. Op.63. A song went to my heart. So many songs = Es zog manch Lied : for four-part chorus of mixed voices a cappella. *Schirmer. £0.35* EZDW (B79-50890)
Amid nature. Op.63. Birch tree by the verdant slope. Birch tree on green hill = Birke am grünen Bergeshang : for four-part chorus of mixed voices a cappella. *Schirmer. £0.45* EZDW (B79-50891)
Amid nature. Op.63. Golden fields. Golden meadows = Goldne Fluren : for four-part chorus of mixed voices a cappella. *Schirmer. £0.35* EZDW (B79-50892)
Amid nature. Op.63. This is in truth a day of joy. A summer day = Ein Sommertag : for four-part chorus of mixed voices a cappella. *Schirmer. £0.45* EZDW (B79-50893)
Bouquet of Czech folk songs. B72. The betrayed shepherd. The abducted shepherd = Der entführte Hirt : for four-part chorus of men's voices a cappella. *Schirmer. £0.35* GEZDW (B79-50925)
Bouquet of Czech folk songs. B72. The sweetheart's resolve. If you should go away = Wenn du fortgehst : for four-part chorus of men's voices a cappella. *Schirmer. £0.35* GEZDW (B79-50926)

Dwight, Timothy. I love thy church, O God : for four-part chorus of mixed voices with optional piano accompaniment. (Snyder, Wesley). *Schirmer. Unpriced* EZDH (B79-50880)

Dylan, Bob. Bob Dylan in his own words. *Omnibus Press.* Pbk. *£2.50* AKDW/HKR/E(P) (B79-31930) ISBN 0-86001-542-4

Eames, Vera MacNess-. *See* MacNess-Eames, Vera.

Ear training and sight-singing : an integrated approach
Book 1. (Trubitt, Allen R). *Schirmer Books : Collier Macmillan.* Pbk. *£8.25* A/EF (B79-25327) ISBN 0-02-870810-5

Earl, Gillian. Carols for piano. *Oxford University Press. Unpriced* QPK/DP/LF/AY (B79-50223) ISBN 0-19-372608-4

Early Georgian songs
Book 1: Medium voice. *Stainer and Bell. Unpriced* KFVDW (B79-50559) ISBN 0-85249-459-9

Early German music for clarinet choir.
Erbach, Christian. Canzona. (La paglia). *Schirmer. Unpriced* VVNK (B79-50779)
Graupner, Christoph. Sonata in G major. *Schirmer. £9.10* VVNK/AE (B79-50781)
Scheidt, Samuel. Paduana, galliarda. *arr.* Canzon super intradam aechiopicam. *Schirmer. £7.55* VVNK (B79-50780)

Early music hall in Bristol. (Barker, Kathleen). *74 Bell Barn Rd, Stoke Bishop, Bristol BS9 2DG : Historical Association, Bristol Branch.* Sd. *£0.60* A/JV(YDHDB) (B79-23405)

Early part-songs 1890-1891 : for SATB with divisions. (Elgar, *Sir* Edward, *bart*). *Novello. £1.15* EZDW (B79-50894)

Earnest, David. The Son has risen : mixed chorus and organ. *Broude : Breitkopf und Härtel. £0.45* DH/LL (B79-50434)

East Anglia University. *See* University of East Anglia.

Easton, M. Just friends, in print : Marian Montgomery with Richard Rodney Bennett in words, music and pictures. *Novello. £2.95* KDW/GB/AY (B79-50536)

Eastwood, Tom. Romance et plainte : for guitar. *Bèrben Breitkopf and Härtel. £2.35* TSPMJ (B79-51185)

Easy decision : soprano voice & piano. (Bedford, David). *Universal. Unpriced* KFLDW (B79-50997)

Easy stretch guitar : new method for the complete beginner. (Pairman, David). *Galliard.* Pbk. *£3.00* TS/AC (B79-50697) ISBN 0-85249-447-5

Eatanswill candidates. (Cruft, Adrian). *(1 The Retreat, S.W.14) : Joad Press. Unpriced* WSNTQK/DW (B79-50391)

Eatanswill election. The Anti-Buffs song. *arr.* The Anti-buffs song : arranged for B flat trumpet (or cornet) and piano. (Cruft, Adrian). *(1 The Retreat, S.W.14) : Joad Press. Unpriced* WSPK/DW (B79-50397)

Eatanswill election. The Eatanswill candidates. *arr.* The Eatanswill candidates. (Cruft, Adrian). *(1 The Retreat, S.W.14) : Joad Press. Unpriced* WSNTQK/DW (B79-50391)

Eatanswill election. The last voter's song. *arr.* The last voter's song. (Cruft, Adrian). *(1 The Retreat, S.W.14) : Joad Press. Unpriced* WTPK/DW (B79-50400)

Eatanswill series.
Cruft, Adrian. The Eatanswill election. The Anti-Buffs song. *arr.* The Anti-buffs song : arranged for B flat trumpet (or cornet) and piano. *(1 The Retreat, S.W.14) : Joad Press. Unpriced* WSPK/DW (B79-50397)
Cruft, Adrian. The Eatanswill election. The Eatanswill candidates. *arr.* The Eatanswill candidates. *(1 The Retreat, S.W.14) : Joad Press. Unpriced* WSNTQK/DW (B79-50391)
Cruft, Adrian. The Eatanswill election. The last voter's song. *arr.* The last voter's song. *(1 The Retreat, S.W.14) : Joad Press. Unpriced* WTPK/DW (B79-50400)

Ebb, Fred. Chicago : a musical vaudeville. *French.* Sd. *£1.65* BKDEACM (B79-06704) ISBN 0-573-68081-7

Eben, Peter. Laudes : for organ. *United Music. Unpriced* RJ (B79-51125)

Eboracum choral series.
Bullard, Alan. Praise the Lord out of heaven : S.A.T.B. *Banks. Unpriced* DK (B79-50438)
Carter, Andrew. De Virgin Mary : West Indian traditional carol. S.A.T.B. unacc. *Banks. Unpriced* EZDP/LF (B79-50884)
Carter, Andrew. The twelve days of Christmas : English traditional carol, S.A.T.B. unacc. *Banks. Unpriced* EZDW/LF (B79-50904)
Jackson, Francis. Versicles and responses (including the Sovereign's Accession) : S.A.(T.)T.B. *Banks. Unpriced* EZDGMM (B79-50459)
Nelson, Havelock. Kitty of Coleraine : traditional Irish, S.A.T.B. unacc. *Banks. Unpriced* EZDW (B79-50899)
Ross, Colin. Gently the breeze blows : two-part. *Banks. Unpriced* FDW (B79-50496)
Swale, David. This endris night : S.A.T.B. *Banks. Unpriced* DP/LF (B79-50842)
Whitter, Mark. Stardance carol : S.A.T.B. *Banks. Unpriced* EXRVDP/LF (B79-50871)

Ecce quam bonum : See how good, how right : for four-part chorus of mixed voices a cappella. (Richafort, Jean). *Schirmer. £0.30* EZDR (B79-50472)

Ecce sacerdos magnus. Motecta, Sancta Maria. Sancta Maria, and, Ecce sacerdos magnus : for four part chorus of mixed voices unaccompanied. (Victoria, Tomás Luis de). *Roberton. £0.28* EZDJ (B79-50469)

Ehmann, Wilhelm.
Leichte Choral-Partiten : für Bläser. *Bärenreiter. £3.96* WMG (B79-50369)
'Weihnachtskonzert' : Zyklus zu Advent bis Epiphanians, für Blechbläser und Orgel. (Wenzel, Eberhard). *Bärenreiter. £2.31* NWXPF (B79-50603)

Ehret, Walter.
Gypsy. Everything's coming up roses. *arr.* Everything's coming up roses : for S.A. cambiata, B. or S.A.T.B, with piano. (Styne, Jule). *Williamson. Unpriced* DW (B79-50859)
Hush! My dear. (Nettleton carol) : for mixed chorus and piano. *Broude : Breitkopf and Härtel. £0.42* DP/LF (B79-50839)
The King and I. Getting to know you. *arr.* Getting to know you : for S.A. cambiata, B. or S.A.T.B. (Rodgers, Richard). *Williamson. Unpriced* DW (B79-50855)
Kiss me, Kate. Another op'nin, another show. *arr.* Another op'nin', another show : for S.A. cambiata, B. or S.A.T.B. with piano. (Porter, Cole). *Chappell. Unpriced* DW (B79-50852)
My masters, be merry! : for mixed voices (SATB) and accompaniment. *Broude : Breitkopf and Härtel. £0.42* DP/LF (B79-50840)
Oklahoma!. Oh, what a beautiful mornin'. *arr.* Oh, what a beautiful mornin' : S.A.C.(T)B. with piano. (Rodgers, Richard). *Williamson Music. Unpriced* DW (B79-50856)
Paint your wagon. They call the wind Maria. *arr.* They call the wind Maria : S.A.C.(T.) B. with piano. (Loewe, Frederick). *Chappell. Unpriced* DW (B79-50850)
Porgy and Bess. Summertime. *arr.* Summertime : S.A.C.(T.) B. with piano. (Gershwin, George). *Chappell. Unpriced* DW (B79-50849)
The sound of music. Climb ev'ry mountain. *arr.* Climb ev'ry mountain : for S.A. cambiata, B. or S.A.T.B. with piano. (Rodgers, Richard). *Williamson Music. Unpriced* DW (B79-50857)
State fair. Its a grand night for singing. *arr.* Its a grand night for singing : S.A.C.(T).B, with piano. (Rodgers, Richard). *Williamson. Unpriced* DW (B79-50858)
Wasn't that a mighty day! : Christmas spiritual for mixed voices, accompanied (S.A.T.B.). *Broude : Breitkopf and Härtel. £0.42* DW/LC/LF (B79-50863)

Wasn't that a mighty day! : Christmas spiritual for mixed voices, accompanied (S.A.T.B.). (Ehret, Walter). *Broude : Breitkopf and Härtel. £0.42* DW/LC/LF (B79-50863)

Ehrlich, Bettina. *See* Bettina, b.1903.

Eight songs for high voice and piano. (Bush, Geoffrey). *Novello. £2.40* KFTDW (B79-51005)

Eight traditional Japanese pieces. *Novello. £1.55* VSPM/AYVU (B79-50765)

Elastic band. *Novello. Score, £5.00, Parts, Unpriced* LNK/AAY (B79-50160)

Electric bass guitar : a complete guide. (Canty, Laurence). *Chappell. Unpriced* TSUPV/AC (B79-50716)

Electric guitar : its history and construction. (Brosnac, Donald). *Omnibus Press.* Pbk. *£3.50* ATSPV/B(X) (B79-33557) ISBN 0-86001-491-6

Electronic music and creative tape recording. (Berry, M K). *Babani.* Pbk. *£1.25* APV (B79-32721) ISBN 0-900162-72-4

Electronic projects for musicians. (Anderton, Craig). *Guitar Player Productions; 25 East St., Farnham, Surrey Distributed by Omnibus Book Service.* Pbk. *£5.95* APV (B79-09656) ISBN 0-89122-011-9

Electronic projects in music. (Flind, A J). *Newnes Technical Books.* Pbk. *£2.25 : CIP rev.* APV/BC (B79-17724) ISBN 0-408-00391-x

Elegy : for string orchestra. (Gould, Morton). *Schirmer. Unpriced* RXMJ (B79-50665)

Element books. Hamel, Peter Michael. Through music to the self : how to appreciate and experience music anew. *Compton Press. £5.95* A/CC (B79-08926) ISBN 0-900193-53-0

Elgar, *Sir* Edward, *bart.*
5 part songs. Op.45. From the Greek Anthology : five unaccompanied part-songs for TTBB. Opus 45. *Novello. £1.15* GEZDW (B79-50927)
The early part-songs 1890-1891 : for SATB with divisions. *Novello. £1.15* EZDW (B79-50894)
Elgar piano album. *Novello. Unpriced* QPK (B79-50220)

Elgar Society. Elgar Society journal. *For earlier issues of this periodical see* Elgar Society. Elgar Society newsletter, new series.

Elgar Society. The Elgar Society journal
Vol.1, no.1- ; Jan. 1979-. *104 Crescent Rd, New Barnet, Herts. : 'The Elgar Society Journal'.* Sd. *Free to members* BEP(B) (B79-23400)

Elgar Society. Elgar Society newsletter, new series. *For later issues of this periodical see* Elgar Society. Elgar Society journal.

Elisabeth, *Saint.* Father of mercies : for chorus of unison voices with organ accompaniment. (Hamble, William R). *Chappell. Unpriced* JDH (B79-50930)

Elley, Derek. International music guide
1979. *Tantivy Press etc.*. Pbk. *£3.50* A(BC) (B79-28897) ISBN 0-498-02242-0

Ellison, J Audrey. In memoriam N.W.G.T., 1910-1978. *74 Doneraile St., SW6 6EP : J.A. Ellison.* Sd. *£1.30* AC(WB/P) (B79-16101) ISBN 0-904677-09-5

Elms, Albert. Parade of champions. *Boosey and Hawkes. Unpriced* UMMJ (B79-51207)

Eloy, Jean Claude. Kâmakalâ. Le triangle des énergies : pour trois ensembles d'orchestres et de choeurs. *Universal. Unpriced* EMDX (B79-50868)

Elvira Madigan theme ... (Mozart, Wolfgang Amadeus). *Studio Music. Unpriced* WMK (B79-50376)

Elvis lives! *Galaxy Publications Ltd : Distributed by Wells Gardner Darton.* Sd. *£0.75* AKDW/HK/E(P) (B79-02989)

Emanuel Moór Double Keyboard Piano Trust. The history of the Emanuel Moór double keyboard piano. (Shead, Herbert A). *Emanuel Moór Double Keyboard Piano Trust; The Gresham Press, Old Woking, Surrey GU22 9LH : Distributed by Unwin Brothers Ltd.* Pbk. *£15.00* AQ/BC(P) (B79-08930) ISBN 0-9506023-0-2

Empty arms. *arr.* Empty arms : for SATB chorus and piano with optional bass and drums. (Blackley, Terry J). *Warner : Blossom. Unpriced* DW (B79-50847)

Empty arms : for SATB chorus and piano with optional bass and drums. (Blackley, Terry J). *Warner : Blossom. Unpriced* DW (B79-50847)

Enfant prodigue. Opus 46 : ballet in three scenes by Boris Kochno. (Prokofiev, Sergei). 1st ed. *Boosey and Hawkes. Unpriced* MM/HM (B79-50164)

English church music.
Fayrfax, Robert. Aeternae laudis lilium : for 5 voices. *72 Brewery Rd, N.7 : Mapa mundi. Unpriced* EZDJ (B79-50061)
Philips, Peter. Cantiones sacrae, octonis vocibus. Tu es Petrus. Tu es Petrus : for 8 voices. *Mapa mundi. Unpriced* EZDJ (B79-50065)
Shepherd, John. Salvator mundi, Domine : Compline hymn for the Vigil of Christmas in the Sarum Use. *72 Brewery Rd, N.7 : Mapa mundi. Unpriced* EZDJ/LF (B79-50078)
Tallis, Thomas. Sancte Deus. *72 Brewery Rd, N.7 : Mapa mundi. Unpriced* EZDJ (B79-50066)
Tallis, Thomas. Videte miraculum : for 6 voices. *72 Brewery Rd, N.7 : Mapa Mundi. Unpriced* EZDJ (B79-50067)
Tye, Christopher. The Mass Euge bone : for 6 voices. *72 Brewery Rd, N.7 : Mapa mundi. Unpriced* EZDG (B79-50051)

English church music : a collection of essays
1979. *Addington Palace, Croydon CR9 5AD : Royal School of Church Music.* Pbk. *£2.24* AD/LD(YD/D) (B79-33554) ISBN 0-85402-081-0

English folksinger : 159 modern and traditional folksongs. *Collins. £3.95(hardback), £1.95(pbk)* KE/TSDW/G/AYD (B79-50994) ISBN 0-00-411067-6

English lyrics. *selections.* Seven songs for high voice. (Parry, *Sir* Charles Hubert, *bart*). *Stainer and Bell. Unpriced* KFTDW (B79-51006)

English madrigalists. Bennet, John. Madrigals to foure voices (1599). *Stainer and Bell. Unpriced* EZDU (B79-50473) ISBN 0-85249-456-4

English recital song
Vol.1. *Chappell. Unpriced* KDW/AY (B79-50528)

Ensemble/séparé : fur 1-4 Instrumentalspieler = for 1 to 4 players. (Hoch, Peter). *Schott. £6.00* LN (B79-50563)

Enzberg, Hans.
Top Music an der Orgel : leicht verständlicher Einfuhrungskurs, für elektronische Heimorgel in 5 Bänden mit 40 Lektionen
Band 1: Lektion 1-8. *Schott. £5.60* RPV/AC (B79-50243)
Band 2: Lektion 9-16. *Schott. £5.60* RPV/AC (B79-50244)
Band 3: Lektion 17-24. *Schott. £5.60* RPV/AC (B79-50245)
Band 4: Lektion 25-32. *Schott. £5.60* RPV/AC (B79-50246)
Band 5: Lektion 33-40. *Schott. £5.60* RPV/AC (B79-50247)
Die Weihnachts-Orgel : Top Music an der Orgel, die schönsten Weihnachtslieder für elektrönische Heimorgel im Schwierigkeitsgrad 1-5 der Hans Enzberg-Schule. *Schott. £4.80* RPVK/DP/LF/AY (B79-51134)

Erbach, Christian. Canzona. (La paglia). *Schirmer. Unpriced* VVNK (B79-50779)

Erber, James.
Sacra cantiones, lib. 2. Magnificat. Magnificat. (Gagliano, Marco da). *Cathedral Music. Unpriced* EZDGKK (B79-50054)
Sacra cantiones, lib.2. Veni creator spiritus. Veni creator spiritus. (Gagliano, Marco da). *Cathedral Music. Unpriced* EZDJ/LN (B79-50087)
Suite, harpsichord, no.6 (1st collection), F sharp minor. Suite no.6, F sharp minor. (Handel, George Frideric). *Peters. Unpriced* QRPG (B79-50645)

Erbrecht, Lothar Hoffman-. *See* Hoffman-Erbrecht, Lothar.

Erie Canal, and, Great grandad : American folk songs, for two-part chorus of equal voices and piano. (De Cormier, Robert). *Roberton. £0.28* FDW (B79-50494)

Erig, Richard. L'alphabet de la musique : Op.30. Sonatas 4, 7, 16. 3 Sonaten aus 'L'alphabet de la musique' = 3 sonatas from 'L'alphabet de la musique' : für Altblockflöte und Basso continuo = for alto recorder and basso continuo. (Schickhard, Johann Christian). *Pelikan : Bärenreiter. £9.10* VSSPE (B79-50769)

Erinnerungen an Orpheus : Musik für Orchester (1977/78). (Kelterborn, Rudolf). *Bote and Bock. £11.50* MMJ (B79-51024)

Erzittert und fallet. *Vocal score.* Erzittert und fallet = Oh, tremble and falter : Kantate zum Ostersonntag von, Easter cantata. (Bach, Wilhelm Friedemann). *Belwin-Mills. £2.25* DE/LL (B79-50423)

Es ist ein Ros entsprungen = Now blooms a rose so tender. (Brahms, Johannes). *Boosey and Hawkes. Unpriced* EZDW (B79-50888)

Escarraman : a suite of Spanish dances from the XVIth century (after Cervantes), op.177, for guitar. (Castelnuovo-Tedesco, Mario). *Bèrben : Breitkopf and Härtel. £4.70* TSPMHG (B79-51180)

Escobar, Pedro de. Clamabat autem mulier. *72 Brewery Rd, N.7 : Mapa mundi. Unpriced* GEZDJ (B79-50111)

Escribano, Juan. Paradisi porta : motet for 6 voices. *72 Brewery Rd, N.7 : Mapa mundi. Unpriced* EZDJ (B79-50059)

España. Op.165. *Selections : arr.* Two pieces from España. (Albéniz, Isaac). *Oxford University Press. Unpriced* VVNTQK (B79-50782) ISBN 0-19-355137-3

Espansioni : Sinfonie III für grosses Orchester, Bariton und Tonband, 1974/1975. (Kelterborn, Rudolf). *Bärenreiter. £11.55* KGNE/MDX (B79-50156)

Esquivel, Juan.
Motecta festorum. Sancta Maria. Sancta Maria. *72 Brewery Rd, N.7 : Mapa mundi. Unpriced* EZDJ (B79-50060)
Veni Domine : motet for the Advent season for 5 voices. *72 Brewery Rd, N.7 : Mapa mundi. Unpriced* EZDJ/LEZ (B79-50070)
Vox clamantis in deserto : motet for the Advent season for 4 voices. *72 Brewery Rd, N.7 : Mapa mundi. Unpriced* EZDJ/LEZ (B79-50071)
Essays on Armenian music. *Kahn and Averill for the Institute of Armenian Music. £6.95* A(D/YVVA) (B79-33551) ISBN 0-900707-49-6
Essercizi (1738) : 30 sonatas for keyboard. (Scarlatti, Domenico). *Schirmer. £7.55* QRPE (B79-51112)
Estro armonico. Op.3. *Selections : arr.* Two concerto movements. (Vivaldi, Antonio). *Banks. Unpriced* TSNUK (B79-50302)
Eta Cohen Violinschule
1. Band. (Cohen, Eta). *Paxton. Unpriced* S/AC (B79-50272)
Etkin, Ruth. The rhythm band book. *Sterling : Oak Tree Press. Unpriced* XMK/AAY (B79-50402)
Europäische Kunstlied : eine Auswahl von Klavierliedern aus vier Jahrhunderten für den Musikunterricht ... *Schott. £6.00* KDW/AY (B79-50962)
Evans, Colin. Fun with xylophones : four pieces in popular style for group music making. *Paxton. £1.30* NYL (B79-50202)
Evans, David, *b.1940 (May)*. Sing a song
1. Teacher's book. *Nelson : ILEA Learning Materials Service.* Sp. *£2.75* A/GR(VG) (B79-07467) ISBN 0-17-413002-3
Evans, John, *b.1953*. Benjamin Britten, 1913-1976 : pictures from a life : a pictorial biography. *Faber. £15.00 : CIP rev.* BBU(EM) (B78-29832) ISBN 0-571-11261-7
Evans, Peter, *b.1929*. The music of Benjamin Britten. *Dent. £15.00 : CIP entry* BBU (B79-00563) ISBN 0-460-04350-1
Evans, Sarah. Someone's singing, Lord. Melody part. Someone's singing, Lord : hymns and songs for children. *A & C Black. Unpriced* JFADM/AY (B79-50125) ISBN 0-7136-1847-7
Even such is time : for mixed chorus. (Brown, Christopher). *J. and W. Chester. Unpriced* EZDW (B79-50476)
Everett, Paul J.
L'alphabet de la musique, op.30 : 24 sonatas in all the keys, for treble recorder and basso continuo ...
Vol.4: Sonatas 13-16. (Schickhard, Johann Christian). *Musica rara. Unpriced* VSSPE (B79-50344)
Vol.5: Sonatas 17-20. (Schickhard, Johann Christian). *Musica rara. Unpriced* VSSPE (B79-50345)
Vol.6: Sonatas 21-24. (Schickhard, Johann Christian). *Musica rara. Unpriced* VSSPE (B79-50346)
Everyman's book of English country songs. *Dent. £7.95 : CIP rev.* AKDW/G(YC) (B79-15558) ISBN 0-460-12048-4
Everything's coming up roses : for S.A. cambiata, B. or S.A.T.B, with piano. (Styne, Jule). *Williamson. Unpriced* DW (B79-50859)
Experiencing of musical sound : prelude to a phenomenology of music. (Smith, F Joseph). *Gordon and Breach. £8.10* A/CC (B79-02983) ISBN 0-677-04430-5
Exploring music series.
Baroque music for trumpet : including music by Albinoni, Charpentier, Keller, Molter, Telemann, Torelli. *Boosey and Hawkes. £1.65* WSP/AY (B79-50393)
Renaissance Scottish dances. *Boosey and Hawkes. Unpriced* NYEPNQK/AH/AYDL (B79-50200)
Exploring music series : Ensemble series. Schwertsik, Kurt. Kleine Blasmusik. Op.32 : five short movements for two trumpets and two trombones. *Boosey and Hawkes. Unpriced* WNS (B79-50388)
Eybler, Joseph von. Quintet, strings, D major. Quintet, vln., viola, viola d'amore, cello, bass. *(Little Margaret, Penmans Green, Chipperfield) : E.L. White. Unpriced* RXNR (B79-50672)
Eymwag, Joachim. Lamento. *(Little Margaret, Penmans Green, Chipperfield) : E.L. White. Unpriced* KE/NXNRDW (B79-50544)
Ezell, Helen Ingle. Next week Terry & I ... : 5 easy pieces for the piano. *Oxford University Press. Unpriced* QPJ (B79-51080)
Faber guitar series. Giuliani, Mauro. Rossiniana, no.1, op.119. Rossiniana no.1 : for solo guitar, op.119. *Faber Music. Unpriced* TSPMG (B79-50704)
Façade 2 : a further entertainment. (Walton, *Sir* William). *Oxford University Press. Unpriced* KHYE/NYENQ (B79-51010) ISBN 0-19-359406-4
Facsimile classics series.
Gilbert, *Sir* William Schwenck. The Mikado, or, The town of Titipu. *42 Bloomsbury St., W.C.1 : Godfrey Cave Associates. £5.50* BSWACF (B79-16839) ISBN 0-906223-05-9
Gilbert, *Sir* William Schwenck. The yeomen of the guard, or, The merryman and his maid. *42 Bloomsbury St., W.C.1 : Godfrey Cave Associates Ltd. £5.50* BSWACF (B79-16840) ISBN 0-906223-06-7
Fact finders.
Ardley, Neil. Musical instruments. *Macmillan. £0.95* AL/B (B79-50008) ISBN 0-333-24465-6
Ardley, Neil. Musical instruments. *Macmillan.* Pbk. *£0.50* AL/B (B79-22637) ISBN 0-333-26156-9
Fall of Lucifer. *Vocal score.* The fall of Lucifer : for countertenor, tenor and bass soloists, chamber choir and instrumental ensemble. (Burgon, Geoffrey). *Chester Music. Unpriced* CM/L (B79-50015)
Falla, Manuel de. On music and musicians. *Boyars Distributed by Calder and Boyars. £5.95* A (B79-14910) ISBN 0-7145-2600-2
Falla y Matheu, Manuel Maria de Los Dolores de. *See* Falla, Manuel de.
Fallersleben, Hoffmann von. Wie die Wolke. Op.6, no.5. *arr.* As the clouds with longing wander : Wie die Wolke : for three-part chorus of women's voices with piano accompaniment. (Brahms, Johannes). *Schirmer. £0.35* FDW (B79-50493)
Famous solo in E minor : for double bass and piano. (Dragonetti, Domenico). *Yorke. Unpriced* SSPJ (B79-50290)
Fanfare der Stadt Wien. *arr.* Festmusik der Stadt Wien. (Strauss, Richard). *Boosey and Hawkes. Unpriced* UMMK/AGN (B79-50729)
Fanshawe, David.
African sanctus ... : for soprano solo, mixed chorus, instrumental ensemble and pre-recorded tape. *Chappell. Unpriced* ENYLDE (B79-50456)
Tarka the otter. Theme. *arr.* Tarka the otter. *Chappell. Unpriced* QPK/JR (B79-51106)
Fantaisie and variations on a theme of Danzi. Op.81 : for clarinet and string quartet. (Spohr, Louis). *Musica rara. Unpriced* NVVNR/T (B79-51045)
Fantasia a 5. (Schütz, Heinrich). *Ricordi. Unpriced* VSNRK/DJ (B79-50338)
Fantasia for brass quartet : for 2 trumpets and 2 trombones. (Saunders, Neil). *Roberton. £3.00* WNS (B79-51315)
Fantasia super 'Urbs Turegem, urbs famosa' sive 'Lauda Sion salvatorem' : fur Orgel ... (Müller, Paul). *Verlag der Zentralbibliothek Zurich in Kommission bei Amadeus Verlag : Bärenreiter. Unpriced* RJ (B79-50649)
Fantasy for euphonium and brass band. (Sparke, Philip). *R. Smith. Unpriced* WMPWW (B79-50384)
Fare well. (Benger, Richard). *Edwin Ashdown. £0.20* FDW (B79-50101)
Faris, Alexander. M'sieur Offenbach : a suite for clarinet, alto and tenor saxophones. (Offenbach, Jacques). *7 Garrick St., W.C.2 : Middle Eight Music. Unpriced* VNTK/DW (B79-50324)
Farjeon, Eleanor. Four miniatures for unaccompanied chorus SATB. (Maconchy, Elizabeth). *Chester Music. Unpriced* EZDW (B79-50479)
Farmer, Paul.
Into the classics. *Longman.* Sd. *£0.65* A(XFWE101) (B79-33549) ISBN 0-582-21576-5
Pop. *Longman.* Sd. *£0.65* A/GB (B79-32712) ISBN 0-582-21577-3
Ragtime & blues. *Longman.* Sd. *£0.65* AQPHXJ (B79-36912) ISBN 0-582-21579-x
Farnsworth, Barry.
Original music and alternative music for the Modern Dance Grade Examinations
Grades 2 and 3: including pieces needed for the course of movement for boys. (Imperial Society of Teachers of Dancing. *Modern Dance Branch*). *Imperial Society of Teachers of Dancing. £3.50* QPH/H/AL (B79-51070)
Primary and Grade 1: including pieces needed for the course of movement for boys. (Imperial Society of Teachers of Dancing. *Modern Dance Branch*). *Imperial Society of Teachers of Dancing. £3.00* QPH/H/AL (B79-51071)
Farrar, John. Hopelessly devoted to you. *arr.* Hopelessly devoted to you. *Chappell. Unpriced* UMK/DW (B79-51202)
Father of mercies : for chorus of unison voices with organ accompaniment. (Hamble, William R). *Chappell. Unpriced* JDH (B79-50930)
Fatinitza march. *arr.* Fatinitza march : based on themes from the operetta 'Fatinitza'. (Suppé, Franz von). *Bosworth & Co. £1.25* MK/AGM (B79-51012)
Fatinitza march : based on themes from the operetta 'Fatinitza'. (Suppé, Franz von). *Bosworth & Co. £1.25* MK/AGM (B79-51012)
Fats Waller. (Waller, Thomas). *EMI. Unpriced* KDW/GB (B79-50138)
Fauré, Gabriel.
Quartet, strings & keyboard, no.1, op.15. First piano quartet. Op.15. *Eulenburg. £2.05* NXNT (B79-50604)
Quartet, strings & keyboard, no.2, op.45. Second piano quartet. Op.45. *Eulenburg. Unpriced* NXNT (B79-50605)
Fawcett, Trevor. Music in eighteenth-century Norwich and Norfolk. *Norwich NR4 7TJ : Centre of East Anglian Studies, University of East Anglia.* Sd. *£1.75* A(YDDS/XF101) (B79-33550)
Faychild, Janie. Sisters in song : a collection of new songs from the women's liberation movement. *Onlywoman Press. Unpriced* KFE/TSDW/AY (B79-50996)
Faychild, Junie. Sisters in song : a collection of new songs from the women's liberation movement. (Burgon, Geoffrey). *Onlywomen Press. Unpriced* KDGPR (B79-50951)
Fayrfax, Robert. Aeternae laudis lilium : for 5 voices. *72 Brewery Rd, N.7 : Mapa mundi. Unpriced* EZDJ (B79-50061)
Feast of easy carols. *Chester Music. Unpriced* QPK/DP/LF/AY (B79-51098)
Feel like going home : portraits in blues & rock'n'roll. (Guralnick, Peter). *Omnibus Press.* Pbk. *£2.95* AKDW/HHW/E(M) (B79-10476) ISBN 0-86001-493-2
Feld, Jindřich. Suite rhapsodica : for clarinet solo, 1976. *Schirmer. £1.80* VVPMJ (B79-51288)
Feldman, Morton.
Chorus and orchestra. *Universal. Unpriced* EM (B79-50039)
Piano and orchestra. *Universal. Unpriced* MPQ (B79-50181)
Three clarinets, cello and piano. *Universal. Unpriced* NUVNR (B79-50186)
Fellowes, Edmund Horace. Madrigals to foure voices (1599). (Bennet, John). *Stainer and Bell. Unpriced* EZDU (B79-50473) ISBN 0-85249-456-4
Fenby, Eric. The magic fountain. *Vocal score.* The magic fountain : lyric drama in 3 acts. (Delius, Frederick). *Delius Trust, Boosey and Hawkes. Unpriced* CC (B79-50010)
Fénelon, Fania. The musicians of Auschwitz. *Sphere.* Pbk. *£0.95* A(M/YLCO/XPC3) (B79-19444) ISBN 0-7221-3466-5
Ferandiere, Fernando. Arte de tocar la guitarra española por música, (Madrid, 1799). *Tecla. Unpriced* TS/AC (B79-51163) ISBN 0-8494-0093-7
Ferguson, Barry. Aubade : song cycle for speaker, SATB and piano (or harp). *Novello. Unpriced* DW (B79-50033)
Ferguson, Howard.
Piéces de clavecin, livre 3, ordre 24,15,16. *Selections : arr.* Four duos for flute or oboe and keyboard (harpsichord or piano). (Couperin, François). *Oxford University Press. Unpriced* VRPK (B79-50331) ISBN 0-19-355912-9
Sonatas, piano. Complete pianoforte sonatas, including the unfinished works
Volume 3. (Schubert, Franz). *Associated Board of the Royal Schools of Music. Unpriced* QPE/AZ (B79-51069)
Ferial antiphons on Venite, Benedictus and Magnificat with simple tones. (Communities Consultative Council. *Anglican Office Book Committee*). *Communities Consultative Council. Unpriced* JEZDGNPE (B79-50932)
Ferienkurse '78. (Internationale Ferienkurse für Neue Musik, *29, Darmstadt, 1978*). *Schott.* Pbk. *£9.60* A(XR9) (B79-14011)

Ferrari, Ermanno Wolf-. *See* Wolf-Ferrari, Ermanno.
Ferris, William.
Indian summer : for mixed chorus and piano. *Oxford University Press. Unpriced* DW (B79-50848)
Te Deum : for unison, boys', and mixed choirs combined, with organ. *Oxford University Press. Unpriced* DGKHB (B79-50426)
Festival service book
9: Voice and verse : a meditation with words and music. *Royal College of Church Music. Unpriced* DGM (B79-50428) ISBN 0-85402-079-9
Festmusik der Stadt Wien. (Strauss, Richard). *Boosey and Hawkes. Unpriced* UMMK/AGN (B79-50729)
Fétis, François Joseph.
Concerto, flute, B minor. Konzert für Flöte und Orchester in h-moll. *Eulenburg. £3.50* MPVRF (B79-50587)
Concerto, flute, B minor. *arr.* Konzert in h-moll für Flote und Orchester. *Eulenburg. £3.25* VRPK/LF (B79-50752)
Fiddler's ten : easy tunes for violin with piano accompaniment. (Rose, Michael). *Novello. £1.65* SPJ (B79-50277)
Fietta, Hector Lagna.
Album para piano. (Madi, Tito). *Fermata do Brasil Clifford Essex. Unpriced* QPK/AH (B79-51096)
Prelúdio pra Ninar Gente Grande. *arr.* Prelúdio pra Ninar Gente Grande. (Vieira, Luiz). *Rio Musical : Essex Music. Unpriced* QPK (B79-51093)
Fifteenth-century liturgical music
2: Four anonymous masses. *Stainer and Bell. Unpriced* EZDFF/AYD (B79-50873) ISBN 0-85249-544-7
Final covenent : for symphonic band or wind ensemble. (Tull, Fisher). *Boosey and Hawkes. Unpriced* UMMJ (B79-50725)
Find a bin : a song/mime for children. (Diamond, Eileen). *Chappell, in association with Keep Britain Tidy. Unpriced* JFDW/JN (B79-50941)
Finger, Gottfried.
Pastorelle, recorders (treble) (3), G major. Pastorelle and sonata : for three treble recorders. *Oxford University Press. Unpriced* VSSNT (B79-50343) ISBN 0-19-363204-7
Sonata, oboes (2) & continuo, B flat major. Sonata in B flat for 2 oboes/violins (or recorders in C) and basso continuo. *Nova Music. Unpriced* VTNTPWE (B79-51256)
Sonata, recorder (treble) & continuo, op.3, no.2, C minor. Sonata in C, opus 3, no.2, for treble recorder and basso continuo. *Nova Music. Unpriced* VSSPE (B79-51252)
Finishing school : comic operetta in one act (two scenes). (Suppé, Franz von). *Weinberger. Unpriced* CF (B79-50414)
Fink, Siegfried. Krenzpunkte : zwei Studien für Schlagzengtrio. *Schott. £3.20* XNT/AF (B79-50812)
Finke, Fidelio Fritz. Acht Musiken : für zwei Geigen und Bratsche (1923). *Neue Musik : Breitkopf and Härtel. £3.60* RXNT (B79-51144)
Finzi, Gerald. Bagatelles, clarinet & piano. *arr.* Five bagatelles. *Boosey and Hawkes. Unpriced* VRPK (B79-51225)
Firemen's galop. (Hertel, Peter Ludwig). *Harmer Music : Studio Music. Unpriced* WMK/AHLF (B79-50378)
First book for the guitar
Part 1. (Noad, Frederick). *Schirmer. £1.75* TS/AC (B79-51166)
Part 2. (Noad, Frederick). *Schirmer. £1.75* TS/AC (B79-51167)
First book of bassoon solos. *Faber Music. Unpriced* VWP/AY (B79-50787)
First book of organ pieces. Six organ pieces. (Bridge, Frank). *Boosey and Hawkes. Unpriced* RJ (B79-51123)
First nursery suite : four traditional songs. *Novello. £0.98* NYFSRK/DW/GJ/AY (B79-50608)

First violin book. (Whiteley, Faith). *Oxford University Press. Unpriced* S/AF (B79-51145) ISBN 0-19-359511-7

First year violin method. Eta Cohen Violinschule

1. Band. (Cohen, Eta). *Paxton. Unpriced* S/AC (B79-50272)

Fisk, Eliot. Essercizi. *Selections.* Five sonatas. (Scarlatti, Domenico). *DeCamera : Schirmer. £2.50* TSPMK/AE (B79-51192)

Fiske, Roger. Beethoven's Missa solemnis. *Elek. £5.95* BBJADG (B79-14016) ISBN 0-236-40146-7

Fitzgerald, Edward. Symphony no.24, op.273, 'Majnun'. Majnun symphony. (Symphony no.24). Op.273 : for tenor solo, four-part chorus of mixed voices, trumpet in C, solo violin and string orchestra. (Hovhaness, Alan). *Associated Music. £9.10* EMDX (B79-50869)

Five bagatelles. (Finzi, Gerald). *Boosey and Hawkes. Unpriced* VRPK (B79-51225)

Five Blake songs : for high voice and piano. (Chapple, Brian). *Chester Music. Unpriced* KFTDW (B79-50154)

Five concert pieces : for young pianists. (Hedges, Anthony). *Universal. Unpriced* QPJ (B79-51081)

Five incantations = Cinque incantesimi : for piano. (Scelsi, Giacinto). *Schirmer. £3.05* QPJ (B79-50638)

Five nativity carols : for unison voices, piano and simple percussion. (Brown, Gerald Edgar). *7 Garrick St. W.C.2 : Middle Eight Music. Unpriced* JFE/NYLDP/LF (B79-50946)

Five part-songs. Op.45. 5 part songs. Op.45. From the Greek Anthology : five unaccompanied part-songs for TTBB. Opus 45. (Elgar, *Sir* Edward, *bart*). *Novello. £1.15* GEZDW (B79-50927)

Five ricercare in four parts for brass. (Gabrieli, Andrea). *Musica rara. Unpriced* WSN (B79-50798)

Five ricercare in four parts : for brass or recorders. (Gabrieli, Andrea). *Musica rara. Unpriced* VSNS (B79-51235)

Five ricercare in four parts for recorders. (Gabrieli, Andrea). *Musica rara. Unpriced* VSN (B79-50759)

Fix-it man. *Melody part.* The fix-it man : songs for schools. (Milne, Lorraine). *Macmillan. Unpriced* JFADW/GJ (B79-50514) ISBN 0-333-25190-3

Flaherty, Gloria. Opera in the development of German critical thought. *Princeton University Press. £11.70* AC/CC(YE/XE201) (B79-14914) ISBN 0-691-06370-2

Flanders, Michael. A waltz dream : operetta in three acts. (Dunn, Bernard). *10 Rathbone St., W1P 2BJ : Josef Weinberger.* Pbk. *£1.25* BSOTACF (B79-06705)

Flauto traverso.

Boehm, Theobald. 24 Caprices-Études, opus 26 : für Flöte solo = for solo flute = pour flûte seule. Reprint der Schott-Originalausgabe von 1852. *Schott. £4.00* VR/AF (B79-51213)

Drouet, Louis. Méthode pour la flûte. Exercices de tous genres. 25 Etüden für Flöte = 25 studies for flute = 25 exercices pour flûte. Reprint der Schott-Originalausgabe von 1827. *Schott. £4.00* VR/AF (B79-51214)

Platti, Giovanni Benedetto. Sonata, flute & continuo, op.3, no.3, E minor. Sonate e-Moll, e minor, mi mineur, opus III, no.3, für Flöte und Basso continuo, for flute and basso continuo, pour flûte et basse continue. *Schott. £4.80* VRPE (B79-51222)

Flecker, James Elroy. Hassan : the incidental music to the play by James Elroy Flecker. (Delius, Frederick). *Boosey and Hawkes. Unpriced* EM/JM (B79-50040)

Fleming, Antony le. *See* Le Fleming, Antony.

Fletcher, Andrew. Versicles and responses : Series 3 Morning and Evening Prayer. *Royal School of Church Music. Unpriced* EZDGMM (B79-50458)

Fletcher, John.

Away, delights : for men's chorus a cappella. (Diemer, Emma Lou). *Broude : Breitkopf and Härtel. £0.42* GEZDW (B79-50924)

Tell me, dearest, what is love? : for mixed chorus a cappella. (Diemer, Emma Lou). *Broude : Breitkopf and Härtel. £0.42* EZDW (B79-50889)

Weep no more : for women's chorus a cappella. (Diemer, Emma Lou). *Broude : Breitkopf and Härtel. £0.42* FEZDW (B79-50917)

Flick und Flock's Abenteuer. Feuerwehr Galopp. *arr.* The firemen's galop. (Hertel, Peter Ludwig). *Harmer Music : Studio Music. Unpriced* WMK/AHLF (B79-50378)

Flind, A J. Electronic projects in music. *Newnes Technical Books.* Pbk. *£2.25 : CIP rev.* APV/BC (B79-17724) ISBN 0-408-00391-x

Flindell, Fred.

Ach, dass du den Himmel zerrissest. *Vocal score.* Ach, dass du den Himmel zerrissest = Oh! you who doth rend heav'n asunder : festo nativit Christi, Weihnachtskantate von, Christmas cantata. (Bach, Wilhelm Friedemann). *Belwin Mills. £2.25* DE/LF (B79-50421)

Erzittert und fallet. *Vocal score.* Erzittert und fallet = Oh, tremble and falter : Kantate zum Ostersonntag von, Easter cantata. (Bach, Wilhelm Friedemann). *Belwin-Mills. £2.25* DE/LL (B79-50423)

Wie schön leuchtet der Morgenstern. *Vocal score.* Wie schon leuchtet der Morgenstern = How fair the morning star doth glow : Kantate Dom. II. p. Epiph. (Bach, Wilhelm Friedemann). *Belwin-Mills. £2.25* DE/LFP (B79-50422)

Flute encores

Vol.1. *Chester Music. Unpriced* VRPK/AAY (B79-50750)

Flute magic. *Chappell. Unpriced* VRPK/AAY (B79-50332)

Flute magic

2. *Chappell. Unpriced* VRPK/DW/GB/AY (B79-51226)

Flute trios

Vol.1. *Chester Music. Unpriced* VRNT/AY (B79-51216)

Vol.2. *Chester Music. Unpriced* VRNT/AY (B79-51217)

Fodor, Akos. Magnificat, D major, (1758). Magnificat. (Bach, Johann Christian). *Editio musica : Eulenburg. Unpriced* EMDGKK (B79-50044)

Foellmer, Oscar.

Erzittert und fallet. *Vocal score.* Erzittert und fallet = Oh, tremble and falter : Kantate zum Ostersonntag von, Easter cantata. (Bach, Wilhelm Friedemann). *Belwin-Mills. £2.25* DE/LL (B79-50423)

Wie schön leuchtet der Morgenstern. *Vocal score.* Wie schon leuchtet der Morgenstern = How fair the morning star doth glow : Kantate Dom. II. p. Epiph. (Bach, Wilhelm Friedemann). *Belwin-Mills. £2.25* DE/LFP (B79-50422)

Folies de Paris : the rise and fall of French operetta. (Harding, James, *b.1929*). *Chappell : Elm Tree Books. £7.95* ACF(YH) (B79-19445) ISBN 0-903443-28-7

'Folk guitar styles of today'. (Shipton, Russ). *Oak Publications : Music Sales (dist.). Unpriced* TS/ED (B79-50298) ISBN 0-86001-077-5

Folk revival : the rediscovery of a national music. (Woods, Fred). *Blandford Press. £3.95 : CIP rev.* A/G (B79-14913) ISBN 0-7137-0970-7

Folk song fantasy : for brass quintet. (Horovitz, Joseph). *J. & W. Chester. Unpriced* WNR (B79-50386)

Folksong 2. (Royal, Timothy). *16 Oldfield Place, Hotwells, Bristol BS8 4QJ : Shed Music. Unpriced* TSPMJ (B79-50706)

Folksong book 1. *Helicon Press. Unpriced* LK/DW/G/AY (B79-50158) ISBN 0-905684-01-x

Fond kiss : for four-part chorus of mixed voices with baritone solo a cappella. (Rhein, Robert). *Schirmer. £0.35* EZDW (B79-50901)

Fontyn, Jacqueline. Seven little pieces for woodwind trio. *Schirmer. £4.85* VNT (B79-50734)

Foot tapping : the Shadows, 1958-1978. (Geddes, George Thomson). *102 Dorchester Ave., Glasgow G12 0EB : The author.* Sp. *£1.00* AKDW/GB/FD(P/WT) (B79-00884)

Forbes, Watson. Thirty easy classical duets : for unaccompanied clarinets. *Oxford University Press. Unpriced* VVNUK/AAY (B79-50356) ISBN 0-19-356566-8

Ford, Charles. Making musical instruments, strings and keyboard. *Faber. £15.00 : CIP rev.* AL/BC (B79-00571) ISBN 0-571-10870-9

Form in tonal music : an introduction to analysis. (Green, Douglas Marshall). 2nd ed. *Holt, Rinehart and Winston. £10.00* A/S (B79-24591) ISBN 0-03-020286-8

Förster, Dieter H.

Concertino, flute, op.60, D major. *arr.* Concertino für Flöte und Orchester in D-dur. op.60. (Reissiger, Carl Gottlieb). *Eulenburg. £3.70* VRPK/LFL (B79-50753)

Concerto, flute, op.30, B minor. Konzert für Flöte und Orchester in h-moll, op.30 (17). (Romberg, Bernhard). *Eulenburg. £4.20* MPVRF (B79-50588)

Introduction, variations & finale, flute & piano, op.80, C major. Introduktion, Variationen und Finale für Flöte oder Violine und Klavier in C-dur. Op.80. (Czerny, Carl). *Eulenburg. £3.25* VRP/T (B79-50746)

Forster, Dieter H. Sechs Ragtimes für Flöte oder Klarinette in B and Klavier. (Joplin, Scott). *Eulenburg. £4.20* VRPK/AHXJ (B79-50751)

Forsyth, Ella Marie. Building a chamber music collection : a descriptive guide to published scores. *Scarecrow Press Distributed by Bailey and Swinfen. £6.30* AN(T) (B79-32195) ISBN 0-8108-1215-0

Fortner, Wolfgang.

Trio, strings & piano, 1978. Trio, für Violine, Violoncello und Klavier, for violin, cello and piano, (1978). *Schott. £12.00* NXNT (B79-50198)

Triptychon : für Orchester (1977). *Schott. £20.00* MMJ (B79-50175)

Forty-two piano classics. 42 piano classics. *EMI. Unpriced* QP/AY (B79-51065) ISBN 0-86175-057-8

Foss, Hugh. The Foss Collection of Scottish dances. *H. Foss. Unpriced* QPK/AH/AYDL (B79-50222)

Foss, Michael. Orchestra. *Macdonald and Jane's. £7.95* AMM/E (B79-35974) ISBN 0-354-04420-6

Foss, Peter. Roots, rock and reggae. *Chappell. Unpriced* KDW/HKR/AY (B79-50543)

Foss Collection of Scottish dances. *H. Foss. Unpriced* QPK/AH/AYDL (B79-50222)

Fosse, Bob. Chicago : a musical vaudeville. (Ebb, Fred). *French.* Sd. *£1.65* BKDEACM (B79-06704) ISBN 0-573-68081-7

Foster, Bob. Chopbuster march : an outrageous trumpet feature. *Warner : Blossom. Unpriced* UMMGM (B79-50719)

Four American settings. Song of Thyrsis. 4 American settings. Song of Thyrsis. Song of Thyrsis : S.A.T.B. & piano. (Tepper, Albert). *Boosey and Hawkes. £0.35* DW (B79-50860)

Four Burns songs : for high voice and piano. (Britten, Benjamin, *Baron Britten*). *Faber Music. Unpriced* KFTDW (B79-50153)

Four duos for flute or oboe and keyboard (harpsichord or piano). (Couperin, François). *Oxford University Press. Unpriced* VRPK (B79-50331) ISBN 0-19-355912-9

Four introits : unison chorus and hand bells. (McCray, James). *Broude : Breitkopf und Härtel. £0.42* JE/XSQDH (B79-50511)

Four miniatures for unaccompanied chorus SATB. (Maconchy, Elizabeth). *Chester Music. Unpriced* EZDW (B79-50479)

Four motets

No.1: Help us, O Lord .. (Copland, Aaron). *Boosey and Hawkes. Unpriced* EZDJ (B79-50464)

No.2: Thou, O Jehovah .. (Copland, Aaron). *Boosey and Hawkes. Unpriced* EZDJ (B79-50465)

No.3: Have mercy on us, O my Lord .. (Copland, Aaron). *Boosey and Hawkes. Unpriced* EZDJ (B79-50466)

No.4: Sing ye praises to our King .. (Copland, Aaron). *Boosey and Hawkes. Unpriced* EZDJ (B79-50467)

Four seasons, op.8 (Concerto for violin and orchestra) Autumn : for violin and piano. (Vivaldi, Antonio). *Schirmer. £2.40* SPK/LF (B79-50682)

Four seasons, op.8. (Concerto for violin and orchestra Op.8, no.4: Winter : for violin and piano. (Vivaldi, Antonio). *Schirmer. £2.40* SPK/LF (B79-51154)

Four solo pieces : for trombone (in bass and treble clefs). (Nash, Harold). *Paterson. Unpriced* WUPJ (B79-51324)

Four sonatas for treble recorder and basso continuo. Der getreue Music Meister. *Selections.* 4 sonatas for treble recorder and basso continuo. (Telemann, Georg Philipp). *Musica rara. Unpriced* VSSPE (B79-50347)

Françaix, Jean. Quasi improvvisando : pour ensemble à vent = für Bläserensemble. *Schott. £12.00* UN (B79-50320)

Franco-Flemish church music.

Brumel, Antoine. Laudate Dominum de caelis : for 4 voices. *72 Brewery Rd, N.7 : Mapa mundi. Unpriced* EZDR (B79-50097)

La Rue, Pierre de. Missa cum iucunditate : for 4 and 5 voices. *72 Brewery Rd, N.7 : Mapa mundi. Unpriced* GEZDG (B79-50109)

Lasso, Orlando di. Magnificat praetur rerum seriem : upon the motet by Josquin, for 6 voices. *72 Brewery Rd, N.7 : Mapa mundi. Unpriced* EZDGKK (B79-50055)

Okeghem, Jean. Missa pro defunctis : for 2,3 and 4 voices. *72 Brewery Rd, N.7 : Mapa mundi. Unpriced* EZDGKAV (B79-50052)

Okeghem, Jean. Salve regina : for 4 voices. *72 Brewery Rd, N.7 : Mapa mundi. Unpriced* GEZDJ (B79-50113)

Silva, Andreas de. Omnis pulchritudo Domini : motet for the Ascension of our Lord, for 5 voices. *72 Brewery Rd, N.7 : Mapa mundi. Unpriced* EZDJ/LM (B79-50086)

Frank, Alan.

The clarinet : a comprehensive method for the Boehm clarinet. (Thurston, Frederick J). 3rd ed. (revised and enlarged). *Boosey and Hawkes. Unpriced* VV/AC (B79-51272)

España. Op.165. *Selections : arr.* Two pieces from España. (Albéniz, Isaac). *Oxford University Press. Unpriced* VVNTQK (B79-50782) ISBN 0-19-355137-3

Thirty easy classical duets : for unaccompanied clarinets. *Oxford University Press. Unpriced* VVNUK/AAY (B79-50356) ISBN 0-19-356566-8

Frankie and Johnny : for four-part chorus of mixed voices with soprano, alto, baritone and tenor solos a cappella. (De Cormier, Robert). *Roberton. £0.28* EZDW (B79-50478)

Franz, Robert. Mutter, o sing 'mich zur Ruh', op.10, no.3. *arr.* Mother, O sing me to sleep = Mutter, O sing mich zur ruh' : for three-part chorus of female voices and piano. *Roberton. £0.24* FDW (B79-50910)

Franz Schubert Lieder : Urtext der Neuen Schubert-Ausgabe

Heft 1: Die schöne Müllerin, op.25: Mittlere Stimme (Transposition). (Schubert, Franz). *Bärenreiter. £5.28* KDW (B79-50133)

Heft 3: Leider nach Texten von Goethe: Mittlere Stimme (Transposition). (Schubert, Franz). *Bärenreiter. £4.80* KDW (B79-50134)

Fraser, Shena. Grannies to sell. Grannies to sell, and, Boating. *Roberton. £0.20* JFDW (B79-50518)

Frazer, Alan.

A little theatre music : for flute, clarinet, trumpet, violin, cello and percussion. *7 Garrick St., W.C.2 : Middle Eight Music. Unpriced* NYE/J (B79-50199)

Music from the ballet. (Delibes, Leo). *(7 Garrick St., W.C.2) : Middle Eight Music. Unpriced* UNSK/HM (B79-50732)

Music from the ballet. (Tchaikovsky, Peter). *(7 Garrick St., W.C.2) : Middle Eight Music. Unpriced* UNSK/HM (B79-50733)

Two ragtime trios : for 2 clarinets and tenor saxophone (or bass clarinet). *7 Garrick St., W.C.2 : Middle Eight Music. Unpriced* VNTK/AHXJ (B79-50323)

Frédéric François Chopin, 1810-1844. (Chopin, Frédéric). *East-West. Unpriced* QPJ (B79-50213) ISBN 0-904499-04-9

French's musical library. Ebb, Fred. Chicago : a musical vaudeville. *French.* Sd. *£1.65* BKDEACM (B79-06704) ISBN 0-573-68081-7

Freneau, Philip Morin. 4 American settings. Song of Thyrsis. Song of Thyrsis : S.A.T.B. & piano. (Tepper, Albert). *Boosey and Hawkes. £0.35* DW (B79-50860)

Frescobaldi, Girolamo. Libro della canzoni, no.1. Canzona 2 'La Bernadina'. Canzona (II) 'La Bernadina' per canto solo : für Sopranblockflüte (Flüte, Oboe, Violine) und Generalbass = for descant recorder (flute, oboe, violin) and continuo. *Schott. £3.20* VSRPJ (B79-51242)

Friedman, Laura. Jazz-rock fusion : the people - the music. (Coryell, Julie). *Boyars : Distributed by Calder and Boyars. £12.00* AKDW/HKRJ (B79-32718) ISBN 0-7145-2667-3

Friend, Lionel. Thérèse. *Vocal score.* Thérèse ... (Tavener, John). *Chester Music. Unpriced* CC (B79-50817)

Frith, Simon. Rock file

5. *Panther.* Pbk. *£1.25* ADW/GB (B79-03804) ISBN 0-586-04680-1

Fröhlich, Johannes Frederik. March and hunting piece. Op.40. *arr.* Nonet for... horns. *(116 Long Acre, W.C.2) : Paxman. £4.00* WTNM (B79-51321)

Fröhliche Weihnacht : Weihnachtslieder aus aller Welt. *Schott. £2.40* JE/TSDP/LF/AY (B79-50118)

Fröhlicher Reigen = Cheerful round dance : Tänze für zwei Sopranblockflöten mit Gitarre ad lib. = dances for two soprano recorders with guitarre sic ad lib. (Biebl, Franz).

Pelikan : Bärenreiter. £1.49 VSRNUH (B79-50766)
From Liszt to music hall. (Middleton, Richard). *Open University Press.* Pbk. *Unpriced* A(XFY101) (B79-36911) ISBN 0-335-05423-4
From the Greek Anthology : five unaccompanied part-songs for TTBB. Opus 45. (Elgar, *Sir* Edward, *bart*). *Novello. £1.15* GEZDW (B79-50927)
Front line sax solos. *Chappell. Unpriced* VUPMHX (B79-50776)
Fruit of the vine : for full chorus of mixed voices a cappella. (Berger, Jean). *Schirmer. Unpriced* EZDX (B79-50905)
Fuellmer, Oscar. Ach, dass du den Himmel zerrissest. *Vocal score.* Ach, dass du den Himmel zerrissest = Oh! you who doth rend heav'n asunder : festo nativit Christi, Weihnachtskantate von, Christmas cantata. (Bach, Wilhelm Friedemann). *Belwin Mills. £2.25* DE/LF (B79-50421)
Fuller, Frederick. Stravinsky. (Vlad, Roman). 3rd ed. *Oxford University Press. £5.95* BSV(N) (B79-11126) ISBN 0-19-315444-7
Fun chord organ : for young people of any age. *EMI. Unpriced* RPVCK/DW/GB/AY (B79-51133) ISBN 0-86175-064-0
Fun clarinet : for young people of any age. *EMI. Unpriced* VVPK/DW/GB/AY (B79-51283) ISBN 0-86175-060-8
Fun flute : for young people of any age. *EMI. Unpriced* VRPK/DW/GB/AY (B79-51227) ISBN 0-86175-058-6
Fun music : for clarinet
Vol.1. *Chappell. Unpriced* VVPK/AAY (B79-50357)
Vol.2. *Chappell. Unpriced* VVPK/AAY (B79-50358)
Fun music : for flute
Vol.1. *Chappell. Unpriced* VRPK/AAY (B79-50333)
Vol.2. *Chappell. Unpriced* VRPK/AAY (B79-50334)
Fun music for recorder
Vol.1. *Chappell. Unpriced* VSPK/AAY (B79-50341)
Fun music : for recorder
Vol.2. *Chappell. Unpriced* VSPK/AAY (B79-50342)
Fun music : for trumpet
Vol.1. *Chappell. Unpriced* WSPK/AAY (B79-50394)
Fun music : for trumpets
Vol.2. *Chappell. Unpriced* WSPK/AAY (B79-50395)
Fun music : for violin
Vol.1. *Chappell. Unpriced* SPK/AAY (B79-50278)
Vol.2. *Chappell. Unpriced* SPK/AAY (B79-50279)
Fun organ : arrangements ... for all electronic and 'C' chord organs
Folio no.2. *EMI. Unpriced* RPVCK/AAY (B79-50660)

Fun piano : for young people of any age. *EMI. Unpriced* QPK/DW/GB/AY (B79-51101) ISBN 0-86175-062-4

Fun violin : for young people of any age. *EMI. Unpriced* SPK/DW/GB/AY (B79-51153) ISBN 0-86175-066-7
Fun with xylophones : four pieces in popular style for group music making. (Evans, Colin). *Paxton. £1.30* NYL (B79-50202)
Fundamental classroom music skills : theory and performing techniques. (Wachhaus, Gustav). *Holt, Rinehart and Winston.* Sp. *£7.75* A(VG) (B79-12529) ISBN 0-03-041775-9
Fünf Choralvorspiele : für Trompete und Orgel, 1975. (Zipp, Friedrich). *Merseburger : Bärenreiter. £4.46* WSPLR (B79-50805)
Fünf Gesänge für gemischten Chor nach Gedichten von Richard Dehmel, Opus 26. (Burkhard, Willy). *Bärenreiter. £1.16* EZDW (B79-50477)
Fünf Lieder ohne Worte. Lieder ohne Worte. *Selections : arr.* 5 Lieder ohne Worte : für zwei Gitarren = for two guitars. (Mendelssohn, Felix). *Schott. £4.00* TSNUK (B79-51172)
Fünfundzwanzig Etüden für Flöte = Twenty-five studies for flute = Vingtcing exercices pour flûte. Méthode pour la flûte. Exercices de tous genres. 25 Etüden für Flöte = 25 studies for flute = 25 exercices pour flûte. (Drouet, Louis). Reprint der Schott-Originalausgabe von 1827. *Schott. £4.00* VR/AF (B79-51214)
Furze, Jessie. In the days of long ago. *Selections.* The tin soldiers, and, Lords and ladies : two simple piano duets from the suite 'In the days of long ago'. *Roberton. £0.50* QNV (B79-50614)
Gabrieli, Andrea.
Madrigali et ricercari a quattro voci. *Selections.* Five ricercare in four parts for brass. *Musica rara. Unpriced* WSN (B79-50798)
Madrigali et ricercari a quattro voci. *Selections.* Five ricercare in four parts : for brass or recorders. *Musica rara. Unpriced* VSNS (B79-51235)
Madrigali et ricercari a quattro voci. *Selections.* Five ricercare in four parts for recorders. *Musica rara. Unpriced* VSN (B79-50759)
Maria stabat. *36 Ranelagh Gdns W.6 : Cathedral Music. Unpriced* EZDJ/LK (B79-50084)
Gabrieli, Giovanni. Sacrae symphoniae, bk.2. O quam suavis. O quam suavis : for eight-part chorus of mixed voices with organ accompaniment. *Schirmer. £0.75* DGKJ/LNC (B79-50427)
Gabrielli, Domenico.
Sonata, trumpet & string orchestra, D. XI, 8, D major. Sonata D. XI, 8 in D, for trumpet, strings and basso continuo. *Musica rara. Unpriced* RXMPWSE (B79-50670)
Sonata, trumpet & string orchestra, D. XI, 8, D major. *arr.* Sonata D. XI, 8 in D for trumpet, strings and basso continuo. *Musica rara. Unpriced* WSPK/LE (B79-50803)
Sonata, trumpet, string quintet & continuo, D.XI.7, D major. Sonata D.XI.7 in D for trumpet, strings and basso continuo. *Musica rara. Unpriced* NUXSNPE (B79-50598)
Sonata, trumpet, string quintet & continuo, D.XI.7, D major. *arr.* Sonata D.XI.7 in D for trumpet, strings and basso continuo. *Musica rara. Unpriced* WSPK/AE (B79-50800)
Gaelic blessing. (Rutter, John). *Royal School of Church Music. Unpriced* DH (B79-50432)
Gagliano, Marco da.
Sacra cantiones, lib. 2. Magnificat. Magnificat. *Cathedral Music. Unpriced* EZDGKK (B79-50054)
Sacra cantiones, lib.2. Veni creator spiritus. Veni creator spiritus. *Cathedral Music. Unpriced* EZDJ/LN (B79-50087)
Gál, Hans.
Quintet, clarinet & string quartet, op.107. Quintet for clarinet and string quartet, op.107. *Simrock. Unpriced* NVVNR (B79-50190)
Quintet, clarinet & string quartet, op.107. Quintet for clarinet and string quartet, op.107. *Simrock. £5.20* NVVNR (B79-50191)
Quintet for 2 violins, 2 violas and violoncello, op.106. *Simrock. Unpriced* RXNR (B79-50264)
Quintet, violins (2), violas (2) & cello. Quintet for 2 violins, 2 violas and violoncello, op.106. *Simrock. Unpriced* RXNR (B79-50265)
Galliards and airs : fünf altenglische Lautenstucke nach Tabulaturen übertragen und für Gitarre bearbeitet von = five old English lute pieces. *Schott. £3.20* TSPMK/AYD (B79-50711)
Galway, James. The magic flute of James Galway. *Novello. Unpriced* VRPL/AAY (B79-50754)
Gambaccini, Paul. Critics' choice top 200 albums. *Omnibus Press; 78 Newman St., W1P 3LA : Distributed by Book Sales Limited.* Pbk. *£2.25* A/HKR/FD(WT) (B79-09962) ISBN 0-86001-494-0
Gamble, Peter William. Kemps music & recording industry year book international
1979. *Kemps.* Pbk. *£10.50* A/GB(YC/BC) (B79-22267) ISBN 0-905255-52-6
Gangi, Mario. Improvvisazione : per chitarra. (Ravinale, Irma). *Berben : Breitkopf und Härtel. £1.70* TSPMK (B79-50708)
Garcia, Gerald. More guitar pieces : folktunes and Elizabethan pieces. *Holley Music. Unpriced* TSPMK/AAY (B79-50310)
García Lorca, Federico. Sinfonia come un grade lamento (1977). Dem Andenken Frederico sic García Lorca. (Zimmermann, Ildo). *VEB Deutscher Verlag für Musik. £3.30* MME (B79-51015)
Gardiner, John. 'Big Al' : a new musical based on the life and times of the infamous Chicago gangster Al Capone. *6 Friday Furlong, Hitchin, Herts. SG5 2ND Gardiner-Parr Musicals.* Pbk. *£1.50* BPDRACM (B79-31928)
Garland reference library of the humanities. Woll, Allen L. Songs from Hollywood musical comedies, 1927 to the present : a dictionary. *Garland. £15.00* ACM/JR(WT) (B79-50406) ISBN 0-8240-9958-3
Garvin, Wilbert. The Irish bagpipes : their construction and maintenance. *Blackstaff Press for Na Píobairí Uileann.* Pbk. *£3.95* AVYR/BT (B79-17765) ISBN 0-85640-149-8
Gather your rosebuds. (Lawes, William). *Pro Cantione Antiqua : Breitkopf und Härtel. Unpriced* GEZDU (B79-50505)
Gavall, John.
L'estro armonico. Op.3. *Selections : arr.* Two concerto movements. (Vivaldi, Antonio). *Banks. Unpriced* TSNUK (B79-50302)
A ground in gamut. Z645. *arr.* A ground in gamut. (Purcell, Henry). *Banks. Unpriced* TSNUK (B79-50703)

Geddes, George Thomson. Foot tapping : the Shadows, 1958-1978. *102 Dorchester Ave., Glasgow G12 0EB : The author.* Sp. *£1.00* AKDW/GB/FD(P/WT) (B79-00884)
Geistliche Chormusik. Die mit Thränen säen. *arr.* Fantasia a 5. (Schütz, Heinrich). *Ricordi. Unpriced* VSNRK/DJ (B79-50338)
Gems of British social history series. Burns, Robert. The merry muses of Caledonia. The secret cabinet of Robert Burns : merry muses of Caledonia. New ed.. *P. Harris. £3.50* AKDW/K/G/KDX (B79-36915) ISBN 0-904505-84-7
Genesis *(Group).* Genesis lyrics. *Sidgwick and Jackson. £8.95 : CIP rev.* AKDW/HKR(P) (B79-14920) ISBN 0-283-98526-7
Gentleman's bottle companion. *P. Harris. £4.50 : CIP entry* AKDW/K/G/KDX (B79-00568) ISBN 0-904505-60-x
Gently the breeze blows : two-part. (Ross, Colin). *Banks. Unpriced* FDW (B79-50496)
Genzmer, Harald.
Lied des Vogelstellers : drei leichte Chorlieder No.1. *Schott. £0.72* EZDW (B79-50895)
Rechenstunde : drei leichte Chorlieder, für gemischten Chor No.3. *Schott. £0.72* EZDW (B79-50896)
Stadturlaub : drei leichte Chorlieder No.2. *Schott. £0.72* EZDW (B79-50897)
Geraedts, Jaap. Canzonetta for flute and piano (1947). *Donemus : Lengnick. Unpriced* VRPJ (B79-50748)
German-Slav church music.
Ammon, Blasius. Sacrae cantiones. Parvulus filius. Parvulus filius : for 6 voices. *72 Brewery Rd, N.7 : Mapa mundi. Unpriced* EZDJ/LF (B79-50074)
Ammon, Blasius. Sacrae cantiones. Tenebrae factae sunt. Tenebrae factae sunt : for 4 voices. *72 Brewery Rd, N.7 : Mapa mundi. Unpriced* EZDJ/LK (B79-50083)
Handl, Jacob. Secundus tomus musici operis. Ascendens Christus. Ascendens Christus : motet for the Ascension of our Lord, for 4 voices. *72 Brewery Rd, N.7 : Mapa mundi. Unpriced* EZDJ/LM (B79-50085)
Handl, Jacob. Tomus primus operis musici. Rorate coeli. Rorate coeli : motet for the Advent season, for 6 voices. *Mapa mundi. Unpriced* EZDJ/LEZ (B79-50072)
Gershwin, George.
Porgy and Bess. *Selections : arr.* Porgy and Bess. *Elm Tree Books : Chappell. Unpriced* KDW (B79-50131)
Porgy and Bess. Summertime. *arr.* Summertime : S.A.C.(T.) B. with piano. *Chappell. Unpriced* DW (B79-50849)
Gershwin, Ira. Porgy and Bess. *Selections : arr.* Porgy and Bess. (Gershwin, George). *Elm Tree Books : Chappell. Unpriced* KDW (B79-50131)
Gerster, Ottmar. Die Amsel : für Sopranstimme und Oboe. *Neue Musik : Breitkopf und Härtel. £1.20* KFLE/VTDW (B79-50551)
Gervaise, Claude. Danceries, liv.3. *Selections : arr.* Tanz-Suite ... für Blockflötenquartett (SATB ; ATTB) oder andere Melodieinstrumente (Violen oder Flöten), Schlagwerk ad lib. = Dance suite ... for recorder quartet (SATB ; ATTB) or other melodic instruments (viols or flutes), percussion instruments ad lib. *Schott. Unpriced* VSNSK/AH/AYH (B79-51236)
Getreue Music Meister. Duet, flute & viola pomposa. *arr.* Dueto in G-dur für Flote und Violine = Duet in G major for flute and violin. (Telemann, Georg Philipp). *Amadeus : Bärenreiter. £1.85* VRPLS (B79-50755)
Getreue Music Meister. *Selections.* 4 sonatas for treble recorder and basso continuo. (Telemann, Georg Philipp). *Musica rara. Unpriced* VSSPE (B79-50347)
Getreue Music Meister. Sonata, bassoon & continuo, F minor. Sonate in f-moll für Fagott oder Violoncello und Basso continuo = Sonata in F minor for bassoon or cello and basso continuo. (Telemann, Georg Philipp). *Amadeus : Schott. Unpriced* VWPE (B79-50363)
Getting closer and Baby's request. (McCartney, Paul). *MPL Communications. Unpriced* KDW/GB (B79-50967)
Getting to know you : for S.A. cambiata, B. or S.A.T.B. (Rodgers, Richard). *Williamson. Unpriced* DW (B79-50855)
Gibb, Barry. (Our love). Don't throw it all away. *arr.* (Our love). Don't throw it all away. *Stigwood Music. Unpriced* UMK/DW (B79-51203)
Gibbons, Orlando. Orlando Gibbons II : full anthems, hymns and fragmentary verse anthems. *Stainer and Bell. Unpriced* DK (B79-50026) ISBN 0-85249-517-x
Gifted children of music : the young lives of the great musicians. (Ingman, Nicholas). *Ward Lock. £3.95 : CIP rev.* A/D(M/C) (B78-27520) ISBN 0-7063-5721-3
Gigon, Olof. Consolatio philosophiae. *Vocal score.* Consolatio philosophiae : scène dramatique voix haute et orchestre in memoriam Ernest Ansermet (1977). (Sutermeister, Heinrich). *Schott. £10.80* KFTDX (B79-50155)

Gigue for piano solo. (Parke, Dorothy). *Banks. Unpriced* QPHP (B79-51074)
Gilardino, Angelo.
Escarraman : a suite of Spanish dances from the XVIth century (after Cervantes), op.177, for guitar. (Castelnuovo-Tedesco, Mario). *Bèrben : Breitkopf and Härtel. £4.70* TSPMHG (B79-51180)
The oceans of the moon : eight variations and a theme, op.75 : for guitar. (Blyton, Carey). *Bèrben : Breitkopf and Härtel. £2.85* TSPM/T (B79-51176)
Romance et plainte : for guitar. (Eastwood, Tom). *Bèrben : Breitkopf and Härtel. £2.35* TSPMJ (B79-51185)
Sonata, guitar, no.4, 'Italiana', 'Sonovidades 1977'. Sonata n.4 (Italiana), ! Sonoridades 1977! : para guitarra. (Santórsola, Güido). *Bèrben : Breitkopf and Härtel. £2.85* TSPME (B79-51177)
Gilbert, *Sir* William Schwenck.
The Mikado, or, The town of Titipu. *42 Bloomsbury St., W.C.1 : Godfrey Cave Associates. £5.50* BSWACF (B79-16839) ISBN 0-906223-05-9
The yeomen of the guard, or, The merryman and his maid. *42 Bloomsbury St., W.C.1 : Godfrey Cave Associates Ltd. £5.50* BSWACF (B79-16840) ISBN 0-906223-06-7
Gilbertson, Moyna. Music to help disabled children to move. (Kennard, Daphne). *A.P.C.P. Publications, 25 Goff's Park Rd, Southgate, Crawley, W. Sussex RH11 8AX : Association of Paediatric Chartered Physiotherapists.* Sd. *£0.50* A(VMX) (B79-13819)
Gillett, Charlie. Rock file
5. *Panther.* Pbk. *£1.25* ADW/GB (B79-03804) ISBN 0-586-04680-1
Gitarre
4. *Verlag Neue Musik : Breitkopf and Härtel. £2.10* TS/AY (B79-50699)
5. *Neue Musik : Breitkopf and Härtel. £2.10* TS/AY (B79-51168)
Gitarren - Archiv. Hindemith, Paul. Rondo, guitars (3). Rondo für zwei Gitarren, for two guitars. *Schott. £2.00* TSNUK/W (B79-50304)
Gitarren-Archiv.
Debussy, Claude. Danse bohémienne. *arr.* Danse bohémienne : für zwei Gitarren oder Oktavgitarre und Gitarre = for two guitars or octave guitar and guitar = pour deux guitares ou guitare octave et guitare. *Schott. £3.20* TSNUK/AH (B79-51175)
Dowland, John. Zwei Duette. *Schott. £2.20* TSNUK (B79-51171)
Mendelssohn, Felix. Lieder ohne Worte. *Selections : arr.* 5 Lieder ohne Worte : für zwei Gitarren = for two guitars. *Schott. £4.00* TSNUK (B79-51172)

Vogel, Vladimir. Musette. *arr.* Musette : für Gitarre solo = for guitar solo. *Schott.* *£2.00* TSPMK/AHS (B79-50311)
Weiss, Sylvius Leopold. Suite, lute, A major. *arr.* Suite in A. *Schott.* *£3.20* TSPMK/AG (B79-51194)
Weiss, Sylvius Leopold. Suite, lute, D major. *arr.* Suite in D. *Schott.* *£2.60* TSPMK/AG (B79-51195)
Gitarrenschule
Band 2. (Kreidler, Dieter). *Schott.* *£8.50* TS/AC (B79-51165)
Giuliani, Mauro. Rossiniana, no.1, op.119. Rossiniana no.1 : for solo guitar, op.119. *Faber Music.* *Unpriced* TSPMG (B79-50704)
Give thanks to the Lord : for three-part chorus of women's voices a cappella. (Staden, Johann). *Schirmer.* *£0.35* FEZDH (B79-50500)
Give your child music. (Phillips, Jill). *Elek.* *£5.95* A(VC) (B79-14614) ISBN 0-236-40145-9
Glasgow University. *See* University of Glasgow.
Glen, Robert. Out of this world. *Vocal score.* Out of this world : musical in two scenes. *Weinberger.* *Unpriced* CM (B79-50818)
Gloucester organ album. *Novello.* *£2.15* R/AY (B79-51118)

Glover, David Carr.
The three bears go on a picnic : a piano suite with narration. Revised ed. *Schroeder and Gunther.* *£1.35* QPG (B79-50626)
Three sonatinas and a sonata : for piano solo. *Schroeder and Gunther.* *£1.75* QPEM (B79-50625)
Glyn, Gareth. Triban : telyn = harp. *Adlais.* *Unpriced* TQPMJ (B79-50296)
Go go Gabriel : unison with optional descant. (Hudson, Hazel). *Ashdown.* *Unpriced* JFDP/LF (B79-50937)

Goehr, Alexander.
Metamorphosis : dance. *Schott.* *Unpriced* MMJ (B79-50176)
Psalm 4 : for soprano, alto, female chorus, viola solo, and organ. *Schott.* *£1.85* FE/SQPLRDR (B79-50914)
Goethe, Johann Wolfgang von. Franz Schubert Lieder : Urtext der Neuen Schubert-Ausgabe
Heft 3: Leider nach Texten von Goethe: Mittlere Stimme (Transposition). (Schubert, Franz). *Bärenreiter.* *£4.80* KDW (B79-50134)
Goffe, Toni. Wonder why book of XYZ of musical instruments. *Transworld.* Sd. *£0.75* AL/B (B79-16838) ISBN 0-552-57030-3
Golden bond : a spectacular revue. (Barrow, Kenneth). *2 Cromwell Place, SW7 2JG : National Union of Townswomen's Guilds.* Pbk. *£1.50* BAPACP (B79-27787)
Golden cockerel. *Suite.* Suite from the opera, 'The golden cockerel'. (Rimsky-Korsakoff, Nikolai). *Eulenburg.* *Unpriced* MMG (B79-51018)
Golden meadows = Goldne Fluren : for four-part chorus of mixed voices a cappella. (Dvořák, Antonín). *Schirmer.* *£0.35* EZDW (B79-50892)
Goldman, Maurice. Sleep, little Jesus, sleep : Spanish-American folk song for full chorus of mixed voices with soprano solo and piano. *Roberton.* *£0.20* DP/LF (B79-50446)
Gone to earth. *Selections: arr.* Music from two hit albums, Gone to earth and XII. (Barclay James Harvest). *Chappell.* *Unpriced* KDW/HKR (B79-50982)
Good morning, Jesus : twenty-four songs for children. (White, Estelle). *(55 Leigh Rd) : Kevin Mayhew.* *Unpriced* JFDW/GJ (B79-50940)
Good old songs : (Selection no.1). (Siebert, Edrich). *Studio Music.* *Unpriced* WMK (B79-50377)
Good old songs : selections no.2. (Siebert, Edrich). *Studio Music.* *Unpriced* WMK/DW (B79-50382)
Goodnight sweetheart : songs and memories of the Second World War. (Huggett, Frank Edward). *W.H. Allen.* *£5.95* ADW/GB(XNU7) (B79-37421) ISBN 0-491-02308-1
Goodnight to Flamboro' : the life and music of William Baines. (Carpenter, Roger). *22 Pheasants Way, Rickmansworth, Herts. : Triad Press.* Pbk. *£6.95 : CIP rev.* BBCN (B77-21345) ISBN 0-902070-22-3
Goodrum, Randy.
You needed me. *Chappell.* *Unpriced* UMK/DW (B79-51204)
You needed me. *arr.* You needed me : S.A.B. with piano and optional drums. *Chappell.* *Unpriced* DW/GBB (B79-50862)
You needed me. *arr.* You needed me : S.S.A. with piano and optional drums. *Chappell.* *Unpriced* FDW/GBB (B79-50912)
Gordon, Christopher.
Sonatina, oboe & clarinet. Sonatina for oboe and clarinet (or flute and clarinet). *Janus Music.* *Unpriced* VTPLVVEM (B79-50353)
Twelve oboe duets. *265 Magdalen Road, SW18 3NZ : Janus Music.* *Unpriced* VTNU (B79-50771)
Gordon, Gary. C. John Taylor's islands of beauty : ballad in English and Gaelic. (Taylor, Cecil John). *Isle of Seil, Oban, Argyll, Scotland : Highland Arts Studios.* *Unpriced* KDW (B79-50527)
Gordon H. Lamb conductors choral series. Beadell, Robert. I saw water flowing = Vidi aquam : anthem for Eastertide for four-part chorus of mixed voices a cappella. *Schirmer.* *Unpriced* EZDH/LL (B79-50881)
Gordon-Smith, Maria. Chopin. (Marek, George Richard). *Weidenfeld and Nicolson.* *£8.50* BCE(N) (B79-11134) ISBN 0-297-77616-9
Gorgon's head. (Withams, Eric). *Universal.* *Unpriced* CQN (B79-50824)
Gorman, Clem. Backstage rock : behind the scenes with the bands. *Pan Books.* Pbk. *£0.90* AKDW/HKR/E(P/YC) (B79-50007) ISBN 0-330-25583-5
Gostling, John. The Gostling manuscript. *University of Texas Press.* *£24.50* ADK(XEYK37) (B79-04542) ISBN 0-292-72713-5
Gostling manuscript. *University of Texas Press.* *£24.50* ADK(XEYK37) (B79-04542) ISBN 0-292-72713-5
Gothic symphony. Havergal Brian's 'Gothic symphony' : two studies. (Truscott, Harold). *33 Coopers Rd, Little Heath, Potters Bar, Herts. EN6 1JQ : Havergal Brian Society.* Pbk. *£6.95(£4.75 to members of the Havergal Brian Society)* BBTNADX (B79-10481) ISBN 0-9505185-1-4
Gottlieb, Jack. Leonard Bernstein : a complete catalogue of his works. *Amberson Enterprises : Distributed by Boosey and Hawkes.* Sd. *£2.50* BBMM(TC) (B79-06192) ISBN 0-913932-40-x
Gottlieb, Jay. Appello : for piano. (Kolb, Barbara). *Boosey and Hawkes.* *Unpriced* QPJ (B79-50218)
Gould, Morton.
American ballads : settings of familiar tunes ... for orchestra
1: Star-spangled overture (on 'The star-spangled banner'). *Schirmer.* *£6.10* MMJ (B79-50570)
2: Amber waves (on 'America the beautiful'). *Schirmer.* *£6.10* MMJ (B79-50571)
3: Jubilo (on 'Year of Jubilo'). *Schirmer.* *£6.10* MMJ (B79-50572)
4: Memorials (on 'Taps'). *Schirmer.* *£6.10* MMJ (B79-50573)
5: Saratoga quickstep (on 'The girl I left behind me'). *Schirmer.* *£6.10* MMJ (B79-50574)
6: Hymnal (on 'We shall overcome'). *Schirmer.* *£6.10* MMJ (B79-50575)
Elegy : for string orchestra. *Schirmer.* *Unpriced* RXMJ (B79-50665)
Gould, Murray Joseph. Paths to musical thought : an approach to ear singing through sight singing. *Holt, Rinehart and Winston.* *Unpriced* CB/EG (B79-50412) ISBN 0-03-020421-6
Gradualia, lib. 2. Alleluia, ascendit Deus. Alleluia, our Lord is risen : for mixed chorus SSATB. (Byrd, William). *Broude : Breitkopf und Härtel.* *£0.42* EZDJ/LM (B79-50470)
Graf von Luxemburg. *Selections: arr.* Der Graf von Luxemburg : Melodienfolge. (Lehár, Franz). Neue Ausgabe. *Glocken.* *Unpriced* UMK/DW (B79-50318)
'Gramophone' guide to classical composers and recordings. (Salter, Lionel). *Salamander Books.* *£6.95* A/D(M/FD) (B79-00562) ISBN 0-86101-025-6
Granados, Enrique. 2 Marchas militares, no.1. *arr.* Marcha militar no.1. *Leonard, Gould and Bolttler.* *£0.40* QPK/AGM (B79-50641)
Grandi, Alessandro. Il quatro libro de motetti. Plorabo die ac nocte. Plorabo die ac nocte. *36 Ranelagh Gdns W.6 : Cathedral Music.* *Unpriced* DJ (B79-50025)
Grannies to sell. Grannies to sell, and, Boating. (Fraser, Shena). *Roberton.* *£0.20* JFDW (B79-50518)
Grannies to sell, and, Boating. (Fraser, Shena). *Roberton.* *£0.20* JFDW (B79-50518)
Grantham, G P. Rejoice, then, Christ is born : Christmas song for mixed voices, optional a cappella S.A.T.B., Italian carol-tune (traditional). (Kingsbury, John). *Broude : Breitkopf und Härtel.* *£0.42* DP/LF (B79-50841)
Graupner, Christoph. Sonata in G major. *Schirmer.* *£9.10* VVNK/AE (B79-50781)
Graves, Richard. Sonata, violins (2), op.1, no.12, G major. Gigue. *arr.* Jig. (Humphries, J S). *Banks.* *Unpriced* VVPK/AHP (B79-50785)
Grease. *arr.* Grease : original soundtrack songs from the motion picture. (Casey, Warren). *Warner : Blossom.* *Unpriced* KDW/JR (B79-50143)
Grease. *arr.* Grease : original soundtrack songs from the motion picture. (Casey, Warren). *Chappell.* *Unpriced* KDW/JR (B79-50144)
Grease. *Selections : arr.* Grease : easy guitar, original sound track songs from the motion picture. *Chappell.* *Unpriced* TSPMK/DW/HKR/JR/AY (B79-50714)
Grease. *Selections : arr.* Grease : organ, original soundtrack songs from the motion picture. *Chappell.* *Unpriced* RK/DW/HKR/JR/AY (B79-50659)
Great composers : reviews and bombardments. (Shaw, Bernard). *University of California Press.* *£17.15* A (B79-00561) ISBN 0-520-03253-5
Great grandaad. The Erie Canal, and, Great grandad : American folk songs, for two-part chorus of equal voices and piano. (De Cormier, Robert). *Roberton.* *£0.28* FDW (B79-50494)
Great masters. Kendall, Alan, *b.1939.* Beethoven and his world. *Ward Lock.* *£2.95 : CIP rev.* BBJ(N) (B79-30252) ISBN 0-7063-5867-8
Great performer's edition. Mozart, Wolfgang Amadeus. Fantasia, clock-organ, K.608, F minor. *arr.* Fantasia in F minor for organ (mechanical clock-organ, K.608). *Schirmer.* *£3.65* RK/B/FK (B79-51128)
Greater London Council. *Inner London Education Authority.* *See* Inner London Education Authority.
Greaves, Terence. Comus. Dances. *arr.* Two dances from 'Comus'. (Arne, Thomas Augustine). *Banks.* *Unpriced* RK (B79-50653)
Green, Douglas Marshall. Form in tonal music : an introduction to analysis. 2nd ed. *Holt, Rinehart and Winston.* *£10.00* A/S (B79-24591) ISBN 0-03-020286-8
Greensleeves. (Cutting, Francis). *DeCamera : Schirmer.* *£1.50* TSPMK/T (B79-51198)
Greensleeves. *arr.* Greensleeves. (Cutting, Francis). *DeCamera : Schirmer.* *£1.50* TSPMK/T (B79-51198)
Greer, David. Hamilton Harty : his life and music. *Blackstaff Press.* *£7.50* A/EC(P) (B79-10480) ISBN 0-85640-131-5
Gregg Smith choral series. Gabrieli, Giovanni. Sacrae symphoniae, bk.2. O quam suavis. O quam suavis : for eight-part chorus of mixed voices with organ accompaniment. *Schirmer.* *£0.75* DGKJ/LNC (B79-50427)
Grieg, Edvard.
Sigurd Jorsalfar. Op.56. *Selections.* Three orchestral pieces from the incidental music to Sigurd Jorsalfar, op.56. *Eulenburg.* *Unpriced* MM/JM (B79-50165)
Two elegiac melodies. Op.34. *Eulenburg.* *Unpriced* MMJ (B79-50177)
Griffith, G Wynne. How far is it to Bethlehem? Pa mor bell yur Bethlehem? : unison voices and piano. (Hughes-Jones, Llifon). *Roberton.* *£0.20* JFDP/LF (B79-50517)
Griffiths, Ann. Transformations : for solo harp, op.141. (Rubbra, Edmund). *Lengnick.* *£1.00* TQPMJ (B79-50695)
Griffiths, Paul. Boulez. *Oxford University Press.* Pbk. *£3.50* BBRO (B79-18562) ISBN 0-19-315442-0
Grigg, Carolyn Doub. Music translation dictionary. *Greenwood Press.* *£16.95* A(QTF) (B79-36910) ISBN 0-313-20559-0
Grime, Kitty. Jazz at Ronnie Scott's. *Hale.* *£5.80* AMT(M) (B79-16103) ISBN 0-7091-6907-8
Grones dictionary of music, or, A golden treasury of musical rubbish, or, Misleading lives of the great composers. (Burnham, Howard). *Windmill Farm, Ampleforth, Yorkshire : Emerson Edition.* Pbk. *£2.95* A/D(M/YB) (B79-04539) ISBN 0-9506209-0-4
Groth, Klaus. Komm'bald. Op.97, no.5. *arr.* Come soon = Komm bald : for three-part chorus of women's voices with piano accompaniment. (Brahms, Johannes). *Schirmer.* *£0.35* FDW (B79-50492)
Ground in gamut. (Purcell, Henry). *Banks.* *Unpriced* TSNUK (B79-50703)
Ground in gamut. Z645. *arr.* A ground in gamut. (Purcell, Henry). *Banks.* *Unpriced* TSNUK (B79-50703)
Grubb, Thomas. Singing in French : a manual of French diction and French vocal repertoire. *Schirmer Books : Collier Macmillan.* Pbk. *£7.45* AB/EDD (B79-25332) ISBN 0-02-870790-7
Grüber, Franz Xaver. Stille Nacht, heilige Nacht. *arr.* Silent night. *36 Ranelagh Gdns W.6 : Cathedral Music.* *Unpriced* EZDP/LF (B79-50094)
Gruber, Heinz Karl. Phantom-Bilder auf der Spur eines verdächtingen Themas. Op.30 = Photo-fit pictures on the tracks of a suspect theme = für kleines Orchester = for small orchestra. *Boosey and Hawkes.* *Unpriced* MJ (B79-50564)
Gruber, Josef. ABC. Two at the piano : 50 duets for young pianists. *Faber Music.* *Unpriced* QNV (B79-50615)
Grundman, Clare. Norwegian rhapsody. *Boosey and Hawkes.* *Unpriced* UMMJ (B79-50722)
Guerrero, Francisco.
Missarum liber secundo. Missa de la batalla escoutez. Missa de la batalla escoutez : for 5 voices. *Mapa mundi.* *Unpriced* EZDG (B79-50049)
Motecta ... liber secundus. Pastores loquebantur. Pastores loquebantur. *72 Brewery Rd, N.7 : Mapa mundi.* *Unpriced* EZDJ/LF (B79-50076)
Motecta. Duo seraphim. Duo seraphim. *Mapa mundi.* *Unpriced* EZDJ (B79-50062)
Guet-apens. (Ange). *Chappell.* *Unpriced* KDW/HKR (B79-50981)
Guet-apens. *arr.* Guet-apens. (Ange). *Chappell.* *Unpriced* KDW/HKR (B79-50981)
Guinness book of British hit singles : (the Guinness book of records records). 2nd ed. *Guinness Superlatives.* *£5.25* AKDW/GB/FD(WT) (B79-22108) ISBN 0-900424-89-3
Guitar book. Denny Laine's guitar book. (Laine, Denny). *G. Whizzard : Deutsch.* *£4.95* ATS/E (B79-33558) ISBN 0-233-97101-7
Guitar masters of the century. Spanish masters : 19 original easy pieces. *Ricordi.* *Unpriced* TSPM/AYK (B79-50305)

Guitarcosmos 1 : progressive pieces for guitar. (Brindle, Reginald Smith). *Schott.* *£2.50* TSPMJ (B79-51181)
Guitarcosmos 2 : progressive pieces for guitar. (Brindle, Reginald Smith). *Schott.* *£2.50* TSPMJ (B79-51182)
Guitarcosmos 3 : Progressive pieces for guitar. (Brindle, Reginald Smith). *Schott.* *£2.50* TSPMJ (B79-51183)
Gunslinger. (Buckley, Joss). *Chappell.* *Unpriced* CM (B79-50820)
Gunslinger. *Vocal score.* Gunslinger. (Buckley, Joss). *Chappell.* *Unpriced* CM (B79-50820)
Günther, Dorothee. L'Orfeo. Vieni Imeneo. *arr.* Zwei Chöre aus 'Orpheus' = Two chorusses sic from 'Orpheus'. (Monteverdi, Claudio). *Schott.* *£0.80* EZDW (B79-50898)
Günzerodt, Werner. Jiddische Volkslieder : Liebeslieder, für Singstimme mit Klavier oder Gitarre. *Verlag Neue Musik : Breitkopf und Härtel.* *£3.60* KDW/G/AYEU (B79-50529)
Guralnick, Peter. Feel like going home : portraits in blues & rock'n'roll. *Omnibus Press.* Pbk. *£2.95* AKDW/HHW/E(M) (B79-10476) ISBN 0-86001-493-2
Guy, Barry. Quartet, strings, no.2. String quartet no.2. *Novello.* *£5.50* RXNS (B79-50266)
Gymnastics : piano pieces for beginners. (Last, Joan). *Boosey and Hawkes.* *Unpriced* QPJ (B79-51084)
Gypsy. Everything's coming up roses. *arr.* Everything's coming up roses : for S.A. cambiata, B. or S.A.T.B, with piano. (Styne, Jule). *Williamson.* *Unpriced* DW

(B79-50859)
Haan, Stefan de. Concerto, trumpet, E major. Concerto, E major, for trumpet and orchestra. (Hummel, Johann Nepomuk). *Eulenburg. Unpriced* MPWSF (B79-51032)
Hackforth, Norman. There will always be ... (Coward, *Sir* Noël). *Chappell. Unpriced* KDW (B79-50525)
Hálek, Vitězslav.
Amid nature. Op.63. Birch tree by the verdant slope. Birch tree on green hill = Birke am grünen Bergeshang : for four-part chorus of mixed voices a cappella. (Dvořák, Antonín). *Schirmer. £0.45* EZDW (B79-50891)
Amid nature. Op.63. This is in truth a day of joy. A summer day = Ein Sommertag : for four-part chorus of mixed voices a cappella. (Dvořák, Antonín). *Schirmer. £0.45* EZDW (B79-50893)
Halffter, Cristóbal.
Concerto, cello. Concierto para violoncello y orquesta. *Universal. Unpriced* MPSRF (B79-51030)
Officium defunctorum (1978). *Universal. Unpriced* EMDE (B79-50866)
Hall, Peter. The Scottish folksinger : 118 modern and traditional folksongs. New ed. *Collins. Unpriced* JE/TSDW/G/AYDL (B79-50119) ISBN 0-00-411125-7
Hallelujah amen ... : for four-part chorus of mixed voices a cappella. (Schubert, Franz). *Schirmer. £0.45* EZDH/LK (B79-50463)
Halstead, Anthony. Suite, horn. Suite for solo horn. *22 Woodcote Ave : Dunster Music. Unpriced* WTPMG (B79-51323)
Hamble, William R. Father of mercies : for chorus of unison voices with organ accompaniment. *Chappell. Unpriced* JDH (B79-50930)
Hambledon's cricket glory
Vol.6: The Hambledon cricket song. (Knight, Ronald David). 2nd (revised) ed. *40 Abbotsbury Rd, Weymouth, Dorset DT4 0AE : The author.* Pbk. *£0.50* BCMTADW (B79-29607) ISBN 0-903769-06-9
Hamel, Peter Michael. Through music to the self : how to appreciate and experience music anew. *Compton Press. £5.95* A/CC (B79-08926) ISBN 0-900193-53-0
Hamilton Harty : his life and music. *Blackstaff Press. £7.50* A/EC(P) (B79-10480) ISBN 0-85640-131-5
Hamlisch, Marvin. They're playing our song. *Selections : arr.* They're playing our song. *Chappell. Unpriced* KDW (B79-50956)
Hammar, Russell A. Singing - : an extension of speech. *Scarecrow Press : Distributed by Bailey and Swinfen. £6.75* AB/E (B79-17764) ISBN 0-8108-1182-0
Hammerstein, Oscar, *.1895.* Oklahoma!. Oh, what a beautiful mornin'. *arr.* Oh, what a beautiful mornin' : S.A.C.(T)B. with piano. (Rodgers, Richard). *Williamson Music. Unpriced* DW (B79-50856)
Hammerstein, Oscar, *b.1895.*
The King and I. Getting to know you. *arr.* Getting to know you : for S.A. cambiata, B. or S.A.T.B. (Rodgers, Richard). *Williamson. Unpriced* DW (B79-50855)
The sound of music. Climb ev'ry mountain. *arr.* Climb ev'ry mountain : for S.A. cambiata, B. or S.A.T.B. with piano. (Rodgers, Richard). *Williamson Music. Unpriced* DW (B79-50857)
State fair. Its a grand night for singing. *arr.* Its a grand night for singing : S.A.C.(T).B, with piano. (Rodgers, Richard). *Williamson. Unpriced* DW (B79-50858)
Hammond, David. Songs of Belfast. *25 Shenick Rd, Skerries : Gilbert Dalton. Unpriced* JEZDW/G/AYDTB (B79-50124)
Hand, Colin.
John Taverner : his life and music. *48 Great Marlborough St., W1V 2BN : Eulenberg Books.* Pbk. *£2.00* BTCE (B79-06702) ISBN 0-903873-52-4
Sonatina, guitar, no.2. 'Allotropes'. Sonatina no.2 (Allotropes) for guitar. *Schott. £0.80* TSPME (B79-50306)
Handbook and register of members
1978-79. (Incorporated Society of Musicians). *10 Stratford Place, W1N 9AE : The Society.* Pbk. *£7.00* A(YC/Q/MM) (B79-17756)
Handbook to 'The church hymnary'. 3rd ed. *Oxford University Press. £3.50* ADM/LSF (B79-31512) ISBN 0-19-146811-8
Handel, George Frideric.
Almira. *Selections : arr.* Dances from 'Almira'. *Banks Music. Unpriced* QPK/AH (B79-50221)
The complete sonatas for treble (alto) recorder and basso continuo = Die gesamten Sonaten für Altblockflöte und basso continuo. *Faber Music. Unpriced* VSSPE/AZ (B79-51253)
Dixit Dominus. *Vocal score.* Dixit Dominus : Psalm 110, for two sopranos, alto, tenor and bass soli, SSATB, strings and continuo. *Novello. £2.25* DR (B79-50448)
Handel's greatest hits : all organ. *Chappell. Unpriced* RK (B79-50654)
Let God arise. *Vocal score.* Let God arise : anthem for soprano and tenor soli, SATB and orchestra. *Novello. £1.65* DK (B79-50027)
Sonatas, oboe & continuo. The three authentic sonatas : oboe & basso continuo in F, opus 1, no.5, B flat, 'Fitzwilliam', C minor, opus 1, no.8. *Nova Music. Unpriced* VTPE (B79-51259)
Suite, harpsichord, C.B. 60, no.19, G minor. Suite in A minor. *Oxford University Press. Unpriced* TSNUK/AG (B79-50303) ISBN 0-19-356997-3
Suite, harpsichord, no.6 (1st collection), F sharp minor. Suite no.6, F sharp minor. *Peters. Unpriced* QRPG (B79-50645)
Handel's greatest hits : all organ. (Handel, George Frideric). *Chappell. Unpriced* RK (B79-50654)
Handl, Jacob.
Secundus tomus musici operis. Ascendens Christus. Ascendens Christus : motet for the Ascension of our Lord, for 4 voices. *72 Brewery Rd, N.7 : Mapa mundi. Unpriced* EZDJ/LM (B79-50085)
Tomus primus operis musici. Rorate coeli. Rorate coeli : motet for the Advent season, for 6 voices. *Mapa mundi. Unpriced* EZDJ/LEZ (B79-50072)
Hands across the water. Wings tour USA. (Powell, Aubrey). *High St., Limpsfield, Surrey RH8 0DY : Paper Tiger.* Pbk. *£3.25* AKDW/GB/E(P/EM/XRF) (B79-05872) ISBN 0-905895-10-x
Happy Christmas : accordion. *EMI. Unpriced* RSPMK/DP/LF/AY (B79-51135)
Happy Christmas : B flat clarinet. *EMI. Unpriced* VVPMK/DP/LF/AY (B79-50360)
Happy Christmas : B flat trumpet. *EMI. Unpriced* WSPMK/DP/LF/AY (B79-50399)
Happy Christmas : chord organ. *EMI. Unpriced* RPVCK/DP/LF/AY (B79-50248)
Happy Christmas : easy piano or organ. *EMI. Unpriced* QPK/DP/LF/AY (B79-50224)
Harding, James, *b.1929.*
Folies de Paris : the rise and fall of French operetta. *Chappell : Elm Tree Books. £7.95* ACF(YH) (B79-19445) ISBN 0-903443-28-7
My friends and myself : conversations with Francis Poulenc. (Audel, Stéphane). *Dobson. £4.95* BPO (B78-39780) ISBN 0-234-77251-4
Harding, Rosamond Evelyn Mary. The piano-forte : its history traced to the Great Exhibition of 1851. 2nd ed. *Unwin Brothers Ltd, The Gresham Press, Old Woking, Surrey : Gresham Books. £11.50* AQ/B(XFWK122) (B79-14922) ISBN 0-905418-31-x
Harfleur song : for saxophone quartet. (Harvey, Paul). *Novello. £0.80* VUNS (B79-51266)
Harmonia artificiosa Partia, violas d'amore (2) & continuo, no.7 C minor. *Viola d'amore parts.* Harmonia artificiosa, partita no. VIII in fact, 7 : for two violas d'amore and cello, with optional organ or harpsichord. (Biber, Heinrich). *(Little Margaret, Penmans Green, Chipperfield) : E.L. White. Unpriced* SQQ (B79-50688)
Harmony : a textbook for class use on aural foundations. (Warburton, Annie Osborne). New ed. *Longman.* Pbk. *£1.95* A/R (B79-35972) ISBN 0-582-33071-8
Harnick, Sheldon. Die lustige Witwe. *Selections : arr.* Songs from The merry widow (Die lustige Witwe). (Lehár, Franz). *Glocken. Unpriced* KDW (B79-50957)
Harold E. Cook collection of musical instruments. (Bucknell University. *Music Department*). *Bucknell University Press : Associated University Press. £5.75* AL(YTGLB/WJ) (B79-02987) ISBN 0-8387-1574-5
Harper, Don. Songs for Alice : Alice in Wonderland and Through the looking glass. *Adam & Charles Black. Unpriced* JFDW (B79-50127) ISBN 0-7136-1879-5
Harper, Jeanne. Sound of living waters. Combined Sound of living waters - Fresh sounds. *Hodder and Stoughton. £6.95* DM/AY (B79-50029) ISBN 0-340-23262-5
Harper, John.
Atarah's bandkit
Strand D1: With a friend or two : eight duets for flute and classical guitar, with companion cassette. (Ben-Tovim, Atarah). *Novello. £7.00* VRPLTSK/AAY (B79-50758)
The elastic band. *Novello. Score, £5.00, Parts, Unpriced* LNK/AAY (B79-50160)
Harrison, George. *See* Beatles, The.
Harrison, Max. Modern jazz, the essential records : a critical selection. *Aquarius Books : Distributed by Argus Books.* Pbk. *£2.90* AMT/FD(XPE26) (B79-15562)
Harrop, Beatrice. Someone's singing, Lord. Melody part. Someone's singing, Lord : hymns and songs for children. *A & C Black. Unpriced* JFADM/AY (B79-50125) ISBN 0-7136-1847-7
Harry, Bill. 'Mersey beat', the beginnings of the Beatles. *Omnibus Press; 78 Newman St., W1P 3LA : Distributed by Book Sales Limited.* Pbk. *£2.95* AKDW/GB/E(P) (B79-36913) ISBN 0-86001-415-0
Harte, Frank. Songs of Dublin. *25 Shenick Rd. Skerries : Gilbert Dalton. Unpriced* JEZDW/G/AYDN (B79-50122)
Hartley, Richard. Penmarric : from the BBC classic serial. *EMI. Unpriced* QPK/JS (B79-51107)
Harvest jazz : a cantata for schools. (Cartwright, Kenneth). *Boosey and Hawkes. Unpriced* FDE/LP (B79-50489)
Harvey, Jonathan.
Inner light (1) : for seven players and tape. *Novello. £5.00* NYDPNP/FG (B79-50607)
Inner light (2) : for SSATB soli, instrumental ensemble and tape ... *Faber Music. Unpriced* JNBE/MRDW/FT (B79-50949)
Harvey, Paul.
Clarinet à la carte : a menu for unaccompanied clarinet. *Ricordi. Unpriced* VVPMJ (B79-51289)
The Harfleur song : for saxophone quartet. *Novello. £0.80* VUNS (B79-51266)
Pets : a suite of 8 pieces for unaccompanied clarinet. *Ricordi. Unpriced* VVPMG (B79-51286)
Saxophone solos : B flat tenor with piano accompaniment
Vol.1. *Chester Music. Unpriced* VUTPK/AAY (B79-51269)
Vol.2. *Chester Music. Unpriced* VUTPK/AAY (B79-51270)
Saxophone solos : E flat alto with piano accompaniment
Vol.1. *Chester Music. Unpriced* VUSPK/AAY (B79-50354)
Vol.2. *Chester Music. Unpriced* VUSPK/AAY (B79-50355)
Haskins, James. Scott Joplin. *Robson Books. £4.50 : CIP entry* BJRP(N) (B78-38608) ISBN 0-86051-058-1
Hassan : the incidental music to the play by James Elroy Flecker. (Delius, Frederick). *Boosey and Hawkes. Unpriced* EM/JM (B79-50040)
Haus, Karl. Fröhliche Weihnacht : Weihnachtslieder aus aller Welt. *Schott. £2.40* JE/TSDP/LF/AY (B79-50118)
Hauss-Musik, Tl.3. Danket dem Herren. *arr.* Give thanks to the Lord : for three-part chorus of women's voices a cappella. (Staden, Johann). *Schirmer. £0.35* FEZDH (B79-50500)
Hava nagila : Israeli folk song. (Davies, Bryan). *Roberton. £0.32* GDW (B79-50920)
Havergal Brian Society. Havergal Brian's 'Gothic symphony' : two studies. (Truscott, Harold). *33 Coopers Rd, Little Heath, Potters Bar, Herts. EN6 1JQ : Havergal Brian Society.* Pbk. *£6.95(£4.75 to members of the Havergal Brian Society)* BBTNADX (B79-10481) ISBN 0-9505185-1-4
Havergal Brian's 'Gothic symphony' : two studies. (Truscott, Harold). *33 Coopers Rd, Little Heath, Potters Bar, Herts. EN6 1JQ : Havergal Brian Society.* Pbk. *£6.95(£4.75 to members of the Havergal Brian Society)* BBTNADX (B79-10481) ISBN 0-9505185-1-4
Haverkampf, Ulrich. Brandenburg concerto, flutes (2), violin & string orchestra, no.4, BWV1049, G major. *arr.* Brandenburgisches Konzert Nr.4, G-dur : für 2 Blockflöten (Flöten), Violine, Streicher und Continuo, BWV1049. (Bach, Johann Sebastian). *Breitkopf und Härtel. £8.40* NUSNSK/LF (B79-51040)
Hawkes pocket scores.
Binkerd, Gordon. Trio, string instruments. Trio for strings. *Boosey and Hawkes. Unpriced* RXNT (B79-50677)
Del Tredici, David. Vintage Alice : fantascene on a mad tea-party. *Boosey and Hawkes. Unpriced* KFLE/MDX (B79-51000)
Delius, Frederick. Hassan : the incidental music to the play by James Elroy Flecker. *Boosey and Hawkes. Unpriced* EM/JM (B79-50040)
Holloway, Robin. The rivers of hell. Opus 34 : concertante for seven players. *Boosey and Hawkes. Unpriced* NYDPNPF (B79-51048)
Holloway, Robin. Scenes from Schumann : seven paraphrases for orchestra, opus 13,. *Boosey and Hawkes. Unpriced* MMJ (B79-50178)
Prokofiev, Sergei. Love of three oranges. L'amour des trois oranges. Opus 33 : opéra en 4 actes et 10 tableaux avec un prologue d'après Carlo Gozzi. *Boosey and Hawkes. Unpriced* CQC (B79-50822)
Prokofiev, Sergei. The prodigal son. L'enfant prodigue. Opus 46 : ballet in three scenes by Boris Kochno. 1st ed. *Boosey and Hawkes. Unpriced* MM/HM (B79-50164)
Schwertsik, Kurt. Concerto, violin, op.31. Violinkonzert opus 31 : Romanzen im Schwarztiten-Ton und in der geblümtem Paradies-Weis. *Boosey and Hawkes. Unpriced* MPSF (B79-50582)
Hawkes school series.
Gruber, Heinz Karl. Phantom-Bilder auf der Spur eines verdächtingen Themas. Op.30 = Photo-fit pictures on the tracks of a suspect theme = für kleines Orchester = for small orchestra. *Boosey and Hawkes. Unpriced* MJ (B79-50564)
Khachaturian, Aram. Spartak. Adagio of Spartacus and Phrygia. *arr.* Adagio. *Boosey and Hawkes. Unpriced* MK/HM (B79-50567)
Khachaturian, Aram. Spartak. Adagio of Spartacus and Phrygia. *arr.* Adagio. *Boosey and Hawkes. Unpriced* MK/HM (B79-50568)
Tull, Fisher. Concertino, oboe & string orchestra. Concertino for oboe and strings. *Boosey and Hawkes. Unpriced* RXMPVTFL (B79-51141)
Hayden, Andrew J. British hymn writers and composers : a check-list, giving their dates & places of birth & death 1st ed. reprinted. *c/o Addington Palace, Croydon CR9 5AD : Hymn Society of Great Britain and Ireland.* Pbk. *£3.00* ADM/D(M/WT) (B79-15556)
Haydn, Joseph.
Divertimento for violin, viola d'amore and gamba. *(Little Margaret, Penmans Green, Chipperfield) : E.L. White. Unpriced* RXNTK (B79-50678)
Sechs englische Psalmen. Hob. XXIII Anhang, Nachtrag. Sechs Psalmen = Six psalms : für dreistimmigen gemischten Chor = for three-part mixed chorus, Hob. XXIII Anhang, Nachtrag. *Bärenreiter. £2.31* EZDR (B79-50471)
Headliners
1. *Chappell. Unpriced* KDW/GB/AY (B79-50971)
2. *Chappell. Unpriced* KDW/GB/AY (B79-50972)
3. *Chappell. Unpriced* KDW/GB/AY (B79-50973)
5. *Chappell. Unpriced* KDW/GB/AY (B79-50974)
6. *Chappell. Unpriced* KDW/GB/AY (B79-50975)
Healy, James N. Comic songs of Ireland. *Mercier Press. Unpriced* JE/TSDW/AYDM (B79-50510) ISBN 0-85342-529-9
Hear us, O hear us, Lord : anthem for S.A.T.B. and organ. (Hoiby, Lee). *Broude : Breitkopf und Härtel. £0.55* DH (B79-50431)
Hearn, Lafcadio. A Creole mystery. *Vocal score.* A Creole mystery : a short story for medium voice and string quartet. (Beeson, Jack). *Boosey and Hawkes. Unpriced* KFVDX (B79-50560)
Hebden, John. Sonata, flute & continuo, no.1, D major. Sonata 1 in D major for flute and basso continuo. *Oxford University Press. Unpriced* VRPE (B79-51221) ISBN 0-19-357021-1
Hedges, Anthony.

Five concert pieces : for young pianists. *Universal. Unpriced* QPJ (B79-51081)
Mary's carol. *Universal. Unpriced* EZDP/LF (B79-50886)

Helen comes home, or, Achilles the heel. (Taylor, Jeremy James). *French. £1.50 : CIP entry* BNEACN (B79-17762) ISBN 0-573-15004-4
Hellyer, Roger.
Serenade, wind sextet, no.11, K.375, E flat major. Serenade in E flat. K.375, original version : for two clarinets, two horns, and two bassoons. (Mozart, Wolfgang Amadeus). *Oxford University Press. Unpriced* UNQ (B79-51209) ISBN 0-19-357939-1
Serenade, wind sextet, no.11, K.375, E flat major. *Original version.* Serenade in E flat. K.375. Original version : for two clarinets, two horns and two bassoons. (Mozart, Wolfgang Amadeus). *Oxford University Press. Unpriced* UNQ (B79-51210) ISBN 0-19-357940-5
Helyer, Marjorie.
Awayday : a holiday album of ten pieces for young pianists. *Novello. Unpriced* QPJ (B79-50215)
Polka dot : ten characteristic pieces for piano, grade 2. *Novello. £0.91* QPJ (B79-50216)
Hendrie, Gerald. Introduction to music. *Open University Press.* Pbk. *Unpriced* A (B79-16836) ISBN 0-335-05414-5
Henneberg, Claus H. Lear : Oper in zwei Teilen nach William Shakespeare eingerichtet von Claus H. Henneberg (1976/1978). (Reimann, Aribert). *Schott. Unpriced* CQC (B79-50823)
Hennessey, Mike. Some of my best friends are blues. (Scott, Ronnie). *W.H. Allen. £3.50* AMT(P) (B79-28900) ISBN 0-491-02239-5
Henze, Hans Werner.
Aria de la folía española : für Orchester = for orchestra : (1977). *Schott. £19.60* MMJ (B79-50576)
Sonatina, trumpet. Sonatina for solo trumpet. *22 Woodcote Ave. : Dunster Music. Unpriced* WSPMEM (B79-51319)

Herbert, David. The operas of Benjamin Britten : the complete librettos illustrated with designs of the first productions. *H. Hamilton. £30.00* BBUAC (B79-34989) ISBN 0-241-10256-1
Herbert, George. Let all the world in every corner sing. (Ives, Grayston). *Novello. £0.61* DH (B79-50024)
Here we come as in the beginning. (Nelson, Ron). *Boosey and Hawkes. Unpriced* EZDH (B79-50877)
Herfurth, C Paul. Violin fancies. *Chappell. Unpriced* SPK/AAY (B79-51152)
Herod and the rooster : a legend for all seasons, a dramatic cantata. (Chamberlain, Ronald). *(125 Waxwell Lane) : The Grail. Unpriced* DE/LF (B79-50827) ISBN 0-901829-51-x
Herrick, Robert. A thanksgiving to God, for his house. (Argento, Dominick). *Boosey and Hawkes. Unpriced* EZDH (B79-50875)
Hertel, Peter Ludwig. Flick und Flock's Abenteuer. Feuerwehr Galopp. *arr.* The firemen's galop. *Harmer Music : Studio Music. Unpriced* WMK/AHLF (B79-50378)
Hess, Reimund. Dampflok-Story : ein Kinder - Musical : für Sprecher, 1-3 stg. Kinderchor und Begleitinstrumente auf Text von James Krüss. *Schott. £10.00* CQN (B79-50418)

Hess, Robert. L'Orfeo. Vieni Imeneo. *arr.* Zwei Chöre aus 'Orpheus' = Two chorusses sic from 'Orpheus'. (Monteverdi, Claudio). *Schott. £0.80* EZDW (B79-50898)
Hess, Willy.
Kleine Cammermusic. Die kleine Kammermusik : sechs Partiten für Blockflöte, Querflöte, Oboe oder Violine und Basso continuo = six partitas for recorder, flute, oboe or violin and basso continuo. (Telemann, Georg Philipp). *Amadeus : Eulenburg. £4.70* VSPG (B79-50764)
Quintet, contrabassoon & string quartet, op.63. Quintet für Kontrafagott oder Fagott und Streichquartett op.63. *Amadeus : Schott. Unpriced* VWPK (B79-50364)

Sonata, recorder, violin & continuo, F major. 26 Triosonate in F-dur für Altblockflöte (Querflöte), Violine (Querflöte, Oboe) und Basso continuo. Sonata a tre in F major for treble recorder (flute), violin (flute, oboe) and basso continuo. (Telemann, Georg Philipp). *Amadeus Breitkopf and Härtel. £2.80* NUSNTE (B79-51041)
Hexad : for six players. (Sohal, Naresh). *Novello. £2.25* NYENQ (B79-51049)
Heyward, Du Bose. Porgy and Bess. Summertime. *arr.* Summertime : S.A.C.(T.) B. with piano. (Gershwin, George). *Chappell. Unpriced* DW (B79-50849)
Heyward, Dubose. Porgy and Bess. *Selections : arr.* Porgy and Bess. (Gershwin, George). *Elm Tree Books : Chappell. Unpriced* KDW (B79-50131)

Hieremiae prophetae lamentationes, et alia piae cantiones. *Selections.* Lamentations for Tenebrae on Maundy Thursday, Feria V in Coena Domini ad Matatinum. (Lasso, Orlando di). *72 Brewery Rd, N.7 : Mapa Mundi. Unpriced* EZDJ/LHM (B79-50081)
Hieremiae prophetae lamentationes, et alia piae cantiones. *Selections.* Six responsories for Tenebrae on Maundy Thursday, feria V in Coena Domini ad Matatinum. (Lasso, Orlando di). *72 Brewery Rd, N.7 : Mapa mundi. Unpriced* EZDJ/LHM (B79-50082)
Higham, David. A plainsong mass book. *Catholic Truth Society. Unpriced* JEZDG/AY (B79-50512)
Hill, Jackson. The Harold E. Cook collection of musical instruments. (Bucknell University. *Music Department*). *Bucknell University Press : Associated University Press. £5.75* AL(YTGLB/WJ) (B79-02987) ISBN 0-8387-1574-5
Hilling, Lyndon. First book of bassoon solos. *Faber Music. Unpriced* VWP/AY (B79-50787)
Hilmar, Ernst.
Verzeichnis der Schubert-Handschriften in der Musiksammlung der Wiener Stadt- und Landesbibliothek. (Wiener Stadt- und Landesbibliothek). *17 Bucklersbury, Hutchin, Herts. SG5 1BB : Bärenreiter for the International Association of Music Libraries and the International Musicological Society.* Pbk. *£28.05* BMS(TC) (B79-10755)
Verzeichnis der Schubert-Handschriften in der Musiksammlung der Wiener Stadt- und Landesbibliothek. (Wiener Stadt- und Landesbibliothek). *17 Bucklersbury, Hutchin, Herts. SG5 1BB : Bärenreiter for the International Association of Music Libraries and the International Musicological Society.* Pbk. *£28.05* BSF(TE) (B79-10755)
Hindemith, Paul. Rondo, guitars (3). Rondo für zwei Gitarren, for two guitars. *Schott. £2.00* TSNUK/W (B79-50304)
Hindmarsh, Paul. Oration : (concerto elegiaco) for solo cello and orchestra. (Bridge, Frank). *Faber Music. Unpriced* MPSRF (B79-50584)
Hines, Robert S.
Ear training and sight-singing : an integrated approach Book 1. (Trubitt, Allen R). *Schirmer Books : Collier Macmillan.* Pbk. *£8.25* A/EF (B79-25327) ISBN 0-02-870810-5
Mutter, o sing 'mich zur Ruh', op.10, no.3. *arr.* Mother, O sing me to sleep = Mutter, O sing mich zur ruh' : for three-part chorus of female voices and piano. (Franz, Robert). *Roberton. £0.24* FDW (B79-50910)
Singer's manual of Latin diction and phonetics. *Schirmer Books : Collier Macmillan. £6.75* ADFF/EDD (B79-08691) ISBN 0-02-870800-8
Hinson, Maurice. The piano in chamber ensemble. *Harvester Press. £10.50 : CIP entry* ALP(WT) (B78-23117) ISBN 0-85527-634-7
Historical Association. *Bristol Branch.* Local history pamphlets. Barker, Kathleen. Early music hall in Bristol. *74 Bell Barn Rd, Stoke Bishop, Bristol BS9 2DG : Historical Association, Bristol Branch.* Sd. *£0.60* A/JV(YDHDB) (B79-23405)
History of the Emanuel Moór double keyboard piano. (Shead, Herbert A). *Emanuel Moór Double Keyboard Piano Trust; The Gresham Press, Old Woking, Surrey GU22 9LH : Distributed by Unwin Brothers Ltd.* Pbk. *£15.00* AQ/BC(P) (B79-08930) ISBN 0-9506023-0-2
Hitchcock, Gordon. Carols in consort : Christmas music for two descant, treble, tenor and optional bass recorders. *EMI. Unpriced* VSNSK/DP/LF/AY (B79-50339)
Hits in vision
No.2: 10 top TV themes. *Chappell. Unpriced* QPK/JS/AY (B79-51109)
No.3: 10 top T.V. themes. *Chappell. Unpriced* QPK/JS/AY (B79-51108)
Hoch, Peter. Ensemble/séparé : fur 1-4 Instrumentalspieler = for 1 to 4 players. *Schott. £6.00* LN (B79-50563)
Hoddinott, Alun.
Ancestor worship : four poems of Emyr Humphreys, for baritone and piano. *Oxford University Press. Unpriced* KGNDW (B79-51009) ISBN 0-19-345433-5
A contemplation upon flowers. Op.90. *Vocal score.* A contemplation upon flowers : 3 songs for soprano and orchestra. *Oxford University Press. Unpriced* KFLDW (B79-50998) ISBN 0-19-346719-4
Landscapes, Op.86 : for orchestra. *Oxford University Press. Unpriced* MMJ (B79-50577) ISBN 0-19-364492-4
The magician. Op.88. *Vocal score.* The magician : an opera in one act. *Oxford University Press. Unpriced* CC (B79-50011) ISBN 0-19-336839-0
Hodie Christas natus est. (Marenzio, Luca). *72 Brewery Rd, N.7 : Mapa mundi. Unpiced* EZDJ/LF (B79-50073)
Hodie Christus natus est. (Law, Ronald). *36 Ranelagh Gdns W.6 : Cathedral Music. Unpriced* EZDJ/LF (B79-50077)
Hodkinson, Sydney. Two fanfares for a festival : for brass, timpani, and percussion. *Associated Music. £7.25* WMGN (B79-50791)
Hofbauer, Alfred.
Der Graf von Luxemburg. *Selections: arr.* Der Graf von Luxemburg : Melodienfolge. (Lehár, Franz). Neue Ausgabe. *Glocken. Unpriced* UMK/DW (B79-50318)
Zigeunerliebe. *Selections: arr.* Zigeunerliebe : Melodienfolge. (Lehár, Franz). Neue Ausgabe. *Glocken. Unpriced* UMK/DW (B79-50319)
Hofbauer, Kurt. Praxis der chorischen Stimmbildung. *Schott.* Pbk. *£6.00* AD/E (B79-11133)
Hoffman-Erbrecht, Lothar.
Sonaten für Klavier zu zwei Händen
Band 1. (Beethoven, Ludwig van). *Litolff : Peters. Unpriced* QPE/AZ (B79-50623)
Band 2. (Beethoven, Ludwig van). *Litolff : Peters. Unpriced* QPE/AZ (B79-50624)
Hoffmann, Wolfram.
Blockflöte : Altblockflöte und Klavier, herausgegeben von Wolfram Hoffmann
1. *Neue Musik : Breitkopf und Härtel. £2.10* VRP/AY (B79-50745)
Blockflöte
2: Altblockflöte und Klavier. *Neue Musik : Breitkopf and Härtel. Unpriced* VS/AY (B79-51233)
Hoffmeister, Franz Anton. Prélude ou exercise pour la flûte seule, op.35, nach dem Erstdruck ... *Amadeus : Schott. Unpriced* VRPMJ (B79-50336)
Hogwood, Christopher. The trio sonata. *British Broadcasting Corporation.* Pbk. *£2.50* ANXNSE (B79-33556) ISBN 0-563-17095-6
Hoiby, Lee. Hear us, O hear us, Lord : anthem for S.A.T.B. and organ. *Broude : Breitkopf und Härtel. £0.55* DH (B79-50431)
Hold, Trevor. The walled-in garden : a study of the songs of Roger Quilter (1877-1953). *22 Pheasants Way, Rickmansworth, Herts. : Triad Press.* Pbk. *£4.95* BQI(N) (B79-05249)
Hölderlin, Johann Christian Friedrich. Schicksalslied = Song of destiny. Op.54. (Brahms, Johannes). *Eulenberg. Unpriced* EMDX (B79-50867)
Holiday memories : for elementary string trio (2 violins and cello). (Standford, Patric). *7 Garrick St., W.C.2 : Middle Eight Music. Unpriced* RXNT (B79-50271)
Holliger, Heinz.
Atembogen : für Orchester. *Schott. £18.00* MMJ (B79-51023)
Quartet, strings, (1973). Streichquartett = String quartet : 1973. *Schott. £39.20* RXNS (B79-50673)
Hollingsworth, Louis.
Arabesque, no.1. Ist arabesque : for organ and piano. (Debussy, Claude). *Columns Music : Schirmer (dist.). £1.95* QPLRK (B79-51111)
Uns ist ein Kind geboren. BWV142. Overture. *arr.* Overture to cantata 'For us a Child is born' (Uns ist ein Kind geborn sic) : for organ and piano. (Bach, Johann Sebastian). *Sycamore : Schirmer (dist.). £1.50* QPLRK (B79-51110)

Holloway, Laurie. Pop preludes for piano : easy music in pop style. *Novello. £1.15* QPJ (B79-50631)
Holloway, Robin.
Debussy and Wagner. *48 Great Marlborough St., W1V 2BN : Ernst Eulenburg Ltd. £5.50* BDJ(Z) (B79-35970) ISBN 0-903873-25-7
The rivers of hell. Opus 34 : concertante for seven players. *Boosey and Hawkes. Unpriced* NYDPNPF (B79-51048)
Scenes from Schumann : seven paraphrases for orchestra, opus 13,. *Boosey and Hawkes. Unpriced* MMJ (B79-50178)
Holman, Peter. Sonata, oboes (2) & continuo, B flat major. Sonata in B flat for 2 oboes/violins (or recorders in C) and basso continuo. (Finger, Gottfried). *Nova Music. Unpriced* VTNTPWE (B79-51256)
Holst, Gustav.
The planets. Op.32. *arr.* The planets. *Curwen Edition. Unpriced* QNUK/AG (B79-51062)
The planets : suite for large orchestra. Op.32. *Curwen. Unpriced* MMG (B79-51017)
Songs from 'The princess' : for unaccompanied equal voices (SSA-SSSAA). *Novello. £1.15* FEZDW (B79-50918)
Songs of land, sea and air : a collection of part songs and canons for equal voices with piano accompaniment. *Novello. Unpriced* FDW (B79-50104)
Holst, Imogen. The planets : suite for large orchestra. Op.32. (Holst, Gustav). *Curwen. Unpriced* MMG (B79-51017)

Holstein, Jean Paul. Rêves éveillés. Rêves éveillés et Rêves endormis : pour piano. *Chappell. Unpriced* QPJ (B79-51082)
Holy Boy. *Vocal score.* Holy Boy : a folk oratorio. (Palmer, David). *EMI. Unpriced* DE/LF (B79-50829) ISBN 0-86175-078-0
Holy communion, series 3 ... (Osborne, Hayward). *Weinberger. Unpriced* JDGS (B79-50117)
Home recording for musicians. (Anderton, Craig). *Guitar Player Books; 25 East St., Farnham, Surrey : Distributed by Omnibus Book Service.* Pbk. *£7.95* A/FG (B79-12532) ISBN 0-89122-019-4
Hook, James. Eight songs : for high voice. *Stainer and Bell. Unpriced* KFTDW (B79-50555) ISBN 0-85249-494-7
Hopelessly devoted to you. *arr.* Hopelessly devoted to you. (Farrar, John). *Chappell. Unpriced* UMK/DW (B79-51202)
Hopkins, Antony. Understanding music. *Dent. £6.95 : CIP rev.* A/C (B79-15552) ISBN 0-460-04376-5
Hopkins, Bill, *b.1943.* Selected letters of Gustav Mahler. (Mahler, Gustav). *Faber. £15.00 : CIP rev.* BME(N) (B79-14911) ISBN 0-571-08643-8
Hören und Singen : ein Solfège-Übungsbuch zur Gehörbildung. (Nobis, Herbert). *Schott. £5.60* CB/AF (B79-50816)
Horn, James van. *See* Van Horn, James.
Hornpype. *arr.* A hornpype. (Aston, Hugh). *Novello. £1.55* WNK (B79-51308)
Horovitz, Joseph. Folk song fantasy : for brass quintet. *J. & W. Chester. Unpriced* WNR (B79-50386)
Horse, his name was Henry Fencewaver Watkins. (Bedford, David). *Universal. Unpriced* NUPNP (B79-50185)
Hört ihr den Trommelschlag : Variationen für Streichorchester. (Schwaen, Kurt). *VEB Deutscher Verlag : Breitkopf and Härtel. £2.10* RXM/T (B79-51136)
Horton, John. Fughettas, piano, op.1. *arr.* Six fughettas. Op.1. (Weber, Carl Maria von, *Freiherr*). *Schott. Unpriced* VVNSK (B79-51275)
Hortus musicus. Ariosti, Attilio. Sonatas, viola d'amore &

continuo, 'Stockholm'. 'Stockholmer Sonaten' für Viola d'amore (Viola) und Basso continuo = 'Stockholm sonatas' for viola d'amore (viola) and basso continuo
2: Sonatas in ... B flat major ... G minor ... A minor. *Bärenreiter. £5.28* SQQPE (B79-50287)
Horvit, Michael. Techniques and materials of tonal music : with an introduction to twentieth-century techniques. (Benjamin, Thomas). 2nd ed. *Houghton Mifflin. £9.75* A/R (B79-18563) ISBN 0-395-27066-9
Hosier, John. The sorcerer's apprentice, and other stories. *Oxford University Press.* Pbk. *£1.50* ABN (B79-50005) ISBN 0-19-314922-2
Hotteterre, Jacques Martin.
Sonatas, flutes (2) & continuo, op.3. Triosonaten für zwei Flöten, (Flöte und Violine) und Basso continuo, op.3
Nos 1 & 2 : E-moll, D-dur. *Eulenburg. £3.50* VRNTPWE (B79-50741)
Sonatas, flutes (2) & continuo, op.3. Triosonaten für zwei Flöten (Flöte und Violine) und Basso continuo, op.3
Nos 3 & 4 : B-moll, E-moll. *Eulenburg. £3.50* VRNTPWE (B79-50742)
Sonatas, flutes (2) & continuo, op.3. Triosonaten für zwei Flöten (Flöte und Violine) und Basso continuo, op.3
Nos 5 & 6 : A-dur, G-dur. *Eulenburg. £3.50* VRNTPWE (B79-50743)
Hounsome, Terry. Rockmaster
1978. *13 Stanton Rd, Regents Park, Southampton, Hants. : Rockmaster.* Sd. *Unpriced* AKDW/HKR/FD(WT) (B79-35642)
Hovhaness, Alan. Symphony no.24, op.273, 'Majnun'. Majnun symphony. (Symphony no.24). Op.273 : for tenor solo, four-part chorus of mixed voices, trumpet in C, solo violin and string orchestra. *Associated Music. £9.10* EMDX (B79-50869)
How, Martin. Psalm 23. *Weinberger. Unpriced* FDR (B79-50908)
How far is it to Bethlehem? Pa mor bell yur Bethlehem? : unison voices and piano. (Hughes-Jones, Llifon). *Roberton. £0.20* JFDP/LF (B79-50517)
How to play rock guitar. (Daniels, Charlie). *Warner-Tamerlane : Blossom. Unpriced* TS/AC (B79-50297)
How to succeed in the music business. (Dann, Allan). *Wise Publications; 78 Newman St., W1P 3LA : Distributed by Music Sales Limited.* Pbk. *£2.50* A/GB (B79-10119) ISBN 0-86001-454-1
How to teach piano successfully. (Bastien, James W). 2nd ed. *General Words and Music etc.; 20 Earlham St., WC2H 9LN : Distributed by Breitkopf and Hartel (London) Ltd.* Pbk. *£7.90* AQ/E(VC) (B79-25333) ISBN 0-8497-6109-3
Howarth, Elgar.
A hornpype. *arr.* A hornpype. (Aston, Hugh). *Novello. £1.55* WNK (B79-51308)
Pictures at an exhibition. *arr.* Pictures at an exhibition. (Mussorgsky, Modest). *Chester Music. Unpriced* WMK (B79-51302)
Variations, brass quintet. Variations for brass quintet. *Novello. £1.95* WNR/T (B79-50794)
Howe, Lyn. Wacky and his fuddlejig : a chidren's Christmas musical play. (Swann, Donald). *Universal. Unpriced* CN/LF (B79-50017)
Howells, Herbert. I would be true. *Addington Press. Unpriced* EZDH (B79-50876)
Huber, Klaus. '... inwendig voller Figur ...'. Traumgesicht. Traumgesicht : für Männerstimme allein (1971). *Ars viva : Schott. £3.00* GEZDW (B79-50506)
Huber, Paul. Symphonic music. *R. Smith. Unpriced* WMJ (B79-51299)
Hudson, Hazel.
Go go Gabriel : unison with optional descant. *Ashdown. Unpriced* JFDP/LF (B79-50937)
Will you be my partner? : a quodlibet. *Edwin Ashdown. £0.25* FDW (B79-50911)
Huggett, Frank Edward. Goodnight sweetheart : songs and memories of the Second World War. *W.H. Allen. £5.95* ADW/GB(XNU7) (B79-37421) ISBN 0-491-02308-1
Hughes-Jones, Llifon. How far is it to Bethlehem? Pa mor bell yur Bethlehem? : unison voices and piano. *Roberton. £0.20* JFDP/LF (B79-50517)
Hugo Riemann's 'Theory of harmony' : a study / by William C. Mickelsen. And, History of music theory, Book III / by Hugo Riemann ; translated from the German and edited by William C. Mickelsen. (Mickelsen, William C). *University of Nebraska Press. £10.50* A/R (B79-04541) ISBN 0-8032-0891-x
Humanities Research Center, *University of Texas at Austin. See* University of Texas at Austin. *Humanities Research Center.*
Hume, Arthur Wolfgang Julius Gerald Ord-. *See* Ord-Hume, Arthur Wolfgang Julius Gerald.
Humel, Gerald. Arabesque : für Gitarre, Violoncello und Schlagzeug = for guitar, violoncello and percussion. *Schott. £10.80* NYJNT (B79-50201)
Hummel, Johann Nepomuk.
Concerto, trumpet, E major. Concerto, E major, for trumpet and orchestra. *Eulenburg. Unpriced* MPWSF (B79-51032)
Potpourri, viola & orchestra, op.94. Potpourri for viola and orchestra, op.94. *Musica rara. Unpriced* SQPK (B79-50282)
Humphreys, Emyr. Ancestor worship : four poems of Emyr Humphreys, for baritone and piano. (Hoddinott, Alun). *Oxford University Press. Unpriced* KGNDW (B79-51009) ISBN 0-19-345433-5

Humphries, J S. Sonata, violins (2), op.1, no.12, G major. Gigue. *arr.* Jig. *Banks. Unpriced* VVPK/AHP (B79-50785)
Humphries, John, *b.1941.* Music master
1979. *1 De Cham Ave., Hastings, Sussex : John Humphries. £30.00* A/FD(WT) (B79-28369) ISBN 0-904520-07-2
Hunt, Oliver.
Ricercare for three guitars. *Schott. £0.80* TSNT (B79-50300)
Two quartets : for four guitars. *Schott. Unpriced* TSNS (B79-50700)
Huray, Peter le. *See* Le Huray, Peter.
Hurd, Michael.
Round the town : five Charles Causley poems. *Novello. £0.74* JFDW (B79-50128)
This day to man. *Vocal score.* This day to man : six hymns for the Nativity for SATB and orchestra. *Novello. Unpriced* DE/LF (B79-50828)
Husa, Karel.
Le ballet des muses : for baroque ensemble. (Lully, Jean Baptiste). *Associated Music. £15.10* RXM/HM (B79-50663)
Concerto, saxophone (alto) & wind band. Concerto for alto saxophone and concert band. *Associated Music. £45.30* UMPVUSF (B79-50730)
Sonata, piano, no.2. Sonata no.2 for piano. *Associated Music. £4.55* QPE (B79-50621)
Hush! My dear. (Nettleton carol) : for mixed chorus and piano. (Ehret, Walter). *Broude : Breitkopf and Härtel. £0.42* DP/LF (B79-50839)
Husler, Frederick. Singer : die physische Natur des Stimmorganes : Anleitung zum Aufschliessen der Singstimme. 2.Aufl. *Schott.* Pbk. *£9.60* AB/E (B79-13063)
Hymn Society of Great Britain and Ireland. British hymn writers and composers : a check-list, giving their dates & places of birth & death. (Hayden, Andrew J). 1st ed. reprinted. *c/o Addington Palace, Croydon CR9 5AD : Hymn Society of Great Britain and Ireland.* Pbk. *£3.00* ADM/D(M/WT) (B79-15556)
Hymn to Saint John the Baptist. Ut queant laxis. (Monteverdi, Claudio). *36 Ranelagh Gdns W.6 : Cathedral Music. Unpriced* JNFLEE/SNTPWDJ (B79-50130)
Hymnes sacrées. Ave Maria. *arr.* Ave Maria. Offertorium. (Cherubini, Luigi). *Fentone Music : Breitkopf and Härtel. Unpriced* KFLE/VVPDJ (B79-51001)

I love thy church, O God : for four-part chorus of mixed voices with optional piano accompaniment. (Snyder, Wesley). *Schirmer. Unpriced* EZDH (B79-50880)
I saw the world end : a study of Wagner's 'Ring'. (Cooke, Deryck). *Oxford University Press. £6.50* BWCAC (B79-15554) ISBN 0-19-315318-1
I saw water flowing = Vidi aquam : anthem for Eastertide for four-part chorus of mixed voices a cappella. (Beadell, Robert). *Schirmer. Unpriced* EZDH/LL (B79-50881)
I wanna share. *arr.* I wanna share : for vocal solo, SATB chorus and piano with optional bass and drums. (Radlbauer, Dan). *Warner : Blossom. Unpriced* DW (B79-50853)
I wanna share : for vocal solo, SATB chorus and piano with optional bass and drums. (Radlbauer, Dan). *Warner Blossom. Unpriced* DW (B79-50853)

I want to walk like an elephant : musical fun for 'tinies' with chord symbols for piano, piano accordion and guitar. (McNess-Eames, Vera). *Stockwell.* Pbk. *£0.65* JFDW (B79-50938) ISBN 0-7223-1256-3
I will always need you : for vocal solo, SATB chorus and piano with optional bass and drums. (Pierce, Brent). *Warner : Blossom. Unpriced* DW (B79-50851)
I will give thanks : for four-part chorus of mixed voices with piano accompaniment. (Vance, Margaret). *Schirmer. £0.45* EZDK (B79-50883)
I will thank thee, O Lord. (Purcell, Daniel). *36 Ranelagh Gdns W.6 : Cathedral Music. Unpriced* EZDH (B79-50058)
I would be true. (Howells, Herbert). *Addington Press. Unpriced* EZDH (B79-50876)
Idee der absoluten Musik. (Dahlhaus, Carl). *12 Bucklesbury, Hitchin, Herts. SG5 1BB : Bärenreiter-Verlag etc.:* Pbk. *£2.31* A(YB/XG151) (B79-17758)
Idyll : for violoncello and piano. (Sullivan, *Sir* Arthur Seymour). *Leonard, Gould and Bolttler. £0.50* SRPJ (B79-50691)
If you should go away = Wenn du fortgehst : for four-part chorus of men's voices a cappella. (Dvořák, Antonín). *Schirmer. £0.35* GEZDW (B79-50926)
ILEA. *See* Inner London Education Authority.
I'll be seeing you ... : featuring the songs, the artists and the memories of the Second World War. *EMI. Unpriced* KDW/GB/AY(XNU7) (B79-50977) ISBN 0-86175-042-x
Illustrated 'Which one's Cliff?'. (Richard, Cliff). *Hodder and Stoughton.* Pbk. *£2.95 : CIP entry* AKDW/GB/E(P) (B78-29837) ISBN 0-340-23413-x
Illustrations : for brass band. (Tate, Phyllis). *Novello. Unpriced* WMJ (B79-50375)
I'm Popeye the sailor man : for two-part chorus and piano. (Lerner, Samuel). *Warner : Blossom. Unpriced* FDW/JR (B79-50106)
Imberscheid, Albrecht. Concerto, flute, B minor. *arr.* Konzert in h-moll für Flote und Orchester. (Fétis, François Joseph). *Eulenburg. £3.25* VRPK/LF (B79-50752)
Imbescheid, Albrecht. Concerto, flute, B minor. Konzert für Flöte und Orchester in h-moll. (Fétis, François Joseph). *Eulenburg. £3.50* MPVRF (B79-50587)
Imperial Society of Teachers of Dancing. *Modern Dance Branch.*
Original music and alternative music for the Modern Dance Grade Examinations
Grades 2 and 3: including pieces needed for the course of movement for boys. *Imperial Society of Teachers of Dancing. £3.50* QPH/H/AL (B79-51070)
Primary and Grade 1: including pieces needed for the course of movement for boys. *Imperial Society of Teachers of Dancing. £3.00* QPH/H/AL (B79-51071)
Improvisation. Op.48 : for solo viola. (Stevens, Bernard). *Roberton. £1.50* SQPMJ (B79-51157)
Improvvisazione : per chitarra. (Ravinale, Irma). *Berben Breitkopf und Härtel. £1.70* TSPMK (B79-50708)
Imrie, Martyn.
Clamabat autem mulier. (Escobar, Pedro de). *72 Brewery Rd, N.7 : Mapa mundi. Unpriced* GEZDJ (B79-50111)
Laudate Dominum de caelis : for 4 voices. (Brumel, Antoine). *72 Brewery Rd, N.7 : Mapa mundi. Unpriced* EZDR (B79-50097)
Liber primus motectorum quatuor vocum. Vidi turbam magnam. Vidi turbam magnam : motet for All Saints' Day, for 4 voices. (Porta, Constanzo). *72 Brewery Rd, N.7 : Mapa mundi. Unpriced* EZDJ/LQ (B79-50090)
Missa El ojo : for 4 voices. (Peñalosa, Francisco de). *72 Brewery Rd, N.7 : Mapa mundi. Unpriced* EZDG (B79-50050)
Missarum liber secundo. Missa de la batalla escoutez. Missa de la batalla escoutez : for 5 voices. (Guerrero, Francisco). *Mapa mundi. Unpriced* EZDG (B79-50049)
Motecta ... liber secundus. Pastores loquebantur. Pastores loquebantur. (Guerrero, Francisco). *72 Brewery Rd, N.7 : Mapa mundi.. Unpriced* EZDJ/LF (B79-50076)
Motecta festorum totius anni ... liber primus. Hodie Christus natus est. Hodie Christas natus est. (Marenzio, Luca). *72 Brewery Rd, N.7 : Mapa mundi. Unpiced* EZDJ/LF (B79-50073)
Motecta festorum totius anni ... liber primus. O sacrum convivium. O sacrum convivium : motet for the Feast of Corpus Christi, for 4 voices. (Marenzio, Luca). *72 Brewery Rd, N.7 : Mapa mundi. Unpriced* EZDJ/LNC (B79-50089)
Omnis pulchritudo Domini : motet for the Ascension of our Lord, for 5 voices. (Silva, Andreas de). *72 Brewery Rd, N.7 : Mapa mundi. Unpriced* EZDJ/LM (B79-50086)
Paradisi porta : motet for 6 voices. (Escribano, Juan). *72 Brewery Rd, N.7 : Mapa mundi. Unpriced* EZDJ (B79-50059)
Psalmodia vespertina. lauda Hierusalem Dominum. Lauda Hierusalem Dominum. (Porta, Constanzo). *72 Brewery Rd, N.7 : Mapa mundi. Unpriced* DR (B79-50032)
Sacrae cantiones. Parvulus filius. Parvulus filius : for 6 voices. (Ammon, Blasius). *72 Brewery Rd, N.7 : Mapa mundi. Unpriced* EZDJ/LF (B79-50074)
Sacrae cantiones. Tenebrae factae sunt. Tenebrae factae sunt : for 4 voices. (Ammon, Blasius). *72 Brewery Rd, N.7 : Mapa mundi. Unpriced* EZDJ/LK (B79-50083)
Salve Regina. (Anchieta, Juan de). *72 Brewery Rd, N.7 : Mapa mundi. Unpriced* GEZDJ (B79-50110)
Secundus tomus musici operis. Ascendens Christus. Ascendens Christus : motet for the Ascension of our Lord, for 4 voices. (Handl, Jacob). *72 Brewery Rd, N.7 : Mapa mundi. Unpriced* EZDJ/LM (B79-50085)
Tomus primus operis musici. Rorate coeli. Rorate coeli : motet for the Advent season, for 6 voices. (Handl, Jacob). *Mapa mundi. Unpriced* EZDJ/LEZ (B79-50072)

Two motets sic : for four voices. (Martin de Rivafrencha). *72 Brewery Rd, N.7 : Mapa mundi. Unpriced* GEZDJ (B79-50112)
In a Persian market. *arr.* Persian market swing. (In a Persian market). (Ketelbey, Albert). *Bosworth & Co. £1.35* MK (B79-50565)
In memoriam : Margaret James : a treasury of bamboo pipe music. (Pipers' Guild). *Pipers' Guild. Unpriced* VSY/AY (B79-51255)
In memoriam N.W.G.T., 1910-1978. *74 Doneraile St., SW6 6EP : J.A. Ellison.* Sd. *£1.30* AC(WB/P) (B79-16101) ISBN 0-904677-09-5
In my own key. (Söderström, Elisabeth). *H. Hamilton. £5.95 : CIP entry* AKFL/E(P) (B79-25330) ISBN 0-241-10318-5
In praise of music : (seven songs for orchestra). (Argento, Dominick). *Boosey and Hawkes. Unpriced* MMJ (B79-50172)
In the days of long ago. *Selections.* The tin soldiers, and, Lords and ladies : two simple piano duets from the suite 'In the days of long ago'. (Furze, Jessie). *Roberton. £0.50* QNV (B79-50614)
Incorporated Society of Musicians.
Handbook and register of members
1978-79. *10 Stratford Place, W1N 9AE : The Society.* Pbk. *£7.00* A(YC/Q/MM) (B79-17756)
Professional register of artists
1977. *10 Stratford Place, W1N 9AE : The Society.* Sd. *£1.00* A(YC/MM) (B79-27780)
Indes galantes. (Rameau, Jean Philippe). *Oxford University Press. Unpriced* QRPK/HM (B79-51115) ISBN 0-19-373556-3
Indes galantes. *arr.* Les Indes galantes. (Rameau, Jean Philippe). *Oxford University Press. Unpriced* QRPK/HM (B79-51115) ISBN 0-19-373556-3
Indian prayer. (Tull, Fisher). *Boosey and Hawkes. Unpriced*

DW (B79-50452)
Indian summer : for mixed chorus and piano. (Ferris, William). *Oxford University Press. Unpriced* DW (B79-50848)
Ingman, Nicholas. Gifted children of music : the young lives of the great musicians. *Ward Lock. £3.95 : CIP rev.* A/D(M/C) (B78-27520) ISBN 0-7063-5721-3
Inner light (1) : for seven players and tape. (Harvey, Jonathan). *Novello. £5.00* NYDPNP/FG (B79-50607)
Inner light (2) : for SSATB soli, instrumental ensemble and tape ... (Harvey, Jonathan). *Faber Music. Unpriced* JNBE/MRDW/FT (B79-50949)
Inner London Education Authority. *Learning Materials Service.* Sing a song
1. Teacher's book. *Nelson : ILEA Learning Materials Service.* Sp. *£2.75* A/GR(VG) (B79-07467) ISBN 0-17-413002-3
Institut für Neue Musik und Musikerziehung. Veröffentlichungen. Avantgarde, Jazz, Pop : Tenderzen zwischen Tonalität und Atonalität : neun Vorragstexte. *Schott.* Pbk. *£7.20* A/PF (B79-11128)
Institut für Neue Musik und Musikerziehung, *Internationales Musikinstitut Darmstadt. See* Internationales Musikinstitut Darmstadt. *Institut für Neue Musik und Musikerziehung.*
Institute of Armenian Music. Essays on Armenian music. *Kahn and Averill for the Institute of Armenian Music. £6.95* A(D/YVVA) (B79-33551) ISBN 0-900707-49-6
Intabulatura de lauto. *Selections : arr.* Two pieces. (Dalza, Joan Ambrosio). *DeCamera : Schirmer. £1.50* TSPMK (B79-51187)
International Association of Music Libaries. Catalogus musicus. *See* Catalogus musicus.
International electronic music discography. Internationale Diskographie elektronischer Musik = International electronic music discography = Discographie internationale de la musique electronique. (Kondracki, Miroslaw). *Schott.* Pbk. *£11.20* APV/FD(WT) (B79-35641)
International music education. ISME yearbook
Vol.6 : 1979: Music education - the person first : papers of the 13th International Conference, London, Ontario, Canada, 1978. (International Society for Music Education). *Schott.* Pbk. *£9.60* A(V/BC) (B79-32713)
International music guide
1979. *Tantivy Press etc..* Pbk. *£3.50* A(BC) (B79-28897) ISBN 0-498-02242-0
International Musicological Society. Catalogus musicus. *See* Catalogus musicus.
International series of contemporary organ music. Wills, Arthur. Variations on 'Amazing Grace'. Variations on 'Amazing grace' and Toccata : for organ. *Novello. £2.25* RJ (B79-51127)
International Society for Music Education. ISME yearbook
Vol.6 : 1979: Music education - the person first : papers of the 13th International Conference, London, Ontario, Canada, 1978. *Schott.* Pbk. *£9.60* A(V/BC) (B79-32713)

Internationale Diskographie elektronischer Musik = International electronic music discography = Discographie internationale de la musique electronique. (Kondracki, Miroslaw). *Schott.* Pbk. *£11.20* APV/FD(WT) (B79-35641)
Internationale Ferienkurse für Neue Musik, *29, Darmstadt, 1978.* Ferienkurse '78. *Schott.* Pbk. *£9.60* A(XR9) (B79-14011)
Internationales Musikinstitut Darmstadt. Ferienkurse '78. (Internationale Ferienkurse für Neue Musik, *29, Darmstadt, 1978*). *Schott.* Pbk. *£9.60* A(XR9) (B79-14011)
Internationales Musikinstitut Darmstadt. *Institut für Neue Musik und Musikerziehung.* Veröffentlichungen. Neue Musik und die Tradition *(Conference), Darmstadt, 1978.* Die neue Musik und die Tradition : sieben Kongressbeiträge und eine analytische Studie. *Schott.* Pbk. *£10.80* A(XPK19) (B79-11940)
Interpreting Mozart's piano sonatas. (Richner, Thomas). *Paterson's Publications.* Pbk. *£2.00* BMSAQPE/E (B79-04545)
Intervals, scales and temperaments ... (Lloyd, Llewelyn Southworth). New ed. *Macdonald and Jane's. £9.95* A/B (B79-50003) ISBN 0-354-04229-7
Into the classics. (Farmer, Paul). *Longman.* Sd. *£0.65* A(XFWE101) (B79-33549) ISBN 0-582-21576-5
Introduction to music. (Hendrie, Gerald). *Open University Press.* Pbk. *Unpriced* A (B79-16836) ISBN 0-335-05414-5
Introduction to music fundamentals : a programmed textbook for the elementary classroom teacher. (Andrews, J Austin). 4th ed. *Prentice-Hall.* Sp. *£8.00* A/M(VG) (B79-00564) ISBN 0-13-489575-4
Introduction to music theory. (Winold, Allen). 2nd ed. *Prentice-Hall.* Pbk. *£8.40* A/AM (B79-30253) ISBN 0-13-489666-1
Introduction to the cello. (Smith, Doreen). *Oxford University Press. Unpriced* SR/AC (B79-51159) ISBN 0-19-322345-7
Ireland, John. The collected piano works of John Ireland
Vol.4. *Stainer and Bell. Unpriced* QP/AZ (B79-50209) ISBN 0-85249-396-7
Irische Lieder und Balladen. *Schott. £4.00* KE/TSDW/K/G/AYDM (B79-50995)
Irish bagpipes : their construction and maintenance. (Garvin, Wilbert). *Blackstaff Press for Na Píobairí Uileann.* Pbk. *£3.95* AVYR/BT (B79-17765) ISBN 0-85640-149-8
Islands of beauty. C. John Taylor's islands of beauty : ballad in English and Gaelic. (Taylor, Cecil John). *Isle of Seil, Oban, Argyll, Scotland : Highland Arts Studios. Unpriced* KDW (B79-50527)
Isles of the sea : anthem for unaccompanied choir ... (Dearnley, Christopher). *36 Ranelagh Gdns W.6 : Cathedral Music. Unpriced* EZDK (B79-50092)
ISME. *See* International Society for Music Education.
ISME yearbook
Vol.6 : 1979: Music education - the person first : papers of the 13th International Conference, London, Ontario, Canada, 1978. (International Society for Music Education). *Schott.* Pbk. *£9.60* A(V/BC) (B79-32713)
Ist arabesque : for organ and piano. (Debussy, Claude). *Columns Music : Schirmer (dist.). £1.95* QPLRK (B79-51111)
Italian 17th and 18th century sinfonias and sonatas for trumpet and strings. Gabrielli, Domenico. Sonata, trumpet, string quintet & continuo, D.XI.7, D major. Sonata D.XI.7 in D for trumpet, strings and basso continuo. *Musica rara. Unpriced* NUXSNPE (B79-50598)
Italian 17th and 18th century sinfonias and sonatas for trumpets and strings.
Gabrielli, Domenico. Sonata, trumpet & string orchestra, D. XI, 8, D major. Sonata D. XI, 8 in D, for trumpet, strings and basso continuo. *Musica rara. Unpriced* RXMPWSE (B79-50670)
Gabrielli, Domenico. Sonata, trumpet & string orchestra, D. XI, 8, D major. *arr.* Sonata D. XI, 8 in D for trumpet, strings and basso continuo. *Musica rara. Unpriced* WSPK/LE (B79-50803)
Gabrielli, Domenico. Sonata, trumpet, string quintet & continuo, D.XI.7, D major. *arr.* Sonata D.XI.7 in D for trumpet, strings and basso continuo. *Musica rara. Unpriced* WSPK/AE (B79-50800)
Italian 17th & 18th century sinfonias and sonatas for trumpets and strings.
Jacchini, Giuseppe Maria. Sonata, trumpet, strings & continuo, D XII 5, D major. *arr.* Sonata, D XII 5 for tromba, (trumpet), strings and continuo. *Musica rara. Unpriced* WSPK/AE (B79-50801)
Jacchini, Giuseppe Maria. Sonata, trumpet, strings & continuo, D XII 6, D major. Sonata, D XII 6 for tromba, (trumpet), strings and continuo. *Musica rara. Unpriced* NUXSNRE (B79-50599)
Jacchini, Giuseppe Maria. Sonata, trumpet, violins (2) & continuo, D XII 5, D major. *arr.* Sonata, D XII 5 for tromba, (trumpet), strings and continuo. *Musica rara. Unpriced* WSPK/AE (B79-50802)
Jacchini, Giuseppe Maria. Sonata, trumpet, violins(2) & continuo, D XII 5, D major. Sonata, D XII 5 for tromba, (trumpet), strings and continuo. *Musica rara. Unpriced* NUXSNSE (B79-50600)
Jacchini, Giuseppe Maria. Trattenimenti per camera, op.5. Sonata, trumpets (2), strings & continuo, op.5, no.1, D major. Sonata, op.5, no.1, for 2 trombe (trumpets) strins and continuo. *Musica rara. Unpriced* RXMPWSNUE (B79-50263)
Italian 17th and 18th century sinfonias and sonatas for trumpets and strings.
Jacchini, Giuseppe Maria. Trattenimenti per camera, op.5. Sonata, trumpets (2), strings & continuo, op.5, no.1, D major. *arr.* Sonata, op.5, no.1, for 2 trombe (trumpets), strings and continuo. *Musica rara. Unpriced* WSNTQK/LE (B79-50392)
Jacchini, Giuseppe Maria. Trattenimenti per camera. Sinfonia, trumpets (2) & string orchestra, op.5, no.8, D major. Sinfonia, op.5 no.8 for 2 trumpets, strings and basso continuo. *Musica rara. Unpriced* RXMPWSNUE (B79-50671)
Jacchini, Giuseppe Maria. Trattenimenti per camera. Sinfonia, trumpets (2) & string orchestra, op.5, no.8, D major. *arr.* Sinfonia, op.5 no.8 for 2 trumpets, strings and basso continuo. *Musica rara. Unpriced* WSNTQK/AE (B79-50799)
Italian church music.
Marenzio, Luca. Motecta festorum totius anni ... liber primus. Hodie Christus natus est. Hodie Christas natus est. *72 Brewery Rd, N.7 : Mapa mundi. Unpiced* EZDJ/LF (B79-50073)
Marenzio, Luca. Motecta festorum totius anni ... liber primus. O sacrum convivium. O sacrum convivium : motet for the Feast of Corpus Christi, for 4 voices. *72 Brewery Rd, N.7 : Mapa mundi. Unpriced* EZDJ/LNC (B79-50089)
Porta, Constanzo. Liber primus motectorum quatuor vocum. Vidi turbam magnam. Vidi turbam magnam : motet for All Saints' Day, for 4 voices. *72 Brewery Rd, N.7 : Mapa mundi. Unpriced* EZDJ/LQ (B79-50090)
Porta, Constanzo. Psalmodia vespertina. lauda Hierusalem Dominum. Lauda Hierusalem Dominum. *72 Brewery Rd, N.7 : Mapa mundi. Unpriced* DR (B79-50032)
Ito, Ako. Suite française. Op.61 : pour deux guitares. (Duarte, John William). *Bèrben : Breitkopf and Härtel. £3.30* TSNUG (B79-51170)
It's - rock scene. *Purnell. £1.50* AKDW/HKR/E(M) (B79-28896) ISBN 0-361-04558-1
Its a grand night for singing : S.A.C.(T).B, with piano. (Rodgers, Richard). *Williamson. Unpriced* DW (B79-50858)
Ives, Charles. Waltz-rondo for piano. *Schirmer. £3.65* QPHW/W (B79-50629)
Ives, Edward D. Joe Scott : the woodsman-songmaker. *University of Illinois Press. £15.75* AKDW/GNL(P) (B79-22639) ISBN 0-252-00683-6
Ives, Grayston. Let all the world in every corner sing. *Novello. £0.61* DH (B79-50024)
Jacchini, Giuseppe Maria.
Sonata, trumpet, strings & continuo, D XII 5, D major. *arr.* Sonata, D XII 5 for tromba, (trumpet), strings and continuo. *Musica rara. Unpriced* WSPK/AE (B79-50801)
Sonata, trumpet, strings & continuo, D XII 6, D major. Sonata, D XII 6 for tromba, (trumpet), strings and continuo. *Musica rara. Unpriced* NUXSNRE (B79-50599)
Sonata, trumpet, violins (2) & continuo, D XII 5, D major. *arr.* Sonata, D XII 5 for tromba, (trumpet), strings and continuo. *Musica rara. Unpriced* WSPK/AE (B79-50802)
Sonata, trumpet, violins(2) & continuo, D XII 5, D major. Sonata, D XII 5 for tromba, (trumpet), strings and continuo. *Musica rara. Unpriced* NUXSNSE (B79-50600)
Trattenimenti per camera, op.5. Sonata, trumpets (2), strings & continuo, op.5, no.1, D major. Sonata, op.5, no.1, for 2 trombe (trumpets) strins and continuo. *Musica rara. Unpriced* RXMPWSNUE (B79-50263)
Trattenimenti per camera, op.5. Sonata, trumpets (2), strings & continuo, op.5, no.1, D major. *arr.* Sonata, op.5, no.1, for 2 trombe (trumpets), strings and continuo. *Musica rara. Unpriced* WSNTQK/LE (B79-50392)
Trattenimenti per camera. Sinfonia, trumpets (2) & string orchestra, op.5, no.8, D major. Sinfonia, op.5 no.8 for 2 trumpets, strings and basso continuo. *Musica rara. Unpriced* RXMPWSNUE (B79-50671)
Trattenimenti per camera. Sinfonia, trumpets (2) & string orchestra, op.5, no.8, D major. *arr.* Sinfonia, op.5 no.8 for 2 trumpets, strings and basso continuo. *Musica rara. Unpriced* WSNTQK/AE (B79-50799)
Jack of shadows. (Bedford, David). *Universal. £8.06* MRJ (B79-51035)
Jackson, Chuck.
Our love. *arr.* Our love. (Yancy, Marvin). *Chappell. Unpriced* DW (B79-50036)
Our love. *arr.* Our love. (Yancy, Marvin). *Chappell. Unpriced* DW (B79-50037)
Our love. *arr.* Our love. (Yancy, Marvin). *Chappell. Unpriced* FDW (B79-50105)
Jackson, Francis.
Two flourishes : for organ. *Banks. Unpriced* RGN (B79-50233)
Versicles and responses (including the Sovereign's Accession) : S.A.(T.)T.B. *Banks. Unpriced* EZDGMM (B79-50459)
Jacobs, Jim.
Grease. *arr.* Grease : original soundtrack songs from the motion picture. (Casey, Warren). *Warner : Blossom. Unpriced* KDW/JR (B79-50143)
Grease. *arr.* Grease : original soundtrack songs from the motion picture. (Casey, Warren). *Chappell. Unpriced* KDW/JR (B79-50144)
Jacobson, Bernard, *b.1936.* Conductors on conducting. *Macdonald and Jane's. £6.95* A/EC (B79-32716) ISBN 0-354-04416-8
Jacobson, Maurice. The music room. Selections. Sarabande and Rustic ballet ... : two miniatures for piano solo. *Roberton. £0.50* QPH (B79-50627)
Jacques, Michael. Midsummer suite : for treble recorder or flute and piano. *Roberton. £1.50* VSSPG (B79-50770)
Jagger, Mick. Some girls. (Richard, Keith). *EMI. Unpriced* KDW/GB (B79-50137)
Jahn, Thomas. Ten dance studies in jazz idiom : for trombone quintet. *Schirmer. £8.50* WUNRHX (B79-50807)
James, Burnett. Manuel de Falla and the Spanish musical renaissance. *Gollancz. £6.95* BFB (B79-16837) ISBN 0-575-02645-6
Jāmī. Symphony no.24, op.273, 'Majnun'. Majnun symphony. (Symphony no.24). Op.273 : for tenor solo, four-part chorus of mixed voices, trumpet in C, solo violin and string orchestra. (Hovhaness, Alan). *Associated Music. £9.10* EMDX (B79-50869)
Janáček, Leoš.
Our father. Otčenáš = Our Father : for full chorus of mixed voices, tenor or soprano solo, organ and harp. *Roberton. £0.75 (Chorus score £0.28)* EJQPLRDTF (B79-50865)
Sinfonietta. *Eulenburg. £2.50* MMEM (B79-50168)

Janacopoulos, Véra. Love of three oranges. L'amour des trois oranges. Opus 33 : opéra en 4 actes et 10 tableaux avec un prologue d'après Carlo Gozzi. (Prokofiev, Sergei). *Boosey and Hawkes. Unpriced* CQC (B79-50822)
Jarman, Douglas. The music of Alban Berg. *Faber. £18.00 : CIP entry* BBKR (B78-37095) ISBN 0-571-10956-x
Jazz. (Chilton, John). *Teach Yourself Books.* Pbk. *£1.95 : CIP rev.* AMT(X) (B79-15559) ISBN 0-340-23847-x
Jazz at Ronnie Scott's. *Hale. £5.80* AMT(M) (B79-16103) ISBN 0-7091-6907-8
Jazz city : the impact of our cities on the development of jazz. (Ostransky, Leroy). *Prentice-Hall. £8.00* AMT(YT/X) (B79-04544) ISBN 0-13-509380-5
Jazz fiddle. *Chappell. Unpriced* SPHX (B79-50681)
Jazz improvisation. (Kynaston, Trent P). *Prentice-Hall. Unpriced* MT/DZ (B79-50184) ISBN 0-13-509307-4
Jazz Parnass : Etüden, Stücke und Studien, für Klavier. (Schmitz, Manfred). *Schott. £7.20* QPHX/AF (B79-50212)
Jazz players library : 10 classic tunes in their original versions and in completely notated jazz versions. (Dentato, John). *Chappell. Unpriced* QPHX (B79-51075)

Jazz players library : 10 classic tunes in their original versions and in completely notated jazz versions. (Dentato, John). *Chappell. Unpriced* VRPMHX (B79-51230)
Jazz players library : 10 classic tunes in their original

versions and in completely notated jazz versions. (Dentato, John). *Chappell. Unpriced* VUSPMHX (B79-51268)
Jazz players library : 10 classic tunes in their original versions and in completely notated jazz versions. (Dentato, John). *Chappell. Unpriced* VUTPMHX (B79-51271)
Jazz players library : 10 classic tunes in their original versions and in completely notated jazz versions. (Dentato, John). *Chappell. Unpriced* WSPMHX (B79-51320)
Jazz-rock fusion : the people - the music. (Coryell, Julie). *Boyars : Distributed by Calder and Boyars. £12.00* AKDW/HKRJ (B79-32718) ISBN 0-7145-2667-3
Jazz text. (Nanry, Charles). *D. Van Nostrand.* Pbk. *£6.70* AMT (B79-21878) ISBN 0-442-25908-5
Jazzpublikum : zur Sozialpsychologie einer kulturellen Minderheit. (Dollase, Rainer). *Schott.* Pbk. *£9.60* AMT(Z) (B79-10482)
Jefferson, Alan. Sir Thomas Beecham : a centenary tribute. *Macdonald and Jane's. £6.50* A/EC(P) (B79-11942) ISBN 0-354-04205-x
Jeffery, Brian.
Arte de tocar la guitarra española por música, (Madrid, 1799). (Ferandiere, Fernando). *Tecla. Unpriced* TS/AC (B79-51163) ISBN 0-8494-0093-7
Doce canciones. Op.24. Doce canciones = Twelve songs : with guitar accompaniment ... (Moretti, Federico). *Tecla. Unpriced* KE/TSDW (B79-50993) ISBN 0-8494-0140-2
Jenkyns, Peter.
First nursery suite : four traditional songs. *Novello. £0.98* NYFSRK/DW/GJ/AY (B79-50608)
Second nursery suite : three traditional songs. *Novello. £0.98* NYFSRK/DW/GJ/AY (B79-50609)
Jenni, Donald. Cherry valley : an ensemble for nine flutes. *Associated Music. Unpriced* VRNM (B79-51215)
Jenns, Timm. Christmas carols for young children : for piano, guitar and recorder. *East West : Breitkopf and Härtel. £1.50* JFE/NUSNTDP/LF/AY (B79-50943)
Jergenson, Dale. Sacrae symphoniae, bk.2. O quam suavis. O quam suavis : for eight-part chorus of mixed voices with organ accompaniment. (Gabrieli, Giovanni). *Schirmer. £0.75* DGKJ/LNC (B79-50427)
Jesus, our Lord, doth live again : Easter anthem, for mixed voices, S.A.T.B. (Kingsbury, John). *Broude : Breitkopf und Härtel. £0.42* DH/LL (B79-50435)
Jiddische Volkslieder : Liebeslieder, für Singstimme mit Klavier oder Gitarre. *Verlag Neue Musik : Breitkopf und Härtel. £3.60* KDW/G/AYEU (B79-50529)
Jkesutora no toki no toki = Time of orchestral time. (Yūasa, Jōji). *Zen-on Music : Schott. £12.00* MMJ (B79-51026)
Johann Sebastian Bach : life, times, influence. *17 Bucklersbury, Hitchin, Herts. SG5 1BB : Bärenreiter. £21.12* BBC(N) (B79-11127)
John, Elton. A single man. *Big Pig Music : Music Sales. Unpriced* KDW/HKR (B79-50139)
John Blow's anthology : Froberger, Strungk, Fischer, Blow : a selection of keyboard music (twenty suites, capriccios, ricercars, toccatas, etc.) copied out by John Blow around 1700. *Stainer and Bell. Unpriced* QRPJ (B79-50646) ISBN 0-85249-446-7
John III, 16 = Johannes III, 16 : for mixed chorus a capp;ella = für gemischten Chor a cappella. (Reimann, Aribert). *Schott. Unpriced* EZDK (B79-50093)
John Williams series.
Brahms, Johannes. Sextet, string instruments, op.18, B flat major. Andante. *arr.* Theme and variations. *Boosey and Hawkes. Unpriced* TSNUK (B79-50702)
Paganini, Nicolò. Caprice, violin, op.1, no.24, A minor. *arr.* Caprice no.24. *Boosey and Hawkes. Unpriced* TSPMK/T (B79-50715)
Praetorius, Michael. Terpsichore. *Selections : arr.* Four dances ... guitar. *Boosey and Hawkes. Unpriced* TSPMK/AH (B79-50710)
Johnny : a Northumbrian fishergirl's song. (Noble, Harold). *Lengnick. Unpriced* KDW (B79-50132)
Johnson, David. Overture a quattro. Op.4, no.2. Ouverture, Opus 4, No.2 : für Streicher und Basso continuo = for strings and basso continuo. (Barsanti, Francesco). *Schott. £6.00* RXMG (B79-50257)
Johnson, Robert Sherlaw. Sonata, piano, no.3. Sonata no.3 for piano. *Oxford University Press. Unpriced* QPE (B79-51067) ISBN 0-19-373004-9
Johnson, Stuart. Second intermediate band book. *R. Smith. Unpriced* WM/AY (B79-50788)
Johnstone, Duncan. Duncan Johnstone collection of pipe tunes
Vol.1. *Duncan Johnston Piping School. Unpriced* VY/AYDL (B79-50365)
Jones, Arthur.
The little place where I was born : setting for male voices (T.T.B.B.). (Larbalestier, Philip George). *(Fford yr Osaf) : Cyngor Gwasanaethau Gwirfoddol Clwyd (Clwyd Voluntary Services Council). Unpriced* GDW (B79-50503)
The little place where I was born : setting for male voices, T.T.B.B. (Larbalestier, Philip George). *Ffordd yr osaf : Cyngor Gwasanapthau Gwiyfiddol Clwyd = Clwyd Voluntary Services Council. Unpriced* GDW (B79-50921)
Jones, Clayton S. Simple gifts for the dulcimer : an instruction manual for beginners, a collection of songs and tunes for dulcimer players. *TRO Ludlow Music Essex Music. Unpriced* TWT/AC (B79-50717)
Jones, Ivor Wynne. Llandudno's operatic tradition. *71 Llandudno Rd, Penrhyn Bay. Llandudno, Gwynedd : Pegasus.* Sd. *£0.50* AC/E(YDKP/X) (B79-27786)
Jones, John Cynan. Hava nagila : Israeli folk song. (Davies, Bryan). *Roberton. £0.32* GDW (B79-50920)
Jones, Kenneth Victor. Serpentine dances : for harpsichord. *Chester Music. Unpriced* QRPH (B79-51113)
Jones, Llifon Hughes-. *See* Hughes-Jones, Llifon.
Jones, Malcolm, *b.1943.* Music librarianship. *Bingley etc.. £4.00 : CIP rev.* A(U) (B79-11403) ISBN 0-85157-274-x
Jones, Richard Elfyn. David Wynne. *University of Wales Press for the Welsh Arts Council.* Pbk. *£1.50 : CIP rev.* BWY (B79-09705) ISBN 0-7083-0714-0
Joplin, Scott.
Ragtime. Selections. *arr.* String along with Scott : 10 ragtime pieces. *Schirmer. £7.85* RXNSK/AHXJ (B79-50674)
Ragtimes. *Selections : arr.* Ragtimes ... *Schott. £2.60* TSPMK/AHXJ (B79-51196)
Sechs Ragtimes für Flöte oder Klarinette in B and Klavier. *Eulenburg. £4.20* VRPK/AHXJ (B79-50751)
Josquin des Prés.
Domine, ne in furore tuo arguas me. Oh my Lord, let not your blinding fury - My heart = Domine, ne in furore - Cor meum : for four-part chorus of men's voices a cappella. *Schirmer. £0.75* GEZDJ (B79-50504)
Missa Pange lingua : for voices. *Chester Music. Unpriced* EZDG (B79-50874)
Joubert, John. Pro pace motets. Op.19, 32, 29. Pro pace motets : for unaccompanied chorus. *Novello. £1.95* EZDJ (B79-50468)
Journal of the Plainsong & Mediaeval Music Society
Vol.1- ; 1978-. (Plainsong and Mediaeval Music Society). *46 Bond St., Englefield Green, Surrey TW20 0PY : The Society.* Sd. *£1.50(free to members)* A(XA1600/B) (B79-36420)
Joy on this day. (Law, Ronald). *36 Ranelagh Gdns W.6 : Cathedral Music. Unpriced* EZDP/LF (B79-50096)
Joyful songs. (Auckland, Bessie H). *Oliver and Boyd. Unpriced* JFE/LDM/GJ (B79-50521) ISBN 0-05-003260-7
Joyful sound : Christian hymnody. (Reynolds, William Jensen). 2nd ed. *Holt, Rinehart and Winston. £8.75* ADM(X) (B79-05497) ISBN 0-03-040831-8
Judd, Margaret. Dawn : piano solo. *Bosworth and Co. Unpriced* QPJ (B79-50217)
Jürgenson-Rupprecht, Margarete. Das europäische Kunstlied : eine Auswahl von Klavierliedern aus vier Jahrhunderten für den Musikunterricht ... *Schott. £6.00* KDW/AY (B79-50962)
Just brass.
Horovitz, Joseph. Folk song fantasy : for brass quintet. *J. & W. Chester. Unpriced* WNR (B79-50386)
Lear, Hogarth. Mr. Lear's carnival : for brass band. *Chester Music. Unpriced* WMJ (B79-51300)
Mussorgsky, Modest. Pictures at an exhibition. *arr.* Pictures at an exhibition. *Chester Music. Unpriced* WMK (B79-51302)
Old French dances. *Chester Music. Unpriced* WNH/AYH (B79-51307)
Premru, Raymond. Quartet, trumpets (2), horn & trombone. Quartet for two trumpets, horn and trombone. *Chester Music. Unpriced* WNS (B79-50796)
Woods, Stanley. Little blue boy : for tenor horn and brass band. *Chester Music. Unpriced* WMPWTT (B79-51305)
Just friends, in print : Marian Montgomery with Richard Rodney Bennett in words, music and pictures. *Novello. £2.95* KDW/GB/AY (B79-50536)
Kagel, Mauricio. MM51 : ein Stück Filmmusik für Klavier, 1976. *Universal. Unpriced* QPJ (B79-51083)
Kaiser, Ernst. Selected letters of Gustav Mahler. (Mahler, Gustav). *Faber. £15.00 : CIP rev.* BME(N) (B79-14911) ISBN 0-571-08643-8
Kalidas. ... Surya : for S.A.T Bar. B. soli, chorus, flute and percussion. (Sohal, Naresh). *Novello. Unpriced* EVRPLXDW (B79-50048)
Kalliwoda, Jan Václav. Morceau de salon. Op.228 : for oboe and piano. *Nova Music. Unpriced* VTPJ (B79-51262)
Kāmakalā. Le triangle des énergies : pour trois ensembles d'orchestres et de choeurs. (Eloy, Jean Claude). *Universal. Unpriced* EMDX (B79-50868)
Kanazawa, Masakata. The musical manuscript Montecassino 871 : a Neapolitan repertory of sacred and secular music of the late fifteenth century. (Monte Cassino *(Monastery). Biblioteca. MSS. (Codex 871)). Clarendon Press. £25.00* CB/AY (B79-50411) ISBN 0-19-816132-8
Kander, John. Chicago : a musical vaudeville. (Ebb, Fred). *French.* Sd. *£1.65* BKDEACM (B79-06704) ISBN 0-573-68081-7
Katz, Jonathan. Two Beethoven sketchbooks : a description with musical extracts. (Nottebohm, Gustav). *Gollancz. £4.95* BBJ(QVB) (B79-14912) ISBN 0-575-02583-2
Kebszakállú herceg vara. *See* Balázs, Béla.
Kehr, Günter. Symphony, no.14, K.114, A major. Symphonie A-Dur, KV114. (Mozart, Wolfgang Amadeus). *Schott. £4.80* MRE (B79-51033)
Keil, Charles. Tiv song. *University of Chicago Press. £7.00* BZMQTADW (B79-26553) ISBN 0-226-42962-8
Keller, Gottfried. Sonata, recorders (treble) (2) & continuo, G major. Sonata in G, 2 treble recorders (or flutes), 2 oboes/violins (or flutes) & basso continuo. *Nova Music. Unpriced* VSSNTPWE (B79-51246)
Keller-Löwy, Walter.
A tre : Tänze und Stücke alter Meister für 2 Sopran-und 1 Altblockflöte = dances and tunes of old masters for two soprano - and one alto-recorder. *Pelikan : Bärenreiter. £1.23* VSNTK/AH/AY (B79-50763)
Der Siebensprung : und andere Tänze aus aller Welt, leicht gesetzt für zwei Sopranblockflöten = and other dances from all over the world, in easy arrangements for two soprano-recorders. *Pelikan : Bärenreiter. £1.47* VSRNUK/AH/AY (B79-50767)
Kelly, Bryan. Partita : for oboe and piano. *Chester Music. Unpriced* VTPG (B79-50773)
Kelterborn, Rudolf.
Erinnerungen an Orpheus : Musik für Orchester (1977/78). *Bote and Bock. £11.50* MMJ (B79-51024)
Phantasmen : für grosses Orchester, 1965-1966. *Bärenreiter. £10.89* MMJ (B79-50578)
Sevenminute - Play : für Flöte und Klavier = for flute and piano. *Bärenreiter. £4.95* VRPJ (B79-50749)
Symphony no.3, 'Espansioni'. Espansioni : Sinfonie III für grosses Orchester, Bariton und Tonband, 1974/1975. *Bärenreiter. £11.55* KGNE/MDX (B79-50156)
Kelvingrove : for four-part chorus of mixed voices a cappella with optional piano. (Rhein, Robert). *Schirmer. £0.55* EZDW (B79-50902)
Kemps music & recording industry year book international 1979. *Kemps.* Pbk. *£10.50* A/GB(YC/BC) (B79-22267) ISBN 0-905255-52-6
Kendall, Alan, *b.1939.*
Beethoven and his world. *Ward Lock. £2.95 : CIP rev.* BBJ(N) (B79-30252) ISBN 0-7063-5867-8
Vivaldi. *Panther.* Pbk. *£1.50* BVJ(N) (B79-33548) ISBN 0-586-05065-5
Kennard, Daphne. Music to help disabled children to move. *A.P.C.P. Publications, 25 Goff's Park Rd, Southgate, Crawley, W. Sussex RH11 8AX : Association of Paediatric Chartered Physiotherapists.* Sd. *£0.50* A(VMX) (B79-13819)
Kennard, Daphne J. Access to music for the physically handicapped schoolchild and school leaver : report on 3-year project, 1973-1976. *346 Kensington High St., W14 8NS : Disabled Living Foundation.* Sp. *£2.00* A(VMX) (B79-33201) ISBN 0-901908-31-2
Kennedy, Kenneth Thomas. Piano action repairs and maintenance. *Kaye and Ward etc.. £7.95* AQ/BT (B79-11135) ISBN 0-7182-1205-3
Ketcham, J. Stichomythia : for flute and guitar, 1976. (Antioniou, Theodore). *Bärenreiter. £8.58* VRPLTS (B79-50335)
Ketelbey, Albert. In a Persian market. *arr.* Persian market swing. (In a Persian market). *Bosworth & Co. £1.35* MK (B79-50565)
Kettlebury hill : for oboe and piano (or strings). (Butterworth, Neil). *Banks. Unpriced* VTPJ (B79-50350)
Keys, Ivor. Christus. *Selections : arr.* There shall a star from Jacob come forth : three excerpts from Christus. (Mendelssohn, Felix). *Addington Press. Unpriced* DH/LF (B79-50834)
Khachaturian, Aram.
Spartak. Adagio of Spartacus and Phrygia. *arr.* Adagio. *Boosey and Hawkes. Unpriced* MK/HM (B79-50567)
Spartak. Adagio of Spartacus and Phrygia. *arr.* Adagio. *Boosey and Hawkes. Unpriced* MK/HM (B79-50568)
Kidd, J Michael. Thou madest all things well : anthem for unison voices and organ. *Weinberger. Unpriced* JFDH (B79-50935)
Kieler Schriften zur Musikwissenschaft. Krummacher, Friedhelm. Die Choralbearbeitung in der protestantischen Figuralmusik zwischen Praetorius und Bach. *17 Bucklesbury, Hitchin, Herts. SG51 BB : Bärenreiter.* Pbk. *Unpriced* ADGTCW(YE/XE151) (B79-17763)
Kievman, Carson.
Concerto, bassoon & percussion ensemble. Concerto for bassoon and percussion ensemble (fire alarm system). *Associated Music. £2.75* WVPLXF (B79-50811)
Sirocco (1975) : for wood-wind quintet (flute, oboe, B flat clarinet, bassoon, F horn). *Associated Music. Unpriced* UNR (B79-50731)
Kilian, Werner. The two fiddlers. *Vocal score.* The two fiddlers = Die beiden Musikanten : opera in two acts = Oper in zwei Akten. (Davies, Peter Maxwell). *Boosey and Hawkes. Unpriced* CN (B79-50016)
Killmayer, Wilhelm. Quartet, strings & keyboard. Quartett für 2 Violinen, Violoncello und Klavier. *Schott. £11.20* NXNS (B79-50196)
King, Thea. The clarinet : a comprehensive method for the Boehm clarinet. (Thurston, Frederick J). 3rd ed. (revised and enlarged). *Boosey and Hawkes. Unpriced* VV/AC (B79-51272)
King and I. Getting to know you. *arr.* Getting to know you : for S.A. cambiata, B. or S.A.T.B. (Rodgers, Richard). *Williamson. Unpriced* DW (B79-50855)
King shall rejoice. (Tomkins, John). *36 Ranelagh Gdns, W.6 : Cathedral Music. Unpriced* DK (B79-50028)
Kingfisher library. Kendall, Alan, *b.1939.* Beethoven and his world. *Ward Lock. £2.95 : CIP rev.* BBJ(N) (B79-30252) ISBN 0-7063-5867-8
Kingman, Daniel. American music : a panorama. *Schirmer : Collier Macmillan.* Pbk. *£7.45* A(YT/X) (B79-25329) ISBN 0-02-871260-9
Kingsbury, John.
Gradualia, lib. 2. Alleluia, ascendit Deus. Alleluia, our Lord is risen : for mixed chorus SSATB. (Byrd, William). *Broude : Breitkopf und Härtel. £0.42* EZDJ/LM (B79-50470)
Jesus, our Lord, doth live again : Easter anthem, for mixed voices, S.A.T.B. *Broude : Breitkopf und Härtel. £0.42* DH/LL (B79-50435)
Rejoice, then, Christ is born : Christmas song for mixed voices, optional a cappella S.A.T.B., Italian carol-tune (traditional). *Broude : Breitkopf and Härtel. £0.42* DP/LF (B79-50841)
Kingsbury, Roy. Seasons and people and other songs. *Melody part.* Seasons and people and other songs. *Oxford University Press. Unpriced* JFADW (B79-50513) ISBN 0-19-450558-8
Kingsley, Charles. The gorgon's head. (Withams, Eric).

Universal. Unpriced CQN (B79-50824)
Kirby, Frank Eugene. Music in the classic period : an anthology with commentary. *Schirmer : Collier Macmillan. £11.20* C/AY (B79-50409) ISBN 0-02-870710-9
Kirk, Theron. Let all on earth their voices raise : for four-part chorus of mixed voices with piano accompaniment. *Schirmer. Unpriced* DH (B79-50832)
Kirkpatrick, John. Waltz-rondo for piano. (Ives, Charles). *Schirmer. £3.65* QPHW/W (B79-50629)
Kirkpatrick, William Jerome. Away in a manger. *arr.* Away in a manger. *36 Ranelagh Gdns W.6 : Cathedral Music. Unpriced* EZDP/LF (B79-50095)
Kiss. Double platinum. *Almo : EMI. Unpriced* KDW/HKR (B79-50140)
Kiss me, Kate. Another op'nin, another show. *arr.* Another op'nin', another show : for S.A. cambiata, B. or S.A.T.B. with piano. (Porter, Cole). *Chappell. Unpriced* DW (B79-50852)
Kite, Christopher James. Sonatas for harpsichord
Book one. (Scarlatti, Domenico). *Stainer and Bell. Unpriced* QRPE (B79-50644) ISBN 0-85249-513-7
Kitty of Coleraine : traditional Irish, S.A.T.B. unacc. (Nelson, Havelock). *Banks. Unpriced* EZDW (B79-50899)
Klebe, Giselher. Symphony, no.3, op.52. Dritte Sinfonie für grosses Orchester, Op.52 = Third symphony for grand orchestra, op.52. *Bärenreiter. £13.20* MME (B79-50167)
Klefisch, Walter. Lasset uns singen : Volkslied von Tahiti. *Schott. £0.24* FEZDW (B79-50501)
Klein, Maynard.
Canzonetti ... libro quarto a quattro voci. Partiro si. Partirò sì = Parting is pain : for four-part chorus of mixed voices a cappella. (Vecchi, Horatio). *Schirmer. £0.35* EZDU (B79-50475)
Ecce quam bonum : See how good, how right : for four-part chorus of mixed voices a cappella. (Richafort, Jean). *Schirmer. £0.30* EZDR (B79-50472)
Libro de villanelle. O occhi manza mia. O occhi manza mia = Thine eyes, oh, my beloved : for four-part chorus of mixed voices a cappella. (Lasso, Orlando di). *Schirmer. £0.35* EZDU (B79-50887)
Libro de villanelle. Tutto lo di. Day after day, they all say 'sing' : Tutto lo di mi dici : for eight-part chorus of mixed voices a cappella. (Lasso, Orlando di). *Schirmer. £0.45* EZDU (B79-50474)
Stabat mater. Amen. *arr.* Hallelujah amen ... : for four-part chorus of mixed voices a cappella. (Schubert, Franz). *Schirmer. £0.45* EZDH/LK (B79-50463)
Klein, Theodor. Sonatas, viola d'amore & continuo, 'Stockholm'. 'Stockholmer Sonaten' für Viola d'amore (Viola) und Basso continuo = 'Stockholm sonatas' for viola d'amore (viola) and basso continuo
2: Sonatas in ... B flat major ... G minor ... A minor. (Ariosti, Attilio). *Bärenreiter. £5.28* SQQPE (B79-50287)

Kleine Blasmusik. Op.32 : five short movements for two trumpets and two trombones. (Schwertsik, Kurt). *Boosey and Hawkes. Unpriced* WNS (B79-50388)
Kleine Cammermusic. Die kleine Kammermusik : sechs Partiten für Blockflöte, Querflöte, Oboe oder Violine und Basso continuo = six partitas for recorder, flute, oboe or violin and basso continuo. (Telemann, Georg Philipp). *Amadeus : Eulenburg. £4.70* VSPG (B79-50764)
Kleinen Jahreszeiten. *Choral score.* Die kleinen Jahreszeiten : Fraunchor und Klavier. (Schubert, Heino). *Schott. £1.00* FADW (B79-50906)
Kleinen Jahreszeiten : Fra nuenchur und Klavier. (Schubert, Heino). *Schott. £4.10* FDX (B79-50497)
Kleinen Jahreszeiten : Fraunchor und Klavier. (Schubert, Heino). *Schott. £1.00* FADW (B79-50906)
Klopčič, Rok.
Il cimento dell'armonia e dell'inventione. Op.8. Le quattro stagione. Autunno.. *arr.* Four seasons, op.8 (Concerto for violin and orchestra)
Autumn : for violin and piano. (Vivaldi, Antonio). *Schirmer. £2.40* SPK/LF (B79-50682)
Il cimento dell'armonia e dell'inventione. Op.8, nos 1-4. *arr.* Four seasons, op.8. (Concerto for violin and orchestra
Op.8, no.4: Winter : for violin and piano. (Vivaldi, Antonio). *Schirmer. £2.40* SPK/LF (B79-51154)
Knight, Ronald David. Hambledon's cricket glory
Vol.6: The Hambledon cricket song. 2nd (revised) ed. *40 Abbotsbury Rd, Weymouth, Dorset DT4 0AE : The author.* Pbk. *£0.50* BCMTADW (B79-29607) ISBN 0-903769-06-9
Knopf, Bill. Songs from the stage and screen : for 5-string bluegrass banjo. *Chappell. Unpriced* TSPMK/DW (B79-51197)
Knorr, Ernst Lothar von.

Duo, viola & cello, (1961). Duo für Viola und Violoncello (1961). *Amadeus : Eulenburg. £3.70* SQPLSR (B79-50685)
Kochan, Günter. Sieben Miniaturen (1977) : für vier Tuben. *Neue Musik : Breitkopf und Härtel. £4.20* WVNS (B79-50810)
Köhler, Johannes Ernst. Pro organo : Zeitgenössische Orgelmusik von Komponisten der Deutschen Demokratischen Republik. *VEB Deutscher Verlag für Musik : Breitkopf und Härtel. £4.80* R/AYEA (B79-50647)
Kohlhase, Thomas. Regini coeli laetare = Freu dich, Maria, Himmelsköningin : für vierstimmigen gemischten Chor und Basso continuo = for four-part mixed chorus and basso continuo. (Caldara, Antonio). *Bärenreiter. £2.97* DJ (B79-50436)
Kolb, Barbara. Appello : for piano. *Boosey and Hawkes. Unpriced* QPJ (B79-50218)
Komm'bald. Op.97, no.5. *arr.* Come soon = Komm bald : for three-part chorus of women's voices with piano accompaniment. (Brahms, Johannes). *Schirmer. £0.35* FDW (B79-50492)
Kondracki, Miroslaw. Internationale Diskographie elektronischer Musik = International electronic music discography = Discographie internationale de la musique electronique. *Schott.* Pbk. *£11.20* APV/FD(WT) (B79-35641)
Korngold, Erich Wolfgang.
Quartet, strings, no.3, op.34, D major. Streichquartett No.3, opus 34, D-Dur, für 2 Violinen, Viola und Violoncello = String quartet no.3, opus 34, D major, for 2 violins, viola and violoncello. *Schott. £14.00* RXNS (B79-50268)
Quartet, strings, no.3, op.34, D major. Streichquartett No.3, opus 34, D-Dur : für Violine, Viola und Violoncello. *Schott. £16.00* RXNS (B79-50267)
Korsakoff, Nikolai Rimsky-. *See* Rimsky-Korsakoff, Nickolai.
Kossoff, David. Six songs from the psalms : six of the best songs from the BBC TV series 'Kossoff and company'. (Ridout, Alan). *Weinberger. Unpriced* KDR (B79-50954)
Kraus, Egon. ISME yearbook
Vol.6 : 1979: Music education - the person first : papers of the 13th International Conference, London, Ontario, Canada, 1978. (International Society for Music Education). *Schott.* Pbk. *£9.60* A(V/BC) (B79-32713)
Krebs, Johann Ludwig. Chorale preludes, trumpet & organ. Die sechs Choralvorspiele für Trompete und Orgel = The six chorale preludes for trumpet and organ. *Simrock. Unpriced* WSPLR (B79-50398)
Kreidler, Dieter.
Galliards and airs : fünf altenglische Lautenstucke nach Tabulaturen übertragen und für Gitarre bearbeitet von = five old English lute pieces. *Schott. £3.20* TSPMK/AYD (B79-50711)
Gitarrenschule
Band 2. *Schott. £8.50* TS/AC (B79-51165)
Ragtimes. *Selections : arr.* Ragtimes ... (Joplin, Scott). *Schott. £2.60* TSPMK/AHXJ (B79-51196)
Zwei Duette. (Dowland, John). *Schott. £2.20* TSNUK (B79-51171)
Krěnek, Ernst. Die vier Winde = Four-winds : suite ; für Orgel, for organ, 1975. *Bärenreiter. £6.60* RG (B79-50232)
Krenzpunkte : zwei Studien für Schlagzengtrio. (Fink, Siegfried). *Schott. £3.20* XNT/AF (B79-50812)
Kresky, Jeffrey. Tonal music : twelve analytic studies. *Indiana University Press. £8.75* A/CB (B79-10475) ISBN 0-253-37011-6
Krug, Reinhold. Zwota-Sonate, 1974 : Blockflöte und Klavier. *Neue Musik : Breitkopf and Härtel. £3.90* VSPE (B79-51237)
Krummacher, Friedhelm. Die Choralbearbeitung in der protestantischen Figuralmusik zwischen Praetorius und Bach. *17 Bucklesbury, Hitchin, Herts. SG51 BB : Bärenreiter.* Pbk. *Unpriced* ADGTCW(YE/XE151) (B79-17763)
Krumpfer, Hans Joachim. Trompetenëtuden II = Trumpet studies II = Etudy pro trubku II. *Deutscher Verlag für Musik : Breitkopf und Härtel. Unpriced* WS/AC (B79-50797)
Krüss, James. Dampflok-Story : ein Kinder - Musical : für Sprecher, 1-3 stg. Kinderchor und Begleitinstrumente auf Text von James Krüss. (Hess, Reimund). *Schott. £10.00* CQN (B79-50418)
Kuhn, Terry Lee. Fundamental classroom music skills : theory and performing techniques. (Wachhaus, Gustav). *Holt, Rinehart and Winston.* Sp. *£7.75* A(VG) (B79-12529) ISBN 0-03-041775-9
Kynaston, Trent P. Jazz improvisation. *Prentice-Hall. Unpriced* MT/DZ (B79-50184) ISBN 0-13-509307-4
La Rue, Pierre de. Missa cum iucunditate : for 4 and 5 voices. *72 Brewery Rd, N.7 : Mapa mundi. Unpriced* GEZDG (B79-50109)
Laburda, Jiří.
Dobry den. What a day : Dobry den : a choral cycle, for two-part chorus of young voices with piano accompaniment or a cappella. *Schirmer. £2.10* FDW (B79-50495)
Stabat mater : for four-part chorus of mixed voices a cappella. *Schirmer. £2.75* EZDGKADD/LK (B79-50457)
Lade, John. Building a library. *Oxford University Press.* Pbk. *£2.95 : CIP entry* A/FD (B79-25861) ISBN 0-19-311324-4
Laine, Denny.
Denny Laine's guitar book. *G. Whizzard : Deutsch. £4.95* ATS/E (B79-33558) ISBN 0-233-97101-7
Mull of Kintyre. *arr.* Mull of Kintyre. (McCartney, Paul). *Music Sales. Unpriced* DW (B79-50034)
Laken, Alan. Flute magic. *Chappell. Unpriced* VRPK/AAY (B79-50332)
Lally, Maureen. Listen, sing and play
1 : Senior infants, lessons 1-10. Workbook. *Educational Company of Ireland.* Sd. *£0.35* A/M (B79-02026)
Lamentations for Tenebrae on Maundy Thursday, Feria V in Coena Domini ad Matatinum. (Lasso, Orlando di). *72 Brewery Rd, N.7 : Mapa Mundi. Unpriced* EZDJ/LHM (B79-50081)
Lamento. (Eymwag, Joachim). *(Little Margaret, Penmans Green, Chipperfield) : E.L. White. Unpriced* KE/NXNRDW (B79-50544)
Land, Thomas Orszäg-. *See* Orszäg-Land, Thomas.
Landry, Judith. The musicians of Auschwitz. (Fénelon, Fania). *Sphere.* Pbk. *£0.95* A(M/YLCO/XPC3) (B79-19444) ISBN 0-7221-3466-5
Landscapes, Op.86 : for orchestra. (Hoddinott, Alun). *Oxford University Press. Unpriced* MMJ (B79-50577) ISBN 0-19-364492-4
Lane, Philip.
Concertino. *R. Smith. Unpriced* WMFL (B79-51297)
Suite of Cotswold folkdances. *Edwin Ashdown. £5.00* MMHG (B79-50171)
A wedding album. *Edwin Ashdown. Unpriced* RK/KDD/AY (B79-50242)
Laniere, Nicholas. Gather your rosebuds. (Lawes, William). *Pro Cantione Antiqua : Breitkopf und Härtel. Unpriced* GEZDU (B79-50505)
Lannoy, Eduard von. Quintet, wind & piano, op.2, E flat major. Quintett Es-dur für Klavier, Oboe, Klarinette, Horn und Fagott, Op.2. *Eulenburg. Unpriced* NWNR (B79-50193)
Larbalestier, Philip George.
The little place where I was born : setting for male voices (T.T.B.B.). *(Fford yr Osaf) : Cyngor Gwasanaethau Gwirfoddol Clwyd (Clwyd Voluntary Services Council). Unpriced* GDW (B79-50503)
The little place where I was born : setting for male voices, T.T.B.B. *Ffordd yr osaf : Cyngor Gwasanapthau Gwiyfiddol Clwyd = Clwyd Voluntary Services Council. Unpriced* GDW (B79-50921)
Larrad, Jennifer. Suite, harpsichord, C.B. 60, no.19, G minor. Suite in A minor. (Handel, George Frideric). *Oxford University Press. Unpriced* TSNUK/AG (B79-50303) ISBN 0-19-356997-3
Lascelles, Maria Donata, *Countess.*
Piano playtime : very first solos and duets
Book 2. *faber Music. Unpriced* QP/AY (B79-50207)

Lasocki, David.
L'art de la flûte traversière. *Selections.* 12 caprices : for solo flute. (Lusse, Charles de). *Nova Music. Unpriced* VRPMJ (B79-51232)
The complete sonatas for treble (alto) recorder and basso continuo = Die gesamten Sonaten für Altblockflöte und basso continuo. (Handel, George Frideric). *Faber Music. Unpriced* VSSPE/AZ (B79-51253)
Concerto grosso, op.6, no.3, C major. *arr.* Trio sonata in d. (Corelli, Arcangelo). *Nova Music. Unpriced* VSSNTPWK/LF (B79-51248)
Sonata, oboe & continuo, op.2, no.5, G minor. Sonata in g, op.2, no.5 for oboe or violin and basso continuo. (Schickhardt, Johann Christian). *Nova Music. Unpriced* VTPE (B79-51260)
Sonata, oboe, bassoon & continuo, K.46, G major. Trio sonata in G. K.46, oboe (or flute, violin, descant recorder), bassoon or violoncello and basso continuo. (Quantz, Johann Joachim). *Nova Music. Unpriced* NWPNT (B79-51047)
Sonata, recorders (treble) (2) & continuo, G major. Sonata in G, 2 treble recorders (or flutes), 2 oboes/violins (or flutes) & basso continuo. (Keller, Gottfried). *Nova Music. Unpriced* VSSNTPWE (B79-51246)
Sonata, recorders (treble) (2) & continuo, op.6, no.6, D minor, 'La Folia'. Variations on La folia, op.6, no.6 : for 2 treble recorders and basso continuo. (Schickhardt, Johann Christian). *Nova Music. Unpriced* VSSNTPW/T (B79-51244)
Sonatas, oboe & continuo. The three authentic sonatas : oboe & basso continuo in F, opus 1, no.5, B flat, 'Fitzwilliam', C minor, opus 1, no.8. (Handel, George Frideric). *Nova Music. Unpriced* VTPE (B79-51259)
Lasset uns singen : Volkslied von Tahiti. (Klefisch, Walter). *Schott. £0.24* FEZDW (B79-50501)
Lasso, Orlando di.
Hieremiae prophetae lamentationes, et alia piae cantiones. *Selections.* Lamentations for Tenebrae on Maundy Thursday, Feria V in Coena Domini ad Matatinum. *72 Brewery Rd, N.7 : Mapa Mundi. Unpriced* EZDJ/LHM (B79-50081)
Hieremiae prophetae lamentationes, et alia piae cantiones. *Selections.* Six responsories for Tenebrae on Maundy Thursday, feria V in Coena Domini ad Matatinum. *72 Brewery Rd, N.7 : Mapa mundi. Unpriced* EZDJ/LHM (B79-50082)
Libro de villanelle. O occhi manza mia. O occhi manza mia = Thine eyes, oh, my beloved : for four-part chorus of mixed voices a cappella. *Schirmer. £0.35* EZDU (B79-50887)
Libro de villanelle. Tutto lo di. Day after day, they all say 'sing' : Tutto lo di mi dici : for eight-part chorus of mixed voices a cappella. *Schirmer. £0.45* EZDU (B79-50474)
Magnificat praetur rerum seriem : upon the motet by Josquin, for 6 voices. *72 Brewery Rd, N.7 : Mapa mundi. Unpriced* EZDGKK (B79-50055)
Lassus, Roland de. *See* Lasso, Orlando di.
Last, Joan. Gymnastics : piano pieces for beginners. *Boosey and Hawkes. Unpriced* QPJ (B79-51084)
Last voter's song. (Cruft, Adrian). *(1 The Retreat, S.W.14) : Joad Press. Unpriced* WTPK/DW (B79-50400)

Latham, Bill. The illustrated 'Which one's Cliff?'. (Richard, Cliff). *Hodder and Stoughton.* Pbk. *£2.95 : CIP entry* AKDW/GB/E(P) (B78-29837) ISBN 0-340-23413-x
Lauda Hierusalem Dominum. (Porta, Constanzo). *72 Brewery Rd, N.7 : Mapa Mundi. Unpriced* DR (B79-50032)
Laudate Dominum de caelis : for 4 voices. (Brumel,

Antoine). *72 Brewery Rd, N.7 : Mapa mundi. Unpriced* EZDR (B79-50097)
Laudes : for organ. (Eben, Peter). *United Music. Unpriced* RJ (B79-51125)
Laudi alla vergine Maria = Prayer to the Virgin Mary : for four-part chorus of female voices. (Verdi, Giuseppe). *Roberton. £0.32* FEZDH (B79-50916)
Law, Ronald.
Hodie Christus natus est. *36 Ranelagh Gdns W.6 : Cathedral Music. Unpriced* EZDJ/LF (B79-50077)
Joy on this day. *36 Ranelagh Gdns W.6 : Cathedral Music. Unpriced* EZDP/LF (B79-50096)
Lawes, William.
Consort sets in five and six parts. *Faber Music. Unpriced* STNQR (B79-51162)
Gather your rosebuds. *Pro Cantione Antiqua : Breitkopf und Härtel. Unpriced* GEZDU (B79-50505)
Lawrance, F W J. The Bristol and District Organists' Association : a brief history. *57 Burnham Drive, Bleadon Hill, Weston-super-Mare, Avon BS24 9LF : The author.* Sd. *£1.00* AR(QB/DFEB/X) (B79-27792)
Lawrence, Alan.
Ten traditional English carols. *Fenone Music, Breitkopf und Härtel. £0.95* TSPMK/DP/LF/AY (B79-50313)
Time pieces : a collection of works for musical clocks by Handel and Haydn. *Fentone Music : Breitkopf und Härtel. Unpriced* TSPMK/B/FK (B79-50312)
Lawrence, Ian. Composers and the nature of music education. *Scolar Press. £10.00* A(VC/Z) (B79-00558) ISBN 0-85967-401-0
Lawson-Gould sacred choral series. Victoria, Tomás Luis de. Motecta, Sancta Maria. Sancta Maria, and, Ecce sacerdos magnus : for four part chorus of mixed voices unaccompanied. *Roberton. £0.28* EZDJ (B79-50469)
Lawton, Sidney. Le prophète. March. *arr.* Coronation march. (Le prophète). (Meyerbeer, Giacomo). *Novello. £2.00* UMK/AGM (B79-50315)
Layer analysis : a primer of elementary tonal structures. (Warfield, Gerald). *Longman.* Sp. *£6.35* A/PF (B79-50004) ISBN 0-582-28069-9
Layton, Robert. Sibelius. 2nd ed. *Dent. £4.50 : CIP entry* BSH (B78-37096) ISBN 0-460-03169-4
Lazarus : an Easter cantata, for solo, mixed chorus and orchestra. (Schubert, Franz). *Schirmer. £1.80* DE (B79-50420)
Lazarus. *Vocal score.* Lazarus : an Easter cantata, for solo, mixed chorus and orchestra. (Schubert, Franz). *Schirmer. £1.80* DE (B79-50420)
Le Fleming, Antony. Jazz fiddle. *Chappell. Unpriced* SPHX (B79-50681)
Le Huray, Peter. Music and the Reformation in England, 1549-1660. *Cambridge University Press. £19.50* AD/LD(YD/XDXJ112) (B79-16102) ISBN 0-521-21958-2
Leaf, David. Bee Gees : the authorized biography. (Bee Gees, *Group*). *Octopus Books.* Pbk. *£2.99* AKDW/GB/E(P) (B79-20269) ISBN 0-7064-1091-2
Leaper, Kenneth. Yule : for two speakers, children's voices, games players, piano, with occasional recorders : melodicas, tuned and untuned percussion. *Chappell. Unpriced* FE/NYHSDE/LF (B79-50913)
Lear, Hogarth. Mr. Lear's carnival : for brass band. *Chester Music. Unpriced* WMJ (B79-51300)
Lear : Oper in zwei Teilen nach William Shakespeare eingerichtet von Claus H. Henneberg (1976/1978). (Reimann, Aribert). *Schott. Unpriced* CQC (B79-50823)
Learn as you play. Wastall, Peter. Learn as you play trumpet & cornet. *Boosey and Hawkes. Unpriced* WS/AC (B79-51316)
Learn as you play clarinet. (Wastall, Peter). *Boosey and Hawkes. Unpriced* VV/AC (B79-51273)
Learn as you play flute. (Wastall, Peter). *Boosey and Hawkes. £0.85* VR/AC (B79-51212)
Learn as you play trumpet & cornet. (Wastall, Peter). *Boosey and Hawkes. Unpriced* WS/AC (B79-51316)
Learning tree songbook. (Page, Ian). *Chappell. Unpriced* JFDW/GJ (B79-50939)
Learning with traditional rhymes. Singing rhymes. *Ladybird Books. £0.30* AJFDW/GR(VJ) (B79-06706) ISBN 0-7214-0537-1
Lebowsky, Stanley. The children's crusade. The children's crusade : a morality play for the young, for four-part chorus of mixed voices, three soloists, narrator, piano and guitar accompaniment. *Schirmer. £5.15* CN/L (B79-50416)
Led Zeppelin. (Mylett, Howard). *Panther.* Pbk. *£0.75* AKDW/HKR/E(P) (B79-10479)
Lee, Clifford. Concertos, double bass, Krebs 171, 172. *arr.* Concertos for double bass and orchestra. (Dittersdorf, Carl Ditters von). *Yorke. Unpriced* SSPK/LF (B79-50292)
Lees, Benjamin. Variations, piano & orchestra. *arr.* Variations for piano and orchestra. *Boosey and Hawkes. Unpriced* QNUK/L/T (B79-50204)
Legnani, Luigi. 6 capriccetti, che servono di compimento dell' op.250. Sei capricci ... per chitarra. *Berben. £1.70* TSPMJ (B79-50705)
Lehár, Franz.
Der Graf von Luxemburg. *Selections: arr.* Der Graf von Luxemburg : Melodienfolge. Neue Ausgabe. *Glocken. Unpriced* UMK/DW (B79-50318)
Die lustige Witwe. *Selections : arr.* Songs from The merry widow (Die lustige Witwe). *Glocken. Unpriced* KDW (B79-50957)
Zigeunerliebe. *Selections: arr.* Zigeunerliebe : Melodienfolge. Neue Ausgabe. *Glocken. Unpriced* UMK/DW (B79-50319)
Leichte Choral-Partiten : für Bläser. (Ehmann, Wilhelm). *Bärenreiter. £3.96* WMG (B79-50369)
Leichte Klavierstücke und Sonatinen des 17-20 Jahrhunderts. *Schott. £6.00* QP/AY (B79-50617)
Leighton, Kenneth. Quartet in one movement. Contrasts and variants : for violin, viola, cello and piano, opus 63. *Novello. Unpriced* NXNS (B79-50197)
Lemesurier, Peter. Through music to the self : how to appreciate and experience music anew. (Hamel, Peter Michael). *Compton Press. £5.95* A/CC (B79-08926) ISBN 0-900193-53-0
Lengnick (Alfred) & Company. *See* Alfred Lengnick & Company.
Lennon, John. *See* Beatles, The.
Leon, Victor. Die lustige Witwe. *Selections : arr.* Songs from The merry widow (Die lustige Witwe). (Lehár, Franz). *Glocken. Unpriced* KDW (B79-50957)
Leonard, Maurice. Slobodskaya : a biography of Oda Slobodskaya. *Gollancz. £6.50* AKFL/E(P) (B79-22638) ISBN 0-575-02622-7
Leppard, Raymond. Salve regina. *Vocal score.* Salve regina : sacred cantata for soprano and keyboard. (Scarlatti, Domenico). *Faber Music. Unpriced* KFLDJ (B79-50148)
Lerner, Alan Jay. Paint your wagon. They call the wind Maria. *arr.* They call the wind Maria : S.A.C.(T.) B. with piano. (Loewe, Frederick). *Chappell. Unpriced* DW (B79-50850)
Lerner, Samuel. Popeye the sailor. I'm Popeye the sailorman. *arr.* I'm Popeye the sailor man : for two-part chorus and piano. *Warner : Blossom. Unpriced* FDW/JR (B79-50106)
Lester, Bryan. The arpeggio = L'arpeggio = Das Arpeggio : essential guitar skill = tecnica essenziale per la chitarra = Grundlagen der Fertigkeit im Gitarrenspiel. *Ricordi. Unpriced* TS/AC (B79-51164)
Let all on earth their voices raise : for four-part chorus of mixed voices with piano accompaniment. (Kirk, Theron). *Schirmer. Unpriced* DH (B79-50832)
Let all the world in every corner sing. (Ives, Grayston). *Novello. £0.61* DH (B79-50024)
Let God arise. *Vocal score.* Let God arise : anthem for soprano and tenor soli, SATB and orchestra. (Handel, George Frideric). *Novello. £1.65* DK (B79-50027)
Let's explore music : the Russell-Smith method based on Kodály and Orff principles
Book 1: Junior. (Russell-Smith, Geoffry). *EMI. Unpriced* C/AC (B79-50408)
Let's explore music : the Russell-Smith method based on Kodaly and Orff principles
Book 1: Junior, pupils edition. (Russell-Smith, Geoffry). *EMI. Unpriced* C/M (B79-50410)
Let's go band! : for beginning band. (Balent, Andrew). *Warner : Blossom. Unpriced* UMJ (B79-51201)
Levitt, Rod.
Babylon : for stage band. *Associated Music. £7.55* MTJ (B79-50594)
Mamma's eyes : for stage band. *Schirmer. Unpriced* MTJ (B79-50595)
Mon plaisir : for stage band. *Associated Music. £7.55* MSHJK (B79-50593)
Lewendon, Vanessa. Play keyboards today. *Hamlyn. £3.50* APW/E (B79-24593) ISBN 0-600-37201-4
Liber magnificarum. Magnificat octavi toni. Magnificat octavi toni : for 8 voices. (Vivanco, Sebastian de). *Mapa mundi. Unpriced* EZDGKK (B79-50056)
Liber primus missarum. Ave maria. Ave Maria : for 8 voices. (Lobo, Alfonso). *72 Brewery Rd, N.7 : Mapa mundi. Unpriced* EZDJ (B79-50063)
Liber primus missarum. Ave regina coelorum. Ave regina coelorum : Compline and votive antiphon for the season from Christmas to the Purification. (Lobo, Alfonso). *72 Brewery Rd, N.7 : Mapa mundi. Unpriced* EZDGKR/LF (B79-50057)
Liber primus missarum. Credo quod redemptor mens vivit. Credo quod redemptor mens vivit : pro defunctis, for 4 voices. (Lobo, Alfonso). *Mapa mundi. Unpriced* EZDJ/KDN (B79-50068)
Liber primus missarum. O quam suavis est, Domine. O quam suavis est, Domine : motet for the Feast of Corpus Christi, for 6 voices. (Lobo, Alfonso). *72 Brewery Rd, N.7 : Mapa mundi. Unpriced* EZDJ/LNC (B79-50088)
Liber primus missarum. Quam pulchri sunt gressus tui. Quam pulchri sunt gressus tui. (Lobo, Alfonso). *Mapa mundi. Unpriced* EZDJ (B79-50064)
Liber primus missarum. Versa est in luctum. Versa est in luctum : ad exsequias Philip II, cathol. regis Hisp. = for the funeral of Philip II, Catholic King of Spain. (Lobo, Alfonso). *72 Brewery Rd, N.7 : Mapa mundi. Unpriced* EZDJ/KDN (B79-50069)
Liber primus missarum. Vivo ego, dicit Dominus. Vivo ego, dicit Dominus : motet for Lent for 4 voices. (Lobo, Alfonso). *72 Brewery Rd, N.7 : Mapa mundi. Unpriced* EZDJ/LG (B79-50080)
Liber primus motectorum quatuor vocum. Vidi turbam magnam. Vidi turbam magnam : motet for All Saints' Day, for 4 voices. (Porta, Constanzo). *72 Brewery Rd, N.7 : Mapa mundi. Unpriced* EZDJ/LQ (B79-50090)
Libro de villanelle. O occhi manza mia. O occhi manza mia = Thine eyes, oh, my beloved : for four-part chorus of mixed voices a cappella. (Lasso, Orlando di). *Schirmer. £0.35* EZDU (B79-50887)
Libro de villanelle. Tutto lo di. Day after day, they all say 'sing' : Tutto lo di mi dici : for eight-part chorus of mixed voices a cappella. (Lasso, Orlando di). *Schirmer. £0.45* EZDU (B79-50474)
Libro della canzoni, no.1. Canzona 2 'La Bernadina'. Canzona (II) 'La Bernadina' per canto solo : für Sopranblockflüte (Flüte, Oboe, Violine) und Generalbass = for descant recorder (flute, oboe, violin) and continuo. (Frescobaldi, Girolamo). *Schott. £3.20* VSRPJ (B79-51242)
Liebeserklärung für ein verkanntes Instrument : 6 Stücke für Akkordeon, 1977. (Motte, Diether de la). *Bärenreiter. Unpriced* RSPMJ (B79-50255)
Lied des Vogelstellers : drei leichte Chorlieder No.1. (Genzmer, Harald). *Schott. £0.72* EZDW (B79-50895)
Lied im Freien. D.572. (Schubert, Franz). *Bärenreiter. £0.99* GEZDW (B79-50115)
Lieder ohne Worte. *Selections : arr.* 5 Lieder ohne Worte : für zwei Gitarren = for two guitars. (Mendelssohn, Felix). *Schott. £4.00* TSNUK (B79-51172)
Lieder und Tänze des Todes. (Mussorgsky, Modest). *Breitkopf und Härtel. £8.40* KDW (B79-50960)
Ligeti, György. Passacaglia ungherese : für Cembalo = for harpsichord. *Schott. £3.70* QRPHT (B79-51114)
Liliencron, Detlev von. Die Musik kommt : Männerchor und kleines Blasorchester. (Scheck, Helmut). *Schott. £5.60* GE/UMDW (B79-50922)
Lind, Jon. Boogie wonderland. (Willis, Allee). *Rondor : Chappell. Unpriced* KDW/GB (B79-50534)
L'invitation au voyage. *arr.* Voyage : for string orchestra. (Corigliano, John). *Schirmer. Unpriced* RXMJ (B79-50664)
Lion of Suffolk : for organ. (Williamson, Malcolm). *Weinberger. Unpriced* RJ (B79-50652)
Lionheart. *arr.* Lionheart. (Bush, Kate). *EMI. Unpriced* KDW/GB (B79-50135)
Lipka, Alfred. Viola
1: Stücke für Viola und Klavier. *Neue Musik : Breitkopf und Härtel. £2.10* SQP/AY (B79-51156)
Listen, sing and play
1 : Senior infants, lessons 1-10. Workbook. (Lally, Maureen). *Educational Company of Ireland.* Sd. *£0.35* A/M (B79-02026)
Liszt, Franz.
Consolations. G.172. Consolations. *Stainer and Bell. Unpriced* QPJ (B79-50632) ISBN 0-85249-526-9
Klavierwerke = Piano works
Heft 12: Einzelne Charakterstücke 2 = Individual character pieces. *Bärenreiter. £5.94* QP/AZ (B79-50618)
Phantasie über ungarische Volksmelodien = Fantasia on Hungarian folk themes. *Eulenburg. £1.20* MMJ (B79-50179)
Littell, Barbara.
March for a celebration. *Warner : Blossom. Unpriced* UMMGM (B79-50720)
Strawberry rock. *Warner : Blossom. Unpriced* UMMJ (B79-50723)
Little bitty baby : for SAB-SA chorus and piano. (Rocherolle, Eugénie R). *Warner : Blossom. Unpriced* DW (B79-50035)
Little blue boy : for tenor horn and brass band. (Woods, Stanley). *Chester Music. Unpriced* WMPWTT (B79-51305)
Little lamb : for unison treble choir with piano, four hands accompaniment. (Smith, Gregg). *Schirmer. £0.35* JFLDW (B79-50948)
Little place where I was born : setting for male voices (T.T.B.B.). (Larbalestier, Philip George). *(Ffordd yr Osaf) : Cyngor Gwasanaethau Gwirfoddol Clwyd (Clwyd Voluntary Services Council). Unpriced* GDW (B79-50503)
Little place where I was born : setting for male voices, T.T.B.B. (Larbalestier, Philip George). *Ffordd yr osaf : Cyngor Gwasanapthau Gwiyfiddol Clwyd = Clwyd Voluntary Services Council. Unpriced* GDW (B79-50921)
Little theatre music : for flute, clarinet, trumpet, violin, cello and percussion. (Frazer, Alan). *7 Garrick St., W.C.2 : Middle Eight Music. Unpriced* NYE/J (B79-50199)
Living in the city : a songbook. (Swift, Dave). *59 Watney St., E.1 : Basement Writers.* Sd. *£0.15* KE/TSDW (B79-50545)
Living Lord : eighty hymns for the eighties. *Weinberger. Unpriced* DM/AY (B79-50838)
Living music. (Spence, Keith). *H. Hamilton. £6.95* A (B79-20262) ISBN 0-241-10116-6
Livingston, Jerry. Casper the friendly ghost. *arr.* Casper the friendly ghost. *Warner : Blossom. Unpriced* WMK/DW (B79-50379)
Llandudno's operatic tradition. (Jones, Ivor Wynne). *71 Llandudno Rd, Penrhyn Bay. Llandudno, Gwynedd : Pegasus.* Sd. *£0.50* AC/E(YDKP/X) (B79-27786)
Lloyd, Llewelyn Southworth. Intervals, scales and temperaments ... New ed. *Macdonald and Jane's. £9.95* A/B (B79-50003) ISBN 0-354-04229-7
Llwyd, Jethro. Sonatina, harp, op.20, no.6, E flat major. Sonatina in E flat for harp. (Dussek, Jan Ladislav). *Adlais. Unpriced* TQPMEM (B79-50295)
Lobo, Alfonso.
Liber primus missarum. Ave maria. Ave Maria : for 8 voices. *72 Brewery Rd, N.7 : Mapa mundi. Unpriced* EZDJ (B79-50063)
Liber primus missarum. Ave regina coelorum. Ave regina coelorum : Compline and votive antiphon for the season from Christmas to the Purification. *72 Brewery Rd, N.7 : Mapa mundi. Unpriced* EZDGKR/LF (B79-50057)
Liber primus missarum. Credo quod redemptor mens vivit. Credo quod redemptor mens vivit : pro defunctis, for 4 voices. *Mapa mundi. Unpriced* EZDJ/KDN (B79-50068)
Liber primus missarum. O quam suavis est, Domine. O quam suavis est, Domine : motet for the Feast of Corpus Christi, for 6 voices. *72 Brewery Rd, N.7 : Mapa mundi. Unpriced* EZDJ/LNC (B79-50088)
Liber primus missarum. Quam pulchri sunt gressus tui.

Quam pulchri sunt gressus tui. *Mapa mundi. Unpriced* EZDJ (B79-50064)

Liber primus missarum. Versa est in luctum. Versa est in luctum : ad exsequias Philip II, cathol. regis Hisp. = for the funeral of Philip II, Catholic King of Spain. *72 Brewery Rd, N.7 : Mapa mundi. Unpriced* EZDJ/KDN (B79-50069)

Liber primus missarum. Vivo ego, dicit Dominus. Vivo ego, dicit Dominus : motet for Lent for 4 voices. *72 Brewery Rd, N.7 : Mapa mundi. Unpriced* EZDJ/LG (B79-50080)

Lockspeiser, Edward.

Debussy : his life and mind

Vol.1: 1862-1902. 2nd ed. *Cambridge University Press. £12.00* BDJ(N) (B79-20263) ISBN 0-521-22053-x

Vol.2: 1902-1918. *Cambridge University Press. £15.00* BDJ(N) (B79-20264) ISBN 0-521-22054-8

Loeillet, Jean Baptiste.

Sonatas, flutes (2), op.5, bk.2. Six sonatas, opus 5, book 2 for 2 flutes/oboes/recorders in C without bass (Priestman VI). *Musica rara. Unpriced* VRNUE (B79-51220)

Sonatas, recorders (treble) (2). Six sonatas for 2 treble recorders (flutes) without bass ... *Musica rara. Unpriced* VSSNUE (B79-51249)

Loevendie, Johannes Theodorus. Six Turkish folkpoems : for female voice and 7 instruments (1977). *Donemus Lengnick. Unpriced* KFE/NYDPNPDW (B79-50548)

Loewe, Frederick. Paint your wagon. They call the wind Maria. *arr.* They call the wind Maria : S.A.C.(T.) B. with piano. *Chappell. Unpriced* DW (B79-50850)

Loewenburg, Alfred. Annals of opera, 1597-1940. 3rd ed., revised and corrected. *J. Calder. £30.00* AC/E(X25344) (B79-02988) ISBN 0-7145-3657-1

Lollipop lady : a musical play for primary schools. (Adams, Chris). *43 Clifton Rd. : Youngsong. Unpriced* CQN (B79-50825)

London, Elizabeth. Twelve oboe duets. (Gordon, Christopher). *265 Magdalen Road, SW18 3NZ : Janus Music. Unpriced* VTNU (B79-50771)

London. *Inner London Education Authority. See* Inner London Education Authority.

London Lassus series.

Lasso, Orlando di. Hieremiae prophetae lamentationes, et alia piae cantiones. *Selections.* Lamentations for Tenebrae on Maundy Thursday, Feria V in Coena Domini ad Matatinum. *72 Brewery Rd, N.7 : Mapa Mundi. Unpriced* EZDJ/LHM (B79-50081)

Lasso, Orlando di. Hieremiae prophetae lamentationes, et alia piae cantiones. *Selections.* Six responsories for Tenebrae on Maundy Thursday, feria V in Coena Domini ad Matatinum. *72 Brewery Rd, N.7 : Mapa mundi. Unpriced* EZDJ/LHM (B79-50082)

London suite : for elementary string quartets. (Standford, Patric). *7 Garrick St., W.C.2 : Middle Eight Music. Unpriced* RXNS (B79-50269)

London University. *See* University of London.

Longman music topics.

Farmer, Paul. Into the classics. *Longman.* Sd. *£0.65* A(XFWE101) (B79-33549) ISBN 0-582-21576-5

Farmer, Paul. Pop. *Longman.* Sd. *£0.65* A/GB (B79-32712) ISBN 0-582-21577-3

Farmer, Paul. Ragtime & blues. *Longman.* Sd. *£0.65* AQPHXJ (B79-36912) ISBN 0-582-21579-x

Lorca, Federico García. *See* García Lorca, Federico.

Lord of the dance. (Carter, Sydney). *Galliard. Unpriced* ELDM (B79-50453)

Louis Moyse flute collection. Weber, Carl Maria von, *Freiherr.* Trio, flute, cello & piano, op.63. Trio, op.63, for flute, cello (or viola) and piano. *Schirmer. £6.10* NURNT (B79-51039)

Love of three oranges. L'amour des trois oranges. Opus 33 : opéra en 4 actes et 10 tableaux avec un prologue d'après Carlo Gozzi. (Prokofiev, Sergei). *Boosey and Hawkes. Unpriced* CQC (B79-50822)

Lowden, Bob.

Hopelessly devoted to you. *arr.* Hopelessly devoted to you. (Farrar, John). *Chappell. Unpriced* UMK/DW (B79-51202)

Stayin' alive, You need me, plus 12 hot hits. *Chappell. Unpriced* LK/DW/GBB/AY (B79-51011)

Löwy, Walter Keller-. *See* Keller-Löwy, Walter.

Lully, Jean Baptiste. Le ballet des muses : for baroque ensemble. *Associated Music. £15.10* RXM/HM (B79-50663)

Luminos. Op.16a : for basset horn (or clarinet B flat) and piano. (Pert, Morris). *Weinberger. Unpriced* VVXPJ (B79-50361)

Luna. (Shipley, Edward). *Fentone Music : Breitkopf and Härtel. Unpriced* QPJ (B79-51088)

Luna : for piano. (Shipley, Edward). *Fentone Music. £3.00* QPJ (B79-51089)

Lusse, Charles de. L'art de la flûte traversière. *Selections.* 12 caprices : for solo flute. *Nova Music. Unpriced* VRPMJ (B79-51232)

Lustige Witwe. *Selections : arr.* Songs from The merry widow (Die lustige Witwe). (Lehár, Franz). *Glocken. Unpriced* KDW (B79-50957)

Lute music. *Selections : arr.* Four pieces. (Newsidler, Hans). *DeCamera : Schirmer. £1.50* TSPMK (B79-51190)

Lyell, Margaret. Barcarollina : for flute and piano. *Roberton. £1.00* VRPJ (B79-51223)

Lyle, Thomas. Kelvingrove : for four-part chorus of mixed voices a cappella with optional piano. (Rhein, Robert). *Schirmer. £0.55* EZDW (B79-50902)

Lyons, Graham.

Set two : clarinet duets for teacher and pupil

Vol.1. *Chester Music. Unpriced* VVNU/AF (B79-51277)

Vol.1. *Chester Music. Unpriced* VVNU/AF (B79-51278)

Set two : flute duets for teacher and pupil

Vol.1. *Chester Music. Unpriced* VRNU/AF (B79-51219)

Vol.2. *Chester Music. Unpriced* VRNU/AF (B79-51218)

Starting together : easy duets for recorder and guitar groups

Vol.1. *Chester Music. Unpriced* VSPLTSK/DW/AY (B79-51238)

Starting together : easy duets for recorders and guitar groups

Vol.2. *Chester Music. Unpriced* VSPLTSK/DW/AY (B79-51239)

Vol.3. *Chester Music. Unpriced* VSPLTSK/DW/AY (B79-51240)

Ma bonny lad : five traditional songs from Northumbria. *Roberton. £1.50* KDW/G/AYDJJ (B79-50963)

Maasz, Gerhard. Wir sind die Musikanten : eine kleine Instrumentenschau für Orchester, Chor ad lib. (2 gl. Stimmen) und Sprecher ad lib. *Schott. £6.00* MJ (B79-50161)

McAfferty, Maureen. Out of this world. *Vocal score.* Out of this world : musical in two scenes. (Glen, Robert). *Weinberger. Unpriced* CM (B79-50818)

McAuliffe, Gary. Sing a song

1. Teacher's book. *Nelson : ILEA Learning Materials Service.* Sp. *£2.75* A/GR(VG) (B79-07467) ISBN 0-17-413002-3

McBride, Angus. Musical instruments. (Ardley, Neil). *Macmillan.* Pbk. *£0.50* AL/B (B79-22637) ISBN 0-333-26156-9

McCabe, Rose Mary. Cantors : a collection of Gregorian chants. *Cambridge University Press. Unpriced* JEZDTD (B79-50933) ISBN 0-521-22149-8

McCarthy, John. Broadway Joe. *arr.* She was an acrobat's daughter, an English music hall song : for four-part chorus of mixed voices with piano accompaniment. (Ruby, Harry). *Roberton. Unpriced* DW (B79-50450)

McCartney, Paul.

B-side the seaside. Seaside woman. *arr.* Seaside woman. *MPL Communications. Unpriced* KDW/GB (B79-50968)

Back to the egg. *MPL Communications. Unpriced* KDW/GB (B79-50966)

Back to the egg. Getting closer. *arr.* Getting closer and Baby's request. *MPL Communications. Unpriced* KDW/GB (B79-50967)

Mull of Kintyre. *arr.* Mull of Kintyre. *Music Sales. Unpriced* DW (B79-50034)

Wings greatest. *MPL : Music Sales. Unpriced* KDW/GB (B79-50136)

McCartney, Paul. *See* Beatles, The.

McCray, James. Four introits : unison chorus and hand bells. *Broude : Breitkopf und Härtel. £0.42* JE/XSQDH (B79-50511)

McCrea, Lilian. Diddly, diddly, dumpty : finger plays, face games, action rhymes, fun songs, for nursery and infant schools. (Staton, Kathleen). *EMI. Unpriced* JFEZDW/GR (B79-50524)

Macdonald, Hugh. Les Troyens, part 2. Chasse royale et orage. Chase royale et orage. (Berlioz, Hector). *Bärenreiter. Unpriced* MMJ (B79-50173)

MacDonald, John. High surge of the sea. *arr.* The song of the sea. An ataireachd ard = ('High surge of the sea'). *Bosworth and Co. Unpriced* KDW (B79-50526)

McDonough, Edward J. Come to me, your gentle shepherd. (Gentle shepherd) : theme song. *TRO : Essex Music. Unpriced* KDH (B79-50952)

McGegan, Nicolas. Tom Jones. *Vocal score.* Tom Jones : comic opera in three acts based on the novel by Henry Fielding = opera comique en trois actes d'après le roman de Henry Fielding. (Philidor, François André Danican). *Boosey and Hawkes. £7.50* CC (B79-50013)

McGuire, Edward. Rant : for solo violin. *Scotus Music. Unpriced* SPMH (B79-50684) ISBN 0-86100-009-9

Machine : a music mime, for choir, percussion and tape. (Wesley-Smith, Martin). *Universal. Unpriced* FE/XMDW/JN (B79-50915)

MacIver, Donald. High surge of the sea. *arr.* The song of the sea. An ataireachd ard = ('High surge of the sea'). (MacDonald, John). *Bosworth and Co. Unpriced* KDW (B79-50526)

McJazz manuscripts : a collection of the writings of Sandy Brown. (Brown, Sandy). *Faber. £6.95 : CIP rev.* AMT(P) (B79-10483) ISBN 0-571-11319-2

McLarnon, Gerard. Thérèse. *Vocal score.* Thérèse ... (Tavener, John). *Chester Music. Unpriced* CC (B79-50817)

McLeish, Kenneth.

Brahms. *Heinemann. £2.50* BBT(N) (B79-27782) ISBN 0-434-95128-5

Schubert. *Heinemann. £2.50* BSF(N) (B79-26550) ISBN 0-434-95127-7

McLeish, Valerie.

Brahms. (McLeish, Kenneth). *Heinemann. £2.50* BBT(N) (B79-27782) ISBN 0-434-95128-5

Schubert. (McLeish, Kenneth). *Heinemann. £2.50* BSF(N) (B79-26550) ISBN 0-434-95127-7

McLeod, Morag. Music and song from The Boys of the Lough : music and songs of Ireland, Scotland and Shetland. *Gilderoy. Unpriced* KEZDW/G/AYDL (B79-50546) ISBN 0-9505982-0-8

McNess-Eames, Vera.

I want to walk like an elephant : musical fun for 'tinies' with chord symbols for piano, piano accordion and guitar. *Stockwell.* Pbk. *£0.65* JFDW (B79-50938) ISBN 0-7223-1256-3

Maconchy, Elizabeth. Four miniatures for unaccompanied chorus SATB. *Chester Music. Unpriced* EZDW (B79-50479)

MacPhee, James. High surge of the sea. *arr.* The song of the sea. An ataireachd ard = ('High surge of the sea'). (MacDonald, John). *Bosworth and Co. Unpriced* KDW (B79-50526)

MacRae, Ian. High surge of the sea. *arr.* The song of the sea. An ataireachd ard = ('High surge of the sea'). (MacDonald, John). *Bosworth and Co. Unpriced* KDW (B79-50526)

M'sieur Offenbach : a suite for clarinet, alto and tenor saxophones. (Offenbach, Jacques). *7 Garrick St., W.C.2 : Middle Eight Music. Unpriced* VNTK/DW (B79-50324)

Madden, John.

Concerto grosso, op.6, no.3, C major. *arr.* Trio sonata in d. (Corelli, Arcangelo). *Nova Music. Unpriced* VSSNTPWK/LF (B79-51248)

Potpourri, viola & orchestra, op.94. Potpourri for viola and orchestra, op.94. (Hummel, Johann Nepomuk). *Musica rara. Unpriced* SQPK (B79-50282)

Sonata, oboe & continuo, op.2, no.5, G minor. Sonata in g, op.2, no.5 for oboe or violin and basso continuo. (Schickhardt, Johann Christian). *Nova Music. Unpriced* VTPE (B79-51260)

Sonata, recorders (treble) (2) & continuo, G major. Sonata in G, 2 treble recorders (or flutes), 2 oboes/violins (or flutes) & basso continuo. (Keller, Gottfried). *Nova Music. Unpriced* VSSNTPWE (B79-51246)

Sonata, trumpet, bassoon & continuo, C major. Sonata à 3 for trumpet/oboe/flute/violin, bassoon & basso continuo. (Poglietti, Alessandro). *Musica rara. Unpriced* NWNTE (B79-51046)

Sonatae tam aris quam aulis servientes. Sonata, trumpet & string orchestra, no.4, C major. *arr.* Sonata 4 for trumpet, violin, 2 violas and basso continuo. (Biber, Heinrich Ignaz Franz). *Musica rara. Unpriced* NUXSNTK/LE (B79-51043)

Sonatae tam aris quam aulis servientes. Sonata, trumpet & string orchestra, no.12, C. major. *arr.* Sonata 12 for 2 trumpets, 2 violins, 2 violas, cello. (Biber, Heinrich Ignaz Franz). *Muscia rara. Unpriced* NUXSNTK/LE (B79-51044)

Sonatae tam aris quam aulis servientes. Sonata, trumpets (2) & string orchestra, no.1, C major. *arr.* Sonata 1 for 2 trumpets, 2 violins, 2 violas, cello & basso continuo. (Biber, Heinrich Ignaz Franz). *Musica rara. Unpriced* NUXSNRK/LE (B79-51042)

Madi, Tito. Album para piano. *Fermata do Brasil : Clifford Essex. Unpriced* QPK/AH (B79-51096)

Madrigal : für achtstimmigen Chor, 1975. (Trojahn, Manfred). *Bärenreiter. £3.96* EZDW (B79-50099)

Madrigali et ricercari a quattro voci. *Selections.* Five ricercare in four parts for brass. (Gabrieli, Andrea). *Musica rara. Unpriced* WSN (B79-50798)

Madrigali et ricercari a quattro voci. *Selections.* Five ricercare in four parts : for brass or recorders. (Gabrieli, Andrea). *Musica rara. Unpriced* VSNS (B79-51235)

Madrigali et ricercari a quattro voci. *Selections.* Five ricercare in four parts for recorders. (Gabrieli, Andrea). *Musica rara. Unpriced* VSN (B79-50759)

Madrigals to foure voices (1599). (Bennet, John). *Stainer and Bell. Unpriced* EZDU (B79-50473) ISBN 0-85249-456-4

Magic flute of James Galway. *Novello. Unpriced* VRPL/AAY (B79-50754)

Magic fountain. *Vocal score.* The magic fountain : lyric drama in 3 acts. (Delius, Frederick). *Delius Trust, Boosey and Hawkes. Unpriced* CC (B79-50010)

Magician. Op.88. *Vocal score.* The magician : an opera in one act. (Hoddinott, Alun). *Oxford University Press. Unpriced* CC (B79-50011) ISBN 0-19-336839-0

Magnificat and Nunc dimittis. (Burgon, Geoffrey). *Chester Music. Unpriced* FDGPP (B79-50907)

Magnificat octavi toni : for 8 voices. (Vivanco, Sebastian de). *Mapa mundi. Unpriced* EZDGKK (B79-50056)

Magnificat praetur rerum seriem : upon the motet by Josquin, for 6 voices. (Lasso, Orlando di). *72 Brewery Rd, N.7 : Mapa mundi. Unpriced* EZDGKK (B79-50055)

Mahler, Alma. Selected letters of Gustav Mahler. (Mahler, Gustav). *Faber. £15.00 : CIP rev.* BME(N) (B79-14911) ISBN 0-571-08643-8

Mahler, Gustav. Selected letters of Gustav Mahler. *Faber. £15.00 : CIP rev.* BME(N) (B79-14911) ISBN 0-571-08643-8

Maichelbek, Franz Anton. Die auf dem Clavier spielende und das Gehör vergnügeude Caecilia (1736) : acht Sonaten, für Tasteninstrumente. *Merseburger Bärenreiter. £5.45* PWPE (B79-50610)

Majnun symphony. (Symphony no.24). Op.273 : for tenor solo, four-part chorus of mixed voices, trumpet in C, solo violin and string orchestra. (Hovhaness, Alan). *Associated Music. £9.10* EMDX (B79-50869)

Makin' your own country instruments. (De Paule, Andy). *Van Nostrand Reinhold.* Pbk. *£4.45* AL/BC (B79-32720) ISBN 0-442-26117-9

Making musical instruments, strings and keyboard. *Faber. £15.00 : CIP rev.* AL/BC (B79-00571) ISBN 0-571-10870-9

Mamma's eyes : for stage band. (Levitt, Rod). *Schirmer. Unpriced* MTJ (B79-50595)

Man of iron : a portrait of Willy Eisenhart, for piano. (Thomson, Virgil). *Schirmer. £1.20* QPJ (B79-50639)

Mann, Robert. Duet, flute & piano. *arr.* Duo for violin and piano. (Copland, Aaron). *Boosey and Hawkes. Unpriced* SPK (B79-51150)

Manuel de Falla and the Spanish musical renaissance.

(James, Burnett). *Gollancz. £6.95* BFB (B79-16837) ISBN 0-575-02645-6

Marais, Marin. Pièces de violes, liv. 4. *Selections : arr.* Cinque antiche danze francesi. *Berben : Breitkopf und Härtel. £1.90* SQPLTSK (B79-50686)

March and hunting piece. Op.40. *arr.* Nonet for... horns. (Fröhlich, Johannes Frederik). *(116 Long Acre, W.C.2) : Paxman. £4.00* WTNM (B79-51321)

March for a celebration. (Littell, Barbara). *Warner Blossom. Unpriced* UMMGM (B79-50720)

Marcha militar no.1. (Granados, Enrique). *Leonard, Gould and Bolttler. £0.40* QPK/AGM (B79-50641)

Marchbank, Pearce.

Beatles in their own words. (Beatles, The). *Omnibus Press.* Pbk. *£2.50* AKDW/GB/E(P) (B79-26552) ISBN 0-86001-540-8

Bob Dylan in his own words. (Dylan, Bob). *Omnibus Press.* Pbk. *£2.50* AKDW/HKR/E(P) (B79-31930) ISBN 0-86001-542-4

Marche slave. Op.31. *arr.* Marche slave. (Tchaikovsky, Peter). *Oxford University Press. Unpriced* MK/AGM (B79-50162) ISBN 0-19-367910-8

Mare, Walter de la. *See* De la Mare, Walter.

Marek, George Richard. Chopin. *Weidenfeld and Nicolson. £8.50* BCE(N) (B79-11134) ISBN 0-297-77616-9

Marenzio, Luca.

Motecta festorum totius anni ... liber primus. Hodie Christus natus est. Hodie Christas natus est. *72 Brewery Rd, N.7 : Mapa mundi. Unpiced* EZDJ/LF (B79-50073)

Motecta festorum totius anni ... liber primus. O sacrum convivium. O sacrum convivium : motet for the Feast of Corpus Christi, for 4 voices. *72 Brewery Rd, N.7 : Mapa mundi. Unpriced* EZDJ/LNC (B79-50089)

Margitay, Sándor. Anthologia organi : Orgelmusik aus acht Jahrhunderten

Band 5: Die Meister der Sweelinck-Schule. *Schott. £8.00* R/AY (B79-50227)

Margittay, Sándor.

Anthologia organi : Orgelmusik aus acht Jahrhunderten Band 6: Frescobaldi und sein Wirkungskreis. *Schott. £8.00* R/AY (B79-50228)

Band 7: Das italienische Barock. *Schott. £8.00* R/AY (B79-51116)

Band 8: Französische Orgelmusik von Titelouze bis d'Aquin. *Schott. £8.00* R/AY (B79-51117)

Maria stabat. (Gabrieli, Andrea). *36 Ranelagh Gdns W.6 : Cathedral Music. Unpriced* EZDJ/LK (B79-50084)

Mark, Michael L. Contemporary music education. *Schirmer Books : Collier Macmillan. £11.25* A(VC/YT) (B79-19443) ISBN 0-02-871640-x

Markus-Passion für Solostimmen und vierstimmigen Chor a cappella. (Peranda, Marco Giuseppe). *VEB Deutscher Verlag : Breitkopf and Härtel. £2.70* EZDD/LK (B79-50872)

Marling, Yvonne Rodd-. *See* Rodd-Marling, Yvonne.

Marshall, Arthur W. Sonata, recorder (treble) & continuo, op.3, no.2, C minor. Sonata in C, opus 3, no.2, for treble recorder and basso continuo. (Finger, Gottfried). *Nova Music. Unpriced* VSSPE (B79-51252)

Marshall, D J. Regimental quick march, Worcestershire and Sherwood Foresters Regiment, 'Young May moon' and 'Royal Windsor'. *Boosey and Hawkes. Unpriced* UMMGM/KH (B79-50721)

Martin, Bill. The water babies. *Selections: arr.* The water babies. (Coulter, Phil). *Chappell. Unpriced* QPK/JR (B79-51105)

Martin, Frank.

Agnus Dei : pour orgue = für Orgel. *Bärenreiter. £2.97* RDGF (B79-50231)

Dédicace de Pierre de Ronsard : 1945 : pour ténor et piano = für Tenor und Klavier. *Bärenreiter. £2.64* KGHDW (B79-50561)

Ode à la musique. *Choral score.* Ode à musique. *Bärenreiter. £1.16* DADH (B79-50419)

Martin, James. John Denver : Rocky Mountain wonderboy. *Everest.* Pbk. *£0.75* AKDW/GB/E(P) (B79-50006) ISBN 0-905018-56-7

Martìn de Rivafrencha. Two motets sic : for four voices. *72 Brewery Rd, N.7 : Mapa mundi. Unpriced* GEZDJ (B79-50112)

Martinu, Bohuslav. Rhapsody - concerto : für Viola und Orchester = pro violu a orchestr = for viola and orchestra. *Bärenreiter. £12.54* MPSQF (B79-50583)

Martner, Knud. Selected letters of Gustav Mahler. (Mahler, Gustav). *Faber. £15.00 : CIP rev.* BME(N) (B79-14911) ISBN 0-571-08643-8

Mary's carol. (Hedges, Anthony). *Universal. Unpriced* EZDP/LF (B79-50886)

Marzuki, Marilyn S. Mikrokosmos. *arr.* Mikrokosmos for harp : 20 intermediate solos and ensembles for harps with and without pedals. (Bartók, Béla). *Boosey and Hawkes. Unpriced* TQK/AF (B79-50694)

Mason, H B. Memoirs of a gunner bandsman, 1907-1932. *The author : Distributed by Stockwell.* Pbk. *Unpriced* AUMM/E(QB/P) (B79-06708) ISBN 0-7223-1185-0

Mason, Tony.

The night sky : for elementary brass quartet (2 trumpets, 2 trombones). *7 Garrick St., W.C.2 : Middle Eight Music. Unpriced* WNS (B79-50387)

Three ways to go : a suite for three guitars. *7 Garrick St., London W.C.2 : Middle Eight Music. Unpriced* TSNTK/AAY (B79-50301)

Mass Euge bone : for 6 voices. (Tye, Christopher). *72 Brewery Rd, N.7 : Mapa mundi. Unpriced* EZDG (B79-50051)

Mass for Elizabeth Seton. Missa brevis : for SATB chorus with organ or piano accompaniment. (Reinhardt, Stephen). *Broude : Breitkopf und Härtel. £2.10* DG (B79-50424)

Master musicians series. Layton, Robert. Sibelius. 2nd ed. *Dent. £4.50 : CIP entry* BSH (B78-37096) ISBN 0-460-03169-4

Master of Ashmore : opera in three acts. (Olive, Leslie). *Jon Adams. Unpriced* CC (B79-50012)

Master of Ashmore. *Vocal score.* The Master of Ashmore : opera in three acts. (Olive, Leslie). *Jon Adams. Unpriced* CC (B79-50012)

Masters, Anthony Smith-. *See* Smith-Masters, Anthony.

Masters, Stanley Smith-. *See* Smith-Masters, Stanley.

Masterworks of choral music.

Fiske, Roger. Beethoven's Missa solemnis. *Elek. £5.95* BBJADG (B79-14016) ISBN 0-236-40146-7

Steinitz, Paul. Bach's passions. *Elek. £5.95* BBCADD/LK (B79-14916) ISBN 0-236-40132-7

Matheu, Manuel Maria de los Dolores de Falla y. *See* Falla, Manuel de.

Mathews, Eve. Sound tracks

3: Sound poems. (Paynter, John). *Cambridge University Press. £1.95* A/D(VF) (B78-23591) ISBN 0-521-20580-8

Mathias, William. Dance variations : for orchestra. *Oxford University Press. Unpriced* MRH/T (B79-51034) ISBN 0-19-365669-8

Matthews, Colin.

A birthday hansel. Op.92. *Selections : arr.* Four Burns songs : for high voice and piano. (Britten, Benjamin, *Baron Britten*). *Faber Music. Unpriced* KFTDW (B79-50153)

Un colloque sentimental = A sentimental conversation : cycle for medium voice and piano. *Faber Music. Unpriced* KFVDW (B79-51007)

The planets : suite for large orchestra. Op.32. (Holst, Gustav). *Curwen. Unpriced* MMG (B79-51017)

Matthews, David. Paul Bunyan. Op.17. *Vocal score.* Paul Bunyan : an operetta in two acts and a prologue, op.17. (Britten, Benjamin, *Baron Britten*). *Faber Music. Unpriced* CF (B79-50014)

Matthews, Denis. Sonata, piano, no.6, K.284, D major. Sonata in D, K.284, 205b, 1775. (Mozart, Wolfgang Amadeus). *Associated Board of the Royal Schools of Music. Unpriced* QPE (B79-50622)

Matthus, Siegfried.

Concerto, cello (1975). Konzert für Violoncello und Orchester. *VEB Deutscher Verlag für Musik : Breitkopf und Härtel. £5.40* MPSRF (B79-50585)

Trio, flute, viola & harp. Trio für Flöte, Bratsche und Harfe. *VEB Deutscher Verlag für Musik : Breitkopf und Härtel. £2.10* NVRNT (B79-50602)

May, Jane.

Amid nature. Op.63. A song went to my heart. So many songs = Es zog manch Lied : for four-part chorus of mixed voices a cappella. (Dvořák, Antonín). *Schirmer. £0.35* EZDW (B79-50890)

Amid nature. Op.63. Birch tree by the verdant slope. Birch tree on green hill = Birke am grünen Bergeshang : for four-part chorus of mixed voices a cappella. (Dvořák, Antonín). *Schirmer. £0.45* EZDW (B79-50891)

Amid nature. Op.63. Golden fields. Golden meadows = Goldne Fluren : for four-part chorus of mixed voices a cappella. (Dvořák, Antonín). *Schirmer. £0.35* EZDW (B79-50892)

Amid nature. Op.63. This is in truth a day of joy. A summer day = Ein Sommertag : for four-part chorus of mixed voices a cappella. (Dvořák, Antonín). *Schirmer. £0.45* EZDW (B79-50893)

Bouquet of Czech folk songs. B72. The betrayed shepherd. The abducted shepherd = Der entführte Hirt : for four-part chorus of men's voices a cappella. (Dvořák, Antonín). *Schirmer. £0.35* GEZDW (B79-50925)

Bouquet of Czech folk songs. B72. The sweetheart's resolve. If you should go away = Wenn du fortgehst : for four-part chorus of men's voices a cappella. (Dvořák, Antonín). *Schirmer. £0.35* GEZDW (B79-50926)

Dobry den. What a day : Dobry den : a choral cycle, for two-part chorus of young voices with piano accompaniment or a cappella. (Laburda, Jiří). *Schirmer. £2.10* FDW (B79-50495)

Domine, ne in furore tuo arguas me. Oh my Lord, let not your blinding fury - My heart = Domine, ne in furore - Cor meum : for four-part chorus of men's voices a cappella. (Josquin des Prés). *Schirmer. £0.75* GEZDJ (B79-50504)

Mayr, Simon. Sinfonia concertante, violins (3). *arr.* Sinfonia concertante für drei Violinen und Orchester. Zum ersten Mal. *Litolff : Peters. Unpriced* SNSQK/LE (B79-50680)

Meacham, Frank W. The American patrol. *Studio Music. Unpriced* WMJ (B79-50373)

Meadow, hedge, cuckoo : variations for solo alto recorder on John Dowland's ayre 'Away with these self-loving lads'. (Sterne, Colin). *Galaxy Music : Galliard. Unpriced* VSSPM/T (B79-50348)

Medway, Carol. Divertimentos, K. Anh. 229. *Selections: arr.* Six movements from the Mozart divertimenti. (Mozart, Wolfgang Amadeus). *Cramer. Unpriced* VSNTK (B79-50340)

Meek, Bill. Songs of the Irish in America. *25 Shonick Rd. Skerries : Gilbert Dalton. Unpriced* JEZDW/G/AYDM (B79-50121)

Meerwein, Georg. Quintet, wind & piano, op.2, E flat major. Quintett Es-dur für Klavier, Oboe, Klarinette, Horn und Fagott, Op.2. (Lannoy, Eduard von). *Eulenburg. Unpriced* NWNR (B79-50193)

Meira, Augusto. Ciranda do bom barqueiro : cantiga da infância. *Sonata : Clifford Essex. Unpriced* KDW (B79-50958)

Melusine. *Chappell. Unpriced* KDW/G/AYH (B79-50964)

Memoirs of a gunner bandsman, 1907-1932. (Mason, H B). *The author : Distributed by Stockwell.* Pbk. *Unpriced* AUMM/E(QB/P) (B79-06708) ISBN 0-7223-1185-0

Mendelssohn, Felix.

Eine Auswahl aus 'Sechs Kinderstücke'. Op.72 und 'Lieder ohne Worte'. *Breitkopf und Härtel. £2.10* QPJ (B79-51085)

Christus. *Selections : arr.* There shall a star from Jacob come forth : three excerpts from Christus. *Addington Press. Unpriced* DH/LF (B79-50834)

Lieder ohne Worte. *Selections : arr.* 5 Lieder ohne Worte : für zwei Gitarren = for two guitars. *Schott. £4.00* TSNUK (B79-51172)

Mendoza, Anne.

Olé : twelve Spanish songs. *Oxford University Press. Unpriced* JFE/LDW/G/AYK (B79-50523) ISBN 0-19-330597-6

See-saw sacaradown : fourteen childrens sic songs with simple accompaniments for classroom instruments. *Chappell. Unpriced* JFE/XDW/GJ/AY (B79-50947)

Menotti, Gian Carlo. Amahl and the night visitors. *Selections : arr.* Amahl and the night visitors : piano selections. *Schirmer. £3.00* QPK/CC (B79-51097)

Menuhin, Yehudi. Unfinished journey. *Futura Publications.* Pbk. *£1.60* AS/E(P) (B79-11136) ISBN 0-7088-1329-1

Merewether, Richard. March and hunting piece. Op.40. *arr.* Nonet for... horns. (Fröhlich, Johannes Frederik). *(116 Long Acre, W.C.2) : Paxman. £4.00* WTNM (B79-51321)

Merry muses of Caledonia. The secret cabinet of Robert Burns : merry muses of Caledonia. (Burns, Robert). New ed.. *P. Harris. £3.50* AKDW/K/G/KDX (B79-36915) ISBN 0-904505-84-7

'Mersey beat', the beginnings of the Beatles. *Omnibus Press; 78 Newman St., W1P 3LA : Distributed by Book Sales Limited.* Pbk. *£2.95* AKDW/GB/E(P) (B79-36913) ISBN 0-86001-415-0

Mersson, Boris. Fünf Klavierstücke. Op.23. *Eulenburg. £2.80* QPJ (B79-50633)

Mésalliance : for piano and orchestra. (Rands, Bernard). *Universal. Unpriced* MPQ (B79-50182)

Messa di requiem. Requiem. (Verdi, Giuseppe). *Dover Publications : Constable. Unpriced* EMDGKAV (B79-50043) ISBN 0-486-23682-x

Metamorphoses : for large orchestra. (Blake, David). *Novello. £2.75* MMJ (B79-50174)

Metamorphosis : dance. (Goehr, Alexander). *Schott. Unpriced* MMJ (B79-50176)

Méthode pour la flûte. Exercices de tous genres. 25 Etüden für Flöte = 25 studies for flute = 25 exercices pour flûte. (Drouet, Louis). Reprint der Schott-Originalausgabe von 1827. *Schott. £4.00* VR/AF (B79-51214)

Methodist Church. *Division of Education and Youth.* Partners in praise. *Stainer & Bell : Chester House Publications for the Methodist Church Division of Education and Youth. £5.50* DM/LSJ/AY (B79-50444)

Metropolitan Opera Guild. Composer series. Culshaw, John. Wagner : the man and his music. *Hutchinson. £5.95 : CIP rev.* BWC(N) (B78-37864) ISBN 0-09-136210-5

Meyerbeer, Giacomo. Le prophète. March. *arr.* Coronation march. (Le prophète). *Novello. £2.00* UMK/AGM (B79-50315)

Meylan, Raymond.

Concertino, clarinet, B flat major. Concertino für Klarinette und Kammerorchester B-dur. (Donizetti, Gaetano). *Litolff : Peters. Unpriced* MPVVFL (B79-50590)

Concertino, clarinet, B flat major. *arr.* Concertino für Klarinette und Kammerorchester. B-dur. (Donizetti, Gaetano). *Litolff : Peters. Unpriced* VVPK/LFL (B79-50786)

Mezö, Imre. Klavierwerke = Piano works

Heft 12: Einzelne Charakterstücke 2 = Individual character pieces. (Liszt, Franz). *Bärenreiter. £5.94* QP/AZ (B79-50618)

Michaels, Ross. George Harrison : yesterday and today. *Flash Books; 78 Newman St., W.1 : Distributed by Book Sales Ltd.* Pbk. *£1.95* AKDW/GB/E(P) (B79-11130) ISBN 0-8256-3913-1

Michel, Winfried. Der getreue Music Meister. Sonata, bassoon & continuo, F minor. Sonate in f-moll für Fagott oder Violoncello und Basso continuo = Sonata in F minor for bassoon or cello and basso continuo. (Telemann, Georg Philipp). *Amadeus : Schott. Unpriced* VWPE (B79-50363)

Mickelsen, William C. Hugo Riemann's 'Theory of harmony' : a study / by William C. Mickelsen. And, History of music theory, Book III / by Hugo Riemann ; translate from the German and edited by William C. Mickelsen. *University of Nebraska Press. £10.50* A/R (B79-04541) ISBN 0-8032-0891-x

Middle eight ensemble series.

Beament, Peter. The Oregon trail : a suite for percussion ensemble. *7 Garrick St., W.C.2 : Middle Eight Music. Unpriced* XNS (B79-50403)

Frazer, Alan. A little theatre music : for flute, clarinet, trumpet, violin, cello and percussion. *7 Garrick St., W.C.2 : Middle Eight Music. Unpriced* NYE/J (B79-50199)

Mason, Tony. The night sky : for elementary brass quartet (2 trumpets, 2 trombones). *7 Garrick St., W.C.2 : Middle Eight Music. Unpriced* WNS (B79-50387)

Offenbach, Jacques. M'sieur Offenbach : a suite for

clarinet, alto and tenor saxophones. *7 Garrick St., W.C.2 : Middle Eight Music. Unpriced* VNTK/DW (B79-50324)
Standford, Patric. Holiday memories : for elementary string trio (2 violins and cello). *7 Garrick St., W.C.2 : Middle Eight Music. Unpriced* RXNT (B79-50271)
Standford, Patric. A London suite : for elementary string quartets. *7 Garrick St., W.C.2 : Middle Eight Music. Unpriced* RXNS (B79-50269)
Three ways to go : a suite for three guitars. *7 Garrick St., London W.C.2 : Middle Eight Music. Unpriced* TSNTK/AAY (B79-50301)
Two ragtime trios : for 2 clarinets and tenor saxophone (or bass clarinet). *7 Garrick St., W.C.2 : Middle Eight Music. Unpriced* VNTK/AHXJ (B79-50323)
Middleton, Richard. From Liszt to music hall. *Open University Press.* Pbk. *Unpriced* A(XFY101) (B79-36911) ISBN 0-335-05423-4
Midsummer suite : for treble recorder or flute and piano. (Jacques, Michael). *Roberton. £1.50* VSSPG (B79-50770)
Mieg, Peter. Concerto, flutes (2) & string orchestra. Concerto pour deux flûtes et orchestre à cordes, 1974. *Amadeus : Schott. Unpriced* RXMPVRNUF (B79-50259)
Mikado, or, The town of Titipu. (Gilbert, *Sir* William Schwenck). *42 Bloomsbury St., W.C.1 : Godfrey Cave Associates. £5.50* BSWACF (B79-16839) ISBN 0-906223-05-9
Mikrokosmos. *arr.* Mikrokosmos for harp : 20 intermediate solos and ensembles for harps with and without pedals. (Bartók, Béla). *Boosey and Hawkes. Unpriced* TQK/AF (B79-50694)
Miles.
Beatles in their own words. (Beatles, The). *Omnibus Press.* Pbk. *£2.50* AKDW/GB/E(P) (B79-26552) ISBN 0-86001-540-8
Bob Dylan in his own words. (Dylan, Bob). *Omnibus Press.* Pbk. *£2.50* AKDW/HKR/E(P) (B79-31930) ISBN 0-86001-542-4
Milgate, Wesley.
Australian hymn book. With one voice : a hymn book for all the churches with Catholic supplement. *Collins. Unpriced* DM/AY (B79-50443)
Australian hymn book. *Melody part.* With one voice : a hymn book for all the churches, with Catholic supplements. *Collins. Unpriced* JADM (B79-50929) ISBN 0-00-599636-8
With one voice. *Congregation part.* With one voice : a hymn book for all the churches. 2nd ed. *Collins. Unpriced* JDADM/AY (B79-50116) ISBN 0-00-599581-7
Miller, Ambrose. Quintet, strings, D major. Quintet, vln., viola, viola d'amore, cello, bass. (Eybler, Joseph von). *(Little Margaret, Penmans Green, Chipperfield) : E.L. White. Unpriced* RXNR (B79-50672)
Mills, Frank. Music box dancer : piano solo. *Valentine Music. Unpriced* QPJ (B79-51086)
Milne, Lorraine. The fix-it man. *Melody part.* The fix-it man : songs for schools. *Macmillan. Unpriced* JFADW/GJ (B79-50514) ISBN 0-333-25190-3
Milsom, John. Videte miraculum : for 6 voices. (Tallis, Thomas). *72 Brewery Rd, N.7 : Mapa Mundi. Unpriced* EZDJ (B79-50067)
Milson, John. Salve regina : for 4 voices. (Okeghem, Jean). *72 Brewery Rd, N.7 : Mapa mundi. Unpriced* GEZDJ (B79-50113)
Mingled chime : leaves from an autobiography. (Beecham, *Sir* Thomas, *bart*). *Hutchinson. £5.95 : CIP rev.* A/EC(P) (B79-08131) ISBN 0-09-138430-3
Miniature scores:.
Argento, Dominick. In praise of music : (seven songs for orchestra). *Boosey and Hawkes. Unpriced* MMJ (B79-50172)
Berlioz, Hector. Les Troyens, part 2. Chasse royale et orage. Chase royale et orage. *Bärenreiter. Unpriced* MMJ (B79-50173)
Binkerd, Gordon. Trio, string instruments. Trio for strings. *Boosey and Hawkes. Unpriced* RXNT (B79-50677)
Brahms, Johannes. Schicksalslied = Song of destiny. Op.54. *Eulenberg. Unpriced* EMDX (B79-50867)
Del Tredici, David. Vintage Alice : fantascene on a mad tea-party. *Boosey and Hawkes. Unpriced* KFLE/MDX (B79-51000)
Fanshawe, David. African sanctus ... : for soprano solo, mixed chorus, instrumental ensemble and pre-recorded tape. *Chappell. Unpriced* ENYLDE (B79-50456)
Fauré, Gabriel. Quartet, strings & keyboard, no.1, op.15. First piano quartet. Op.15. *Eulenburg. £2.05* NXNT (B79-50604)
Fauré, Gabriel. Quartet, strings & keyboard, no.2, op.45. Second piano quartet. Op.45. *Eulenburg. Unpriced* NXNT (B79-50605)
Grieg, Edvard. Sigurd Jorsalfar. Op.56. *Selections.* Three orchestral pieces from the incidental music to Sigurd Jorsalfar, op.56. *Eulenburg. Unpriced* MM/JM (B79-50165)
Grieg, Edvard. Two elegiac melodies. Op.34. *Eulenburg. Unpriced* MMJ (B79-50177)
Holloway, Robin. The rivers of hell. Opus 34 : concertante for seven players. *Boosey and Hawkes. Unpriced* NYDPNPF (B79-51048)
Hummel, Johann Nepomuk. Concerto, trumpet, E major. Concerto, E major, for trumpet and orchestra. *Eulenburg. Unpriced* MPWSF (B79-51032)
Janáček, Leoš. Sinfonietta. *Eulenburg. £2.50* MMEM (B79-50168)
Klebe, Giselher. Symphony, no.3, op.52. Dritte Sinfonie für grosses Orchester, Op.52 = Third symphony for grand orchestra, op.52. *Bärenreiter. £13.20* MME (B79-50167)
Liszt, Franz. Phantasie über ungarische Volksmelodien = Fantasia on Hungarian folk themes. *Eulenburg. £1.20* MMJ (B79-50179)
Mozart, Wolfgang Amadeus. Adagio and rondo for glass harmonica, flute, oboe, viola and cello. K.617. *Eulenburg. £1.20* NYEPNR/W (B79-51051)
Mozart, Wolfgang Amadeus. Concerto, piano, no.19, K.459, F major. Konzert in F für Klavier und Orchester KV459 = Concerto in F major for pianoforte and orchestra K.459. *Bärenreiter. £3.96* MPQF (B79-50580)
Mozart, Wolfgang Amadeus. Quintet, strings, no.1, K.174, B flat major. Quintet, B flat major for 2 violins, 2 violas and cello K.174. *Eulenburg. £1.55* RXNR (B79-51142)
Prokofiev, Sergei. Love of three oranges. L'amour des trois oranges. Opus 33 : opéra en 4 actes et 10 tableaux avec un prologue d'après Carlo Gozzi. *Boosey and Hawkes. Unpriced* CQC (B79-50822)
Purcell, Henry. Chacony, string orchestra, Z.730, G minor. Chacony for strings. *Eulenberg. Unpriced* RXMHJN (B79-51137)
Rachmaninoff, Sergei. The bells : Opus 35 : poem for soprano, tenor and baritone soli, chorus and orchestra. *Boosey and Hawkes. Unpriced* EMDX (B79-50455)
Rimsky-Korsakoff, Nikolai. The golden cockerel. *Suite.* Suite from the opera, 'The golden cockerel'. *Eulenburg. Unpriced* MMG (B79-51018)
Schwertsik, Kurt. Concerto, violin, op.31. Violinkonzert opus 31 : Romanzen im Schwarztiten-Ton und in der geblümtem Paradies-Weis. *Boosey and Hawkes. Unpriced* MPSF (B79-50582)
Tchaikovsky, Peter. Suite, orchestra, no.3, op.55, G major. Suite no.3 in G, op.55. *Eulenburg. Unpriced* MMG (B79-50170)
Victoria, Tomás Luis de. Motecta. O quam gloriosum est regnum. Motet and mass, O quam gloriosum est regnum. *Eulenburg. Unpriced* EZDJ/LQ (B79-50091)
Wagner, Richard. Wesendonk-Lieder : for soprano voice and orchestra. *Eulenburg. £2.15* KFLE/MDW (B79-50999)
Mirror on which to dwell : six poems of Elizabeth Bishop, for soprano and chamber orchestra. (Carter, Elliott). *Associated Music. £24.20* KFLE/MDW (B79-50550)
Miss Havisham's fire : opera in two acts. (Olon-Scrymgeour, John). *Boosey and Hawkes.* Sd. *£1.00* BARGAC (B79-26551)
Missa cum iucunditate : for 4 and 5 voices. (La Rue, Pierre de). *72 Brewery Rd, N.7 : Mapa mundi. Unpriced* GEZDG (B79-50109)
Missa de la batalla escoutez : for 5 voices. (Guerrero, Francisco). *Mapa mundi. Unpriced* EZDG (B79-50049)
Missa El ojo : for 4 voices. (Peñalosa, Francisco de). *72 Brewery Rd, N.7 : Mapa mundi. Unpriced* EZDG (B79-50050)
Missa in memoriam Benjamin Britten : Holy Communion series 3 for S.A.T.B. and organ. (Wills, Arthur). *Addington Press. Unpriced* DGS (B79-50830)
Missa Pange lingua : for voices. (Josquin des Prés). *Chester Music. Unpriced* EZDG (B79-50874)
Missa pro defunctis : for 2,3 and 4 voices. (Okeghem, Jean). *72 Brewery Rd, N.7 : Mapa mundi. Unpriced* EZDGKAV (B79-50052)
Missarum liber secundo. Missa de la batalla escoutez. Missa de la batalla escoutez : for 5 voices. (Guerrero, Francisco). *Mapa mundi. Unpriced* EZDG (B79-50049)
Mississippi Valley rags : for piano. *Schirmer. £1.75* QPHXJ (B79-51076)
Mitchell, Donald. Benjamin Britten, 1913-1976 : pictures from a life : a pictorial biography. *Faber. £15.00 : CIP rev.* BBU(EM) (B78-29832) ISBN 0-571-11261-7
MM51 : ein Stück Filmmusik für Klavier, 1976. (Kagel, Mauricio). *Universal. Unpriced* QPJ (B79-51083)
Modern accordionist. *EMI. Unpriced* RSPMK/DW/GB/AY (B79-50662)
Modern jazz, the essential records : a critical selection. *Aquarius Books : Distributed by Argus Books.* Pbk. *£2.90* AMT/FD(XPE26) (B79-15562)
Modern recorder series. Casken, John. Thymehaze : for alto recorder and piano. *Schott. Unpriced* VSSPJ (B79-51254)
Modern rhythmic notation. (Read, Gardner). *Indiana University Press. £15.75* A(QU) (B79-21876) ISBN 0-253-33867-0
Mohr, J. Stille Nacht, heilige Nacht. *arr.* Silent night. (Grüber, Franz Xaver). *36 Ranelagh Gdns W.6 : Cathedral Music. Unpriced* EZDP/LF (B79-50094)
Moldenhauer, Hans. Anton von Webern : a chronicle of his life and work. *Gollancz. £20.00* BWM(N) (B79-02986) ISBN 0-575-02436-4
Moldenhauer, Rosaleen. Anton von Webern : a chronicle of his life and work. (Moldenhauer, Hans). *Gollancz. £20.00* BWM(N) (B79-02986) ISBN 0-575-02436-4
Moll, Philip. The magic flute of James Galway. *Novello. Unpriced* VRPL/AAY (B79-50754)
Mon plaisir : for stage band. (Levitt, Rod). *Associated Music. £7.55* MSHJK (B79-50593)
Monahan, Brent Jeffrey. The art of singing : a compendium of thoughts on singing published between 1777 and 1927. *Scarecrow Press : Distributed by Bailey and Swinfen. £9.35* AK/E(VC/XFYS201) (B79-08929) ISBN 0-8108-1155-3
Monge napolitano : tarantela para órgão. (Salles, Anita). *Fermata do Brasil : Clifford Essex. Unpriced* RHVS (B79-51120)
Montagu, Jeremy.
Choose your instrument : a beginner's guide to making music. *Gollancz. £2.95* AL/E (B79-08927) ISBN 0-575-02495-x
The world of baroque & classical musical instruments. *David and Charles. £8.95 : CIP rev.* AL/B(XEG194) (B79-07466) ISBN 0-7153-7593-8
Montanari, Nunzio. 24 momenti musicali : per flauto e pianoforte nelle 24 tunalità del sistema temperato 1° volume: 1-12. *Bèrben. Unpriced* VRPJ (B79-51224)
Monte Cassino *(Monastery). Biblioteca. MSS. (Codex 871).* The musical manuscript Montecassino 871 : a Neapolitan repertory of sacred and secular music of the late fifteenth century. *Clarendon Press. £25.00* CB/AY (B79-50411) ISBN 0-19-816132-8
Monteverdi, Claudio.
Christmas vespers : antiphons, psalms and hymns for soloists, double choir, instruments and organ continuo. *Novello. £3.50* DJ/LF (B79-50437)
L'Orfeo. Vieni Imeneo. *arr.* Zwei Chöre aus 'Orpheus' = Two chorusses sic from 'Orpheus'. *Schott. £0.80* EZDW (B79-50898)
Selva morale e spirituale. Ut queant laxis. *arr.* Hymn to Saint John the Baptist. Ut queant laxis. *36 Ranelagh Gdns W.6 : Cathedral Music. Unpriced* JNFLEE/SNTPWDJ (B79-50130)
Moods for guitar. (Nunn, Ruth). *Novello. £0.66* TSPMJ (B79-50308)
Moór (Emanuel) Double Keyboard Piano Trust. *See* Emanuel Moór Double Keyboard Piano Trust.
Moore, Jack.
Fun chord organ : for young people of any age. *EMI. Unpriced* RPVCK/DW/GB/AY (B79-51133) ISBN 0-86175-064-0
Fun organ : arrangements ... for all electronic and 'C' chord organs
Folio no.2. *EMI. Unpriced* RPVCK/AAY (B79-50660)
Happy Christmas : B flat clarinet. *EMI. Unpriced* VVPMK/DP/LF/AY (B79-50360)
Happy Christmas : chord organ. *EMI. Unpriced* RPVCK/DP/LF/AY (B79-50248)
Happy Christmas : easy piano or organ. *EMI. Unpriced* QPK/DP/LF/AY (B79-50224)
The modern accordionist. *EMI. Unpriced* RSPMK/DW/GB/AY (B79-50662)
Moore, Jerrold Northrop. Music and friends : seven decades of letters to Adrian Boult from Elgar, Vaughan Williams, Holst, Bruno Walter, Yehudi Menuhin and other friends. *H. Hamilton. £6.95 : CIP rev.* A/EC(P) (B79-08128) ISBN 0-241-10178-6
Moore Jack. Happy Christmas : B flat trumpet. *EMI. Unpriced* WSPMK/DP/LF/AY (B79-50399)
Morath, Max. The Mississippi Valley rags : for piano. *Schirmer. £1.75* QPHXJ (B79-51076)
Morceau de salon. Op.228 : for oboe and piano. (Kalliwoda, Jan Václav). *Nova Music. Unpriced* VTPJ (B79-51262)
More guitar pieces : folktunes and Elizabethan pieces. *Holley Music. Unpriced* TSPMK/AAY (B79-50310)
More sing for Jesus : songs for children. (Murcott, Peter). *(23 Park Rd) : Moorley's Bible and Bookshop. £0.55* JFDM/GJ (B79-50516) ISBN 0-86071-054-8
Morehen, John. 40 freym Anrerlieder. Anhang. Two masonic pieces for organ. (Naumann, Johann Gottlieb). *Oxford University Press. Unpriced* RJ (B79-50650)
Moretti, Federico. Doce canciones. Op.24. Doce canciones = Twelve songs : with guitar accompaniment ... *Tecla. Unpriced* KE/TSDW (B79-50993) ISBN 0-8494-0140-2
Morgan, John. The magician. Op.88. *Vocal score.* The magician : an opera in one act. (Hoddinott, Alun). *Oxford University Press. Unpriced* CC (B79-50011) ISBN 0-19-336839-0
Moroney, Davitt.
John Blow's anthology : Froberger, Strungk, Fischer, Blow : a selection of keyboard music (twenty suites, capriccios, ricercars, toccatas, etc.) copied out by John Blow around 1700. *Stainer and Bell. Unpriced* QRPJ (B79-50646) ISBN 0-85249-446-7
Madrigals to foure voices (1599). (Bennet, John). *Stainer and Bell. Unpriced* EZDU (B79-50473) ISBN 0-85249-456-4
Motecta ... liber secundus. Pastores loquebantur. Pastores loquebantur. (Guerrero, Francisco). *72 Brewery Rd, N.7 : Mapa mundi. Unpriced* EZDJ/LF (B79-50076)
Motecta. Duo seraphim. Duo seraphim. (Guerrero, Francisco). *Mapa mundi. Unpriced* EZDJ (B79-50062)
Motecta festorum. Sancta Maria. Sancta Maria. (Esquivel, Juan). *72 Brewery Rd, N.7 : Mapa mundi. Unpriced* EZDJ (B79-50060)
Motecta festorum totius anni ... liber primus. Hodie Christus natus est. Hodie Christas natus est. (Marenzio, Luca). *72 Brewery Rd, N.7 : Mapa mundi. Unpiced* EZDJ/LF (B79-50073)
Motecta festorum totius anni ... liber primus. O sacrum convivium. O sacrum convivium : motet for the Feast of Corpus Christi, for 4 voices. (Marenzio, Luca). *72 Brewery Rd, N.7 : Mapa mundi. Unpriced* EZDJ/LNC (B79-50089)
Motecta festorum. Veni Domine. Veni Domine : motet for the Advent season for 5 voices. (Esquivel, Juan). *72 Brewery Rd, N.7 : Mapa mundi. Unpriced* EZDJ/LEZ (B79-50070)
Motecta. O quam gloriosum est regnum. Motet and mass, O quam gloriosum est regnum. (Victoria, Tomás Luis de). *Eulenburg. Unpriced* EZDJ/LQ (B79-50091)
Motectas festorum. Quem vidistis, pastores? Quem vidistis, pastores? (Victoria, Tomás Luis de). *72 Brewery Rd, N.7 : Mapa mundi. Unpriced* EZDJ/LF (B79-50079)
Motet and mass, O quam gloriosum est regnum. (Victoria, Tomás Luis de). *Eulenburg. Unpriced* EZDJ/LQ (B79-50091)
Mother goose. (Astell, Betty). *Evans. Unpriced* CPP (B79-50021) ISBN 0-237-75042-2

Mother, O sing me to sleep = Mutter, O sing mich zur ruh' : for three-part chorus of female voices and piano. (Franz, Robert). *Roberton. £0.24* FDW (B79-50910)
Motorhead. Overkill. *arr.* Overkill. *Chappell. Unpriced* KDW/HKR (B79-50985)
Motte, Diether de la. Liebeserklärung für ein verkanntes Instrument : 6 Stücke für Akkordeon, 1977. *Bärenreiter. Unpriced* RSPMJ (B79-50255)
Mottl, Felix. Wesendonk-Lieder : for soprano voice and orchestra. (Wagner, Richard). *Eulenburg. £2.15* KFLE/MDW (B79-50999)
Motus : für grosses Orchester. (Wimberger, Gerhard). *Bärenreiter. £8.91* MMJ (B79-50579)
Moyes, John, *b.1924.* Singing rhymes. *Ladybird Books. £0.30* AJFDW/GR(VJ) (B79-06706) ISBN 0-7214-0537-1
Moyse, Louis. Trio, flute, cello & piano, op.63. Trio, op.63, for flute, cello (or viola) and piano. (Weber, Carl Maria von, *Freiherr*). *Schirmer. £6.10* NURNT (B79-51039)
Mozart, Wolfgang Amadeus.
Adagio and rondo for glass harmonica, flute, oboe, viola and cello. K.617. *Eulenburg. £1.20* NYEPNR/W (B79-51051)
Concerto, piano, no.19, K.459, F major. Konzert in F für Klavier und Orchester KV459 = Concerto in F major for pianoforte and orchestra K.459. *Bärenreiter. £3.96* MPQF (B79-50580)
Concerto, piano, no.21, K.467, C major. Andante. *arr.* The Elvira Madigan theme ... *Studio Music. Unpriced* WMK (B79-50376)
Divertimentos, K. Anh. 229. *Selections: arr.* Six movements from the Mozart divertimenti. *Cramer. Unpriced* VSNTK (B79-50340)
Fantasia, clock-organ, K.608, F minor. *arr.* Fantasia in F minor for organ (mechanical clock-organ, K.608). *Schirmer. £3.65* RK/B/FK (B79-51128)
Quintet, strings, no.1, K.174, B flat major. Quintet, B flat major for 2 violins, 2 violas and cello K.174. *Eulenburg. £1.55* RXNR (B79-51142)
Serenade, wind sextet, no.11, K.375, E flat major. Serenade in E flat. K.375, original version : for two clarinets, two horns, and two bassoons. *Oxford University Press. Unpriced* UNQ (B79-51209) ISBN 0-19-357939-1
Serenade, wind sextet, no.11, K.375, E flat major. *Original version.* Serenade in E flat. K.375. Original version : for two clarinets, two horns and two bassoons. *Oxford University Press. Unpriced* UNQ (B79-51210) ISBN 0-19-357940-5
Sonata, piano, no.1, K.279, C major. Sonata in C. *Associated Board of the Royal Schools of Music. Unpriced* QPE (B79-51068)
Sonata, piano, no.6, K.284, D major. Sonata in D, K.284, 205b, 1775. *Associated Board of the Royal Schools of Music. Unpriced* QPE (B79-50622)
Symphony, no.14, K.114, A major. Symphonie A-Dur, KV114. *Schott. £4.80* MRE (B79-51033)
Mr. Lear's carnival : for brass band. (Lear, Hogarth). *Chester Music. Unpriced* WMJ (B79-51300)
Muak : tänzerische Fantasie für grosses Orchester, 1978. (Yun, Isang). *Bote und Bock. £9.60* MMH (B79-51019)
Mudarra, Alonso. Tres libros de música en cifra para vihuela. Fantasia no.9. *arr.* Fantasie no.9. *DeCamera : Schirmer. £1.50* TSPMK (B79-51189)
Mull of Kintyre. *arr.* Mull of Kintyre. (McCartney, Paul). *Music Sales. Unpriced* DW (B79-50034)
Mullen, Brian. Sweet Scottish isle. *arr.* Sweet Scottish isle. *(16 Mendip Rd) : Autumn Publications. Unpriced* KDW (B79-50959)
Müller, Paul. Fantasia super 'Urbs Turegem, urbs famosa' sive 'Lauda Sion salvatorem' : fur Orgel ... *Verlag der Zentralbibliothek Zurich in Kommission bei Amadeus Verlag : Bärenreiter. Unpriced* RJ (B79-50649)
Müller, Wilhelm. Franz Schubert Lieder : Urtext der Neuen Schubert-Ausgabe
Heft 1: Die schöne Mûllerin, op.25: Mittlere Stimme (Transposition). (Schubert, Franz). *Bärenreiter. £5.28* KDW (B79-50133)
Muncey, Richard.
Original music and alternative music for the Modern Dance Grade Examinations
Grades 2 and 3: including pieces needed for the course of movement for boys. (Imperial Society of Teachers of Dancing. *Modern Dance Branch*). *Imperial Society of Teachers of Dancing. £3.50* QPH/H/AL (B79-51070)
Primary and Grade 1: including pieces needed for the course of movement for boys. (Imperial Society of Teachers of Dancing. *Modern Dance Branch*). *Imperial Society of Teachers of Dancing. £3.00* QPH/H/AL (B79-51071)
Murcott, Peter.
Complete sing for Jesus : songs for children. *(23 Park Rd) : Moorley's Bible and Bookshop. £1.00* JFDM/GJ (B79-50515) ISBN 0-86071-055-6
More sing for Jesus : songs for children. *(23 Park Rd) : Moorley's Bible and Bookshop. £0.55* JFDM/GJ (B79-50516) ISBN 0-86071-054-8

Musae Sioniae Tl.3. Allein Gott in der Höh sei Ehr. Allein Gott in der Höh sei Ehr : Choralbearbeitung für zwei vierstimmige Chöre. (Praetorius, Michael). *Bärenreiter. £1.16* EZDH (B79-50462)
Musette. *arr.* Musette : für Gitarre solo = for guitar solo. (Vogel, Vladimir). *Schott. £2.00* TSPMK/AHS (B79-50311)
Musgrave, Thea. Sonata for three : for flute, violin and guitar. *Novello. £4.25* NVRNT (B79-50189)

Music. The observer's book of music. (Dinn, Freda). 4th ed. *F. Warne. £1.25* A (B79-50001) ISBN 0-7232-1581-2
Music. (Politoske, Daniel Theodore). 2nd ed. *Prentice-Hall. £9.05* A(X) (B79-34988) ISBN 0-13-607556-8
Music and friends : seven decades of letters to Adrian Boult from Elgar, Vaughan Williams, Holst, Bruno Walter, Yehudi Menuhin and other friends. *H. Hamilton. £6.95 : CIP rev.* A/EC(P) (B79-08128) ISBN 0-241-10178-6
Music and musicians on postage stamps. (Senior, Geoffrey). *299 Gathurst Rd, Orrell, Greater Manchester : The compiler.* Sp. *£3.00* A(ZE) (B79-16833)
Music & recording industry year book international. Kemps music & recording industry year book international
1979. *Kemps.* Pbk. *£10.50* A/GB(YC/BC) (B79-22267) ISBN 0-905255-52-6
Music and song from The Boys of the Lough : music and songs of Ireland, Scotland and Shetland. *Gilderoy. Unpriced* KEZDW/G/AYDL (B79-50546) ISBN 0-9505982-0-8
Music and the Reformation in England, 1549-1660. (Le Huray, Peter). *Cambridge University Press. £19.50* AD/LD(YD/XDXJ112) (B79-16102) ISBN 0-521-21958-2
Music at the Court of Kromeriz.
Biber, Heinrich Ignaz Franz. Sonatae tam aris quam aulis servientes. Sonata, trumpet & string orchestra, no.4, C major. *arr.* Sonata 4 for trumpet, violin, 2 violas and basso continuo. *Musica rara. Unpriced* NUXSNTK/LE (B79-51043)
Biber, Heinrich Ignaz Franz. Sonatae tam aris quam aulis servientes. Sonata, trumpet & string orchestra, no.12, C. major. *arr.* Sonata 12 for 2 trumpets, 2 violins, 2 violas, cello. *Muscia rara. Unpriced* NUXSNTK/LE (B79-51044)
Music at the Court of Kroměříž. Biber, Heinrich Ignaz Franz. Sonatae tam aris quam aulis servientes. Sonata, trumpets (2) & string orchestra, no.1, C major. *arr.* Sonata 1 for 2 trumpets, 2 violins, 2 violas, cello & basso continuo. *Musica rara. Unpriced* NUXSNRK/LE (B79-51042)
Music at the Court of Kromeriz. Poglietti, Alessandro. Sonata, trumpet, bassoon & continuo, C major. Sonata à 3 for trumpet/oboe/flute/violin, bassoon & basso continuo. *Musica rara. Unpriced* NWNTE (B79-51046)
Music box dancer : piano solo. (Mills, Frank). *Valentine Music. Unpriced* QPJ (B79-51086)
Music by Douglas Deroyan. (Deroyan, Douglas). *37 Buckland Cresc. N.W.3 : Douglas Deroyan. Unpriced* QPJ (B79-51079)
Music education - the person first. ISME yearbook
Vol.6 : 1979: Music education - the person first : papers of the 13th International Conference, London, Ontario, Canada, 1978. (International Society for Music Education). *Schott.* Pbk. *£9.60* A(V/BC) (B79-32713)
Music for amateur orchestra. Tchaikovsky, Peter. Marche slave. Op.31. *arr.* Marche slave. *Oxford University Press. Unpriced* MK/AGM (B79-50162) ISBN 0-19-367910-8
Music for handbells : Module AIIN for 1 1/2 octaves : Hymns and things. *(57a Fore St.) : Handbell Ringers of Great Britain. Unpriced* XSQK/AAY (B79-50813) ISBN 0-904289-03-6
Music for Japan : for orchestra. (Sculthorpe, Peter). *Faber Music. Unpriced* MMJ (B79-51025)
Music : for S.S.C. (Benger, Richard). *Edwin Ashdown. £0.25* FDW (B79-50102)
Music for upright piano. (Rautavaara, Einojuhani). *Schirmer. £2.40* QPJ (B79-50635)
Music for upright piano and amplified cello. (Rautavaara, Einojuhani). *Schirmer. £3.05* SRPJ (B79-50690)
Music from the ballet. (Delibes, Leo). *(7 Garrick St., W.C.2) : Middle Eight Music. Unpriced* UNSK/HM (B79-50732)
Music from the ballet. (Tchaikovsky, Peter). *(7 Garrick St., W.C.2) : Middle Eight Music. Unpriced* UNSK/HM (B79-50733)
Music from two hit albums, Gone to earth and XII. (Barclay James Harvest). *Chappell. Unpriced* KDW/HKR (B79-50982)
Music gudie. Richard Baker's music guide. (Baker, Richard, *b.1925*). *David and Charles. £3.95 : CIP rev.* A/C (B79-12528) ISBN 0-7153-7782-5
Music hall records
No.1- ; June 1978-. *50 Reporton Rd, S.W.6 : Tony Barker.* Sd. *£0.60(£3.60 yearly)* AKDW/JV/FD(B) (B79-15561)

Music in America life. Ives, Edward D. Joe Scott : the woodsman-songmaker. *University of Illinois Press. £15.75* AKDW/GNL(P) (B79-22639) ISBN 0-252-00683-6
Music in eighteenth-century Norwich and Norfolk. (Fawcett, Trevor). *Norwich NR4 7TJ : Centre of East Anglian Studies, University of East Anglia.* Sd. *£1.75* A(YDDS/XF101) (B79-33550)
Music in the classic period : an anthology with commentary. *Schirmer : Collier Macmillan. £11.20* C/AY (B79-50409) ISBN 0-02-870710-9
Music librarianship. (Jones, Malcolm, *b.1943*). *Bingley etc.. £4.00 : CIP rev.* A(U) (B79-11403) ISBN 0-85157-274-x
Music makers. Waller, Thomas. Fats Waller. *EMI. Unpriced* KDW/GB (B79-50138)
Music makers. (Rosenberg, Deena). *Columbia University Press. £10.30* A(M) (B79-10473) ISBN 0-231-03953-0
Music master
1979. *1 De Cham Ave., Hastings, Sussex : John Humphries. £30.00* A/FD(WT) (B79-28369) ISBN 0-904520-07-2
Music of Alban Berg. (Jarman, Douglas). *Faber. £18.00 : CIP entry* BBKR (B78-37095) ISBN 0-571-10956-x

Music of Benjamin Britten. (Evans, Peter, *b.1929*). *Dent. £15.00 : CIP entry* BBU (B79-00563) ISBN 0-460-04350-1
Music of three seasons, 1974-1977. (Porter, Andrew). *Chatto and Windus. £12.50 : CIP entry* A/E(XQP4) (B78-37093) ISBN 0-7011-2340-0
Music room. Selections. Sarabande and Rustic ballet ... : two miniatures for piano solo. (Jacobson, Maurice). *Roberton. £0.50* QPH (B79-50627)
Music through sources and documents. (Rowen, Ruth Halle). *Prentice-Hall.* Pbk. *£9.45* A(X) (B79-16099) ISBN 0-13-608331-5
Music to help disabled children to move. (Kennard, Daphne). *A.P.C.P. Publications, 25 Goff's Park Rd, Southgate, Crawley, W. Sussex RH11 8AX : Association of Paediatric Chartered Physiotherapists.* Sd. *£0.50* A(VMX) (B79-13819)
Music trades international buyers guide, yearbook & directory. *For earlier editions of this annual see* Music trades international directory.
Music trades international buyers guide, yearbook & directory
1979. *4 Local Board Rd, Watford, Herts. : Music Trades International.* Pbk. *£6.75* A(YC/BC) (B79-23760)
Music trades international directory. *For later editions of this annual see* Music trades international buyers guide, yearbook & directory.
Music translation dictionary. (Grigg, Carolyn Doub). *Greenwood Press. £16.95* A(QTF) (B79-36910) ISBN 0-313-20559-0
Musica Britannica : a national collection of music
Vol.42: The judgement of Paris. *Stainer and Bell. Unpriced* C/AYD (B79-50009)
Vol.43: English songs, 1800-1860. *Stainer and Bell. Unpriced* C/AYD (B79-50814) ISBN 0-85249-439-4
Musica da camera.
Arne, Thomas Augustine. Sonata, violin & continuo, E major. Sonata in E major for violin and basso continuo. *Oxford University Press. Unpriced* SPE (B79-50273) ISBN 0-19-355216-7
Babell, William. Sonata, violin & continuo, op.posth., pt.1, no.11, G minor. Sonata 11 in G minor for oboe (or violin) and basso continuo. *Oxford University Press. Unpriced* SPE (B79-50274) ISBN 0-19-355226-4
Boismortier, Joseph Bodin de. Sonatas, flutes (2), op.2, nos.3, 4. Two sonatas, Opus 2, Nos. 3 and 4 for two flutes, or oboes, or violins. *Oxford University Press. Unpriced* VRNUE (B79-50327) ISBN 0-19-355578-6
Finger, Gottfried. Pastorelle, recorders (treble) (3), G major. Pastorelle and sonata : for three treble recorders. *Oxford University Press. Unpriced* VSSNT (B79-50343) ISBN 0-19-363204-7
Hebden, John. Sonata, flute & continuo, no.1, D major. Sonata 1 in D major for flute and basso continuo. *Oxford University Press. Unpriced* VRPE (B79-51221) ISBN 0-19-357021-1
Mozart, Wolfgang Amadeus. Serenade, wind sextet, no.11, K.375, E flat major. Serenade in E flat. K.375, original version : for two clarinets, two horns, and two bassoons. *Oxford University Press. Unpriced* UNQ (B79-51209) ISBN 0-19-357939-1
Mozart, Wolfgang Amadeus. Serenade, wind sextet, no.11, K.375, E flat major. *Original version.* Serenade in E flat. K.375. Original version : for two clarinets, two horns and two bassoons. *Oxford University Press. Unpriced* UNQ (B79-51210) ISBN 0-19-357940-5
Paisible, James. Sonata, trumpets (2), violins (2), viola & continuo, no.10, D major. Sonata 10 in D major for two trumpets (or oboes), strings, and continuo. *Oxford University Press. Unpriced* NUXSNQE (B79-50187) ISBN 0-19-366260-4
Roseingrave, Thomas. Sonata, flute & continuo, no.2, D major. Sonata 2 in D major for flute and basso continuo. *Oxford University Press. Unpriced* VRPE (B79-50329) ISBN 0-19-358643-6
Schickhard, Johann Christian. Sonata, recorder, oboe & continuo, op.5, no.2, D major. Sonata D major for flute/recorder, two oboes, viola da gamba/violoncello/bassoon, and basso continuo. *Oxford University Press. Unpriced* NWPNTE (B79-50194) ISBN 0-19-358815-3
Vivaldi, Antonio. Concerto, violin & string orchestra, R.761, C minor, 'Amato bene'. Concerto in C minor 'Amato bene', RV761, for violin and string orchestra. *Oxford University Press. Unpriced* RXMPSF (B79-51138) ISBN 0-19-367972-8
Musica instrumentalis. Schickhard, Johann Christian. L'alphabet de la musique : Op.30. Sonatas 4, 7, 16. 3 Sonaten aus 'L'alphabet de la musique' = 3 sonatas from 'L'alphabet de la musique' : für Altblockflöte und Basso continuo = for alto recorder and basso continuo. *Pelikan : Bärenreiter. £9.10* VSSPE (B79-50769)
Musical companion. Revised ed. *Pan Books.* Pbk. *£2.95* A (B79-50002) ISBN 0-330-25670-x
Musical growth in the elementary school. (Bergethon, Bjornar). 3rd ed. *Holt, Rinehart and Winston.* Pbk. *£9.25* A(VG) (B79-07190)
Musical growth in the elementary school. (Bergethon, Bjornar). 4th ed. *Holt, Rinehart and Winston.* Sp. *£8.50* A(VK) (B79-10207) ISBN 0-03-020856-4
Musical instruments. (Ardley, Neil). *Macmillan. £0.95* AL/B (B79-50008) ISBN 0-333-24465-6
Musical instruments. (Ardley, Neil). *Macmillan.* Pbk. *£0.50* AL/B (B79-22637) ISBN 0-333-26156-9
Musical manuscript Montecassino 871 : a Neapolitan repertory of sacred and secular music of the late fifteenth century. (Monte Cassino *(Monastery). Biblioteca. MSS. (Codex 871)*). *Clarendon Press. £25.00* CB/AY (B79-50411) ISBN 0-19-816132-8

Musician at large. (Race, Steve). *Eyre Methuen. £6.50 : CIP rev.* A/JT(P) (B79-17755) ISBN 0-413-39740-8

Musicians of Auschwitz. (Fénelon, Fania). *Sphere.* Pbk. *£0.95* A(M/YLCO/XPC3) (B79-19444) ISBN 0-7221-3466-5

Musicke of sundrie kindes : handlist to the exhibition held in the Glasgow University Library, Exhibition Room, 11th January-18th February 1978. (University of Glasgow. Library). *Glasgow G12 8QG : The Library.* Sd. *£0.50* A(U/YDLJ/WM) (B79-14348) ISBN 0-85261-148-x

Musicology series. Smith, F Joseph. The experiencing of musical sound : prelude to a phenomenology of music. *Gordon and Breach. £8.10* A/CC (B79-02983) ISBN 0-677-04430-5

Musik for Blechbläser und Tasteninstrumente. Wenzel, Eberhard. 'Weihnachtskonzert' : Zyklus zu Advent bis Epiphanians, für Blechbläser und Orgel. *Bärenreiter. £2.31* NWXPF (B79-50603)

Musik für Flöte und Gitarre. (Suter, Robert). *Eulenburg. £2.10* VRPLTS (B79-50757)

Musik kommt : Männerchor und kleines Blasorchester. (Scheck, Helmut). *Schott. £5.60* GE/UMDW (B79-50922)

Musikpädagogik. Abel-Struth, Sigrid. Ziele des Musik-Lernens

T.1: Beitrag zur Entwicklung ihrer Theorie. *Schott.* Pbk. *£8.00* A(VC/YE) (B79-14009)

Mussorgskij, Modest. *See* Mussorgsky, Modest.

Mussorgsky, Modest.

Pictures at an exhibition. *arr.* Pictures at an exhibition. *Chester Music. Unpriced* WMK (B79-51302)

Songs and dances of death. *arr.* Lieder und Tänze des Todes. *Breitkopf und Härtel. £8.40* KDW (B79-50960)

Mutter, o sing 'mich zur Ruh', op.10, no.3. *arr.* Mother, O sing me to sleep = Mutter, O sing mich zur ruh' : for three-part chorus of female voices and piano. (Franz, Robert). *Roberton. £0.24* FDW (B79-50910)

My friends and myself : conversations with Francis Poulenc. (Audel, Stéphane). *Dobson. £4.95* BPO (B78-39780) ISBN 0-234-77251-4

My gift : for four-part chorus of men's voices a cappella. (Chorbajian, John). *Schirmer. £0.35* GEZDP/LF (B79-50923)

My masters, be merry! : for mixed voices (SATB) and accompaniment. (Ehret, Walter). *Broude : Breitkopf and Härtel. £0.42* DP/LF (B79-50840)

My music. (Race, Steve). *Robson. £5.25 : CIP entry* A(DE) (B79-22652) ISBN 0-86051-072-7

Myers, Stanley. Cavatina. *arr.* Cavatina. *EMI. Unpriced* WMK (B79-50792)

Mylett, Howard. Led Zeppelin. *Panther.* Pbk. *£0.75* AKDW/HKR/E(P) (B79-10479)

Nagel, Frank. Sonatas, flutes (2), op.47. Sechs Sonaten für zwei Querflöten, op.47. (Boismortier, Joseph Bodin de). *Eulenburg. Unpriced* VRNUE (B79-50328)

Nagels Musik-Archiv. Bach, Carl Philipp Emanuel. Concerto, keyboard & string orchestra, Wq 9, C minor. Concerto in C-moll für Cembalo (Klavier) und Streicher = Concerto in C minor for harpsichord (piano) and strings. Erstausgabe = First ed. *Nagel : Editio Musica : Bärenreiter. Unpriced* RXMPPWF (B79-50258)

Nanry, Charles. The jazz text. *D. Van Nostrand.* Pbk. *£6.70* AMT (B79-21878) ISBN 0-442-25908-5

Nash, Alanna. Dolly. *Panther.* Pbk. *£1.25* AKDW/GC/E(P) (B79-33546) ISBN 0-586-05051-5

Nash, Harold. Four solo pieces : for trombone (in bass and treble clefs). *Paterson. Unpriced* WUPJ (B79-51324)

National Union of Townswomen's Guilds. The golden bond : a spectacular revue. (Barrow, Kenneth). *2 Cromwell Place, SW7 2JG : National Union of Townswomen's Guilds.* Pbk. *£1.50* BAPACP (B79-27787)

Naumann, Johann Gottlieb. 40 freym Anrerlieder. Anhang. Two masonic pieces for organ. *Oxford University Press. Unpriced* RJ (B79-50650)

Naylor, Frank.

Fatinitza march. *arr.* Fatinitza march : based on themes from the operetta 'Fatinitza'. (Suppé, Franz von). *Bosworth & Co. £1.25* MK/AGM (B79-51012)

In a Persian market. *arr.* Persian market swing. (In a Persian market). (Ketelbey, Albert). *Bosworth & Co. £1.35* MK (B79-50565)

Unter dem Doppeladler. Op.159. *arr.* Under the double eagle = Unter dem Doppeladler : march, (op.159). (Wagner, Josef Franz). *Bosworth & Co. Unpriced* MK/AGM (B79-50163)

Nazareth. No mean city. *arr.* No mean city. *Chappell. Unpriced* KDW/HKR (B79-50986)

Nazareth, Ernesto, *b.1863.* Album de violão. *Arthur Napoleão : Essex Music. Unpriced* SPMK (B79-50281)

Neary, Martin.

Old French organ music. *Oxford University Press. Unpriced* R/AYH (B79-50230) ISBN 0-19-375616-1

Preces and responses. *Royal School of Church Music. Unpriced* EZDGMM (B79-50460)

Nelson, Havelock. Kitty of Coleraine : traditional Irish, S.A.T.B. unacc. *Banks. Unpriced* EZDW (B79-50899)

Nelson, Robert. Techniques and materials of tonal music : with an introduction to twentieth-century techniques. (Benjamin, Thomas). 2nd ed. *Houghton Mifflin. £9.75* A/R (B79-18563) ISBN 0-395-27066-9

Nelson, Ron.

Here we come as in the beginning. *Boosey and Hawkes. Unpriced* EZDH (B79-50877)

Oh, God, invent a word for us : for two-part children's chorus and SAB adult chorus with organ and/or piano. *Boosey and Hawkes. Unpriced* DH (B79-50833)

Nelson, Shirley. Oh, God, invent a word for us : for two-part children's chorus and SAB adult chorus with organ and/or piano. (Nelson, Ron). *Boosey and Hawkes. Unpriced* DH (B79-50833)

Nersessian, Verej. Essays on Armenian music. *Kahn and Averill for the Institute of Armenian Music. £6.95* A(D/YVVA) (B79-33551) ISBN 0-900707-49-6

Netto, Marianinha Ayres. *See* Ayres Netto, Marianinha.

Neue Musik und die Tradition *(Conference), Darmstadt, 1978.* Die neue Musik und die Tradition : sieben Kongressbeiträge und eine analytische Studie. *Schott.* Pbk. *£10.80* A(XPK19) (B79-11940)

Neumann, Frederick, *b.1907.* Ornamentation in baroque and post-baroque music : with special emphasis on J.S. Bach. *Princeton University Press. £33.40* A(QM/XDZK196) (B79-07465) ISBN 0-691-09123-4

Nevin, Mark.

Christmas songs you like : piano duets for elementary level. *Schroeder and Gunther. £1.75* QNVK/DP/LF/AY (B79-51064)

Piano favorites : seven select solos for intermediate grade. *Schroeder and Gunther. £1.35* QPJ (B79-50634)

New wings suite : music for band. (D'arville, Jasper). *Boosey and Hawkes. £22.00* UMMG (B79-51206)

Newbery, Celia. Vaughan Williams in Dorking : a collection of personal reminiscences of the composer Dr Ralph Vaughan Williams, O.M. (Dorking and Leith Hill District Preservation Society. *Local History Group*). *c/o C. Newbery, 'Wrencot', Partridge La., Newdigate, Dorking, Surrey : The Group.* Sd. *£0.80* BVD(YDCHD/P (B79-21875)

Newlin, Dika. Bruckner, Mahler, Schoenberg. Revised ed.. *Boyars : Distributed by Calder and Boyars. £9.95* BBUE (B79-05247) ISBN 0-7145-2658-4

Newman, Anthony. Fantasia, clock-organ, K.608, F minor. *arr.* Fantasia in F minor for organ (mechanical clock-organ, K.608). (Mozart, Wolfgang Amadeus). *Schirmer. £3.65* RK/B/FK (B79-51128)

Newnes constructors projects. Flind, A J. Electronic projects in music. *Newnes Technical Books.* Pbk. *£2.25 : CIP rev.* APV/BC (B79-17724) ISBN 0-408-00391-x

Newsidler, Hans. Lute music. *Selections : arr.* Four pieces. *DeCamera : Schirmer. £1.50* TSPMK (B79-51190)

Newsome, Roy.

Annie Laurie. *arr.* Annie Laurie. (Scott, Alicia Anne, *Lady John Scott*). *Studio Music. Unpriced* WMK/DW (B79-50381)

Dead man's cave. *Studio Music. Unpriced* WMJ (B79-50374)

Newton, Robert F. British hymn writers and composers : a check-list, giving their dates & places of birth & death. (Hayden, Andrew J). 1st ed. reprinted. *c/o Addington Palace, Croydon CR9 5AD : Hymn Society of Great Britain and Ireland.* Pbk. *£3.00* ADM/D(M/WT) (B79-15556)

Next week Terry & I ... : 5 easy pieces for the piano. (Ezell, Helen Ingle). *Oxford University Press. Unpriced* QPJ (B79-51080)

Nield, David. Helen comes home, or, Achilles the heel. (Taylor, Jeremy James). *French. £1.50 : CIP entry* BNEACN (B79-17762) ISBN 0-573-15004-4

Night sky : for elementary brass quartet (2 trumpets, 2 trombones). (Mason, Tony). *7 Garrick St., W.C.2 : Middle Eight Music. Unpriced* WNS (B79-50387)

Nine carols or ballads. Lord of the dance. *arr.* 9 carols or ballads. Lord of the dance. *arr.* Lord of the dance. (Carter, Sydney). *Galliard. Unpriced* ELDM (B79-50453)

Nisbet, Bob. High surge of the sea. *arr.* The song of the sea. An ataireachd ard = ('High surge of the sea'). (MacDonald, John). *Bosworth and Co. Unpriced* KDW (B79-50526)

Nitz, Gaynor. Johann Sebastian Bach : life, times, influence. *17 Bucklersbury, Hitchin, Herts. SG5 1BB : Bärenreiter. £21.12* BBC(N) (B79-11127)

No mean city. (Nazareth). *Chappell. Unpriced* KDW/HKR (B79-50986)

No mean city. *arr.* No mean city. (Nazareth). *Chappell. Unpriced* KDW/HKR (B79-50986)

Noad, Frederick.

First book for the guitar

Part 1. *Schirmer. £1.75* TS/AC (B79-51166)

Part 2. *Schirmer. £1.75* TS/AC (B79-51167)

Nobis, Herbert. Hören und Singen : ein Solfège-Übungsbuch zur Gehörbildung. *Schott. £5.60* CB/AF (B79-50816)

Noble, Harold. Johnny : a Northumbrian fishergirl's song. *Lengnick. Unpriced* KDW (B79-50132)

Nolte, Charles. The voyage of Edgar Allan Poe. *Vocal score.* The voyage of Edgar Allan Poe : opera in two acts. (Argento, Dominick). *Boosey and Hawkes. Unpriced* CC (B79-50413)

Norton, Mary Dows Herter. Classic and Romantic music : a comprehensive survey. (Blume, Friedrich). *Faber.* Pbk. *£2.50 : CIP rev.* A(XFYK151) (B79-05246) ISBN 0-571-11354-0

Norwegian rhapsody. (Grundman, Clare). *Boosey and Hawkes. Unpriced* UMMJ (B79-50722)

Noth, Hugo. Liebeserklärung für ein verkanntes Instrument : 6 Stücke für Akkordeon, 1977. (Motte, Diether de la). *Bärenreiter. Unpriced* RSPMJ (B79-50255)

Nottebohm, Gustav. Two Beethoven sketchbooks : a description with musical extracts. *Gollancz. £4.95* BBJ(QVB) (B79-14912) ISBN 0-575-02583-2

Novara. (Brown, Earle). *Universal. Unpriced* NUNN (B79-51037)

Novello brass band series. Tate, Phyllis. Illustrations : for brass band. *Novello. Unpriced* WMJ (B79-50375)

Novello church music. Ives, Grayston. Let all the world in every corner sing. *Novello. £0.61* DH (B79-50024)

Novello modern organ repertory. Bennett, Richard Rodney. Alba (1973). *Novello. £1.45* RJ (B79-50234)

Nowak, Jerry. (Our love). Don't throw it all away. *arr.* (Our love). Don't throw it all away. (Gibb, Barry). *Stigwood Music. Unpriced* UMK/DW (B79-51203)

Nowka, Dieter. Sept esquisses : pour flûte et harpe. *Verlag Neue Musik : Breitkopf und Härtel. £2.70* VRPLTQ (B79-50756)

Nunn, Ruth. Moods for guitar. *Novello. £0.66* TSPMJ (B79-50308)

Nursery rhymes. *Helicon Press. Unpriced* LK/DW/GK/AY (B79-50159) ISBN 0-905684-03-6

Ó Canainn, Tomás. Songs of Cork. *25 Shonick Rd. Skerries : Gilbert Dalton. Unpriced* JEZDW/G/AYDQC (B79-50123)

O occhi manza mia = Thine eyes, oh, my beloved : for four-part chorus of mixed voices a cappella. (Lasso, Orlando di). *Schirmer. £0.35* EZDU (B79-50887)

O quam suavis est, Domine : motet for the Feast of Corpus Christi, for 6 voices. (Lobo, Alfonso). *72 Brewery Rd, N.7 : Mapa mundi. Unpriced* EZDJ/LNC (B79-50088)

O quam suavis : for eight-part chorus of mixed voices with organ accompaniment. (Gabrieli, Giovanni). *Schirmer. £0.75* DGKJ/LNC (B79-50427)

O sacrum convivium : motet for the Feast of Corpus Christi, for 4 voices. (Marenzio, Luca). *72 Brewery Rd, N.7 : Mapa mundi. Unpriced* EZDJ/LNC (B79-50089)

Oberthür, Charles. Cadeaux de noces. Op.65. Le désir. 'Le désir' : for clarinet and piano. *Chester Music. Unpriced* VVPJ (B79-51279)

Oboe trios

Vol.1. *Chester. Unpriced* VTNT/AY (B79-50349)

O'Boyle, Manus.

Songs of Belfast. *25 Shenick Rd, Skerries : Gilbert Dalton. Unpriced* JEZDW/G/AYDTB (B79-50124)

Songs of Dublin. *25 Shenick Rd. Skerries : Gilbert Dalton. Unpriced* JEZDW/G/AYDN (B79-50122)

Songs of the Irish in America. *25 Shonick Rd. Skerries : Gilbert Dalton. Unpriced* JEZDW/G/AYDM (B79-50121)

Observer's book of music. (Dinn, Freda). 4th ed. *F. Warne. £1.25* A (B79-50001) ISBN 0-7232-1581-2

Observer's pocket series. Dinn, Freda. The observer's book of music. 4th ed. *F. Warne. £1.25* A (B79-50001) ISBN 0-7232-1581-2

Oceans of the moon : eight variations and a theme, op.75 : for guitar. (Blyton, Carey). *Bèrben : Breitkopf an Härtel. £2.85* TSPM/T (B79-51176)

Ockeghem, Johannes. *See* Okeghem, Jean.

O'Connor, Garry. The pursuit of perfection : a life of Maggie Teyte. *Gollancz. £7.95* AKFL/E(P) (B79-15555) ISBN 0-575-02562-x

Ode à la musique. *Choral score.* Ode à musique. (Martin, Frank). *Bärenreiter. £1.16* DADH (B79-50419)

O'Donovan, Con. Comic songs of Ireland. *Mercier Press. Unpriced* JE/TSDW/AYDM (B79-50510) ISBN 0-85342-529-9

Odoru katachi = Dance patterns : for percussion soloist and chamber orchestra. (Tircuit, Heuwell). *Associated Music. £5.45* MPX (B79-50592)

Offenbach, Jacques. M'sieur Offenbach : a suite for clarinet, alto and tenor saxophones. *7 Garrick St., W.C.2 : Middle Eight Music. Unpriced* VNTK/DW (B79-50324)

Officium defunctorum (1978). (Halffter, Cristóbal). *Universal. Unpriced* EMDE (B79-50866)

Officium defunctorum. Missa pro defunctis. Requiem à 6 (1605). (Victoria, Tomás Luis de). *Oxenford Imprint. Unpriced* EZDGKAV (B79-50053)

Oh, God, invent a word for us : for two-part children's chorus and SAB adult chorus with organ and/or piano. (Nelson, Ron). *Boosey and Hawkes. Unpriced* DH (B79-50833)

Oh my Lord, let not your blinding fury - My heart = Domine, ne in furore - Cor meum : for four-part chorus of men's voices a cappella. (Josquin des Prés). *Schirmer. £0.75* GEZDJ (B79-50504)

Oh, what a beautiful mornin' : S.A.C.(T)B. with piano. (Rodgers, Richard). *Williamson Music. Unpriced* DW (B79-50856)

Okeghem, Jean.

Missa pro defunctis : for 2,3 and 4 voices. *72 Brewery Rd, N.7 : Mapa mundi. Unpriced* EZDGKAV (B79-50052)

Salve regina : for 4 voices. *72 Brewery Rd, N.7 : Mapa mundi. Unpriced* GEZDJ (B79-50113)

Oklahoma!. Oh, what a beautiful mornin'. *arr.* Oh, what a beautiful mornin' : S.A.C.(T)B. with piano. (Rodgers, Richard). *Williamson Music. Unpriced* DW (B79-50856)

Old, Margaret Valerie. Sing to God. *Scripture Union. £0.75* ADM (B79-31511) ISBN 0-85421-722-3

Old French dances. *Chester Music. Unpriced* WNH/AYH (B79-51307)

Old French organ music. *Oxford University Press. Unpriced* R/AYH (B79-50230) ISBN 0-19-375616-1

Old music master : 23 great songs. (Carmichael, Hoagy). *Chappell. Unpriced* KDW/GB (B79-50965)

Olé : twelve Spanish songs. *Oxford University Press. Unpriced* JFE/LDW/G/AYK (B79-50523) ISBN 0-19-330597-6

Olivadoti, Joseph. Castle and woods : overture. *Rubank Novello. Unpriced* UMMJ (B79-50724)

Olive, Leslie. The Master of Ashmore. *Vocal score.* The Master of Ashmore : opera in three acts. *Jon Adams. Unpriced* CC (B79-50012)

Olive, Vicky. Children's songs. (Olive, Vivienne). *Edwin Ashdown. Unpriced* JFDW/GJ (B79-50519)

Olive, Vivienne. Children's songs. *Edwin Ashdown. Unpriced* JFDW/GJ (B79-50519)

Olon-Scrymgeour, John. Miss Havisham's fire : opera in two acts. *Boosey and Hawkes.* Sd. *£1.00* BARGAC

(B79-26551)
Omnis pulchritudo Domini : motet for the Ascension of our Lord, for 5 voices. (Silva, Andreas de). *72 Brewery Rd, N.7 : Mapa mundi. Unpriced* EZDJ/LM (B79-50086)
On music and musicians. (Falla, Manuel de). *Boyars Distributed by Calder and Boyars. £5.95* A (B79-14910) ISBN 0-7145-2600-2
On receiving the first Aspen Award : a speech. (Britten, Benjamin, *Baron Britten*). *Faber.* Sd. *£0.80 : CIP rev.* A (B78-09111) ISBN 0-571-10023-6
On the king's highway. *Chorus score.* On the king's highway : for children's chorus and chamber orchestra. (Binkerd, Gordon). *Boosey and Hawkes. Unpriced* FADW (B79-50488)
On the king's highway : for children's chorus and chamber orchestra. (Binkerd, Gordon). *Boosey and Hawkes. Unpriced* FADW (B79-50488)
Once in royal David's city : carol for two-part mixed chorus and organ with optional chimes. (Wichmann, Russell G). *Oxford University Press. Unpriced* DP/LF (B79-50030)
One dream : for a cappella SATB chorus. (Pierce, Brent). *Warner : Blossom. Unpriced* EZDW (B79-50900)
One pearl : a monody for soprano and string quartet. (Bauld, Alison). *Novello. £4.25* KFLE/RXNSDX (B79-50152)
One world songs : Methodist World Development Action Campaign. *Methodist Church (Division of Social Responsibility). £1.40* JEZDM/LSJ/AY (B79-50120)
Open University.
From Liszt to music hall. (Middleton, Richard). *Open University Press.* Pbk. *Unpriced* A(XFY101) (B79-36911) ISBN 0-335-05423-4
Introduction to music. (Hendrie, Gerald). *Open University Press.* Pbk. *Unpriced* A (B79-16836) ISBN 0-335-05414-5
Opera in the development of German critical thought. (Flaherty, Gloria). *Princeton University Press. £11.70* AC/CC(YE/XE201) (B79-14914) ISBN 0-691-06370-2
Operas of Benjamin Britten : the complete librettos illustrated with designs of the first productions. *H. Hamilton. £30.00* BBUAC (B79-34989) ISBN 0-241-10256-1
Operas. *Selections.* Arien : für hohe Singstimme, Blockflöten, Fagott und Basso continuo. (Schürmann, Georg Caspar). Erstausgabe. *Bärenreiter. £6.60* KFTE/NWPNSDW (B79-50557)

Operetta! : (a stampede through nostalgia). (Sharkey, Jack). *French.* Sd. *£1.80* BSGNHACM (B79-37419) ISBN 0-573-61358-3
Options 4 woodwind.
Delibes, Leo. Music from the ballet. *(7 Garrick St., W.C.2) : Middle Eight Music. Unpriced* UNSK/HM (B79-50732)
Tchaikovsky, Peter. Music from the ballet. *(7 Garrick St., W.C.2) : Middle Eight Music. Unpriced* UNSK/HM (B79-50733)
Opus est. (Rapoport, Paul). *Kahn and Averill. £5.75 : CIP entry* A/D(M/YB) (B78-29830) ISBN 0-900707-48-8
Oration : (concerto elegiaco) for solo cello and orchestra. (Bridge, Frank). *Faber Music. Unpriced* MPSRF (B79-50584)
Orb and sceptre. *arr.* Orb and sceptre. (Walton, *Sir* William). *Oxford University Press. Unpriced* WMK/AGM (B79-51303) ISBN 0-19-368537-x
Orchestra. *Macdonald and Jane's. £7.95* AMM/E (B79-35974) ISBN 0-354-04420-6
Orchestration. (Piston, Walter). *Gollancz.* Pbk. *£3.95* AM/DF (B79-01355) ISBN 0-575-02602-2
Ord-Hume, Arthur Wolfgang Julius Gerald. Barrel organ : the story of the mechanical organ and its repair. *Allen and Unwin. £18.50* A/FK (B79-01356) ISBN 0-04-789005-3
Oregon trail : a suite for percussion ensemble. (Beament, Peter). *7 Garrick St., W.C.2 : Middle Eight Music. Unpriced* XNS (B79-50403)
Orfeo. Ecco Orfeo. *arr.* L'Orfeo. Vieni Imeneo. *arr.* Zwei Chöre aus 'Orpheus' = Two chorusses sic from 'Orpheus'. (Monteverdi, Claudio). *Schott. £0.80* EZDW (B79-50898)
Orfeo. Vieni Imeneo. *arr.* Zwei Chöre aus 'Orpheus' = Two chorusses sic from 'Orpheus'. (Monteverdi, Claudio). *Schott. £0.80* EZDW (B79-50898)
Orff, Carl. L'Orfeo. Vieni Imeneo. *arr.* Zwei Chöre aus 'Orpheus' = Two chorusses sic from 'Orpheus'. (Monteverdi, Claudio). *Schott. £0.80* EZDW (B79-50898)
Orga, Ateş. Chopin. Revised 2nd ed. *Midas Books. £6.50 : CIP entry* BCE(N) (B78-05411) ISBN 0-85936-116-0
Orga, Ates. Sonata, piano, G.162, C major. Piano sonata in C.Wo 051. (Beethoven, Ludwig van). *Roberton. £2.50* QPE (B79-50620)
Organ gold
1. *Chappell. Unpriced* RK/DW/GB/AY (B79-50238)
2. *Chappell. Unpriced* RK/DW/GB/AY (B79-50239)
3. *Chappell. Unpriced* RK/DW/GB/AY (B79-50240)
4. *Chappell. Unpriced* RK/DW/GB/AY (B79-50241)
5. *Chappell. Unpriced* RK/DW/GB/AY (B79-50657)
Organa helvetica.
Schibler, Armin. Rezitativ und Ostinato : für Trompete und Orgel. *Eulenburg. Unpriced* WSPLR (B79-50804)
Wehrle, Heinz. Choral-Toccata, 'O Heiland, reiss die Himmel auf' : Melodie Augsburg 1666. *Eulenburg. £1.85* RJ (B79-50651)
Zbinden, Julien François. Prelude & fugue, organ, op.58. Prélude et fugue pour grand orgue, op.58 (1978). *Eulenburg. £2.10* R/Y (B79-50648)
Orientation for interpreting Mozart's piano sonatas. Interpreting Mozart's piano sonatas. (Richner, Thomas). *Paterson's Publications.* Pbk. *£2.00* BMSAQPE/E (B79-04545)
Original music and alternative music for the Modern Dance Grade Examinations
Grades 2 and 3: including pieces needed for the course of movement for boys. (Imperial Society of Teachers of Dancing. *Modern Dance Branch*). *Imperial Society of Teachers of Dancing. £3.50* QPH/H/AL (B79-51070)
Primary and Grade 1: including pieces needed for the course of movement for boys. (Imperial Society of Teachers of Dancing. *Modern Dance Branch*). *Imperial Society of Teachers of Dancing. £3.00* QPH/H/AL (B79-51071)
Original musik für Blockflöte.
Frescobaldi, Girolamo. Libro della canzoni, no.1. Canzona 2 'La Bernadina'. Canzona (II) 'La Bernadina' per canto solo : für Sopranblockflüte (Flüte, Oboe, Violine) und Generalbass = for descant recorder (flute, oboe, violin) and continuo. *Schott. £3.20* VSRPJ (B79-51242)

Pez, Johann Christoph. Second collection of sonatas for two flutes and a bass. *Selections.* Zwei Suiten für zwei Altblockflöten und Basso continuo
Suite 1: C-Dur = C major. *Schott. £4.00* VSSNTPWG (B79-51247)
Original ragtime, as recorded by Claude Bolling. *Chappell. Unpriced* QPHXJ/AY (B79-51077)
Originalmusik für Blockflöte. Castello, Dario. Sonate concertate, lib. 2, no.1. Sonata prima a soprano solo... : für Sopranblockflöte (Flöte, Violine) und Generalbass = for descant recorder (flute, violin) and continuo. *Schott. £3.20* VSRPE (B79-51241)
Orlando Gibbons II : full anthems, hymns and fragmentary verse anthems. (Gibbons, Orlando). *Stainer and Bell. Unpriced* DK (B79-50026) ISBN 0-85249-517-x
Orledge, Robert.
Gabriel Fauré. *48 Great Marlborough St., W1V 2BN : Eulenberg Books. £7.00* BFD (B79-35971) ISBN 0-903873-40-0
Quartet, strings & keyboard, no.1, op.15. First piano quartet. Op.15. (Fauré, Gabriel). *Eulenburg. £2.05* NXNT (B79-50604)
Quartet, strings & keyboard, no.2, op.45. Second piano quartet. Op.45. (Fauré, Gabriel). *Eulenburg. Unpriced* NXNT (B79-50605)
Ornamentation in baroque and post-baroque music : with special emphasis on J.S. Bach. (Neumann, Frederick, *b.1907*). *Princeton University Press. £33.40* A(QM/XDZK196) (B79-07465) ISBN 0-691-09123-4
Ország-Land, Thomas. Prince Bluebeard's castle : a libretto / adapted from the Hungarian of Béla Balázs ; and, The splendid stags : a Bartók companion. *Top Floor, 64 Highgate High St., N6 5HX : The author.* Sd. *£2.10* BBGAC (B79-30800) ISBN 0-906057-07-8
Osborne, Gary. A single man. (John, Elton). *Big Pig Music : Music Sales. Unpriced* KDW/HKR (B79-50139)
Osborne, Hayward. Holy communion, series 3 ... *Weinberger. Unpriced* JDGS (B79-50117)
O'Shea, Patrick. Seasons and people and other songs. *Melody part.* Seasons and people and other songs. (Kingsbury, Roy). *Oxford University Press. Unpriced* JFADW (B79-50513) ISBN 0-19-450558-8
Ostransky, Leroy. Jazz city : the impact of our cities on the development of jazz. *Prentice-Hall. £8.00* AMT(YT/X) (B79-04544) ISBN 0-13-509380-5
Otčenáš = Our Father : for full chorus of mixed voices, tenor or soprano solo, organ and harp. (Janáček, Leoš). *Roberton. £0.75 (Chorus score £0.28)* EJQPLRDTF (B79-50865)
Ottaway, Hugh. Mozart. *Orbis Books. £10.00* BMS(N) (B79-21148) ISBN 0-85613-069-9
Ottley, John. Praise to God in the highest. *arr.* Praise to God in the highest : Russian melody. (Campbell, Sidney Schofield). *Oxford University Press. Unpriced* FDH/LF (B79-50490) ISBN 0-19-351126-6
Our father. Otčenáš = Our Father : for full chorus of mixed voices, tenor or soprano solo, organ and harp. (Janáček, Leoš). *Roberton. £0.75 (Chorus score £0.28)* EJQPLRDTF (B79-50865)
Our Gracie. (Rochdale Museum). *c/o Rochdale Museum Esplanade, Rochdale, Lancs. : Rochdale Arts and Entertainments Services.* Sd. *£0.70* AKDW/GB/E(P) (B79-08928)
Our love. *arr.* Our love. (Yancy, Marvin). *Chappell. Unpriced* DW (B79-50036)
Our love. *arr.* Our love. (Yancy, Marvin). *Chappell. Unpriced* DW (B79-50037)
Our love. *arr.* Our love. (Yancy, Marvin). *Chappell. Unpriced* FDW (B79-50105)
(Our love). Don't throw it all away. *arr.* (Our love). Don't throw it all away. (Gibb, Barry). *Stigwood Music. Unpriced* UMK/DW (B79-51203)
Out of this world. *Vocal score.* Out of this world : musical in two scenes. (Glen, Robert). *Weinberger. Unpriced* CM (B79-50818)
Outlines of modern librarianship. Jones, Malcolm, *b.1943.* Music librarianship. *Bingley etc.. £4.00 : CIP rev.* A(U) (B79-11403) ISBN 0-85157-274-x
Overkill. (Motorhead). *Chappell. Unpriced* KDW/HKR (B79-50985)
Overkill. *arr.* Overkill. (Motorhead). *Chappell. Unpriced* KDW/HKR (B79-50985)
Overture a quattro. Op.4, no.2. Ouverture, Opus 4, No.2 : für Streicher und Basso continuo = for strings and basso continuo. (Barsanti, Francesco). *Schott. £6.00* RXMG (B79-50257)
Overture Beatrice and Benedict. (Berlioz, Hector). *R. Smith. Unpriced* WMK (B79-51301)
Overture to cantata 'For us a Child is born' (Uns ist ein Kind geborn sic) : for organ and piano. (Bach, Johann Sebastian). *Sycamore : Schirmer (dist.). £1.50* QPLRK (B79-51110)
Oxford choral songs.
Arch, Gwen. The spinning wheel : S.S.A.A. (with divisi). *Oxford University Press. Unpriced* FDW (B79-50909) ISBN 0-19-342599-8
Willcocks, *Sir* David. What Child is this? S.A.T.B. (acc. or unacc.), English traditional melody. *Oxford University Press. Unpriced* DP/LF (B79-50447) ISBN 0-19-343071-1
Oxford easy anthems. Campbell, Sidney Schofield. Praise to God in the highest. *arr.* Praise to God in the highest : Russian melody. *Oxford University Press. Unpriced* FDH/LF (B79-50490) ISBN 0-19-351126-6
Oxford studies of composers. Griffiths, Paul. Boulez. *Oxford University Press.* Pbk. *£3.50* BBRO (B79-18562) ISBN 0-19-315442-0
Oxford University. *See* University of Oxford.
Oxtoby, David. Oxtoby's rockers : the eternal fan. *Phaidon.* Pbk. *£4.95* AKDW/HK/E(M) (B79-15543) ISBN 0-7148-1854-2
Pachelbel, Johann. Canon & gigue, violins (3) & continuo, D major. Canon & gigue for three violins and keyboard (cello continuo ad lib.). *Fentone Music : Breitkopf and Härtel. Unpriced* SNSPWHP (B79-51146)
Paganini, Nicolò.
Capriccio, violin solo, op.1, no.24, A minor. *arr.* Paganini caprice 24 : for double woodwind quintet. *Associated Music. £10.60* UMK/T (B79-51205)
Caprice, violin, op.1, no.24, A minor. *arr.* Caprice no.24. *Boosey and Hawkes. Unpriced* TSPMK/T (B79-50715)
Sonata, guitar & violin, op.39, A major. *arr.* Grande sonata in la maggiore. *Bèrben : Breitkopf and Härtel. £3.80* TSNUK/AE (B79-51173)
Page, Ian. Learning tree songbook. *Chappell. Unpriced* JFDW/GJ (B79-50939)
Paint your wagon. They call the wind Maria. *arr.* They call the wind Maria : S.A.C.(T.) B. with piano. (Loewe, Frederick). *Chappell. Unpriced* DW (B79-50850)
Pairman, David. Easy stretch guitar : new method for the complete beginner. *Galliard.* Pbk. *£3.00* TS/AC (B79-50697) ISBN 0-85249-447-5
Paisible, James. Sonata, trumpets (2), violins (2), viola & continuo, no.10, D major. Sonata 10 in D major for two trumpets (or oboes), strings, and continuo. *Oxford University Press. Unpriced* NUXSNQE (B79-50187) ISBN 0-19-366260-4
Palmer, David. Holy Boy. *Vocal score.* Holy Boy : a folk oratorio. *EMI. Unpriced* DE/LF (B79-50829) ISBN 0-86175-078-0
Palmer, Roy.
A ballad history of England : from 1588 to the present day. *Batsford. £6.50* AKDW/K/G(YD) (B79-11132) ISBN 0-7134-0968-1
Everyman's book of English country songs. *Dent. £7.95 : CIP rev.* AKDW/G(YC) (B79-15558) ISBN 0-460-12048-4
Strike the bell : transport by road, canal, rail and sea in the nineteenth century through songs, ballads and contemporary accounts. *Cambridge University Press.* Sd. *£2.25* KEZDW/K/G/AYC (B79-50547) ISBN 0-521-21921-3

Panorama ... (Tchaikovsky, Peter). *R. Smith. Unpriced* WMK/HM (B79-50383)
Parade of champions. (Elms, Albert). *Boosey and Hawkes. Unpriced* UMMJ (B79-51207)
Paradisi porta : motet for 6 voices. (Escribano, Juan). *72 Brewery Rd, N.7 : Mapa mundi. Unpriced* EZDJ (B79-50059)
Parastasis I : for percussion and tape = für Schlagzeug und Tonband. (Antioniou, Theodore). *Bärenreiter. £7.92* XPLPV (B79-50404)
Parke, Dorothy.

Gigue for piano solo. *Banks. Unpriced* QPHP (B79-51074)

Parker, Derek. The story and the song : a survey of English musical plays, 1916-78. *Chappell : Elm Tree Books. £7.50* ACM(YD/XMR53) (B79-35973) ISBN 0-903443-25-2
Parker, Jim. The shepherd king. *Vocal score.* The shepherd king : a musical play in eight scenes. *Weinberger. Unpriced* CN (B79-50415)
Parker, Julia. The story and the song : a survey of English musical plays, 1916-78. (Parker, Derek). *Chappell : Elm Tree Books. £7.50* ACM(YD/XMR53) (B79-35973) ISBN 0-903443-25-2
Parkinson, John Alfred. Sonata, violin & continuo, E major. Sonata in E major for violin and basso continuo. (Arne, Thomas Augustine). *Oxford University Press. Unpriced* SPE (B79-50273) ISBN 0-19-355216-7
Parry, *Sir* Charles Hubert, *bart.* English lyrics. *selections.* Seven songs for high voice. *Stainer and Bell. Unpriced* KFTDW (B79-51006)
Parsons, Tony. 'The boy looked at Johnny' : the obituary of rock and roll. (Burchill, Julie). *Pluto Press.* Pbk. *£1.25* AKDW/HKR/E(M) (B79-02984) ISBN 0-86104-030-9
Partirò sì = Parting is pain : for four-part chorus of mixed

voices a cappella. (Vecchi, Horatio). *Schirmer. £0.35* EZDU (B79-50475)
Partita : for oboe and piano. (Kelly, Bryan). *Chester Music. Unpriced* VTPG (B79-50773)
Partners in praise. *Stainer & Bell : Chester House Publications for the Methodist Church Division of Education and Youth. £5.50* DM/LSJ/AY (B79-50444)
Partsongs
Vol.1: for unaccompained i.e. unaccompanied male voices (A(A)T(T)B(B)). *(Lyndhurst, Denton Rd, Ben Rhydding) : Pro Cantione Antiqua : Breitkopf and Härtel. £2.40* GEZDW (B79-50508)
Parvulus filius : for 6 voices. (Ammon, Blasius). *72 Brewery Rd, N.7 : Mapa mundi. Unpriced* EZDJ/LF (B79-50074)
Passacaglia ungherese : für Cembalo = for harpsichord. (Ligeti, György). *Schott. £3.70* QRPHT (B79-51114)
Pastorelle and sonata : for three treble recorders. (Finger, Gottfried). *Oxford University Press. Unpriced* VSSNT (B79-50343) ISBN 0-19-363204-7
Pastorelle, recorders (treble) (3), G major. Pastorelle and sonata : for three treble recorders. (Finger, Gottfried). *Oxford University Press. Unpriced* VSSNT (B79-50343) ISBN 0-19-363204-7
Pastores loquebantur. (Guerrero, Francisco). *72 Brewery Rd, N.7 : Mapa mundi. Unpriced* EZDJ/LF (B79-50076)
Patchen, Kenneth. An easy decision : soprano voice & piano. (Bedford, David). *Universal. Unpriced* KFLDW (B79-50997)
Paths to musical thought : an approach to ear singing through sight singing. (Gould, Murray Joseph). *Holt, Rinehart and Winston. Unpriced* CB/EG (B79-50412) ISBN 0-03-020421-6
Patrick, David. The English recital song
Vol.1. *Chappell. Unpriced* KDW/AY (B79-50528)
Patterson, John. Who wants to sing? : (what it's all about) 2nd and enlarged ed.. *9 Kinnaird Terrace, Antrim Rd, Belfast BT14 6BN : John Patterson.* Pbk. *£3.80* AB/E (B79-06707)
Patterson, Minna. Who wants to sing? : (what it's all about). 2nd and enlarged ed.. *9 Kinnaird Terrace, Antrim Rd, Belfast BT14 6BN : John Patterson.* Pbk. *£3.80* AB/E (B79-06707)
Paul Bunyan. Op.17. *Vocal score.* Paul Bunyan : an operetta in two acts and a prologue, op.17. (Britten, Benjamin, *Baron Britten*). *Faber Music. Unpriced* CF (B79-50014)
Paule, Andy de. *See* De Paule, Andy.
Päuler, Bernhard.
Prélude ou exercise pour la flûte seule, op.35, nach dem Erstdruck ... (Hoffmeister, Franz Anton). *Amadeus Schott. Unpriced* VRPMJ (B79-50336)
Sonata, flute & piano, op.33, G major. Sonate in G-dur für Flöte und Klavier, op.33. (Schneider, Johann Christian Friedrich). *Amadeus : Schott. Unpriced* VRPE (B79-50330)
Pauli, Werner.
Gitarre
4. *Verlag Neue Musik : Breitkopf and Härtel. £2.10* TS/AY (B79-50699)
5. *Neue Musik : Breitkopf and Härtel. £2.10* TS/AY (B79-51168)

Payne, Roger. Beethoven and his world. (Kendall, Alan, *b.1939*). *Ward Lock. £2.95 : CIP rev.* BBJ(N) (B79-30252) ISBN 0-7063-5867-8
Paynter, John. Sound tracks
3: Sound poems. *Cambridge University Press. £1.95* A/D(VF) (B78-23591) ISBN 0-521-20580-8
Payzant, Geoffrey. Glenn Gould : music & mind. *Van Nostrand Reinhold. £10.45* AQ/E(P) (B79-16841) ISBN 0-442-29802-1
PCA partsongs. Lawes, William. Gather your rosebuds. *Pro Cantione Antiqua : Breitkopf und Härtel. Unpriced* GEZDU (B79-50505)
Peacemakers gospel songs and choruses. (Cowgill, Samuel C). *(Elim Pentecostal Church, Wakefield Rd) : S.C. Cowgill. Unpriced* JE/TSDM (B79-50509)
Pearce, J R. The musical companion. Revised ed. *Pan Books.* Pbk. *£2.95* A (B79-50002) ISBN 0-330-25670-x
Pearn, David. Diversions for percussion and piano. *Lengnick. Unpriced* QPLX (B79-50226)
Pedlar of Swaffham : a children's cantata with simple accompaniments for piano and classroom instruments. (Winch, Richard). *Chappell. Unpriced* JFE/NYDSDX (B79-50944)
Peñalosa, Francisco de.
Missa El ojo : for 4 voices. *72 Brewery Rd, N.7 : Mapa mundi. Unpriced* EZDG (B79-50050)
Sancta mater. *72 Brewery Rd, N.7 : Mapa mundi. Unpriced* GEZDJ (B79-50114)
Penetrating Wagner's Ring : an anthology. *Fairleigh Dickinson University Press : Associated University Presses. £12.00* BWCAC (B79-14015) ISBN 0-8386-1795-6
Penmarric : from the BBC classic serial. (Hartley, Richard). *EMI. Unpriced* QPK/JS (B79-51107)
Pensée petit sic valse. (Atkins, Florrie). *(85 Wakefords Way, West Leigh) : Florrie Atkins. Unpriced* QPHW (B79-50628)
Pensionat. *Vocal score.* The finishing school : comic operetta in one act (two scenes). (Suppé, Franz von). *Weinberger. Unpriced* CF (B79-50414)
Pentecost. Charlton. Take my life : tune, Charlton, words, Frances Ridley Havergal and Come, Holy Ghost : tune, Pentecost, words, Bishop J. Cosin, based on 'Veni creator spiritus'. (Wilson, Alan J). *Weinberger. Unpriced* DM (B79-50442)
Peranda, Marco Giuseppe. St. Mark's Passion. Markus-Passion für Solostimmen und vierstimmigen Chor a cappella. *VEB Deutscher Verlag : Breitkopf and Härtel. £2.70* EZDD/LK (B79-50872)
Percival, Allen. Partners in praise. *Stainer & Bell : Chester House Publications for the Methodist Church Division of Education and Youth. £5.50* DM/LSJ/AY (B79-50444)
Performance and interpretation of music. Conductors on conducting. *Macdonald and Jane's. £6.95* A/EC (B79-32716) ISBN 0-354-04416-8
Periodicals:, *New periodicals and those issued with changed titles.*
Black dwarf
1- ; 1978-. *7 Ivywell Rd, Bristol BS9 1NX : 'Black dwarf'.* Sd. *£0.23* AKDW/HKR(B) (B79-01354)
Country people
No.1- ; 1979-. *IPC Magazines.* Sd. *£0.80* A/GC(B) (B79-27777)
Discowords
Vol.1, no.1- ; 1978-. *Dormbourne Limited : Distributed by Wells Gardner Darton.* Sd. *£0.20* AKDW/GB/E(M/DE) (B79-00580)
Elgar Society. The Elgar Society journal
Vol.1, no.1- ; Jan. 1979-. *104 Crescent Rd, New Barnet, Herts. : 'The Elgar Society Journal'.* Sd. *Free to members* BEP(B) (B79-23400)
Music hall records
No.1- ; June 1978-. *50 Reporton Rd, S.W.6 : Tony Barker.* Sd. *£0.60(£3.60 yearly)* AKDW/JV/FD(B) (B79-15561)

Plainsong and Mediaeval Music Society. Journal of the Plainsong & Mediaeval Music Society
Vol.1- ; 1978-. *46 Bond St., Englefield Green, Surrey TW20 0PY : The Society.* Sd. *£1.50(free to members)* A(XA1600/B) (B79-36420)
Pop star weekly
24 Mar. 1979-. *Spotlight Publications.* Sd. *£0.20(£20.00 yearly)* A/GB(B) (B79-27779)
Superpop
No.1- ; Jan. 27, 1979-. *1B Parkfield St., N1 0PR : 'Superpop'.* Sd. *£0.15* A/GB(B) (B79-24588)
Persian market swing. (In a Persian market). (Ketelbey, Albert). *Bosworth & Co. £1.35* MK (B79-50565)
Persistencies : for piano. (Balada, Leonardo). *Schirmer. £4.55* QPJ (B79-50630)
Perspectives on southern Africa. Berliner, Paul. The soul of Mbira : music and traditions of the Shona people of Zimbabwe. *University of California Press. £12.00* BZNM (B79-19448) ISBN 0-520-03315-9
Pert, Morris. Luminos. Op.16a : for basset horn (or clarinet B flat) and piano. *Weinberger. Unpriced* VVXPJ (B79-50361)
Pet sound plus : 24 greatest hits ... (Beach Boys). *Chappell. Unpriced* KDW/HKR (B79-50540)
Peter and the wolf. *See* Prokof'ev, Sergeĭ Sergeevich.
Petite suite. (Debussy, Claude). 2nd ed. *Peters. Unpriced* QNVG (B79-50205)
Pets : a suite of 8 pieces for unaccompanied clarinet. (Harvey, Paul). *Ricordi. Unpriced* VVPMG (B79-51286)

Petti, Anthony Gaetano. The Chester book of motets : sacred renaissance motets, with Latin texts
7: Motets for 3 voices. *Chester Music. Unpriced* EZDJ/AY (B79-50882)
Pez, Johann Christoph

Second collection of sonatas for two flutes and a bass. *Selections.* Zwei Suiten für zwei Altblockflöten und Basso continuo
Suite 1: C-Dur = C major. *Schott. £4.00* VSSNTPWG (B79-51247)
Pezel, Johann. Bicinia variorum instrumentorum. *Selections.* Six sonatinas, nos 1, 2, 3, 7, 9, 11 for 2 oboes/violins/recorders in C and basso continuo. *Nova Music. Unpriced* VTNTPWEM (B79-51257)
Pfuhl, Sabine. Das bunte Spielbuch : für die Kindergartenflöte. *Schott. £4.00* VR/AF (B79-50325)
Phantasie über ungarische Volksmelodien = Fantasia on Hungarian folk themes. (Liszt, Franz). *Eulenburg. £1.20* MMJ (B79-50179)
Phantasmen : für grosses Orchester, 1965-1966. (Kelterborn, Rudolf). *Bärenreiter. £10.89* MMJ (B79-50578)
Phantom-Bilder auf der Spur eines verdächtingen Themas. Op.30 = Photo-fit pictures on the tracks of a suspect theme = für kleines Orchester = for small orchestra. (Gruber, Heinz Karl). *Boosey and Hawkes. Unpriced* MJ (B79-50564)
Philidor, François André Danican. Tom Jones. *Vocal score.* Tom Jones : comic opera in three acts based on the novel by Henry Fielding = opera comique en trois actes d'aprés le roman de Henry Fielding. *Boosey and Hawkes. £7.50* CC (B79-50013)
Philipp, Isidor. Anthology of French piano music. *Selections.* French piano music : an anthology. *Dover : Constable. Unpriced* QP/AY (B79-50616) ISBN 0-486-23381-2
Philips, Peter. Cantiones sacrae, octonis vocibus. Tu es Petrus. Tu es Petrus : for 8 voices. *Mapa mundi. Unpriced* EZDJ (B79-50065)
Phillips, Jill. Give your child music. *Elek. £5.95* A(VC) (B79-14614) ISBN 0-236-40145-9
Phillips, Peter.
Aeternae laudis lilium : for 5 voices. (Fayrfax, Robert). *72 Brewery Rd, N.7 : Mapa mundi. Unpriced* EZDJ (B79-50061)
Cantiones sacrae, octonis vocibus. Tu es Petrus. Tu es Petrus : for 8 voices. (Philips, Peter). *Mapa mundi. Unpriced* EZDJ (B79-50065)
Sancte Deus. (Tallis, Thomas). *72 Brewery Rd, N.7 : Mapa mundi. Unpriced* EZDJ (B79-50066)
Phillips, Roger. Beethoven and his world. (Kendall, Alan, *b.1939*). *Ward Lock. £2.95 : CIP rev.* BBJ(N) (B79-30252) ISBN 0-7063-5867-8
Pianist's resource guide : piano music in print and literature on the pianistic art
1978-79. *Pallma Music; 20 Earlham St., WC2H 9LN Distributed by Breitkopf and Härtel (London) Ltd.* Pbk. *£32.50* AQ (TC) (B79-24852) ISBN 0-8497-7800-x
Piano action repairs and maintenance. (Kennedy, Kenneth Thomas). *Kaye and Ward etc.. £7.95* AQ/BT (B79-11135) ISBN 0-7182-1205-3
Piano and orchestra. (Feldman, Morton). *Universal. Unpriced* MPQ (B79-50181)
Piano cameos. *EMI. Unpriced* QPK/AAY (B79-51095)
Piano favorites : seven select solos for intermediate grade. (Nevin, Mark). *Schroeder and Gunther. £1.35* QPJ (B79-50634)
Piano-forte : its history traced to the Great Exhibition of 1851. (Harding, Rosamond Evelyn Mary). 2nd ed. *Unwin Brothers Ltd, The Gresham Press, Old Woking, Surrey : Gresham Books. £11.50* AQ/B(XFWK122) (B79-14922) ISBN 0-905418-31-x
Piano in chamber ensemble. (Hinson, Maurice). *Harvester Press. £10.50 : CIP entry* ALP(WT) (B78-23117) ISBN 0-85527-634-7
Piano playtime : very first solos and duets
Book 2. *faber Music. Unpriced* QP/AY (B79-50207)

Piano sonata. (Benjamin, George). *Faber Music. Unpriced* QPE (B79-51066)
Pianoforte examination pieces, 1980
Grade 1: Lists A & B. (Associated Board of the Royal Schools of Music). *Associated Board of the Royal Schools of Music. £0.50* Q/AL (B79-51054)
Grade 2: Lists A & B. (Associated Board of the Royal Schools of Music). *Associated Board of the Royal Schools of Music. £0.50* Q/AL (B79-51055)
Grade 3: Lists A & B. (Associated Board of the Royal Schools of Music). *Associated Board of the Royal Schools of Music. £0.60* Q/AL (B79-51056)
Grade 4: Lists A & B. (Associated Board of the Royal Schools of Music). *Associated Board of the Royal Schools of Music. £0.60* Q/AL (B79-51057)
Grade 5: Lists A & B. (Associated Board of the Royal Schools of Music). *Associated Board of the Royal Schools of Music. £0.90* Q/AL (B79-51058)
Grade 6: Lists A & B. (Associated Board of the Royal Schools of Music). *Associated Board of the Royal Schools of Music. £0.90* Q/AL (B79-51059)
Grade 7: Lists A & B. (Associated Board of the Royal Schools of Music). *Associated Board of the Royal Schools of Music. £1.10* Q/AL (B79-51060)
Pictures at an exhibition. *arr.* Pictures at an exhibition. (Mussorgsky, Modest). *Chester Music. Unpriced* WMK (B79-51302)
Piéces de clavecin, livre 3, ordre 24,15,16. *Selections : arr.* Four duos for flute or oboe and keyboard (harpsichord or piano). (Couperin, François). *Oxford University Press. Unpriced* VRPK (B79-50331) ISBN 0-19-355912-9
Pièces de violes, liv. 4. *Selections : arr.* Cinque antiche danze francesi. (Marais, Marin). *Berben : Breitkopf und Härtel. £1.90* SQPLTSK (B79-50686)
Pieper, Manfred. Swing und Beat, Schwarz auf weiss = Swing and beat. Black on white : Anregungen zum Musizieren auf Klavier und Elektronenorgel = Hints on playing the piano and the electronic organ. *VEB Deutscher Verlag für Musik : Breitkopf und Härtel. £6.30* Q/AC (B79-50612)
Pierce, Brent.
I will always need you : for vocal solo, SATB chorus and piano with optional bass and drums. *Warner : Blossom. Unpriced* DW (B79-50851)
One dream : for a cappella SATB chorus. *Warner Blossom. Unpriced* EZDW (B79-50900)
Piguet, Jean Claude. Consolatio philosophiae. *Vocal score.* Consolatio philosophiae : scène dramatique voix haute et orchestre in memoriam Ernest Ansermet (1977). (Sutermeister, Heinrich). *Schott. £10.80* KFTDX (B79-50155)
Pike, Lionel. Beethoven, Sibelius and the 'profound logic'. *Athlone Press. £12.95 : CIP entry* BBJAMME (B78-37102) ISBN 0-485-11178-0
Pilkington, Michael.
Early Georgian songs
Book 1: Medium voice. *Stainer and Bell. Unpriced* KFVDW (B79-50559) ISBN 0-85249-459-9
Eight songs : for high voice. (Hook, James). *Stainer and Bell. Unpriced* KFTDW (B79-50555) ISBN 0-85249-494-7
Seven songs : for high voice. (Storace, Stephen). *Stainer and Bell. Unpriced* KFTDW (B79-50556) ISBN 0-85249-510-2
Ten songs for high voice. (Blow, John). *Stainer and Bell. Unpriced* KFTDW (B79-51004) ISBN 0-85249-547-1
Ten songs for high voice. (Boyce, William). *Stainer and Bell. Unpriced* KFTDW (B79-50554) ISBN 0-85249-493-9
Twelve songs : for high voice
Book 1. (Arne, Thomas Augustine). *Stainer and Bell. Unpriced* KFTDW (B79-50552) ISBN 0-85249-461-0
Book 2. (Arne, Thomas Augustine). *Stainer and Bell. Unpriced* KFTDW (B79-50553) ISBN 0-85249-462-9
Pilo, Nelson. Album de violão. (Nazareth, Ernesto, *b.1863*). *Arthur Napoleão : Essex Music. Unpriced* SPMK

(B79-50281)
Pinto, David. Consort sets in five and six parts. (Lawes, William). *Faber Music. Unpriced* STNQR (B79-51162)
Píobairí Uileann, Na. The Irish bagpipes : their construction and maintenance. (Garvin, Wilbert). *Blackstaff Press for Na Píobairí Uileann.* Pbk. *£3.95* AVYR/BT (B79-17765) ISBN 0-85640-149-8
Pipers' Guild. In memoriam : Margaret James : a treasury of bamboo pipe music. *Pipers' Guild. Unpriced* VSY/AY (B79-51255)
Pirates of Penzance. *Selections : arr.* Suite from Gilbert and Sullivan's 'The pirates of Penzance. (Sullivan, *Sir* Arthur Seymour). *Lengnick. £1.10* JE/VSNQDW (B79-50931)
Piston, Walter.
Concerto, flute. Concerto, flute and orchestra. *Associated Music. £7.55* MPVRF (B79-51031)
Concerto, flute. *arr.* Concerto for flute and orchestra. *Associated Music. £4.25* VRPK/LF (B79-51228)
Fantasia, violin & orchestra. *arr.* Fantasia for violin and orchestra. *Associated Music. £4.25* SPK (B79-51151)
Orchestration. *Gollancz.* Pbk. *£3.95* AM/DF (B79-01355) ISBN 0-575-02602-2
Pizzicato : tempo de gavota. (Cosentino, Manuel). *Arapuã Clifford Essex. Unpriced* QPHM (B79-51072)
Plainsong and Mediaeval Music Society. Journal of the Plainsong & Mediaeval Music Society
Vol.1- ; 1978-. *46 Bond St., Englefield Green, Surrey TW20 0PY : The Society.* Sd. *£1.50(free to members)* A(XA1600/B) (B79-36420)
Plainsong mass book. *Catholic Truth Society. Unpriced* JEZDG/AY (B79-50512)
Plaistow, Stephen. Catalogue of music broadcast on Radio 3 1975. (British Broadcasting Corporation). *B.B.C.* Pbk. *£4.50* A/JT(XQQ) (B79-29149) ISBN 0-563-17372-6
Planets. Op.32. *arr.* The planets. (Holst, Gustav). *Curwen Edition. Unpriced* QNUK/AG (B79-51062)
Planets : suite for large orchestra. Op.32. (Holst, Gustav). *Curwen. Unpriced* MMG (B79-51017)
Platt, Richard.
Pastorelle, recorders (treble) (3), G major. Pastorelle and sonata : for three treble recorders. (Finger, Gottfried). *Oxford University Press. Unpriced* VSSNT (B79-50343) ISBN 0-19-363204-7
Sonata, trumpets (2), violins (2), viola & continuo, no.10, D major. Sonata 10 in D major for two trumpets (or oboes), strings, and continuo. (Paisible, James). *Oxford University Press. Unpriced* NUXSNQE (B79-50187) ISBN 0-19-366260-4
Platti, Giovanni Benedetto. Sonata, flute & continuo, op.3, no.3, E minor. Sonate e-Moll, e minor, mi mineur, opus III, no.3, für Flöte und Basso continuo, for flute and basso continuo, pour flûte et basse continue. *Schott. £4.80* VRPE (B79-51222)
Platts, Kenneth. Sonatina, guitar, op.47. Sonatina for guitar, opus 47. *Edwin Ashdown. £3.00* TSPMEM (B79-51178)

Play drums today. (Brown, Ashley). *Hamlyn. £3.50* AXQ/E (B79-24596) ISBN 0-600-37199-9
Play guitar today. (Butterfield, Arthur). *Hamlyn. £3.50* ATS/E (B79-22642) ISBN 0-600-37200-6
Play keyboards today. (Lewendon, Vanessa). *Hamlyn. £3.50* APW/E (B79-24593) ISBN 0-600-37201-4
Play of Daniel : a 13th century liturgical drama from Beauvais Cathedral. *(Lyndhurst, Denton Rd, Ben Rhydding) : Pro Cantione Antiqua : Breitkopf und Härtel. £2.95* CQM/L (B79-50417)
Play old-time country fiddle : seventy-five traditional tunes arranged with words and chords including twenty-five square dances with complete calls and instructions, plus transposing guides for guitar, banjo, piano, bass or mandolin. *Oak : Music Sales. Unpriced* SPMK/AH/G/AYT (B79-51155) ISBN 0-86001-506-8
Play rock guitar today. (Butterfield, Graham). *Hamlyn. £3.50* ATSPV/E (B79-24594) ISBN 0-600-37202-2
Playing the harpsichord. (Schott, Howard). 1st ed. reprinted. *Faber.* Pbk. *£2.95 : CIP rev.* AQR/E (B79-05250) ISBN 0-571-11375-3
Playing the string game : strategies for teaching cello and strings. (Young, Phyllis). *University of Texas Press. £10.50* ARW/E(VC) (B79-20274) ISBN 0-292-73814-5
Pledge, Andrew. Concerto, viola d'amore, oboe d'amore & continuo, F major. Concerto for viola d'amore or viola, oboe d'amore or viola and basso continuo with cello. (Böhm, I C F). *(Little Margaret, Penmans Green, Chipperfield) : E.L. White. Unpriced* NUPNTF (B79-50596)

Pleyel, Ignaz Joseph. 3 trios concertants pour flûte, clarinette et basson, Ben.4705. Trio no.2. Trio 2 for flute, clarinet and bassoon. *Musica rara. Unpriced* VNTF (B79-50322)
Pocket manual of musical terms. Schirmer pronouncing pocket manual of musical terms. 4th ed. *Schirmer : Collier Macmillan.* Pbk. *£1.45* A(C) (B79-04535) ISBN 0-02-870250-6
Pocket musical history : with biographical list of famous composers and landmarks in the history of musical development. Revised ed.. *421a Brighton Rd, Croydon, Surrey CR2 6YR : Alfred Lengnick and Co.* Sd. *£0.10* A(X) (B79-07464)
Poems of Wallace Stevens I : for soprano and seven players, opus 9. (Connolly, Justin). *Novello. £3.00* KFLE/NYENPDW (B79-50151)
Poglietti, Alessandro. Sonata, trumpet, bassoon & continuo, C major. Sonata à 3 for trumpet/oboe/flute/violin, bassoon & basso continuo. *Musica rara. Unpriced* NWNTE (B79-51046)
Poinsinet, Antoine Alexandre Henri. Tom Jones. *Vocal score.* Tom Jones : comic opera in three acts based on the novel by Henry Fielding = opera comique en trois actes d'après le roman de Henry Fielding. (Philidor, François André Danican). *Boosey and Hawkes. £7.50* CC (B79-50013)
Polacek, Pavle. Sonatina, piano, op.20, no.1, G major. *arr.* Sonatina für zwei Gitarren. (Dussek, Jan Ladislav). *Breitkopf und Härtel. £2.55* TSNUK/AEM (B79-51174)

Politoske, Daniel Theodore. Music. 2nd ed. *Prentice-Hall. £9.05* A(X) (B79-34988) ISBN 0-13-607556-8
Polka dot : ten characteristic pieces for piano, grade 2. (Helyer, Marjorie). *Novello. £0.91* QPJ (B79-50216)
Polkas and marches : for all organs. *Lewis Music : Phoenix. Unpriced* RPVK/AHVH/AY (B79-50661)
Pollitt, Elizabeth. Our Gracie. (Rochdale Museum). *c/o Rochdale Museum Esplanade, Rochdale, Lancs. Rochdale Arts and Entertainments Services.* Sd. *£0.70* AKDW/GB/E(P) (B79-08928)
Pompaleerie jig. (Thompson, Diana). *E.J. Arnold.* Sd. *£1.30* A(VG/GR) (B79-04968) ISBN 0-560-00319-6
Poor, Elizabeth Kimball de Albuquerque. *See* Poor, Kim.
Poor, Kim. Genesis lyrics. (Genesis *(Group)*). *Sidgwick and Jackson. £8.95 : CIP rev.* AKDW/HKR(P) (B79-14920) ISBN 0-283-98526-7
Poor Jenny : for flutes (1 player) and percussion (1 player). (Buller, John). *Schirmer. £3.50* VRPLX (B79-51229)
Poos, Heinrich.
Suite nach englischen Volksliedern
No.1: The keel row. Einst kam ich nach Sandgate. *Schott. £0.72* EZDW/G/AYD (B79-50481)
No.2: The old true love. Ach komm, tritt ein. *Schott. £0.48* EZDW/G/AYD (B79-50482)
No.3: The keeper. Ein Jager wollte jagen gehn. *Schott. £0.80* EZDW/G/AYD (B79-50483)
No.4: There's none to soothe. Wo weilst du, Lieb. *Schott. £0.48* EZDW/G/AYD (B79-50484)
No.5: The miller of Dee. War einst ein braver Mullersmann. *Schott. £0.72* EZDW/G/AYD (B79-50485)
No.6: Cock a doodle doo. *Schott. £0.48* EZDW/G/AYD (B79-50486)
Tanzlied. (Ritmo di joropo). *Schott. £0.48* FEZDW (B79-50502)
Pop. (Farmer, Paul). *Longman.* Sd. *£0.65* A/GB (B79-32712) ISBN 0-582-21577-3
Pop preludes for piano : easy music in pop style. (Holloway, Laurie). *Novello. £1.15* QPJ (B79-50631)
Pop star weekly
24 Mar. 1979-. *Spotlight Publications.* Sd. *£0.20(£20.00 yearly)* A/GB(B) (B79-27779)
Pope, Isabel. The musical manuscript Montecassino 871 : a Neapolitan repertory of sacred and secular music of the late fifteenth century. (Monte Cassino *(Monastery). Biblioteca. MSS. (Codex 871)*). *Clarendon Press. £25.00* CB/AY (B79-50411) ISBN 0-19-816132-8
Popeye the sailor. I'm Popeye the sailorman. *arr.* I'm Popeye the sailor man : for two-part chorus and piano. (Lerner, Samuel). *Warner : Blossom. Unpriced* FDW/JR (B79-50106)
Popular Cambrian Bacchanalian air, of Gland meddwdod mwyn, or 'Good humored and merry' with an introduction and variations : for the harp. (Davies, Oliver). *Adlais. Unpriced* TQPM/T (B79-50293)
Porgy and Bess. (Gershwin, George). *Elm Tree Books : Chappell. Unpriced* KDW (B79-50131)
Porgy and Bess. *Selections : arr.* Porgy and Bess. (Gershwin, George). *Elm Tree Books : Chappell. Unpriced* KDW (B79-50131)
Porgy and Bess. Summertime. *arr.* Summertime : S.A.C.(T.) B. with piano. (Gershwin, George). *Chappell. Unpriced* DW (B79-50849)
Porta, Constanzo.
Liber primus motectorum quatuor vocum. Vidi turbam magnam. Vidi turbam magnam : motet for All Saints' Day, for 4 voices. *72 Brewery Rd, N.7 : Mapa mundi. Unpriced* EZDJ/LQ (B79-50090)
Psalmodia vespertina. lauda Hierusalem Dominum. Lauda Hierusalem Dominum. *72 Brewery Rd, N.7 : Mapa mundi. Unpriced* DR (B79-50032)
Porter, Andrew. Music of three seasons, 1974-1977. *Chatto and Windus. £12.50 : CIP entry* A/E(XQP4) (B78-37093) ISBN 0-7011-2340-0
Porter, Cole. Kiss me, Kate. Another op'nin, another show. *arr.* Another op'nin', another show : for S.A. cambiata, B. or S.A.T.B. with piano. *Chappell. Unpriced* DW (B79-50852)
Pössinger, Alexander. Trio, flute, viola & horn, op.28, D major. Trio in D-dur für Flöte, Viola and Horn. Op.28 = Trio in D major for flute, viola and horn. *Amadeus Bärenreiter. £3.25* NVPNT (B79-50601)
Poulenc, Francis. My friends and myself : conversations with Francis Poulenc. (Audel, Stéphane). *Dobson. £4.95* BPO (B78-39780) ISBN 0-234-77251-4
Powell, Aubrey. Wings tour USA. *High St., Limpsfield, Surrey RH8 0DY : Paper Tiger.* Pbk. *£3.25* AKDW/GB/E(P/EM/XRF) (B79-05872) ISBN 0-905895-10-x
Power within us : a narrative oratorio for baritone, narrator, chorus and orchestra. (Schuller, Gunther). *Associated Music. Unpriced* EMDE (B79-50454)
Praetorius, Michael.
Es ist ein Ros entsprungen. Op. 122, no.8. *arr.* Es ist ein Ros entsprungen = Now blooms a rose so tender. (Brahms, Johannes). *Boosey and Hawkes. Unpriced* EZDW (B79-50888)
Musae Sioniae Tl.3. Allein Gott in der Höh sei Ehr. Allein Gott in der Höh sei Ehr : Choralbearbeitung für zwei vierstimmige Chöre. *Bärenreiter. £1.16* EZDH (B79-50462)
Terpsichore. *Selections : arr.* Four dances ... guitar. *Boosey and Hawkes. Unpriced* TSPMK/AH (B79-50710)
Praise the Lord out of heaven : S.A.T.B. (Bullard, Alan). *Banks. Unpriced* DK (B79-50438)
Praise to God in the highest. *arr.* Praise to God in the highest : Russian melody. (Campbell, Sidney Schofield). *Oxford University Press. Unpriced* FDH/LF (B79-50490) ISBN 0-19-351126-6
Pratt, George.
Sonata, violin & continuo, op.posth., pt.1, no.11, G minor. Sonata 11 in G minor for oboe (or violin) and basso continuo. (Babell, William). *Oxford University Press. Unpriced* SPE (B79-50274) ISBN 0-19-355226-4
Suites, cello, B.W.V. 1007-1012. Six suites for solo cello. (Bach, Johann Sebastian). *Stainer and Bell. Unpriced* SRPMG (B79-50692) ISBN 0-85249-562-5
Praxis der chorischen Stimmbildung. (Hofbauer, Kurt). *Schott.* Pbk. *£6.00* AD/E (B79-11133)
Preces and responses. (Neary, Martin). *Royal School of Church Music. Unpriced* EZDGMM (B79-50460)
Prelude, interlude and carillon : (for organ). (Veal, Arthur). *Cramer. Unpriced* RJ (B79-50236)
Prélude ou exercise pour la flûte seule, op.35, nach dem Erstdruck ... (Hoffmeister, Franz Anton). *Amadeus Schott. Unpriced* VRPMJ (B79-50336)
Prélude, thème et variations pour cor. Prelude, theme and variations for French horn and piano. (Rossini, Gioacchino Antonio). *Schirmer. £3.65* WTP/T (B79-51322)
Prelúdio pra Ninar Gente Grande. (Vieira, Luiz). *Rio Musical : Essex Music. Unpriced* QPK (B79-51093)
Prelúdio pra Ninar Gente Grande. *arr.* Prelúdio pra Ninar Gente Grande. (Vieira, Luiz). *Rio Musical : Essex Music. Unpriced* QPK (B79-51093)
Premru, Raymond. Quartet, trumpets (2), horn & trombone. Quartet for two trumpets, horn and trombone. *Chester Music. Unpriced* WNS (B79-50796)
Prévert, Jacques.
Lied des Vogelstellers : drei leichte Chorlieder No.1. (Genzmer, Harald). *Schott. £0.72* EZDW (B79-50895)
Rechenstunde : drei leichte Chorlieder, für gemischten Chor No.3. (Genzmer, Harald). *Schott. £0.72* EZDW (B79-50896)
Stadturlaub : drei leichte Chorlieder No.2. (Genzmer, Harald). *Schott. £0.72* EZDW (B79-50897)
Previn, André. Orchestra. *Macdonald and Jane's. £7.95* AMM/E (B79-35974) ISBN 0-354-04420-6
Price, Beryl. Two songs of the nativity : for two-part choir and piano. *Roberton. £0.24* FDP/LF (B79-50491)
Price, Milburn. A joyful sound : Christian hymnody. (Reynolds, William Jensen). 2nd ed. *Holt, Rinehart and Winston. £8.75* ADM(X) (B79-05497) ISBN 0-03-040831-8
Price-Thomas, Brian. Singing rhymes. *Ladybird Books. £0.30* AJFDW/GR(VJ) (B79-06706) ISBN 0-7214-0537-1
Prince Bluebeard's castle : a libretto / adapted from the Hungarian of Béla Balázs ; and, The splendid stags : a Bartók companion. (Ország-Land, Thomas). *Top Floor, 64 Highgate High St., N6 5HX : The author.* Sd. *£2.10* BBGAC (B79-30800) ISBN 0-906057-07-8
Pro organo : Zeitgenössische Orgelmusik von Komponisten der Deutschen Demokratischen Republik. *VEB Deutscher Verlag für Musik : Breitkopf und Härtel. £4.80* R/AYEA (B79-50647)
Pro pace motets : for unaccompanied chorus. (Joubert, John). *Novello. £1.95* EZDJ (B79-50468)
Pro pace motets. Op.19, 32, 29. Pro pace motets : for unaccompanied chorus. (Joubert, John). *Novello. £1.95* EZDJ (B79-50468)
Prodigal son. L'enfant prodigue. Opus 46 : ballet in three scenes by Boris Kochno. (Prokofiev, Sergei). 1st ed. *Boosey and Hawkes. Unpriced* MM/HM (B79-50164)
Professional register of artists
1977. (Incorporated Society of Musicians). *10 Stratford Place, W1N 9AE : The Society.* Sd. *£1.00* A(YC/MM) (B79-27780)
Programmed texts:. Andrews, J Austin. Introduction to music fundamentals : a programmed textbook for the elementary classroom teacher. 4th ed. *Prentice-Hall.* Sp. *£8.00* A/M(VG) (B79-00564) ISBN 0-13-489575-4
Prokof'ev, Sergeĭ Sergeevich. Peter and the wolf. *Adaptations.* Peter and the wolf. (Voigt, Erna). *Blackie. £3.75* BPPAMBN (B79-35567) ISBN 0-216-90875-2
Prokofiev, Sergei.
Love of three oranges. L'amour des trois oranges. Opus 33 : opéra en 4 actes et 10 tableaux avec un prologue d'après Carlo Gozzi. *Boosey and Hawkes. Unpriced* CQC (B79-50822)
The prodigal son. L'enfant prodigue. Opus 46 : ballet in three scenes by Boris Kochno. 1st ed. *Boosey and Hawkes. Unpriced* MM/HM (B79-50164)
Prokofjew, Sergei. *See* Prokof'ev, Sergeĭ Sergeevich.
Promises like pie-crust : SATB. (Binkerd, Gordon). *Boosey and Hawkes. Unpriced* EZDW (B79-50098)
Prophète. March. *arr.* Coronation march. (Le prophète). (Meyerbeer, Giacomo). *Novello. £2.00* UMK/AGM (B79-50315)
Pryce, Larry. The Bee Gees. *Panther.* Pbk. *£0.80* AKDW/GB/E(P) (B79-10478) ISBN 0-586-04854-5
Psalm 4 : for soprano, alto, female chorus, viola solo, and organ. (Goehr, Alexander). *Schott. £1.85* FE/SQPLRDR (B79-50914)
Psalm 23. (How, Martin). *Weinberger. Unpriced* FDR (B79-50908)

Psalm 100 : (anthem), for four-part chorus of mixed voices with organ and 2 trumpets accompaniment. (Badarak, Mary Lynn). *Schirmer. Unpriced* EWSNTPLRDR (B79-50870)
Psalmodia vespertina. lauda Hierusalem Dominum. Lauda Hierusalem Dominum. (Porta, Constanzo). *72 Brewery Rd, N.7 : Mapa mundi. Unpriced* DR (B79-50032)
Psaslm der Nacht : für sechzehnstimmigen Frauenchor, Männerstimmen, Schlagwerk und Orgel. (Zimmermann, Udo). *Bärenreiter. £7.92* ERPLXDH/KDN (B79-50046)

Pulkingham, Betty. Sound of living waters. Combined Sound of living waters - Fresh sounds. *Hodder and Stoughton. £6.95* DM/AY (B79-50029) ISBN 0-340-23262-5
Purcell, Daniel. Bow down thine ear. I will thank thee, O Lord. I will thank thee, O Lord. *36 Ranelagh Gdns W.6 : Cathedral Music. Unpriced* EZDH (B79-50058)
Purcell, Henry.
Chacony, string orchestra, Z.730, G minor. Chacony for strings. *Eulenberg. Unpriced* RXMHJN (B79-51137)
A ground in gamut. Z645. *arr.* A ground in gamut. *Banks. Unpriced* TSNUK (B79-50703)
The works of Henry Purcell
Vol.3: Dido and Aeneas. *Novello. £10.00* C/AZ (B79-50815)
Pursuit of perfection : a life of Maggie Teyte. (O'Connor, Garry). *Gollancz. £7.95* AKFL/E(P) (B79-15555) ISBN 0-575-02562-x
Putze dich mit meinem Tüchlein : Kastilianisches Volkslied aus Avila (Spanien). (Desch, Rudolf). *Schott. £0.48* GEZDW (B79-50507)
Q.M.B. edition. D'arville, Jasper. New wings suite : music for band. *Boosey and Hawkes. £22.00* UMMG (B79-51206)
Q.M.B. Edition. Tull, Fisher. The final covenent : for symphonic band or wind ensemble. *Boosey and Hawkes. Unpriced* UMMJ (B79-50725)
Quadrifoglio : concerto per quattro fiati ed orchestra. (Sutermeister, Heinrich). *Schott. £16.80* MPVNSF (B79-50586)
Quaeramus cum pastoribus : for 4 voices. (Cristo, Pedro de). *72 Brewery Rd, N.7 : Mapa mundi. Unpriced* EZDJ/LF (B79-50075)
Quam pulchri sunt gressus tui. (Lobo, Alfonso). *Mapa mundi. Unpriced* EZDJ (B79-50064)
Quantz, Johann Joachim. Sonata, oboe, bassoon & continuo, K.46, G major. Trio sonata in G. K.46, oboe (or flute, violin, descant recorder), bassoon or violoncello and basso continuo. *Nova Music. Unpriced* NWPNT (B79-51047)
Quartet in one movement. Contrasts and variants : for violin, viola, cello and piano, opus 63. (Leighton, Kenneth). *Novello. Unpriced* NXNS (B79-50197)
Quasi improvvisando : pour ensemble à vent = für Bläserensemble. (Françaix, Jean). *Schott. £12.00* UN (B79-50320)
'Quatro libro de motetti. Plorabo die ac nocte. Plorabo die ac nocte. (Grandi, Alessandro). *36 Ranelagh Gdns W.6 : Cathedral Music. Unpriced* DJ (B79-50025)
Quattro pezzi sacri. Laudi alla vergine Maria. Laudi alla vergine Maria = Prayer to the Virgin Mary : for four-part chorus of female voices. (Verdi, Giuseppe). *Roberton. £0.32* FEZDH (B79-50916)
Queen. Queen gold. *EMI. Unpriced* KDW/HKR (B79-50987)
Queen gold. (Queen). *EMI. Unpriced* KDW/HKR (B79-50987)
Queen of hearts. (Astell, Betty). *Evans. Unpriced* CPP (B79-50022) ISBN 0-237-75047-3
Quem vidistis, pastores? (Victoria, Tomás Luis de). *72 Brewery Rd, N.7 : Mapa mundi. Unpriced* EZDJ/LF (B79-50079)
Quine, Hector. Sonata, violin, no.1, B.W.V. 1001. Adagio and fugue. *arr.* Prelude and fugue in A minor. (Bach, Johann Sebastian). *Oxford University Press. Unpriced* TSPMK/Y (B79-50314) ISBN 0-19-355304-x
Quintet for 2 violins, 2 violas and violoncello, op.106. (Gál, Hans). *Simrock. Unpriced* RXNR (B79-50264)
Race, Steve.
Musician at large. *Eyre Methuen. £6.50 : CIP rev.* A/JT(P) (B79-17755) ISBN 0-413-39740-8
My music. *Robson. £5.25 : CIP entry* A(DE) (B79-22652) ISBN 0-86051-072-7
Rachmaninoff, Sergei. The bells : Opus 35 : poem for soprano, tenor and baritone soli, chorus and orchestra. *Boosey and Hawkes. Unpriced* EMDX (B79-50455)
Radlbauer, Dan. I wanna share. *arr.* I wanna share : for vocal solo, SATB chorus and piano with optional bass and drums. *Warner : Blossom. Unpriced* DW (B79-50853)
Rael, Elsa. Snow White and the seven dwarfs. *Vocal score.* Snow White and the seven dwarfs. (Valenti, Michael). *Associated Music. Unpriced* CM (B79-50819)
Rag bag : for piano. (Waldman, Robert). *Schirmer. £1.75* QPJ (B79-50640)
Ragossnig, Konrad.
Libro della canzoni, no.1. Canzona 2 'La Bernadina'. Canzona (II) 'La Bernadina' per canto solo : für Sopranblockflüte (Flüte, Oboe, Violine) und Generalbass = for descant recorder (flute, oboe, violin) and continuo. (Frescobaldi, Girolamo). *Schott. £3.20* VSRPJ (B79-51242)
Musette. *arr.* Musette : für Gitarre solo = for guitar solo. (Vogel, Vladimir). *Schott. £2.00* TSPMK/AHS (B79-50311)

Sonate concertate, lib. 2, no.1. Sonata prima a soprano solo... : für Sopranblockflöte (Flöte, Violine) und Generalbass = for descant recorder (flute, violin) and continuo. (Castello, Dario). *Schott. £3.20* VSRPE (B79-51241)
Ragtime & blues. (Farmer, Paul). *Longman.* Sd. *£0.65* AQPHXJ (B79-36912) ISBN 0-582-21579-x
Ragtime. Selections. *arr.* String along with Scott : 10 ragtime pieces. (Joplin, Scott). *Schirmer. £7.85* RXNSK/AHXJ (B79-50674)
Ragtimes ... (Joplin, Scott). *Schott. £2.60* TSPMK/AHXJ (B79-51196)
Ragtimes. *Selections : arr.* Ragtimes ... (Joplin, Scott). *Schott. £2.60* TSPMK/AHXJ (B79-51196)
Raleigh, *Sir* Walter. Even such is time : for mixed chorus. (Brown, Christopher). *J. and W. Chester. Unpriced* EZDW (B79-50476)
Rameau, Jean Philippe. Les Indes galantes. *arr.* Les Indes galantes. *Oxford University Press. Unpriced* QRPK/HM (B79-51115) ISBN 0-19-373556-3
Rand âne noir : accordeon de concert. (Abbott, Alan). *Waterloo Music : Roberton. £0.90* RSPMJ (B79-50251)
Rands, Bernard.
Ballad 3 : for soprano and tape. *Universal. Unpriced* KFLEZDW (B79-51003)
Mésalliance : for piano and orchestra. *Universal. Unpriced* MPQ (B79-50182)
Scherzi. *Universal. Unpriced* NUP (B79-51038)
Rant : for solo violin. (McGuire, Edward). *Scotus Music. Unpriced* SPMH (B79-50684) ISBN 0-86100-009-9
Raph, Theodore. The songs we sang : a treasury of American popular music. First paperback ed. *Barnes : Yoseloff. £4.00* KDW/GB/AYT (B79-50538) ISBN 0-498-02050-9
Rapoport, Paul.
Havergal Brian's 'Gothic symphony' : two studies. (Truscott, Harold). *33 Coopers Rd, Little Heath, Potters Bar, Herts. EN6 1JQ : Havergal Brian Society.* Pbk. *£6.95(£4.75 to members of the Havergal Brian Society)* BBTNADX (B79-10481) ISBN 0-9505185-1-4
Opus est. *Kahn and Averill. £5.75 : CIP entry* A/D(M/YB) (B78-29830) ISBN 0-900707-48-8
Rastall, Richard. Six 15th-century English songs : for voice with 1 and 2 instruments. *Antico. Unpriced* KE/LDW/AYD (B79-50146)
Ratcliffe, Desmond. Elgar piano album. (Elgar, *Sir* Edward, *bart*). *Novello. Unpriced* QPK (B79-50220)
Rautavaara, Einojuhani.
Music for upright piano. *Schirmer. £2.40* QPJ (B79-50635)
Music for upright piano and amplified cello. *Schirmer. £3.05* SRPJ (B79-50690)
Second music for upright piano. *Schirmer. £1.80* QPJ (B79-50636)
Ravenor, Terence B. Three Renaissance quartets. *Oxford University Press. Unpriced* WNSK/AAY (B79-50389) ISBN 0-19-358490-5
Ravinale, Irma. Improvvisazione : per chitarra. *Berben Breitkopf und Härtel. £1.70* TSPMK (B79-50708)
Read, Gardner. Modern rhythmic notation. *Indiana University Press. £15.75* A(QU) (B79-21876) ISBN 0-253-33867-0
Ready, Susan. Critics' choice top 200 albums. (Gambaccini, Paul). *Omnibus Press; 78 Newman St., W1P 3LA : Distributed by Book Sales Limited.* Pbk. *£2.25* A/HKR/FD(WT) (B79-09962) ISBN 0-86001-494-0
Rechenstunde : drei leichte Chorlieder, für gemischten Chor No.3. (Genzmer, Harald). *Schott. £0.72* EZDW (B79-50896)
Rechlin, Eva. Tiertanzburlesken. *Vocal score.* Tiertanzburlesken. (Bresgen, Cesar). *Schott. Unpriced* FDW (B79-50103)
Recorder consort : forty seven pieces for recorder consort. *Boosey and Hawkes. Unpriced* VSN/AY (B79-50760)
Recorder music. (Dickinson, Peter). *Novello. £1.95* VS/FT (B79-51234)
Redel, Martin Christoph. Concerto, orchestra, op.27. Konzert für Orchester. Opus 27. *Bote and Bock Schirmer. £14.40* MMF (B79-51016)
Rees, Gordon. Lionheart. *arr.* Lionheart. (Bush, Kate). *EMI. Unpriced* KDW/GB (B79-50135)
Reeve, Peter. Old French dances. *Chester Music. Unpriced* WNH/AYH (B79-51307)
Reeves, James. Grannies to sell. Grannies to sell, and, Boating. (Fraser, Shena). *Roberton. £0.20* JFDW (B79-50518)
Reggae bloodlines : in search of the music and culture of Jamaica. (Davis, Stephen). *Heinemann Educational.* Pbk. *£4.95* AKDW/GBSR (B79-31926) ISBN 0-435-98190-0
Regimental quick march, Worcestershire and Sherwood Foresters Regiment, 'Young May moon' and 'Royal Windsor'. (Marshall, D J). *Boosey and Hawkes. Unpriced* UMMGM/KH (B79-50721)
Regini coeli laetare = Freu dich, Maria, Himmelskönigin : für vierstimmigen gemischten Chor und Basso continuo = for four-part mixed chorus and basso continuo. (Caldara, Antonio). *Bärenreiter. £2.97* DJ (B79-50436)
Register of early music
1977. *Journals Department, Press Rd, NW10 0DD Oxford University Press.* Sd. *£1.50* AL/E(WT/BC) (B79-14012)
Rehm, John. Introduction to music theory. (Winold, Allen). 2nd ed. *Prentice-Hall.* Pbk. *£8.40* A/AM (B79-30253) ISBN 0-13-489666-1
Reichling, Alfred. Die auf dem Clavier spielende und das Gehör vergnügeude Caecilia (1736) : acht Sonaten, für Tasteninstrumente. (Maichelbek, Franz Anton). *Merseburger : Bärenreiter. £5.45* PWPE (B79-50610)
Reihe Kammermusik.
Kochan, Günter. Sieben Miniaturen (1977) : für vier Tuben. *Neue Musik : Breitkopf und Härtel. £4.20* WVNS (B79-50810)
Nowka, Dieter. Sept esquisses : pour flûte et harpe. *Verlag Neue Musik : Breitkopf und Härtel. £2.70* VRPLTQ (B79-50756)
Reimann, Aribert.
John III, 16 = Johannes III, 16 : for mixed chorus a capp;ella = für gemischten Chor a cappella. *Schott. Unpriced* EZDK (B79-50093)
Lear : Oper in zwei Teilen nach William Shakespeare eingerichtet von Claus H. Henneberg (1976/1978). *Schott. Unpriced* CQC (B79-50823)
Reinhardt, Stephen. Mass for Elizabeth Seton. Missa brevis : for SATB chorus with organ or piano accompaniment. *Broude : Breitkopf und Härtel. £2.10* DG (B79-50424)
Reiser, Dave. Operetta! : (a stampede through nostalgia). (Sharkey, Jack). *French.* Sd. *£1.80* BSGNHACM (B79-37419) ISBN 0-573-61358-3
Reissiger, Carl Gottlieb. Concertino, flute, op.60, D major. *arr.* Concertino für Flöte und Orchester in D-dur. op.60. *Eulenburg. £3.70* VRPK/LFL (B79-50753)
Rejoice, then, Christ is born : Christmas song for mixed voices, optional a cappella S.A.T.B., Italian carol-tune (traditional). (Kingsbury, John). *Broude : Breitkopf and Härtel. £0.42* DP/LF (B79-50841)
Renaissance Scottish dances. *Boosey and Hawkes. Unpriced* NYEPNQK/AH/AYDL (B79-50200)
Rennert, Jonathan. George Thalben-Ball. *David and Charles. £5.95 : CIP entry* AR/E(P) (B79-21879) ISBN 0-7153-7863-5
Requiescat : S.S. and piano. (Benger, Richard). *Edwin Ashdown. £0.20* FLDW (B79-50919)
Resources of music.
Cantors : a collection of Gregorian chants. *Cambridge University Press. Unpriced* JEZDTD (B79-50933) ISBN 0-521-22149-8
Strike the bell : transport by road, canal, rail and sea in the nineteenth century through songs, ballads and contemporary accounts. *Cambridge University Press.* Sd. *£2.25* KEZDW/K/G/AYC (B79-50547) ISBN 0-521-21921-3
Resurrection : for organ. (Wills, Arthur). *Weinberger. Unpriced* RJ (B79-51126)
Rêves endormis. Rêves éveillés. Rêves éveillés et Rêves endormis : pour piano. (Holstein, Jean Paul). *Chappell. Unpriced* QPJ (B79-51082)
Rêves éveillés. Rêves éveillés et Rêves endormis : pour piano. (Holstein, Jean Paul). *Chappell. Unpriced* QPJ (B79-51082)
Rêves éveillés et Rêves endormis : pour piano. (Holstein, Jean Paul). *Chappell. Unpriced* QPJ (B79-51082)
Reynolds, William Jensen. A joyful sound : Christian hymnody. 2nd ed. *Holt, Rinehart and Winston. £8.75* ADM(X) (B79-05497) ISBN 0-03-040831-8
Reynolds, William Jensen. Survey of Christian hymnody. *For later edition see* Reynolds, William Jensen. A joyful sound.
Rezitativ und Ostinato : für Trompete und Orgel. (Schibler, Armin). *Eulenburg. Unpriced* WSPLR (B79-50804)
Rezits, Joseph. The pianist's resource guide : piano music in print and literature on the pianistic art
1978-79. *Pallma Music; 20 Earlham St., WC2H 9LN Distributed by Breitkopf und Härtel (London) Ltd.* Pbk. *£32.50* AQ (TC) (B79-24852) ISBN 0-8497-7800-x
Rhapsody - concerto : für Viola und Orchester = pro violu a orchestr = for viola and orchestra. (Martinu, Bohuslav). *Bärenreiter. £12.54* MPSQF (B79-50583)
Rhein, Robert.
The de'il's awa wi'th' exiseman : for four-part chorus of mixed voices with piano accompaniment. *Schirmer. £0.35* DW (B79-50854)
Ae fond kiss : for four-part chorus of mixed voices with baritone solo a cappella. *Schirmer. £0.35* EZDW (B79-50901)
Kelvingrove : for four-part chorus of mixed voices a cappella with optional piano. *Schirmer. £0.55* EZDW (B79-50902)
Rhythm band book. *Sterling : Oak Tree Press. Unpriced* XMK/AAY (B79-50402)
Ricci, Robert J. Jazz improvisation. (Kynaston, Trent P). *Prentice-Hall. Unpriced* MT/DZ (B79-50184) ISBN 0-13-509307-4
Riccio, Giovanni Battista. Divine lodi, lib.3. *Selections.* 3 canzonas for violin (trumpet), trombone and basso continuo. *Musica rara. Unpriced* NUXUNT (B79-50188)

Rice, Jo. The Guinness book of British hit singles : (the Guinness book of records records). 2nd ed. *Guinness Superlatives. £5.25* AKDW/GB/FD(WT) (B79-22108) ISBN 0-900424-89-3
Ricercare for three guitars. (Hunt, Oliver). *Schott. £0.80* TSNT (B79-50300)
Richafort, Jean. Ecce quam bonum : See how good, how right : for four-part chorus of mixed voices a cappella. *Schirmer. £0.30* EZDR (B79-50472)
Richard, Cliff. The illustrated 'Which one's Cliff?'. *Hodder and Stoughton.* Pbk. *£2.95 : CIP entry* AKDW/GB/E(P) (B78-29837) ISBN 0-340-23413-x
Richard, Cliff. Which one's Cliff? *For later reprint see* Richard, Cliff. The illustrated 'Which one's Cliff?'.
Richard, Keith. Some girls. *EMI. Unpriced* KDW/GB (B79-50137)

Richard Wagner and the English. (Sessa, Anne Dzamab). *Fairleigh Dickinson University Press : Associated*

University Presses. £7.00 BWC(ZD) (B79-50407) ISBN 0-8386-2055-8

Richard Wagner's music dramas. (Dahlhaus, Carl). *Cambridge University Press. £7.50* BWCAC (B79-33553) ISBN 0-521-22397-0

Richards, Godfrey.
Concerto, piano, no.21, K.467, C major. Andante. *arr.* The Elvira Madigan theme ... (Mozart, Wolfgang Amadeus). *Studio Music. Unpriced* WMK (B79-50376)
Simple gifts : the traditional melody on which 'Lord of the dance' is based. *Studio Music. Unpriced* WMK/DW (B79-50380)

Richards, Sam. The English folksinger : 159 modern and traditional folksongs. *Collins. £3.95(hardback), £1.95(pbk)* KE/TSDW/G/AYD (B79-50994) ISBN 0-00-411067-6

Richardson, Alan. Sonatina, oboes (2). Sonatina for 2 oboes. *Nova Music. Unpriced* VTPEM (B79-51261)

Richner, Thomas. Interpreting Mozart's piano sonatas. *Paterson's Publications.* Pbk. *£2.00* BMSAQPE/E (B79-04545)

Richner, Thomas. Orientation for interpreting Mozart's piano sonatas. *For later reprint see* Richner, Thomas. Interpreting Mozart's piano sonatas.

Riddgeon, John. Brass for beginners : bass clef, trombone, euphonium and baritone. *Boosey and Hawkes. Unpriced* W/AC (B79-51292)

Ridout, Alan. Six songs from the psalms : six of the best songs from the BBC TV series 'Kossoff and company'. *Weinberger. Unpriced* KDR (B79-50954)

Rimsky-Korsakoff, Nikolai. The golden cockerel. *Suite.* Suite from the opera, 'The golden cockerel'. *Eulenburg. Unpriced* MMG (B79-51018)

Ritz, David. Brother Ray : Ray Charles' own story. (Charles, Ray). *Macdonald and Jane's. £5.95* AMT(P) (B79-21877) ISBN 0-354-04393-5

Rive, Thomas. Motecta. O quam gloriosum est regnum. Motet and mass, O quam gloriosum est regnum. (Victoria, Tomás Luis de). *Eulenburg. Unpriced* EZDJ/LQ (B79-50091)

Rivers of hell. Opus 34 : concertante for seven players. (Holloway, Robin). *Boosey and Hawkes. Unpriced* NYDPNPF (B79-51048)

Rizzo, Jacques.
Our love. *arr.* Our love. (Yancy, Marvin). *Chappell. Unpriced* DW (B79-50036)
Our love. *arr.* Our love. (Yancy, Marvin). *Chappell. Unpriced* DW (B79-50037)
Our love. *arr.* Our love. (Yancy, Marvin). *Chappell. Unpriced* FDW (B79-50105)
You needed me. *arr.* You needed me : S.A.B. with piano and optional drums. (Goodrum, Randy). *Chappell. Unpriced* DW/GBB (B79-50862)
You needed me. *arr.* You needed me : S.S.A. with piano and optional drums. (Goodrum, Randy). *Chappell. Unpriced* FDW/GBB (B79-50912)

Robert De Cormier choral series. De Cormier, Robert. Frankie and Johnny : for four-part chorus of mixed voices with soprano, alto, baritone and tenor solos a cappella. *Roberton. £0.28* EZDW (B79-50478)

Robert de Cormier choruses for young voices. De Cormier, Robert. The Erie Canal, and, Great grandad : American folk songs, for two-part chorus of equal voices and piano. *Roberton. £0.28* FDW (B79-50494)

Roberts, Deborah. Il quatro libro de motetti. Plorabo die ac nocte. Plorabo die ac nocte. (Grandi, Alessandro). *36 Ranelagh Gdns W.6 : Cathedral Music. Unpriced* DJ (B79-50025)

Robinson, Paul. Solti. *Macdonald and Jane's. £5.95* A/EC(P) (B79-24592) ISBN 0-354-04288-2

Rochdale *(Metropolitan District). Arts and Entertainments Services.* Our Gracie. (Rochdale Museum). *c/o Rochdale Museum Esplanade, Rochdale, Lancs. : Rochdale Arts and Entertainments Services.* Sd. *£0.70* AKDW/GB/E(P) (B79-08928)

Rochdale Museum. Our Gracie. *c/o Rochdale Museum Esplanade, Rochdale, Lancs. : Rochdale Arts and Entertainments Services.* Sd. *£0.70* AKDW/GB/E(P) (B79-08928)

Rocherolle, Eugénie R. Little bitty baby : for SAB-SA chorus and piano. *Warner : Blossom. Unpriced* DW (B79-50035)

Rock file
5. *Panther.* Pbk. *£1.25* ADW/GB (B79-03804) ISBN 0-586-04680-1

Rock scene. It's - rock scene. *Purnell. £1.50* AKDW/HKR/E(M) (B79-28896) ISBN 0-361-04558-1

Rock. *Vocal score.* The rock : for soli, choir and orchestra. (Roxburgh, Edwin). *United Music. Unpriced* DE (B79-50826)

Rockers. Oxtoby's rockers : the eternal fan. (Oxtoby, David). *Phaidon.* Pbk. *£4.95* AKDW/HK/E(M) (B79-15543) ISBN 0-7148-1854-2

Rockmaster
1978. *13 Stanton Rd, Regents Park, Southampton, Hants. : Rockmaster.* Sd. *Unpriced* AKDW/HKR/FD(WT) (B79-35642)

Rodd-Marling, Yvonne. Singer : die physische Natur des Stimmorganes : Anleitung zum Aufschliessen der Singstimme. (Husler, Frederick). 2.Aufl. *Schott.* Pbk. *£9.60* AB/E (B79-13063)

Rodemann, Albert. Sonatas, flutes (2), nos.1,2. Zwei Sonaten für zwei Querflöten allein = Two sonatas for two solo flutes. (Bach, Wilhelm Friedemann). *Bärenreiter. Unpriced* VRNUE (B79-50326)

Rodgers, Richard.
The King and I. Getting to know you. *arr.* Getting to know you : for S.A. cambiata, B. or S.A.T.B. *Williamson. Unpriced* DW (B79-50855)
Oklahoma!. Oh, what a beautiful mornin'. *arr.* Oh, what a beautiful mornin' : S.A.C.(T)B. with piano. *Williamson Music. Unpriced* DW (B79-50856)
The sound of music. Climb ev'ry mountain. *arr.* Climb ev'ry mountain : for S.A. cambiata, B. or S.A.T.B. with piano. *Williamson Music. Unpriced* DW (B79-50857)
State fair. Its a grand night for singing. *arr.* Its a grand night for singing : S.A.C.(T).B, with piano. *Williamson. Unpriced* DW (B79-50858)

Roger Wagner choral series. Goldman, Maurice. Sleep, little Jesus, sleep : Spanish-American folk song for full chorus of mixed voices with soprano solo and piano. *Roberton. £0.20* DP/LF (B79-50446)

Rogers, John. Quattro pezzi sacri. Laudi alla vergine Maria. Laudi alla vergine Maria = Prayer to the Virgin Mary : for four-part chorus of female voices. (Verdi, Giuseppe). *Roberton. £0.32* FEZDH (B79-50916)

Romance et plainte : for guitar. (Eastwood, Tom). *Bèrben Breitkopf and Härtel. £2.35* TSPMJ (B79-51185)

Romantic cello. *Chappell. Unpriced* SRPK/AAY (B79-50288)

Romberg, Bernhard. Concerto, flute, op.30, B minor. Konzert für Flöte und Orchester in h-moll, op.30 (17). *Eulenburg. £4.20* MPVRF (B79-50588)

Ronsard, Pierre de. Dédicace de Pierre de Ronsard : 1945 : pour ténor et piano = für Tenor und Klavier. (Martin, Frank). *Bärenreiter. £2.64* KGHDW (B79-50561)

Roots, rock and reggae. *Chappell. Unpriced* KDW/HKR/AY (B79-50543)

Rorate coeli : motet for the Advent season, for 6 voices. (Handl, Jacob). *Mapa mundi. Unpriced* EZDJ/LEZ (B79-50072)

Rorem, Ned.
Serenade on five English poems : for voice, violin, viola and piano. *Boosey and Hawkes. Unpriced* KE/NXNTDW (B79-50147)
Surge, illuminare. *Boosey and Hawkes. Unpriced* DK (B79-50439)
Women's voices : eleven songs for soprano and piano. *Boosey and Hawkes. Unpriced* KFLDW (B79-50549)

Rose, Barry.
Away in a manger. *arr.* Away in a manger. (Kirkpatrick, William Jerome). *36 Ranelagh Gdns W.6 : Cathedral Music. Unpriced* EZDP/LF (B79-50095)
Stille Nacht, heilige Nacht. *arr.* Silent night. (Grüber, Franz Xaver). *36 Ranelagh Gdns W.6 : Cathedral Music. Unpriced* EZDP/LF (B79-50094)

Rose, Bernard. Three Addison anthems : for soprano, alto, tenor and bass. *Addington Press. Unpriced* EZDH (B79-50878)

Rose, Judith. Aubade : song cycle for speaker, SATB and piano (or harp). (Ferguson, Barry). *Novello. Unpriced* DW (B79-50033)

Rose, Michael. Fiddler's ten : easy tunes for violin with piano accompaniment. *Novello. £1.65* SPJ (B79-50277)

Roseingrave, Thomas. Sonata, flute & continuo, no.2, D major. Sonata 2 in D major for flute and basso continuo. *Oxford University Press. Unpriced* VRPE (B79-50329) ISBN 0-19-358643-6

Rosenberg, Bernard. The music makers. (Rosenberg, Deena). *Columbia University Press. £10.30* A(M) (B79-10473) ISBN 0-231-03953-0

Rosenberg, Deena. The music makers. *Columbia University Press. £10.30* A(M) (B79-10473) ISBN 0-231-03953-0

Rosenberg, Steve. The recorder consort : forty seven pieces for recorder consort. *Boosey and Hawkes. Unpriced* VSN/AY (B79-50760)

Rosenthal, Harold. The concise Oxford dictionary of opera. 2nd ed. *Oxford University Press. £6.95* AC(C) (B79-23401) ISBN 0-19-311318-x

Ross, Colin. Gently the breeze blows : two-part. *Banks. Unpriced* FDW (B79-50496)

Ross, Theodor.
Danse bohémienne. *arr.* Danse bohémienne : für zwei Gitarren oder Oktavgitarre und Gitarre = for two guitars or octave guitar and guitar = pour deux guitares ou guitare octave et guitare. (Debussy, Claude). *Schott. £3.20* TSNUK/AH (B79-51175)
Rondo, guitars (3). Rondo für zwei Gitarren, for two guitars. (Hindemith, Paul). *Schott. £2.00* TSNUK/W (B79-50304)

Ross, Walter. Six shades of blue : preludes for piano. *Boosey and Hawkes. Unpriced* QPJ (B79-50637)

Rossetti, Christina.
My gift : for four-part chorus of men's voices a cappella. (Chorbajian, John). *Schirmer. £0.35* GEZDP/LF (B79-50923)
Promises like pie-crust : SATB. (Binkerd, Gordon). *Boosey and Hawkes. Unpriced* EZDW (B79-50098)
Sorrow hath a double voice : for solo high voice, unison male or female chorus and harp. (Binkerd, Gordon). *Boosey and Hawkes. Unpriced* ETQDW (B79-50047)

Rossetti, Dante Gabriel. Promises like pie-crust : SATB. (Binkerd, Gordon). *Boosey and Hawkes. Unpriced* EZDW (B79-50098)

Rossi, Abner. Trenta melodie : per il corso preparatorio di chitarra classica. *Berben : Breitkopf und Härtel. £3.30* TS/AF (B79-50698)

Rossini, Gioacchino Antonio.
Prélude, thème et variations pour cor. Prelude, theme and variations for French horn and piano. *Schirmer. £3.65* WTP/T (B79-51322)
Rossini and Chopin variations for oboe and piano. (Brown, James). *Lordship Publications. Unpriced* VTP/T (B79-51258)

Rossini and Chopin variations for oboe and piano. (Brown, James). *Lordship Publications. Unpriced* VTP/T (B79-51258)

Round the piano with Donald Swann : a collection of songs with piano accompaniments. *Bodley Head. Unpriced* KDW/AY (B79-50961) ISBN 0-370-30173-0

Round the town : five Charles Causley poems. (Hurd, Michael). *Novello. £0.74* JFDW (B79-50128)

Routier, Marcelle. The musicians of Auschwitz. (Fénelon, Fania). *Sphere.* Pbk. *£0.95* A(M/YLCO/XPC3) (B79-19444) ISBN 0-7221-3466-5

Rowen, Ruth Halle. Music through sources and documents. *Prentice-Hall.* Pbk. *£9.45* A(X) (B79-16099) ISBN 0-13-608331-5

Roxburgh, Edwin. The rock. *Vocal score.* The rock : for soli, choir and orchestra. *United Music. Unpriced* DE (B79-50826)

Royal, Timothy. Folksong 2. *16 Oldfield Place, Hotwells, Bristol BS8 4QJ : Shed Music. Unpriced* TSPMJ (B79-50706)

Royal College of Organists. Year book
1978-1979. *Kensington Gore, SW7 2QS : The College.* Sd. *£1.15* AR(YC/VP/Q/BC)

Royal Opera House. Why are Covent Garden seat prices so high? (Blaug, Mark). *Royal Opera House Covent Garden, WC2 7QA : Royal Opera House Covent Garden Ltd.* Sd. *Unpriced* AC/E(YC/QB/K) (B79-04908)

Royal School of Church Music. English church music : a collection of essays
1979. *Addington Palace, Croydon CR9 5AD : Royal School of Church Music.* Pbk. *£2.24* AD/LD(YD/D) (B79-33554) ISBN 0-85402-081-0

Rózsa, Miklós. Toccata capricciosa : für Violoncello-Solo. Op.36. *Breitkopf and Härtel. £3.30* SRPMJ (B79-51160)

Rubank symphonic band library. Olivadoti, Joseph. Castle and woods : overture. *Rubank : Novello. Unpriced* UMMJ (B79-50724)

Rubbra, Edmund.
Three hymn tunes. Op.114. Three hymns tunes. *Lengnick. Unpriced* DM (B79-50441)
Transformations : for solo harp, op.141. *Lengnick. £1.00* TQPMJ (B79-50695)

Ruby, Harry. Broadway Joe. *arr.* She was an acrobat's daughter, an English music hall song : for four-part chorus of mixed voices with piano accompaniment. *Roberton. Unpriced* DW (B79-50450)

Rue, Pierre de la. *See* La Rue, Pierre de.

Ruf, Hugo.
Second collection of sonatas for two flutes and a bass. *Selections.* Zwei Suiten für zwei Altblockflöten und Basso continuo
Suite 1: C-Dur = C major. (Pez, Johann Christoph). *Schott. £4.00* VSSNTPWG (B79-51247)

Runes from a holy island : for chamber ensemble. (Davies, Peter Maxwell). *Chester Music. Unpriced* NYEPNQ (B79-51050)

Runze, Klaus.
Zwei Hände-zwölf Tasten. *English.* Two hands-twelve notes
Book 1: A picture-book for young pianists. *Schott. £3.00* Q/AC (B79-51052)
Zwei Hände-zwölf Tasten. *English.* Two hands-twelve notes
Book 2: Playing with music. *Schott. £2.50* Q/AC (B79-51053)

Rupprecht, Margarete Jürgenson-. *See* Jürgenson-Rupprecht, Margarete.

Rüsenberg, Michael. Das Jazzpublikum : zur Sozialpsychologie einer kulturellen Minderheit. (Dollase, Rainer). *Schott.* Pbk. *£9.60* AMT(Z) (B79-10482)

Rush, Leonard. Casper the friendly ghost. *arr.* Casper the friendly ghost. (Livingston, Jerry). *Warner : Blossom. Unpriced* WMK/DW (B79-50379)

Russell-Smith, Geoffry.
Let's explore music : the Russell-Smith method based on Kodály and Orff principles
Book 1: Junior. *EMI. Unpriced* C/AC (B79-50408)
Book 1: Junior. (Russell-Smith, Geoffry). *EMI. Unpriced* C/AC (B79-50408)
Let's explore music : the Russell-Smith method based on Kodaly and Orff principles
Book 1: Junior, pupils edition. *EMI. Unpriced* C/M (B79-50410)

Russian minstrels : a history of the skomorokhi. (Zguta, Russell). *Clarendon Press. £8.95* AKDW/G(YM/XCE751) (B79-24590) ISBN 0-19-815652-9

Rutter, John.
Carols for choirs
3: Fifty carols ; edited and arranged by David Willcocks and John Rutter. *Oxford University Press. Unpriced* DP/LF/AY (B79-50031) ISBN 0-19-353570-x
A Gaelic blessing. *Royal School of Church Music. Unpriced* DH (B79-50432)
Introduction to music. (Hendrie, Gerald). *Open University Press.* Pbk. *Unpriced* A (B79-16836) ISBN 0-335-05414-5

Sachs, Nelly. Psaslm der Nacht : für sechzehnstimmigen Frauenchor, Männerstimmen, Schlagwerk und Orgel. (Zimmermann, Udo). *Bärenreiter. £7.92* ERPLXDH/KDN (B79-50046)

Sacra cantiones, lib. 2. Magnificat. Magnificat. (Gagliano, Marco da). *Cathedral Music. Unpriced* EZDGKK (B79-50054)

Sacra cantiones, lib.2. Veni creator spiritus. Veni creator

spiritus. (Gagliano, Marco da). *Cathedral Music. Unpriced* EZDJ/LN (B79-50087)
Sacrae cantiones. Parvulus filius. Parvulus filius : for 6 voices. (Ammon, Blasius). *72 Brewery Rd, N.7 : Mapa mundi. Unpriced* EZDJ/LF (B79-50074)
Sacrae cantiones. Tenebrae factae sunt. Tenebrae factae sunt : for 4 voices. (Ammon, Blasius). *72 Brewery Rd, N.7 : Mapa mundi. Unpriced* EZDJ/LK (B79-50083)
Sacrae symphoniae, bk.2. O quam suavis. O quam suavis : for eight-part chorus of mixed voices with organ accompaniment. (Gabrieli, Giovanni). *Schirmer. £0.75* DGKJ/LNC (B79-50427)
Sacred music for mixed voices. Saunders, Neil. Magnificat and Nunc dimittis for five-part chorus of mixed voices unaccompanied. *Roberton. £0.24* EZDGPP (B79-50461)
Sad birds = Oiseaux tristes : concert accordion = accordeon de concert. (Abbott, Alan). *Waterloo Music Roberton. £1.05* RSPMJ (B79-50252)
Sadie, Stanley.
Sonata, piano, no.1, K.279, C major. Sonata in C. (Mozart, Wolfgang Amadeus). *Associated Board of the Royal Schools of Music. Unpriced* QPE (B79-51068)
Sonata, piano, no.6, K.284, D major. Sonata in D, K.284, 205b, 1775. (Mozart, Wolfgang Amadeus). *Associated Board of the Royal Schools of Music. Unpriced* QPE (B79-50622)
Sonata, violins (2) & continuo, no.1, A minor. Trio sonata, no.1, A minor, for 2 violins and continuo. (Boyce, William). *Peters. Unpriced* SNTPWE (B79-51147)
Sonata, violins (2) & continuo, no.3, A major. Trio sonata, no.3, A major, for 2 violins and continuo. (Boyce, William). *Peters. Unpriced* SNTPWE (B79-51148)
Sadler, Graham. Les Indes galantes. *arr.* Les Indes galantes. (Rameau, Jean Philippe). *Oxford University Press. Unpriced* QRPK/HM (B79-51115) ISBN 0-19-373556-3
Saëns, Camille Saint-. *See* Saint-Saëns, Camille.
Saetveit, Adolph. Spirit of peace : for four-part chorus of mixed voices a cappella. *Schirmer. £0.45* EZDH (B79-50879)
Sager, Carole Bayer. They're playing our song. *Selections : arr.* They're playing our song. (Hamlisch, Marvin). *Chappell. Unpriced* KDW (B79-50956)
Saint Paul's series.
Dearnley, Christopher. The isles of the sea : anthem for unaccompanied choir ... *36 Ranelagh Gdns W.6 : Cathedral Music. Unpriced* EZDK (B79-50092)
Tomkins, John. The King shall rejoice. *36 Ranelagh Gdns, W.6 : Cathedral Music. Unpriced* DK (B79-50028)
Saint-Saëns, Camille. Le carnival des animaux. Le cygne. *arr.* Il cigno. *Berben : Breitkopf und Härtel. £1.10* TSPMK (B79-50709)
Salamander books. Salter, Lionel. The 'Gramophone' guide to classical composers and recordings. *Salamander Books. £6.95* A/D(M/FD) (B79-00562) ISBN 0-86101-025-6
Salieri, Antonio. Scherzi armonici. *arr.* Two Salieri canons. *Boosey and Hawkes. Unpriced* GE/XTBDW/X (B79-50108)
Salis-Seewis, Johann Gaudenz von. Lied im Freien. D.572. (Schubert, Franz). *Bärenreiter. £0.99* GEZDW (B79-50115)
Salles, Anita. O monge napolitano : tarantela para órgão. *Fermata do Brasil : Clifford Essex. Unpriced* RHVS (B79-51120)
Salter, Adrian. Tom Jones. *Vocal score.* Tom Jones : comic opera in three acts based on the novel by Henry Fielding = opera comique en trois actes d'aprés le roman de Henry Fielding. (Philidor, François André Danican). *Boosey and Hawkes. £7.50* CC (B79-50013)
Salter, Lionel.
Adagio and rondo for glass harmonica, flute, oboe, viola and cello. K.617. (Mozart, Wolfgang Amadeus). *Eulenburg. £1.20* NYEPNR/W (B79-51051)
The 'Gramophone' guide to classical composers and recordings. *Salamander Books. £6.95* A/D(M/FD) (B79-00562) ISBN 0-86101-025-6
Johann Sebastian Bach : life, times, influence. *17 Bucklersbury, Hitchin, Herts. SG5 1BB : Bärenreiter. £21.12* BBC(N) (B79-11127)
Salvation Army Brass Band Journal (Festival series)
Nos.392-395: Swiss rhapsody for flugel horn (or cornet) by Leslie Condon. Variations on Laudate Dominum by Edward Gregson. Endless song : moto perpetuo, by Michael Kenyon. Near the cross : meditation by Dudley Bright. *Salvationist Publishing and Supplies. Unpriced* WM/AY (B79-50366)
Nos.396-398: The call to arms : selection, by James Curnow. Logos : tone poem by Ray Steadman-Allen. Home on the range : euphonium solo, by Erik Leidzén. *Salvationist Publishing and Supplies. Unpriced* WM/AY (B79-51293)
Salvation Army Brass Band Journal (General series)
Nos. 1709-1712: Kilmarnock Temple - march. *Salvationist Publishing and Supplies. Unpriced* WM/AY (B79-50367)
Nos. 1713-1716: Brooklands, march by Dudley Bright. Sing along with the band, by Norman Bearcroft. I love to sing : song setting, by Leslie Condon. Theodora : hymn tune arrangement by David Jones. Become aware of Him : song setting by Robert Redhead. *Salvationist Publishing and Supplies. Unpriced* WM/AY (B79-50789)
Salvation Army brass band journal
Nos.399-402: Songs of childhood: suite, by David Catherwood. Variations and fugue on 'Rachie' (a young person's guide to the brass band) by Michael Kenyon. The sound of the gospel: festival march, by Robert Redhead. Golden slippers: cornet solo, by Norman Bearcroft. *Salvationist Publishing and Supplies. Unpriced* WM/AY (B79-51294)
Salvation Army Brass Band Journal (Triumph series)
Nos. 829-832: Brazilian jubilee : march, by Leslie Condon. Christ is the answer : air varié, by Erik Silfverberg. Jesus is real to me : trombone solo by Noel Jones, and, Prayer of childhood : cornet solo, by Leslie Condon. Where joy and duty meet : march, by Derek Jordan. *Salvation Army Brass Band Journal. Unpriced* WM/AY (B79-50790)
Salvation Army Brass Band Journal, (Triumph series)
Nos 833-836: It's new : march, by John Larsson. A call to action : tone poem, by Ray Steadman-Allen. The manger scene : carol setting, by Leslie Condon. Coming to the King : meditation, by David Wells. *Salvationist Publishing and Supplies. Unpriced* WM/AY (B79-51295)
Salvation Army Brass Band Journal (Triumph series)
Nos.825-828: God's children, by William Himes. My heavenly home: selection by A.H. Jakeway. By the light of that star: carol setting by John Larsson, arr. Roy Steadman-Allen. Life's dedication: selection by Christopher Cole. *Salvationist Publishing and Supplies. Unpriced* WM/AY (B79-50368)
Salvation Army Brass Band Journal (Unity series)
Nos.81-88: Alice Springs : march by Allen Pengilly. Sleaford : march by Neville McFarlane. Harvest home, fantasy by Ralph Pearce. Mannheim : hymn tune arrangement by Michael Kirk. Trumpet tune, by Purcell, arr. Ray Steadman-Allen. It happened to me : selection songs by John Gowans and John Larsson arr. Ray Steadman-Allen. Three Czech carols, by G. John Swansbury. Chorus time no.1 : selection, choruses by Sidney E. Cox. Christ for all : selection by Erik Silfverberg. *Salvationist Publishing and Supplies. Unpriced* WM/AY (B79-51296)
Salvator mundi, Domine : Compline hymn for the Vigil of Christmas in the Sarum Use. (Shepherd, John). *72 Brewery Rd, N.7 : Mapa mundi. Unpriced* EZDJ/LF (B79-50078)
Salve Regina. (Anchieta, Juan de). *72 Brewery Rd, N.7 : Mapa mundi. Unpriced* GEZDJ (B79-50110)
Salve regina : for 4 voices. (Okeghem, Jean). *72 Brewery Rd, N.7 : Mapa mundi. Unpriced* GEZDJ (B79-50113)
Salve regina. *Vocal score.* Salve regina : sacred cantata for soprano and keyboard. (Scarlatti, Domenico). *Faber Music. Unpriced* KFLDJ (B79-50148)
Sama'i : for flute solo. (Camilleri, Charles). *Basil Ramsey : Roberton. Unpriced* VRPMJ (B79-51231)
Sancta Maria. (Esquivel, Juan). *72 Brewery Rd, N.7 : Mapa mundi. Unpriced* EZDJ (B79-50060)
Sancta Maria, and, Ecce sacerdos magnus : for four part chorus of mixed voices unaccompanied. (Victoria, Tomás Luis de). *Roberton. £0.28* EZDJ (B79-50469)
Sancta mater. (Peñalosa, Francisco de). *72 Brewery Rd, N.7 : Mapa mundi. Unpriced* GEZDJ (B79-50114)
Sancte Deus. (Tallis, Thomas). *72 Brewery Rd, N.7 : Mapa mundi. Unpriced* EZDJ (B79-50066)
Sander, Peter. Quintet, wind, instruments, no.1. Wind quintet no.1. *Eulenburg. Unpriced* UNR (B79-50321)
Sanders, John. Gloucester organ album. *Novello. £2.15* R/AY (B79-51118)
Sandison, David. Oxtoby's rockers : the eternal fan. (Oxtoby, David). *Phaidon.* Pbk. *£4.95* AKDW/HK/E(M) (B79-15543) ISBN 0-7148-1854-2
Sansom, Clive. Mull of Kintyre. *arr.* Mull of Kintyre. (McCartney, Paul). *Music Sales. Unpriced* DW (B79-50034)
Santórsola, Güido. Sonata, guitar, no.4, 'Italiana', 'Sonovidades 1977'. Sonata n.4 (Italiana), ! Sonoridades 1977! : para guitarra. *Bèrben : Breitkopf and Härtel. £2.85* TSPME (B79-51177)
Sarabande and gigue : E-flat alto saxophone and piano. (Tull, Fisher). *Boosey and Hawkes. Unpriced* VUSPH (B79-50777)
Sarabande and Rustic ballet ... : two miniatures for piano solo. (Jacobson, Maurice). *Roberton. £0.50* QPH (B79-50627)
Saturday night fever. *Selections : arr.* Saturday night fever : from the original movie soundtrack. (Bee Gees). *Chappell. Unpriced* RK/DW/HKR/JR (B79-50658)
Saturday night fever. *Selections : arr.* Saturday night fever : from the original movie soundtrack. (Bee Gees). *Chappell. Unpriced* TSPMK/DW/HKR/JR (B79-50713)
Saunders, Gordon. Eight traditional Japanese pieces. *Novello. £1.55* VSPM/AYVU (B79-50765)
Saunders, Neil.
Fantasia for brass quartet : for 2 trumpets and 2 trombones. *Roberton. £3.00* WNS (B79-51315)
Magnificat and Nunc dimittis for five-part chorus of mixed voices unaccompanied. *Roberton. £0.24* EZDGPP (B79-50461)
Saxophone solos : B flat tenor with piano accompaniment
Vol.1. *Chester Music. Unpriced* VUTPK/AAY (B79-51269)
Vol.2. *Chester Music. Unpriced* VUTPK/AAY (B79-51270)
Saxophone solos : E flat alto with piano accompaniment
Vol.1. *Chester Music. Unpriced* VUSPK/AAY (B79-50354)
Vol.2. *Chester Music. Unpriced* VUSPK/AAY (B79-50355)
Scarlatti, Domenico.
Essercizi (1738) : 30 sonatas for keyboard. *Schirmer. £7.55* QRPE (B79-51112)
Essercizi. *Selections.* Five sonatas. *DeCamera : Schirmer. £2.50* TSPMK/AE (B79-51192)
Salve regina. *Vocal score.* Salve regina : sacred cantata for soprano and keyboard. *Faber Music. Unpriced* KFLDJ (B79-50148)
Sonatas for harpsichord
Book one. *Stainer and Bell. Unpriced* QRPE (B79-50644) ISBN 0-85249-513-7
Sonatas, harpsichord. *Selections : arr.* Three sonatas (K.176/L163, K.177/L364,K.208/L238) : guitar solo. *Universal. Unpriced* TSPMK/AE (B79-51193)
Scelsi, Giacinto. Five incantations = Cinque incantesimi : for piano. *Schirmer. £3.05* QPJ (B79-50638)
Scena III : clarinet solo. (Bennett, Richard Rodney). *Novello. £2.60* VVPMJ (B79-51287)
Scenes from Schumann : seven paraphrases for orchestra, opus 13,. (Holloway, Robin). *Boosey and Hawkes. Unpriced* MMJ (B79-50178)
Scenes from the west : flute sextet or choir. (Walters, Harold L). *Rubank : Novello. Unpriced* VRNQ (B79-50740)
Schaffner, Nicholas. The Beatles forever. *McGraw-Hill.* Pbk. *£4.95* AKDW/GB/E(P) (B79-20268) ISBN 0-07-055087-5
Schall, Friedrich.
Ach, dass du den Himmel zerrissest. *Vocal score.* Ach, dass du den Himmel zerrissest = Oh! you who doth rend heav'n asunder : festo nativit Christi, Weihnachtskantate von, Christmas cantata. (Bach, Wilhelm Friedemann). *Belwin Mills. £2.25* DE/LF (B79-50421)
Erzittert und fallet. *Vocal score.* Erzittert und fallet = Oh, tremble and falter : Kantate zum Ostersonntag von, Easter cantata. (Bach, Wilhelm Friedemann). *Belwin-Mills. £2.25* DE/LL (B79-50423)
Wie schön leuchtet der Morgenstern. *Vocal score.* Wie schon leuchtet der Morgenstern = How fair the morning star doth glow : Kantate Dom. II. p. Epiph. (Bach, Wilhelm Friedemann). *Belwin-Mills. £2.25* DE/LFP (B79-50422)
Schallehn, Hilger. Steht auf und singt : festlicher Spruch. *Schott. £0.80* EZDW (B79-50903)
Scheck, Helmut. Die Musik kommt : Männerchor und kleines Blasorchester. *Schott. £5.60* GE/UMDW (B79-50922)
Scheidt, Samuel. Paduana, galliarda. *arr.* Canzon super intradam aechiopicam. *Schirmer. £7.55* VVNK (B79-50780)
Scherzi. (Rands, Bernard). *Universal. Unpriced* NUP (B79-51038)
Scherzi armonici. *arr.* Two Salieri canons. (Salieri, Antonio). *Boosey and Hawkes. Unpriced* GE/XTBDW/X (B79-50108)
Scherzo : for organ (manuals only). (Smith, Peter Melville). *Banks. Unpriced* RJ (B79-50235)
Scherzo : hommage à Prokofieff. (Zabrack, Harold). *Boosey and Hawkes. Unpriced* QNVK (B79-51063) ISBN 0-934286-14-0
Scherzo, piano. *arr.* Scherzo : hommage à Prokofieff. (Zabrack, Harold). *Boosey and Hawkes. Unpriced* QNVK (B79-51063) ISBN 0-934286-14-0
Schevill, James. Here we come as in the beginning. (Nelson, Ron). *Boosey and Hawkes. Unpriced* EZDH (B79-50877)
Schibler, Armin.
Fantasy concertante, alto saxophone & orchestra. *arr.* Konzertante Fantasie für Alt-saxophon und kleines Orchester. *Eulenburg. £4.60* VUSPK/LF (B79-50778)
Rezitativ und Ostinato : für Trompete und Orgel. *Eulenburg. Unpriced* WSPLR (B79-50804)
Schickhard, Johann Christian.
L'alphabet de la musique : Op.30. Sonatas 4, 7, 16. 3 Sonaten aus 'L'alphabet de la musique' = 3 sonatas from 'L'alphabet de la musique' : für Altblockflöte und Basso continuo = for alto recorder and basso continuo. *Pelikan : Bärenreiter. £9.10* VSSPE (B79-50769)
L'alphabet de la musique, op.30 : 24 sonatas in all the keys, for treble recorder and basso continuo ...
Vol.4: Sonatas 13-16. *Musica rara. Unpriced* VSSPE (B79-50344)
Vol.5: Sonatas 17-20. *Musica rara. Unpriced* VSSPE (B79-50345)
Vol.6: Sonatas 21-24. *Musica rara. Unpriced* VSSPE (B79-50346)
Sonata, recorder, oboe & continuo, op.5, no.2, D major. Sonata D major for flute/recorder, two oboes, viola da gamba/violoncello/bassoon, and basso continuo. *Oxford University Press. Unpriced* NWPNTE (B79-50194) ISBN 0-19-358815-3
Schickhardt, Johann Christian.
Concerto grosso, op.6, no.3, C major. *arr.* Trio sonata in d. (Corelli, Arcangelo). *Nova Music. Unpriced* VSSNTPWK/LF (B79-51248)
Sonata, oboe & continuo, op.2, no.5, G minor. Sonata in g, op.2, no.5 for oboe or violin and basso continuo. *Nova Music. Unpriced* VTPE (B79-51260)
Sonata, recorders (treble) (2) & continuo, op.6, no.6, D minor, 'La Folia'. Variations on La folia, op.6, no.6 : for 2 treble recorders and basso continuo. *Nova Music. Unpriced* VSSNTPW/T (B79-51244)
Schicksalslied = Song of destiny. Op.54. (Brahms, Johannes). *Eulenberg. Unpriced* EMDX (B79-50867)
Schiffelholz, Johann Paul. Trio, bassoons & continuo, G major. Trio in G for 2 bassoons and basso continuo. *Musica rara. Unpriced* VWNTPW (B79-50362)
Schininá, Luigi. Sonata, guitar & violin, op.39, A major. *arr.* Grande sonata in la maggiore. (Paganini, Nicolò). *Bèrben : Breitkopf and Härtel. £3.80* TSNUK/AE (B79-51173)
Schirmer pronouncing pocket manual of musical terms. 4th ed. *Schirmer : Collier Macmillan.* Pbk. *£1.45* A(C) (B79-04535) ISBN 0-02-870250-6
Schirmer's library of musical classics.
Beethoven, Ludwig van. Sonata, piano duet, op.6, D major. *arr.* Sonata in D major, op.6, for clarinet and piano.

Schirmer. £3.05 VVPK/AE (B79-50784)
Vivaldi, Antonio. Il cimento dell'armonia e dell'inventione. Op.8. Le quattro stagione. Autunno.. *arr.* Four seasons, op.8 (Concerto for violin and orchestra)
Autumn : for violin and piano. *Schirmer. £2.40* SPK/LF (B79-50682)
Vivaldi, Antonio. Il cimento dell'armonia e dell'inventione. Op.8, nos 1-4. *arr.* Four seasons, op.8. (Concerto for violin and orchestra
Op.8, no.4: Winter : for violin and piano. *Schirmer. £2.40* SPK/LF (B79-51154)
Schmidt. Sinfonia, viola d'amore, violin & continuo, D major. Sinfonia for viola d'amore, violin and basso. *(Little Margaret, Penmans Green, Chipperfield) : E.L. White. Unpriced* NXNTE (B79-50606)
Schmitz, Manfred. Jazz Parnass : Etüden, Stücke und Studien, für Klavier. *Schott. £7.20* QPHX/AF (B79-50212)
Schnabel's interpretation of piano music. (Wolff, Konrad). 2nd ed. *Faber.* Pbk. *£2.50* AQ/E(P) (B79-36916) ISBN 0-571-10029-5
Schneider, Johann Christian Friedrich. Sonata, flute & piano, op.33, G major. Sonate in G-dur für Flöte und Klavier, op.33. *Amadeus : Schott. Unpriced* VRPE (B79-50330)
Scholey, Arthur.
Herod and the rooster : a legend for all seasons, a dramatic cantata. (Chamberlain, Ronald). *(125 Waxwell Lane) : The Grail. Unpriced* DE/LF (B79-50827) ISBN 0-901829-51-x
Wacky and his fuddlejig : a chidren's Christmas musical play. (Swann, Donald). *Universal. Unpriced* CN/LF (B79-50017)
Schönberg und andere : gesammelte Aufsätze zur neuen Musik. (Dahlhaus, Carl). *Schott.* Pbk. *£14.00* A(D/XM78) (B79-08129)
Schonthal, Ruth. By the roadside : six songs to poems by Walt Whitman, for soprano and piano. *Oxford University Press. Unpriced* KFLDW (B79-50150)
School of English Church Music. *See* Royal School of Church Music.
Schott, Howard. Playing the harpsichord. 1st ed., reprinted. *Faber.* Pbk. *£2.95 : CIP rev.* AQR/E (B79-05250) ISBN 0-571-11375-3
Schottes Chorverlag. Schallehn, Hilger. Steht auf und singt : festlicher Spruch. *Schott. £0.80* EZDW (B79-50903)
Schott's Chorblätter. Klefisch, Walter. Lasset uns singen : Volkslied von Tahiti. *Schott. £0.24* FEZDW (B79-50501)
Schott's Chorverlag.
Desch, Rudolf. Putze dich mit meinem Tüchlein : Kastilianisches Volkslied aus Avila (Spanien). *Schott. £0.48* GEZDW (B79-50507)
Genzmer, Harald. Lied des Vogelstellers : drei leichte Chorlieder No.1. *Schott. £0.72* EZDW (B79-50895)
Genzmer, Harald. Stadturlaub : drei leichte Chorlieder No.2. *Schott. £0.72* EZDW (B79-50897)
Monteverdi, Claudio. L'Orfeo. Vieni Imeneo. *arr.* Zwei Chöre aus 'Orpheus' = Two chorusses sic from 'Orpheus'. *Schott. £0.80* EZDW (B79-50898)
Poos, Heinrich. Tanzlied. (Ritmo di joropo). *Schott. £0.48* FEZDW (B79-50502)
Scheck, Helmut. Die Musik kommt : Männerchor und kleines Blasorchester. *Schott. £5.60* GE/UMDW (B79-50922)
Suite nach englischen Volksliedern
No.1: The keel row. Einst kam ich nach Sandgate. *Schott. £0.72* EZDW/G/AYD (B79-50481)
Suite nach englischen Volksliedern
No.2: The old true love. Ach komm, tritt ein. *Schott. £0.48* EZDW/G/AYD (B79-50482)
Suite nach englischen Volksliedern
No.3: The keeper. Ein Jager wollte jagen gehn. *Schott. £0.80* EZDW/G/AYD (B79-50483)
Suite nach englischen Volksliedern
No.4: There's none to soothe. Wo weilst du, Lieb. *Schott. £0.48* EZDW/G/AYD (B79-50484)
Suite nach englischen Volksliedern
No.5: The miller of Dee. War einst ein braver Mullersmann. *Schott. £0.72* EZDW/G/AYD (B79-50485)
Suite nach englischen Volksliedern
No.6: Cock a doodle doo. *Schott. £0.48* EZDW/G/AYD (B79-50486)
Schubert, Franz.
Franz Schubert Lieder : Urtext der Neuen Schubert-Ausgabe
Heft 1: Die schöne Mûllerin, op.25: Mittlere Stimme (Transposition). *Bärenreiter. £5.28* KDW (B79-50133)
Heft 3: Leider nach Texten von Goethe: Mittlere Stimme (Transposition). *Bärenreiter. £4.80* KDW (B79-50134)
Lazarus. *Vocal score.* Lazarus : an Easter cantata, for solo, mixed chorus and orchestra. *Schirmer. £1.80* DE (B79-50420)
Lied im Freien. D.572. *Bärenreiter. £0.99* GEZDW (B79-50115)
Sonatas, piano. Complete pianoforte sonatas, including the unfinished works
Volume 3. *Associated Board of the Royal Schools of Music. Unpriced* QPE/AZ (B79-51069)
Stabat mater. Amen. *arr.* Hallelujah amen ... : for four-part chorus of mixed voices a cappella. *Schirmer. £0.45* EZDH/LK (B79-50463)
Schubert, Heino.
Die kleinen Jahreszeiten. *Choral score.* Die kleinen Jahreszeiten : Fraunchor und Klavier. *Schott. £1.00* FADW (B79-50906)
Die kleinen Jahreszeiten : Fra nuenchur und Klavier. *Schott. £4.10* FDX (B79-50497)
Schubert. (McLeish, Kenneth). *Heinemann. £2.50* BSF(N) (B79-26550) ISBN 0-434-95127-7
Schuller, Gunther. The power within us : a narrative oratorio for baritone, narrator, chorus and orchestra. *Associated Music. Unpriced* EMDE (B79-50454)
Schürmann, Georg Caspar. Operas. *Selections.* Arien : für hohe Singstimme, Blockflöten, Fagott und Basso continuo. Erstausgabe. *Bärenreiter. £6.60* KFTE/NWPNSDW (B79-50557)
Schurmann, Gerard. Concerto, violin. Concerto for violin and orchestra. *Novello. £8.85* MPSF (B79-51029)
Schütz, Heinrich. Geistliche Chormusik. Die mit Thränen säen. *arr.* Fantasia a 5. *Ricordi. Unpriced* VSNRK/DJ (B79-50338)
Schwaen, Kurt.
Hört ihr den Trommelschlag : Variationen für Streichorchester. *VEB Deutscher Verlag : Breitkopf and Härtel. £2.10* RXM/T (B79-51136)
Spatzenmusik für zwei, drei und mehr Geigen. *Neue Musik : Breitkopf and Härtel. £3.00* SN (B79-50679)
Über allen strahlt die Sonne : Variationen für Klavier über allerlei Themen. *Verlag Neue Musik : Breitkopf und Härtel. Unpriced* QP/T (B79-50619)
Schweizerische Musikbibliothek. Müller, Paul. Fantasia super 'Urbs Turegem, urbs famosa' sive 'Lauda Sion salvatorem' : fur Orgel ... *Verlag der Zentralbibliothek Zurich in Kommission bei Amadeus Verlag : Bärenreiter. Unpriced* RJ (B79-50649)
Schwendowius, Barbara. Johann Sebastian Bach : life, times, influence. *17 Bucklersbury, Hitchin, Herts. SG5 1BB : Bärenreiter. £21.12* BBC(N) (B79-11127)
Schwerdtner, Hans Georg. Leichte Klavierstücke und Sonatinen des 17-20 Jahrhunderts. *Schott. £6.00* QP/AY (B79-50617)
Schwertsik, Kurt.
Concerto, violin, op.31. Violinkonzert opus 31 : Romanzen im Schwarztiten-Ton und in der geblümtem Paradies-Weis. *Boosey and Hawkes. Unpriced* MPSF (B79-50582)
Kleine Blasmusik. Op.32 : five short movements for two trumpets and two trombones. *Boosey and Hawkes. Unpriced* WNS (B79-50388)
Scott, Alicia Anne, *Lady John Scott.* Annie Laurie. *arr.* Annie Laurie. *Studio Music. Unpriced* WMK/DW (B79-50381)
Scott, James. Two ragtime trios : for 2 clarinets and tenor saxophone (or bass clarinet). *7 Garrick St., W.C.2 : Middle Eight Music. Unpriced* VNTK/AHXJ (B79-50323)
Scott, Ronnie. Some of my best friends are blues. *W.H. Allen. £3.50* AMT(P) (B79-28900) ISBN 0-491-02239-5
Scottish folksinger : 118 modern and traditional folksongs. New ed. *Collins. Unpriced* JE/TSDW/G/AYDL (B79-50119) ISBN 0-00-411125-7
Scottish winners. *Campbell, Connelly and Connelly. Unpriced* KDW/GB/AYDL (B79-50537)
Scotus guitar series. Wilson, Thomas Brendan. Canción : for solo guitar. *Scotus : Schirmer. Unpriced* TSPMJ (B79-50707)
Scribenery : for solo cello. (Buller, John). *Schirmer. £1.25* SRPMJ (B79-51161)
Scripture Union. Sing to God. *Scripture Union. £0.75* ADM (B79-31511) ISBN 0-85421-722-3
Scrymgeour, John Olon-. *See* Olon-Scrymgeour, John.
Sculthorpe, Peter.
Music for Japan : for orchestra. *Faber Music. Unpriced* MMJ (B79-51025)
Sonata, viola & percussion (1960). Sonata for viola and percussion (1960). *Faber Music. Unpriced* SQPLXE (B79-50687)
Seaman, Ann-Marie. Six 15th-century English songs : for voice with 1 and 2 instruments. *Antico. Unpriced* KE/LDW/AYD (B79-50146)
Seaside woman. (McCartney, Paul). *MPL Communications. Unpriced* KDW/GB (B79-50968)
Seasons = Les saisons. (Apparailly, Yves). *Waterloo Music : Roberton. £1.35* RSPMJ (B79-50254)
Seasons and people and other songs. (Kingsbury, Roy). *Oxford University Press. Unpriced* JFADW (B79-50513) ISBN 0-19-450558-8
Seasons and people and other songs. *Melody part.* Seasons and people and other songs. (Kingsbury, Roy). *Oxford University Press. Unpriced* JFADW (B79-50513) ISBN 0-19-450558-8
Sechs Choralvorspiele für Trompete und Orgel = The six chorale preludes for trumpet and organ. (Krebs, Johann Ludwig). *Simrock. Unpriced* WSPLR (B79-50398)
Sechs englische Psalmen. Hob. XXIII Anhang, Nachtrag. Sechs Psalmen = Six psalms : für dreistimmigen gemischten Chor = for three-part mixed chorus, Hob. XXIII Anhang, Nachtrag. (Haydn, Joseph). *Bärenreiter. £2.31* EZDR (B79-50471)
Sechs Psalmen = Six psalns : für dreistimmigen gemischten Chor = for three-part mixed chorus, Hob. XXIII Anhang, Nachtrag. (Haydn, Joseph). *Bärenreiter. £2.31* EZDR (B79-50471)
Sechs Ragtimes für Flöte oder Klarinette in B and Klavier. (Joplin, Scott). *Eulenburg. £4.20* VRPK/AHXJ (B79-50751)
Sechs Sonaten für zwei Querflöten, op.47. (Boismortier, Joseph Bodin de). *Eulenburg. Unpriced* VRNUE (B79-50328)
Sechsundzwanzigste Triosonate in F-dur für Altblockflöte (Querflöte), Violine (Querflöte, Oboe) und Basso continuo. Sonata, recorder, violin & continuo, F major. 26 Triosonate in F-dur für Altblockflöte (Querflöte), Violine (Querflöte, Oboe) und Basso continuo. Sonata a tre in F major for treble recorder (flute), violin (flute, oboe) and basso continuo. (Telemann, Georg Philipp). *Amadeus : Breitkopf and Härtel. £2.80* NUSNTE (B79-51041)

Second collection of sonatas for two flutes and a bass. *Selections.* Zwei Suiten für zwei Altblockflöten und Basso continuo
Suite 1: C-Dur = C major. (Pez, Johann Christoph). *Schott. £4.00* VSSNTPWG (B79-51247)
Second intermediate band book. (Johnson, Stuart). *R. Smith. Unpriced* WM/AY (B79-50788)
Second music for upright piano. (Rautavaara, Einojuhani). *Schirmer. £1.80* QPJ (B79-50636)
Second nursery suite : three traditional songs. *Novello. £0.98* NYFSRK/DW/GJ/AY (B79-50609)
Second wind band book. *Oxford University Press. Unpriced* UM/AY (B79-50718) ISBN 0-19-369831-5
Secret cabinet of Robert Burns : merry muses of Caledonia. (Burns, Robert). New ed.. *P. Harris. £3.50* AKDW/K/G/KDX (B79-36915) ISBN 0-904505-84-7
Secundus tomus musici operis. Ascendens Christus. Ascendens Christus : motet for the Ascension of our Lord, for 4 voices. (Handl, Jacob). *72 Brewery Rd, N.7 : Mapa mundi. Unpriced* EZDJ/LM (B79-50085)
Sedaine, Jean-Michel. Tom Jones. *Vocal score.* Tom Jones : comic opera in three acts based on the novel by Henry Fielding = opera comique en trois actes d'aprés le roman de Henry Fielding. (Philidor, François André Danican). *Boosey and Hawkes. £7.50* CC (B79-50013)
See-saw sacaradown : fourteen childrens sic songs with simple accompaniments for classroom instruments. *Chappell. Unpriced* JFE/XDW/GJ/AY (B79-50947)
Seewis, Johann Gaudenz von Salis-. *See* Salis-Seewis, Johann Gaudenz von.
Segal, P. Stichomythia : for flute and guitar, 1976. (Antioniou, Theodore). *Bärenreiter. £8.58* VRPLTS (B79-50335)
Segreto di Susanna. Overture. Susanna's secret = Il segreto di Susanna = Susannens Geheimnis : overture. (Wolf-Ferrari, Ermanno). *Weinberger. Unpriced* MMJ (B79-50180)
Sei capriccetti, che servono di compimento dell' op.250. 6 capriccetti, che servono di compimento dell' op.250. Sei capricci ... per chitarra. (Legnani, Luigi). *Berben. £1.70* TSPMJ (B79-50705)
Sei capricci ... per chitarra. (Legnani, Luigi). *Berben. £1.70* TSPMJ (B79-50705)
Selva morale e spirituale. Ut queant laxis. *arr.* Hymn to Saint John the Baptist. Ut queant laxis. (Monteverdi, Claudio). *36 Ranelagh Gdns W.6 : Cathedral Music. Unpriced* JNFLEE/SNTPWDJ (B79-50130)
Sem dizer nada : canto e piano. (Ayres Netto, Marianinha). *Fermata do Brasil : Clifford Essex. Unpriced* KDW (B79-50955)
Senex. (Beeson, Jack). *Boosey and Hawkes. Unpriced* KGNDW (B79-50562)
Senior, Geoffrey. Music and musicians on postage stamps. *299 Gathurst Rd, Orrell, Greater Manchester : The compiler.* Sp. *£3.00* A(ZE) (B79-16833)
Sept esquisses : pour flûte et harpe. (Nowka, Dieter). *Verlag Neue Musik : Breitkopf und Härtel. £2.70* VRPLTQ (B79-50756)
Serenade : for four-part chorus of mixed voices with piano accompaniment. (Albert, *Prince Consort of Victoria, Queen of Great Britain*). *Roberton. £0.24* DW (B79-50449)
Serenade on five English poems : for voice, violin, viola and piano. (Rorem, Ned). *Boosey and Hawkes. Unpriced* KE/NXNTDW (B79-50147)
Sergi, Antonio. Desencontro : improviso no.1. *Seresta Clifford Essex. Unpriced* QPJ (B79-51087)
Sermon on the mount : for four-part chorus of mixed voices with piano accompaniment. (Young, Donald J). *Schirmer. £0.45* DH (B79-50433)
Sermon on the mount. *Vocal score.* Sermon on the mount : for four-part chorus of mixed voices with piano accompaniment. (Young, Donald J). *Schirmer. £0.45* DH (B79-50433)
Serpentine dances : for harpsichord. (Jones, Kenneth Victor). *Chester Music. Unpriced* QRPH (B79-51113)
Sessa, Anne Dzamab.

Richard Wagner and the English. *Fairleigh Dickinson University Press : Associated University Presses. £7.00* BWC(ZD) (B79-50407) ISBN 0-8386-2055-8
Sessions, Roger Huntington. Roger Sessions on music : collected essays. *Princeton University Press. £14.10* A (B79-14909) ISBN 0-691-09126-9
Set of five : for piano. (Van Appledorn, Mary Jeanne). *Oxford University Press. Unpriced* QPJ (B79-50219)
Set two : clarinet duets for teacher and pupil
Vol.1. (Lyons, Graham). *Chester Music. Unpriced* VVNU/AF (B79-51277)
Vol.1. (Lyons, Graham). *Chester Music. Unpriced* VVNU/AF (B79-51278)
Set two : flute duets for teacher and pupil
Vol.1. (Lyons, Graham). *Chester Music. Unpriced* VRNU/AF (B79-51219)
Vol.2. (Lyons, Graham). *Chester Music. Unpriced* VRNU/AF (B79-51218)
Seven brightness : solo B flat clarinet. (Davies, Peter Maxwell). *Boosey and Hawkes. Unpriced* VVPMJ (B79-50359)
Seven little pieces for woodwind trio. (Fontyn, Jacqueline).

Schirmer. £4.85 VNT (B79-50734)
Seven songs for high voice. (Parry, *Sir* Charles Hubert, *bart*). *Stainer and Bell. Unpriced* KFTDW (B79-51006)
Sevenminute - Play : für Flöte und Klavier = for flute and piano. (Kelterborn, Rudolf). *Bärenreiter. £4.95* VRPJ (B79-50749)
Seventeen classical solos.
17 classical solos : for unaccompanied clarinet. *Fentone Music : Breitkopf and Härtel. £1.85* VVPMK/AAY (B79-51290)

Shakespeare, William. All the world's a stage. *Vocal score.* All the world's a stage : prologue, six variations, and epilogue for chorus and orchestra. (Tate, Phyllis). *Oxford University Press. Unpriced* DX (B79-50864) ISBN 0-19-338344-6
Shannon, Randall. Solo, double bass & piano, E minor. The famous solo in E minor : for double bass and piano. (Dragonetti, Domenico). *Yorke. Unpriced* SSPJ (B79-50290)
Sharkey, Jack. Operetta! : (a stampede through nostalgia). *French.* Sd. *£1.80* BSGNHACM (B79-37419) ISBN 0-573-61358-3
Shaw, Bernard. The great composers : reviews and bombardments. *University of California Press. £17.15* A (B79-00561) ISBN 0-520-03253-5
Shaw, George Bernard. *See* Shaw, Bernard.
Shaw, Patrick Shuldham-. *See* Shuldham-Shaw, Patrick.
Shaw, Watkins.
Dixit Dominus. *Vocal score.* Dixit Dominus : Psalm 110, for two sopranos, alto, tenor and bass soli, SSATB, strings and continuo. (Handel, George Frideric). *Novello. £2.25* DR (B79-50448)
Te Deum. *Vocal score.* Te Deum : for soloists, chorus, and orchestra. (Croft, William). *Oxford University Press. Unpriced* DGNQ (B79-50429) ISBN 0-19-335585-x
She was an acrobat's daughter, an English music hall song : for four-part chorus of mixed voices with piano accompaniment. (Ruby, Harry). *Roberton. Unpriced* DW (B79-50450)
Shead, Herbert A.
The anatomy of the piano. *The Gresham Press, Old Woking, Surrey : Unwin Brothers Ltd.* Pbk. *£8.50* AQ/B (B79-15560) ISBN 0-905418-20-4
The history of the Emanuel Moór double keyboard piano. *Emanuel Moór Double Keyboard Piano Trust; The Gresham Press, Old Woking, Surrey GU22 9LH : Distributed by Unwin Brothers Ltd.* Pbk. *£15.00* AQ/BC(P) (B79-08930) ISBN 0-9506023-0-2
Shephard, Richard.
Three short anthems. *Royal School of Church Music. Unpriced* DJ (B79-50835)
The Wiltshire service : Holy Communion series 3, for congregation and choir (SATB) with organ or piano. *Royal School of Church Music. Unpriced* DGS (B79-50430)
Shepherd, John. Salvator mundi, Domine : Compline hymn for the Vigil of Christmas in the Sarum Use. *72 Brewery Rd, N.7 : Mapa mundi. Unpriced* EZDJ/LF (B79-50078)
Shepherd king. *Vocal score.* The shepherd king : a musical play in eight scenes. (Parker, Jim). *Weinberger. Unpriced* CN (B79-50415)
Shepherd's lottery. Symphony. *arr.* Gavot, from symphony no.4. (Boyce, William). *Edwin Ashdown. £0.40* RK/AHM (B79-50237)
Shipley, Edward.
La luna. *Fentone Music : Breitkopf and Härtel. Unpriced* QPJ (B79-51088)
La luna : for piano. *Fentone Music. £3.00* QPJ (B79-51089)
Shipton, Russ. 'Folk guitar styles of today'. *Oak Publications : Music Sales (dist.). Unpriced* TS/ED (B79-50298) ISBN 0-86001-077-5
Shostakovich, Dmitriĭ Dmitrievich. Testimony. *H. Hamilton. £7.95 : CIP entry* BSGR(N) (B79-25857) ISBN 0-241-10321-5
Shout for joy : for four-part chorus of mixed voices with piano accompaniment. (Stocker, David). *Schirmer. £0.75* DR (B79-50844)
Shuldham-Shaw, Patrick. Sociable carols : fifteen Christmas carols. *Oxford University Press. Unpriced* JFE/LDP/AY (B79-50522) ISBN 0-19-330595-x
Sieben Miniaturen (1977) : für vier Tuben. (Kochan, Günter). *Neue Musik : Breitkopf und Härtel. £4.20* WVNS (B79-50810)
Siebensprung : und andere Tänze aus aller Welt, leicht gesetzt für zwei Sopranblockflöten = and other dances from all over the world, in easy arrangements for two soprano-recorders. *Pelikan : Bärenreiter. £1.47* VSRNUK/AH/AY (B79-50767)
Siebert, Edrich.
Flick und Flock's Abenteuer. Feuerwehr Galopp. *arr.* The firemen's galop. (Hertel, Peter Ludwig). *Harmer Music : Studio Music. Unpriced* WMK/AHLF (B79-50378)
The good old songs : (Selection no.1). *Studio Music. Unpriced* WMK (B79-50377)
The good old songs : (Selection no.1). (Siebert, Edrich). *Studio Music. Unpriced* WMK (B79-50377)
The good old songs : selections no.2. *Studio Music. Unpriced* WMK/DW (B79-50382)
Sigurd Jorsalfar. Op.56. *Selections.* Three orchestral pieces from the incidental music to Sigurd Jorsalfar, op.56. (Grieg, Edvard). *Eulenburg. Unpriced* MM/JM (B79-50165)
Silbury air. (Birtwistle, Harrison). *Universal. Unpriced* MMJ (B79-51021)
Silent night. (Grüber, Franz Xaver). *36 Ranelagh Gdns W.6 : Cathedral Music. Unpriced* EZDP/LF (B79-50094)
Silva, Andreas de. Omnis pulchritudo Domini : motet for the Ascension of our Lord, for 5 voices. *72 Brewery Rd, N.7 : Mapa mundi. Unpriced* EZDJ/LM (B79-50086)
Silverman, Jerry. Play old-time country fiddle : seventy-five traditional tunes arranged with words and chords including twenty-five square dances with complete calls and instructions, plus transposing guides for guitar, banjo, piano, bass or mandolin. *Oak : Music Sales. Unpriced* SPMK/AH/G/AYT (B79-51155) ISBN 0-86001-506-8
Simon, Peter. Reggae bloodlines : in search of the music and culture of Jamaica. (Davis, Stephen). *Heinemann Educational.* Pbk. *£4.95* AKDW/GBSR (B79-31926) ISBN 0-435-98190-0
Simple gifts for the dulcimer : an instruction manual for beginners, a collection of songs and tunes for dulcimer players. (Jones, Clayton S). *TRO Ludlow Music : Essex Music. Unpriced* TWT/AC (B79-50717)
Simple gifts : the traditional melody on which 'Lord of the dance' is based. (Richards, Godfrey). *Studio Music. Unpriced* WMK/DW (B79-50380)
Simpson, J Sparrow-. *See* Sparrow-Simpson, J.
Simpson, Robert.
Carl Nielsen : symphonist. Completely revised ed. *Kahn and Averill. £6.95 : CIP rev.* BN1(N) (B79-13062) ISBN 0-900707-46-1
Quartet, strings, no.7. Quartet n.7 (1977). *Lengnick. Unpriced* RXNS (B79-51143)
Sinfonia come un grade lamento (1977). Dem Andenken Frederico sic García Lorca. (Zimmermann, Ildo). *VEB Deutscher Verlag für Musik. £3.30* MME (B79-51015)
Sinfonietta. Donizetti, Gaetano. Concertino, clarinet, B flat major. Concertino für Klarinette und Kammerorchester B-dur. *Litolff : Peters. Unpriced* MPVVFL (B79-50590)
Sing a song
1. Teacher's book. *Nelson : ILEA Learning Materials Service.* Sp. *£2.75* A/GR(VG) (B79-07467) ISBN 0-17-413002-3
Sing to God. *Scripture Union. £0.75* ADM (B79-31511) ISBN 0-85421-722-3
Singalongamax. *EMI. Unpriced* KDW/GB/AY (B79-50976) ISBN 0-86175-043-8
Singer : die physische Natur des Stimmorganes : Anleitung zum Aufschliessen der Singstimme. (Husler, Frederick). 2.Aufl. *Schott.* Pbk. *£9.60* AB/E (B79-13063)
Singer's manual of Latin diction and phonetics. (Hines, Robert S). *Schirmer Books : Collier Macmillan. £6.75* ADFF/EDD (B79-08691) ISBN 0-02-870800-8
Singing - : an extension of speech. (Hammar, Russell A). *Scarecrow Press : Distributed by Bailey and Swinfen. £6.75* AB/E (B79-17764) ISBN 0-8108-1182-0
Singing in French : a manual of French diction and French vocal repertoire. (Grubb, Thomas). *Schirmer Books : Collier Macmillan.* Pbk. *£7.45* AB/EDD (B79-25332) ISBN 0-02-870790-7
Singing rhymes. *Ladybird Books. £0.30* AJFDW/GR(VJ) (B79-06706) ISBN 0-7214-0537-1
Single man. (John, Elton). *Big Pig Music : Music Sales. Unpriced* KDW/HKR (B79-50139)
Siniana, no.1, op.119. Rossiniana no.1 : for solo guitar, op.119. (Giuliani, Mauro). *Faber Music. Unpriced* TSPMG (B79-50704)
Sir Alex K. Butterworth, LL.B. (1854-1946) and Captain G.S.K. Butterworth, M.C.,B.A. (1885-1916). (Angus-Butterworth, Lionel Milner). *Old Hall Hotel, Buxton, Derbyshire : The author.* Sd. *£0.50* BBVT(N) (B79-27781)
Sir Dan Godfrey & the Bournemouth Municipal Orchestra : a biographical discography, copiously illustrated with pictures and facsimile reproductions covering countless famous personalities and related material. (Upton, Stuart). New enlarged ed. *4 Harvest Bank Rd, West Wickham, Kent : Vintage Light Music Society.* Sd. *Unpriced* A/EC/FD(P/WT) (B79-11941)
Sirocco (1975) : for wood-wind quintet (flute, oboe, B flat clarinet, bassoon, F horn). (Kievman, Carson). *Associated Music. Unpriced* UNR (B79-50731)
Sisters in song : a collection of new songs from the women's liberation movement. *Onlywoman Press. Unpriced* KFE/TSDW/AY (B79-50996)
Sisters in song : a collection of new songs from the women's liberation movement. (Burgon, Geoffrey). *Onlywomen Press. Unpriced* KDGPR (B79-50951)
Sitwell, *Dame,* Edith. Façade 2 : a further entertainment. (Walton, *Sir* William). *Oxford University Press. Unpriced* KHYE/NYENQ (B79-51010) ISBN 0-19-359406-4
Six 15th-century English songs : for voice with 1 and 2 instruments. *Antico. Unpriced* KE/LDW/AYD (B79-50146)
Six duos. Op.5, nos.1-3 for 2 clarinets. (Yost, Michel). *Musica rara. Unpriced* VVNU (B79-51276)
Six fughettas. Op.1. (Weber, Carl Maria von, *Freiherr*). *Schott. Unpriced* VVNSK (B79-51275)
Six organ pieces. (Bridge, Frank). *Boosey and Hawkes. Unpriced* RJ (B79-51123)
Six petites pieces faciles. Op.3. Marcia. *arr.* 6 petites pièces faciles. Op.3. Marcia. *arr.* March. Op.3, no.5. (Weber, Carl Maria von, *Freiherr*). *Roberton. Unpriced* SPK/AGM (B79-50280)
Six responsories for Tenebrae on Maundy Thursday, feria V in Coena Domini ad Matatinum. (Lasso, Orlando di). *72 Brewery Rd, N.7 : Mapa mundi. Unpriced* EZDJ/LHM (B79-50082)
Six shades of blue : preludes for piano. (Ross, Walter). *Boosey and Hawkes. Unpriced* QPJ (B79-50637)
Six songs from the psalms : six of the best songs from the BBC TV series 'Kossoff and company'. (Ridout, Alan). *Weinberger. Unpriced* KDR (B79-50954)
Six Turkish folkpoems : for female voice and 7 instruments (1977). (Loevendie, Johannes Theodorus). *Donemus Lengnick. Unpriced* KFE/NYDPNPDW (B79-50548)
Sketches for young pianists : (Grade 3-4). (Clark, Harold Ronald). *(42 Glebe Rd) : Harold R. Clark. Unpriced* QPJ (B79-51078)
Skoda, Eva Badura-. *See* Badura-Skoda, Eva.
Skoda, Paul Badura-. *See* Badura-Skoda, Paul.
Slack, Roy.
Advertising the classics. *Leonard, Gould and Bolttler. £0.75* VSRPK/AAY (B79-50768)
Alacita : a suite for brass band. *Peters. Unpriced* WMG (B79-50370)
Fun clarinet : for young people of any age. *EMI. Unpriced* VVPK/DW/GB/AY (B79-51283) ISBN 0-86175-060-8
Fun flute : for young people of any age. *EMI. Unpriced* VRPK/DW/GB/AY (B79-51227) ISBN 0-86175-058-6

Fun piano : for young people of any age. *EMI. Unpriced* QPK/DW/GB/AY (B79-51101) ISBN 0-86175-062-4

Fun violin : for young people of any age. *EMI. Unpriced* SPK/DW/GB/AY (B79-51153) ISBN 0-86175-066-7
Slatford, Rodney.
Concertos, double bass, Krebs 171, 172. *arr.* Concertos for double bass and orchestra. (Dittersdorf, Carl Ditters von). *Yorke. Unpriced* SSPK/LF (B79-50292)
Sinfonia concertante, viola & double bass, Krebs 127, D major. *arr.* Sinfonia concertante for double bass and viola. (Dittersdorf, Carl Ditters von). *Yorke Edition. Unpriced* SQPLSSK/LE (B79-50285)

Sleep, little Jesus, sleep : Spanish-American folk song for full chorus of mixed voices with soprano solo and piano. (Goldman, Maurice). *Roberton. £0.20* DP/LF (B79-50446)
Sleeping beauty. (Astell, Betty). *Evans. Unpriced* CPP (B79-50023) ISBN 0-237-75043-0
Sleeping beauty. Op.66. Panorama. *arr.* Panorama ... (Tchaikovsky, Peter). *R. Smith. Unpriced* WMK/HM (B79-50383)
Sleeping innocence : a lullaby, for mixed chorus and piano. (Townsend, Douglas). *Broude : Breitkopf and Härtel. £0.42* DW (B79-50451)
Slobodskaya : a biography of Oda Slobodskaya. (Leonard, Maurice). *Gollancz. £6.50* AKFL/E(P) (B79-22638) ISBN 0-575-02622-7
Slonimsky, Nicolas.
Baker's biographical dictionary of musicians. (Baker, Theodore). 6th ed. *Schirmer Books : Collier Macmillan. £55.00* A(M/C) (B79-17757) ISBN 0-02-870240-9
Schirmer pronouncing pocket manual of musical terms. 4th ed. *Schirmer : Collier Macmillan.* Pbk. *£1.45* A(C) (B79-04535) ISBN 0-02-870250-6
Smet, Robin de. *See* De Smet, Robin.
Smith, Doreen.
Cello positions. *Oxford University Press. Unpriced* SR/AC (B79-51158) ISBN 0-19-322346-5
Introduction to the cello. *Oxford University Press. Unpriced* SR/AC (B79-51159) ISBN 0-19-322345-7
Smith, F Joseph. The experiencing of musical sound : prelude to a phenomenology of music. *Gordon and Breach. £8.10* A/CC (B79-02983) ISBN 0-677-04430-5
Smith, Geoffry Russell-. *See* Russell-Smith, Geoffry.
Smith, Glenn P. Divine lodi, lib.3. *Selections.* 3 canzonas for violin (trumpet), trombone and basso continuo. (Riccio, Giovanni Battista). *Musica rara. Unpriced* NUXUNT (B79-50188)
Smith, Gregg. Beware of the soldier. Songs of innocence. Little lamb. *arr.* Little lamb : for unison treble choir with piano, four hands accompaniment. *Schirmer. £0.35* JFLDW (B79-50948)
Smith, H J. Come give your hearts to joy this day. (Barsham, Eve). *Ashdown. Unpriced* JFDP/LF (B79-50936)
Smith, Maria Gordon-. *See* Gordon-Smith, Maria.
Smith, Martin Wesley-. *See* Wesley-Smith, Martin.
Smith, Peter Melville.
Scherzo : for organ (manuals only). *Banks. Unpriced* RJ (B79-50235)
Two flourishes : for organ. *Banks. Unpriced* RGN (B79-50233)
Smith, William Joseph Thomas. Bells, clocks & ringers. *Boreham Vicarage, Chelmsford CM3 3EG : The author.* Pbk. *£0.50* AXSR(YDDEBO) (B79-31934)
Smith-Masters, Anthony. All mimsy : for double bass and piano. *Yorke. Unpriced* SSPJ (B79-50291)
Smith-Masters, Stanley. The American patrol. (Meacham, Frank W). *Studio Music. Unpriced* WMJ (B79-50373)
Snell, Howard. 3 pastiches : trumpet & piano. *22 Woodcote Ave. : Dunster Music. Unpriced* WSPJ (B79-51317)
Snow White and the seven dwarfs. *Vocal score.* Snow White and the seven dwarfs. (Valenti, Michael). *Associated Music. Unpriced* CM (B79-50819)
Snyder, Wesley. I love thy church, O God : for four-part chorus of mixed voices with optional piano accompaniment. *Schirmer. Unpriced* EZDH (B79-50880)

So many songs = Es zog manch Lied : for four-part chorus of mixed voices a cappella. (Dvořák, Antonín). *Schirmer. £0.35* EZDW (B79-50890)
Sociable carols : fifteen Christmas carols. *Oxford University*

Press. Unpriced JFE/LDP/AY (B79-50522)
ISBN 0-19-330595-x
Söderström, Elisabeth. In my own key. *H. Hamilton. £5.95 : CIP entry* AKFL/E(P) (B79-25330)
ISBN 0-241-10318-5
Sohal, Naresh.
... Surya : for S.A.T Bar. B. soli, chorus, flute and percussion. *Novello. Unpriced* EVRPLXDW (B79-50048)
Hexad : for six players. *Novello. £2.25* NYENQ (B79-51049)
Soldan, Kurt. Messa di requiem. Requiem. (Verdi, Giuseppe). *Dover Publications : Constable. Unpriced* EMDGKAV (B79-50043) ISBN 0-486-23682-x

Soliloquy : for guitar. (Wilson, Thomas). *Bèrben : Breitkopf and Härtel. £1.90* TSPMJ (B79-51186)
Some girls. (Richard, Keith). *EMI. Unpriced* KDW/GB (B79-50137)
Some of my best friends are blues. (Scott, Ronnie). *W.H. Allen. £3.50* AMT(P) (B79-28900)
ISBN 0-491-02239-5
Some stars above magnitude 2.9 : soprano voice and piano. (Bedford, David). *Universal. Unpriced* KFLDW (B79-50149)
Someone's singing, Lord : hymns and songs for children. *A & C Black. Unpriced* JFADM/AY (B79-50125)
ISBN 0-7136-1847-7
Someone's singing, Lord. Melody part. Someone's singing, Lord : hymns and songs for children. *A & C Black. Unpriced* JFADM/AY (B79-50125)
ISBN 0-7136-1847-7
Son has risen : mixed chorus and organ. (Earnest, David). *Broude : Breitkopf und Härtel. £0.45* DH/LL (B79-50434)
Sonata in C. (Mozart, Wolfgang Amadeus). *Associated Board of the Royal Schools of Music. Unpriced* QPE (B79-51068)
Sonata la posta : für drei Posaunen und Orgel, 1667. (Vejvanovský, Pavel Josef). *Merseburger : Bärenreiter. £2.97* WUNTRE (B79-50808)
Sonata n.4 (Italiana), ! Sonoridades 1977! : para guitarra. (Santórsola, Güido). *Bèrben : Breitkopf and Härtel. £2.85* TSPME (B79-51177)
Sonata, recorders (treble) (3), F major. Pastorelle, recorders (treble) (3), G major. Pastorelle and sonata : for three treble recorders. (Finger, Gottfried). *Oxford University Press. Unpriced* VSSNT (B79-50343)
ISBN 0-19-363204-7
Sonatae tam aris quam aulis servientes. Sonata, trumpet & string orchestra, no.4, C major. *arr.* Sonata 4 for trumpet, violin, 2 violas and basso continuo. (Biber, Heinrich Ignaz Franz). *Musica rara. Unpriced* NUXSNTK/LE (B79-51043)
Sonatae tam aris quam aulis servientes. Sonata, trumpet & string orchestra, no.12, C. major. *arr.* Sonata 12 for 2 trumpets, 2 violins, 2 violas, cello. (Biber, Heinrich Ignaz Franz). *Muscia rara. Unpriced* NUXSNTK/LE (B79-51044)
Sonatas, piano. Complete pianoforte sonatas, including the unfinished works
Volume 3. (Schubert, Franz). *Associated Board of the Royal Schools of Music. Unpriced* QPE/AZ (B79-51069)
Sonate concertate, lib. 2, no.1. Sonata prima a soprano solo... : für Sopranblockflöte (Flöte, Violine) und Generalbass = for descant recorder (flute, violin) and continuo. (Castello, Dario). *Schott. £3.20* VSRPE (B79-51241)
Sondheim, Stephen. Gypsy. Everything's coming up roses. *arr.* Everything's coming up roses : for S.A. cambiata, B. or S.A.T.B, with piano. (Styne, Jule). *Williamson. Unpriced* DW (B79-50859)
Song of the sea. An ataireachd ard = ('High surge of the sea'). (MacDonald, John). *Bosworth and Co. Unpriced* KDW (B79-50526)
Song of Thyrsis : S.A.T.B. & piano. (Tepper, Albert). *Boosey and Hawkes. £0.35* DW (B79-50860)
Songs and dances of death. *arr.* Lieder und Tänze des Todes. (Mussorgsky, Modest). *Breitkopf und Härtel. £8.40* KDW (B79-50960)
Songs, dances and studies : for band
Set 1. (Turok, Paul). *Schirmer. £2.10* UMMJ (B79-50726)
Set 2. (Turok, Paul). *Schirmer. £2.10* UMMJ (B79-50727)
Set 3. (Turok, Paul). *Schirmer. £2.10* UMMJ (B79-50728)

Songs for Alice : Alice in Wonderland and Through the looking glass. (Harper, Don). *Adam & Charles Black. Unpriced* JFDW (B79-50127) ISBN 0-7136-1879-5
Songs from Hollywood musical comedies, 1927 to the present : a dictionary. (Woll, Allen L). *Garland. £15.00* ACM/JR(WT) (B79-50406) ISBN 0-8240-9958-3
Songs from The merry widow (Die lustige Witwe). (Lehár, Franz). *Glocken. Unpriced* KDW (B79-50957)
Songs from 'The princess' : for unaccompanied equal voices (SSA-SSSAA). (Holst, Gustav). *Novello. £1.15* FEZDW (B79-50918)
Songs from the stage and screen : for 5-string bluegrass banjo. *Chappell. Unpriced* TSPMK/DW (B79-51197)
Songs of Belfast. *25 Shenick Rd, Skerries : Gilbert Dalton. Unpriced* JEZDW/G/AYDTB (B79-50124)
Songs of Cork. *25 Shonick Rd. Skerries : Gilbert Dalton. Unpriced* JEZDW/G/AYDQC (B79-50123)
Songs of Dublin. *25 Shenick Rd. Skerries : Gilbert Dalton. Unpriced* JEZDW/G/AYDN (B79-50122)
Songs of land, sea and air : a collection of part songs and canons for equal voices with piano accompaniment. (Holst, Gustav). *Novello. Unpriced* FDW (B79-50104)
Songs of the Irish in America. *25 Shonick Rd. Skerries : Gilbert Dalton. Unpriced* JEZDW/G/AYDM (B79-50121)
Songs. *Selections.* Eight songs for high voice and piano. (Bush, Geoffrey). *Novello. £2.40* KFTDW (B79-51005)
Songs we sang : a treasury of American popular music. First paperback ed. *Barnes : Yoseloff. £4.00* KDW/GB/AYT (B79-50538) ISBN 0-498-02050-9
Songsmiths. Warren, Harry. The works of Harry Warren. *EMI. Unpriced* KDW/JR (B79-50145)
Sopeña, Federico. On music and musicians. (Falla, Manuel de). *Boyars : Distributed by Calder and Boyars. £5.95* A (B79-14910) ISBN 0-7145-2600-2
Sor, Fernando. Duet, guitars, op.55, no.1, D major. Duo in la maggiore, op.55, n.1. *Bèrben : Breitkopf and Härtel. £1.70* TSNU (B79-51169)
Sorcerer's apprentice, and other stories. (Hosier, John). *Oxford University Press.* Pbk. *£1.50* ABN (B79-50005)
ISBN 0-19-314922-2
Sorrow hath a double voice : for solo high voice, unison male or female chorus and harp. (Binkerd, Gordon). *Boosey and Hawkes. Unpriced* ETQDW (B79-50047)
Soul of Mbira : music and traditions of the Shona people of Zimbabwe. (Berliner, Paul). *University of California Press. £12.00* BZNM (B79-19448)
ISBN 0-520-03315-9

Sound of living waters. Combined Sound of living waters - Fresh sounds. *Hodder and Stoughton. £6.95* DM/AY (B79-50029) ISBN 0-340-23262-5
Sound of music. Climb ev'ry mountain. *arr.* Climb ev'ry mountain : for S.A. cambiata, B. or S.A.T.B. with piano. (Rodgers, Richard). *Williamson Music. Unpriced* DW (B79-50857)
Sound tracks
3: Sound poems. (Paynter, John). *Cambridge University Press. £1.95* A/D(VF) (B78-23591)
ISBN 0-521-20580-8
Sounding strings : an album of Celtic music for clarsach pedal harp or piano. *United Music. £1.80* TQPMK/AYCC (B79-50696)
Souvenir de Prague. Op.24 : for two flutes and piano. (Doppler, Franz). *Musica rara. Unpriced* VRNTQ (B79-50744)
Spanish choral music.
Lobo, Alfonso. Liber primus missarum. Ave regina coelorum. Ave regina coelorum : Compline and votive antiphon for the season from Christmas to the Purification. *72 Brewery Rd, N.7 : Mapa mundi. Unpriced* EZDGKR/LF (B79-50057)
Lobo, Alfonso. Liber primus missarum. Credo quod redemptor mens vivit. Credo quod redemptor mens vivit : pro defunctis, for 4 voices. *Mapa mundi. Unpriced* EZDJ/KDN (B79-50068)
Lobo, Alfonso. Liber primus missarum. O quam suavis est, Domine. O quam suavis est, Domine : motet for the Feast of Corpus Christi, for 6 voices. *72 Brewery Rd, N.7 : Mapa mundi. Unpriced* EZDJ/LNC (B79-50088)
Lobo, Alfonso. Liber primus missarum. Vivo ego, dicit Dominus. Vivo ego, dicit Dominus : motet for Lent for 4 voices. *72 Brewery Rd, N.7 : Mapa mundi. Unpriced* EZDJ/LG (B79-50080)
Spanish church music.
Anchieta, Juan de. Salve Regina. *72 Brewery Rd, N.7 : Mapa mundi. Unpriced* GEZDJ (B79-50110)
Cristo, Pedro de. Quaeramus cum pastoribus : for 4 voices. *72 Brewery Rd, N.7 : Mapa mundi. Unpriced* EZDJ/LF (B79-50075)
Escobar, Pedro de. Clamabat autem mulier. *72 Brewery Rd, N.7 : Mapa mundi. Unpriced* GEZDJ (B79-50111)
Escribano, Juan. Paradisi porta : motet for 6 voices. *72 Brewery Rd, N.7 : Mapa mundi. Unpriced* EZDJ (B79-50059)
Esquivel, Juan. Motecta festorum. Sancta Maria. Sancta Maria. *72 Brewery Rd, N.7 : Mapa mundi. Unpriced* EZDJ (B79-50060)
Esquivel, Juan. Veni Domine : motet for the Advent season for 5 voices. *72 Brewery Rd, N.7 : Mapa mundi. Unpriced* EZDJ/LEZ (B79-50070)
Esquivel, Juan. Vox clamantis in deserto : motet for the Advent season for 4 voices. *72 Brewery Rd, N.7 : Mapa mundi. Unpriced* EZDJ/LEZ (B79-50071)
Guerrero, Francisco. Missarum liber secundo. Missa de la batalla escoutez. Missa de la batalla escoutez : for 5 voices. *Mapa mundi. Unpriced* EZDG (B79-50049)
Guerrero, Francisco. Motecta ... liber secundus. Pastores loquebantur. Pastores loquebantur. *72 Brewery Rd, N.7 : Mapa mundi. Unpriced* EZDJ/LF (B79-50076)
Guerrero, Francisco. Motecta. Duo seraphim. Duo seraphim. *Mapa mundi. Unpriced* EZDJ (B79-50062)
Lobo, Alfonso. Liber primus missarum. Ave maria. Ave Maria : for 8 voices. *72 Brewery Rd, N.7 : Mapa mundi. Unpriced* EZDJ (B79-50063)
Lobo, Alfonso. Liber primus missarum. Quam pulchri sunt gressus tui. Quam pulchri sunt gressus tui. *Mapa mundi. Unpriced* EZDJ (B79-50064)
Lobo, Alfonso. Liber primus missarum. Versa est in luctum. Versa est in luctum : ad exsequias Philip II, cathol. regis Hisp. = for the funeral of Philip II, Catholic King of Spain. *72 Brewery Rd, N.7 : Mapa mundi. Unpriced* EZDJ/KDN (B79-50069)
Martìn de Rivafrencha. Two motets suit : for four voices. *72 Brewery Rd, N.7 : Mapa mundi. Unpriced* GEZDJ (B79-50112)
Peñalosa, Francisco de. Missa El ojo : for 4 voices. *72 Brewery Rd, N.7 : Mapa mundi. Unpriced* EZDG (B79-50050)
Peñalosa, Francisco de. Sancta mater. *72 Brewery Rd, N.7 : Mapa mundi. Unpriced* GEZDJ (B79-50114)
Victoria, Tomás Luis de. Motectas festorum. Quem vidistis, pastores? Quem vidistis, pastores? *72 Brewery Rd, N.7 : Mapa mundi. Unpriced* EZDJ/LF (B79-50079)
Vivanco, Sebastian de. Liber magnificarum. Magnificat octavi toni. Magnificat octavi toni : for 8 voices. *Mapa mundi. Unpriced* EZDGKK (B79-50056)
Spanish masters : 19 original easy pieces. *Ricordi. Unpriced* TSPM/AYK (B79-50305)
Sparke, Philip. Fantasy for euphonium and brass band. *R. Smith. Unpriced* WMPWW (B79-50384)
Sparrow-Simpson, J. The crucifixion. *arr.* The crucifixion : a meditation on the Sacred Passion of the Holy Redeemer. (Stainer, *Sir* John). *Novello. £1.55* FDE/LK (B79-50100)
Spartak. Adagio of Spartacus and Phrygia. *arr.* Adagio. (Khachaturian, Aram). *Boosey and Hawkes. Unpriced* MK/HM (B79-50567)
Spartak. Adagio of Spartacus and Phrygia. *arr.* Adagio. (Khachaturian, Aram). *Boosey and Hawkes. Unpriced* MK/HM (B79-50568)
Spatzenmusik für zwei, drei und mehr Geigen. (Schwaen, Kurt). *Neue Musik : Breitkopf and Härtel. £3.00* SN (B79-50679)
Spence, Keith. Living music. *H. Hamilton. £6.95* A (B79-20262) ISBN 0-241-10116-6
Spink, Ian. Musica Britannica : a national collection of music
Vol.42: The judgement of Paris. *Stainer and Bell. Unpriced* C/AYD (B79-50009)
Spinner, Leopold. Cantata, op.20 on German folksong texts : for mezzo-soprano solo, chorus and chamber orchestra. *Boosey and Hawkes. Unpriced* EMDX (B79-50045)
Spinning wheel : S.S.A.A. (with divisi). (Arch, Gwen). *Oxford University Press. Unpriced* FDW (B79-50909)
ISBN 0-19-342599-8
Spirit of peace : for four-part chorus of mixed voices a cappella. (Saetveit, Adolph). *Schirmer. £0.45* EZDH (B79-50879)
Spirits having flown. (Bee Gees). *Chappell. Unpriced* KDW/HKR (B79-50541)
Spohr, Louis. Fantaisie and variations on a theme of Danzi. Op.81 : for clarinet and string quartet. *Musica rara. Unpriced* NVVNR/T (B79-51045)
Sprink, Eberhard. Love of three oranges. L'amour des trois oranges. Opus 33 : opéra en 4 actes et 10 tableaux avec un prologue d'après Carlo Gozzi. (Prokofiev, Sergei). *Boosey and Hawkes. Unpriced* CQC (B79-50822)
Spurgin, Anthony. The Duke of York'&s patrol. *Studio Music. Unpriced* WMGM (B79-50371)
Srebotnjak, Alojz.
Il cimento dell'armonia e dell'inventione. Op.8. Le quattro stagione. Autunno.. *arr.* Four seasons, op.8 (Concerto for violin and orchestra)
Autumn : for violin and piano. (Vivaldi, Antonio). *Schirmer. £2.40* SPK/LF (B79-50682)
Il cimento dell'armonia e dell'inventione. Op.8, nos 1-4. *arr.* Four seasons, op.8. (Concerto for violin and orchestra
Op.8, no.4: Winter : for violin and piano. (Vivaldi, Antonio). *Schirmer. £2.40* SPK/LF (B79-51154)
St. Mark's Passion. Markus-Passion für Solostimmen und vierstimmigen Chor a cappella. (Peranda, Marco Giuseppe). *VEB Deutscher Verlag : Breitkopf an Härtel. £2.70* EZDD/LK (B79-50872)
Staatlichen Institut für Musikforschung Preussischer Kulturbesitz. Bibliographie des Musikschriftums
1972. *Schott. £30.00* A(T) (B79-30467)
Stabat mater. Amen. *arr.* Hallelujah amen ... : for four-part chorus of mixed voices a cappella. (Schubert, Franz). *Schirmer. £0.45* EZDH/LK (B79-50463)
Staden, Johann. Hauss-Musik, Tl.3. Danket dem Herren. *arr.* Give thanks to the Lord : for three-part chorus of women's voices a cappella. *Schirmer. £0.35* FEZDH (B79-50500)
Stadturlaub : drei leichte Chorlieder No.2. (Genzmer, Harald). *Schott. £0.72* EZDW (B79-50897)
Stainer, *Sir* John. The crucifixion. *arr.* The crucifixion : a meditation on the Sacred Passion of the Holy Redeemer. *Novello. £1.55* FDE/LK (B79-50100)
Staley, James. Danceries, liv.3. *Selections : arr.* Tanz-Suite ... für Blockflötenquartett (SATB ; ATTB) oder andere Melodieinstrumente (Violen oder Flöten), Schlagwerk ad lib. = Dance suite ... for recorder quartet (SATB ; ATTB) or other melodic instruments (viols or flutes), percussion instruments ad lib. (Gervaise, Claude). *Schott. Unpriced* VSNSK/AH/AYH (B79-51236)
Standford, Patric.
Holiday memories : for elementary string trio (2 violins and cello). *7 Garrick St., W.C.2 : Middle Eight Music. Unpriced* RXNT (B79-50271)
A London suite : for elementary string quartets. *7 Garrick St., W.C.2 : Middle Eight Music. Unpriced* RXNS (B79-50269)
Stanford, *Sir* Charles Villiers.
Intermezzos, clarinet & piano, op.13. Three intermezzi, op.13 : for clarinet and piano. *Chester Music. Unpriced* VVPJ (B79-51280)
Six songs for medium voice. *Stainer and Bell. Unpriced* KFVDW (B79-51008) ISBN 0-85249-526-9
Stanier, Tom. The shepherd king. *Vocal score.* The shepherd king : a musical play in eight scenes. (Parker, Jim).

Weinberger. Unpriced CN (B79-50415)
Stankiewicz, Marta. Internationale Diskographie elektronischer Musik = International electronic music discography = Discographie internationale de la musique electronique. (Kondracki, Miroslaw). Schott. Pbk. £11.20 APV/FD(WT) (B79-35641)
Stardance carol : S.A.T.B. (Whitter, Mark). Banks. Unpriced EXRVDP/LF (B79-50871)
Starker, Janos. Sonata, cello & piano. Sonata for cello and piano. (Baker, David). Associated Music. £6.10 SRPE (B79-50689)
Starr, Ringo. See Beatles, The.
Starting together : easy duets for recorder and guitar groups
Vol.1. Chester Music. Unpriced VSPLTSK/DW/AY (B79-51238)
Starting together : easy duets for recorders and guitar groups
Vol.2. Chester Music. Unpriced VSPLTSK/DW/AY (B79-51239)
Vol.3. Chester Music. Unpriced VSPLTSK/DW/AY (B79-51240)
State fair. Its a grand night for singing. arr. Its a grand night for singing : S.A.C.(T).B, with piano. (Rodgers, Richard). Williamson. Unpriced DW (B79-50858)
Staton, Kathleen. Diddly, diddly, dumpty : finger plays, face games, action rhymes, fun songs, for nursery and infant schools. EMI. Unpriced JFEZDW/GR (B79-50524)
Staveacre, Tony. Al Bowlly. (Colin, Sid). Elm Tree Books. £5.95 : CIP entry AKDW/GB/E(P) (B78-37099) ISBN 0-241-10057-7
Stayin' alive, You need me, plus 12 hot hits. Chappell. Unpriced LK/DW/GBB/AY (B79-51011)
Steane, Leonard. Glazounov : an assessment of the value of Glazounov's orchestral music, with tributes from various sources. 1st ed. reprinted and revised. 57 Burns Rd, Coventry, Warwickshire CV2 4AD : The author. Sd. £0.50 BGK (B79-27791)
Stedman, Preston. The symphony. Prentice-Hall. £9.70 AMME(X) (B79-32717) ISBN 0-13-880062-6
Steely Dan. Steely Dan : the best of ... Chappell. Unpriced KDW/HKR (B79-50542)
Steely Dan : the best of ... (Steely Dan). Chappell. Unpriced KDW/HKR (B79-50542)
Steht auf und singt : festlicher Spruch. (Schallehn, Hilger). Schott. £0.80 EZDW (B79-50903)
Stein, Leo. Die lustige Witwe. Selections : arr. Songs from The merry widow (Die lustige Witwe). (Lehár, Franz). Glocken. Unpriced KDW (B79-50957)
Steinberg, Jeffrey. You needed me. (Goodrum, Randy). Chappell. Unpriced UMK/DW (B79-51204)
Steinitz, Paul. Bach's passions. Elek. £5.95 BBCADD/LK (B79-14916) ISBN 0-236-40132-7
Stephens, James. On the king's highway. Chorus score. On the king's highway : for children's chorus and chamber orchestra. (Binkerd, Gordon). Boosey and Hawkes. Unpriced FADW (B79-50488)
Stephenson, Elspeth Mary. Sing to God. Scripture Union. £0.75 ADM (B79-31511) ISBN 0-85421-722-3
Stern, Susan. Women composers : a handbook. Scarecrow Press : Distributed by Bailey and Swinfen. £6.00 A/D(M/C) (B79-02985) ISBN 0-8108-1138-3
Sterne, Colin. Meadow, hedge, cuckoo : variations for solo alto recorder on John Dowland's ayre 'Away with these self-loving lads'. Galaxy Music : Galliard. Unpriced VSSPM/T (B79-50348)
Steude, Wolfram. St. Mark's Passion. Markus-Passion für Solostimmen und vierstimmigen Chor a cappella. (Peranda, Marco Giuseppe). VEB Deutscher Verlag Breitkopf and Härtel. £2.70 EZDD/LK (B79-50872)
Stevens, Bernard.
Ballade no.2 : Op.42 : for piano solo. Roberton. £1.50 QPJ (B79-51090)
Improvisation. Op.48 : for solo viola. Roberton. £1.50 SQPMJ (B79-51157)
Stevens, Cat. Back to earth. arr. Back to earth. Ashtar EMI. Unpriced KDW/HKR (B79-50988)
Stevens, Denis. Monteverdi : sacred, secular and occasional music. Fairleigh Dickinson University Press : Associated University Presses. £4.95 BMN (B79-32715) ISBN 0-8386-1937-1
Stevens, Wallace. Poems of Wallace Stevens I : for soprano and seven players, opus 9. (Connolly, Justin). Novello. £3.00 KFLE/NYENPDW (B79-50151)
Stevenson, Ronald. Sounding strings : an album of Celtic music for clarsach pedal harp or piano. United Music. £1.80 TQPMK/AYCC (B79-50696)
Stewart, John. Bombs away, dream babies. arr. Bombs away, dream babies. Chappell. Unpriced KDW/HKR (B79-50989)
Stewart, Rod. The vintage years. Chappell. Unpriced KDW/HKR (B79-50990)
Stichomythia : for flute and guitar, 1976. (Antioniou, Theodore). Bärenreiter. £8.58 VRPLTS (B79-50335)
Stiles, Frank.
Sonata, oboe & piano. Sonata for oboe and piano. (Paigles, Perry Green, Bradwell) : Anglian Edition. Unpriced VTPE (B79-50772)
Sonata, violin. Sonata for solo violin. (Paigles, Perry Green, Bradwell) : Anglian Edition. Unpriced SPME (B79-50683)
Stilestone suite : for chamber ensemble or wind, brass, percussion op.62a. (Cruft, Adrian). (1 The Retreat, S.W.14) : Joad Press. Unpriced MRK/AG (B79-50183)
Stilestone suite : for piano, op.62. (Cruft, Adrian). (1 The Retreat, S.W.1) : Joad Press. Unpriced QPG (B79-50210)
Stilestone suite. Op.62. arr. Stilestone suite : for chamber ensemble or wind, brass, percussion op.62a. (Cruft, Adrian). (1 The Retreat, S.W.14) : Joad Press. Unpriced MRK/AG (B79-50183)
Still, Barry. Two hundred and fifty years of the Three Choirs Festival : a commemoration in words and pictures. c/o Arts Council of Great Britain, 105 Piccadilly, W1V 0AU : Three Choirs Festival Association. Pbk. £2.00 AD(YDGB/WE/X) (B79-07463)
Still more hidden melodies : six improvisations for piano. (Cooper, Joseph). Novello. Unpriced QPJ (B79-50214)
Stille Nacht, heilige Nacht. arr. Silent night. (Grüber, Franz Xaver). 36 Ranelagh Gdns W.6 : Cathedral Music. Unpriced EZDP/LF (B79-50094)
Stingl, Anton. Lieder ohne Worte. Selections : arr. 5 Lieder ohne Worte : für zwei Gitarren = for two guitars. (Mendelssohn, Felix). Schott. £4.00 TSNUK (B79-51172)
Stocker, David. Shout for joy : for four-part chorus of mixed voices with piano accompaniment. Schirmer. £0.75 DR (B79-50844)
'Stockholmer Sonaten' für Viola d'amore (Viola) und Basso continuo = 'Stockholm sonatas' for viola d'amore (viola) and basso continuo
2: Sonatas in ... B flat major ... G minor ... A minor. (Ariosti, Attilio). Bärenreiter. £5.28 SQQPE (B79-50287)
Stollenwerk, Hans J. Das Jazzpublikum : zur Sozialpsychologie einer kulturellen Minderheit. (Dollase, Rainer). Schott. Pbk. £9.60 AMT(Z) (B79-10482)
Stone, David.
Spartak. Adagio of Spartacus and Phrygia. arr. Adagio. (Khachaturian, Aram). Boosey and Hawkes. Unpriced MK/HM (B79-50567)
Spartak. Adagio of Spartacus and Phrygia. arr. Adagio. (Khachaturian, Aram). Boosey and Hawkes. Unpriced MK/HM (B79-50568)
Storace, Stephen. Seven songs : for high voice. Stainer and Bell. Unpriced KFTDW (B79-50556) ISBN 0-85249-510-2
Story and the song : a survey of English musical plays, 1916-78. (Parker, Derek). Chappell : Elm Tree Books. £7.50 ACM(YD/XMR53) (B79-35973) ISBN 0-903443-25-2
Stranz, Ulrich. Déjà vu : für Oboe d'amore und kleines Orchester. Bärenreiter. £11.22 MPVTQ (B79-50589)
Stratford, Michael D. The pirates of Penzance. Selections : arr. Suite from Gilbert and Sullivan's 'The pirates of Penzance. (Sullivan, Sir Arthur Seymour). Lengnick. £1.10 JE/VSNQDW (B79-50931)
Straus, Oscar. A waltz dream : operetta in three acts. (Dunn, Bernard). 10 Rathbone St., W1P 2BJ : Josef Weinberger. Pbk. £1.25 BSOTACF (B79-06705)
Strauss, Johann, b.1825. Wein, Weib und Gesang. Op.333. arr. Wine, women and song. New revised ed. Schott. £0.90 VSNRQK/AHW (B79-50762)
Strauss, Richard. Fanfare der Stadt Wien. arr. Festmusik der Stadt Wien. Boosey and Hawkes. Unpriced UMMK/AGN (B79-50729)
Stravinsky, Vera. Stravinsky in pictures and documents. Hutchinson. £16.00 BSV(N) (B79-15553) ISBN 0-09-138000-6
Stravinsky in pictures and documents. (Stravinsky, Vera). Hutchinson. £16.00 BSV(N) (B79-15553) ISBN 0-09-138000-6
Strawberry rock. (Littell, Barbara). Warner : Blossom. Unpriced UMMJ (B79-50723)
Strike the bell : transport by road, canal, rail and sea in the nineteenth century through songs, ballads and contemporary accounts. Cambridge University Press. Sd. £2.25 KEZDW/K/G/AYC (B79-50547) ISBN 0-521-21921-3
String along with Scott : 10 ragtime pieces. (Joplin, Scott). Schirmer. £7.85 RXNSK/AHXJ (B79-50674)
Struth, Sigrid Abel-. See Abel-Struth, Sigrid.
Strutte, Wilson. Tchaikovsky : his life and times. Midas Books. £6.50 BTD(N) (B79-27783) ISBN 0-85936-113-6
Stubbs, Leighton. Harvest jazz : a cantata for schools. (Cartwright, Kenneth). Boosey and Hawkes. Unpriced FDE/LP (B79-50489)
Stubbs, Tish. The English folksinger : 159 modern and traditional folksongs. Collins. £3.95(hardback), £1.95(pbk) KE/TSDW/G/AYD (B79-50994) ISBN 0-00-411067-6
Studies in musical science in the late Renaissance. (Walker, Daniel Pickering). Warburg Institute etc.. £15.00 A/AM(XDYAK181) (B79-17759) ISBN 0-85481-056-0
Styne, Jule. Gypsy. Everything's coming up roses. arr. Everything's coming up roses : for S.A. cambiata, B. or S.A.T.B, with piano. Williamson. Unpriced DW (B79-50859)

Suite bergamasque. (Debussy, Claude). Peters. Unpriced QPG (B79-50211)
Suite française. Op.61 : pour deux guitares. (Duarte, John William). Bèrben : Breitkopf and Härtel. £3.30 TSNUG (B79-51170)
Suite from Gilbert and Sullivan's 'The pirates of Penzance. (Sullivan, Sir Arthur Seymour). Lengnick. £1.10 JE/VSNQDW (B79-50931)
Suite nach englischen Volksliedern
No.1: The keel row. Einst kam ich nach Sandgate. Schott. £0.72 EZDW/G/AYD (B79-50481)
No.2: The old true love. Ach komm, tritt ein. Schott. £0.48 EZDW/G/AYD (B79-50482)
No.3: The keeper. Ein Jager wollte jagen gehn. Schott. £0.80 EZDW/G/AYD (B79-50483)
No.4: There's none to soothe. Wo weilst du, Lieb. Schott. £0.48 EZDW/G/AYD (B79-50484)
No.5: The miller of Dee. War einst ein braver Mullersmann. Schott. £0.72 EZDW/G/AYD (B79-50485)
No.6: Cock a doodle doo. Schott. £0.48 EZDW/G/AYD (B79-50486)
Suite of Cotswold folkdances. (Lane, Philip). Edwin Ashdown. £5.00 MMHG (B79-50171)
Suite rhapsodica : for clarinet solo, 1976. (Feld, Jindřich). Schirmer. £1.80 VVPMJ (B79-51288)
Suite variata : per chitarra. (Viozzi, Giulio). Bèrben Breitkopf and Härtel. £2.35 TSPMG (B79-51179)
Sullivan, Sir Arthur Seymour.
An idyll : for violoncello and piano. Leonard, Gould and Bolttler. £0.50 SRPJ (B79-50691)
The pirates of Penzance. Selections : arr. Suite from Gilbert and Sullivan's 'The pirates of Penzance. Lengnick. £1.10 JE/VSNQDW (B79-50931)
Sullivan, J. An unpublished religious song-book of mid-eighteenth century Russia. (Akademiia nauk SSSR. Biblioteka. MSS. (33.3.5)). c/o C.L. Drage, 94 Inverness Terrace, W.2 : The editors. Pbk. £2.00 AKDH/LSC(YM/XFX31) (B79-37420)
Sullivan, Michael. The lollipop lady : a musical play for primary schools. (Adams, Chris). 43 Clifton Rd. : Youngsong. Unpriced CQN (B79-50825)
Sulyok, Imre. Klavierwerke = Piano works
Heft 12: Einzelne Charakterstücke 2 = Individual character pieces. (Liszt, Franz). Bärenreiter. £5.94 QP/AZ (B79-50618)
Summer day = Ein Sommertag : for four-part chorus of mixed voices a cappella. (Dvořák, Antonín). Schirmer. £0.45 EZDW (B79-50893)
Summer in the city : rock music and way of life. (Doney, Malcolm). Lion Publishing. Pbk. £1.25 AKDW/HKR(X) (B79-04538) ISBN 0-85648-085-1
Summertime : S.A.C.(T.) B. with piano. (Gershwin, George). Chappell. Unpriced DW (B79-50849)
Sumsion, Herbert. They that go down to the sea in ships : anthem for S.A.T.B. and organ. Addington Press. Unpriced DK (B79-50836)
Sun rising : threnody for orchestra. Op.45. (Brown, Christopher). Chester Music. Unpriced MMJ (B79-51022)
Superman. Theme. arr. Theme from 'Superman'. (Williams, John). Warner. Unpriced QPK/JR (B79-50225)
Superpop
No.1- ; Jan. 27, 1979-. 1B Parkfield St., N1 0PR : 'Superpop'. Sd. £0.15 A/GB(B) (B79-24588)
Supersound series for young bands.
Balent, Andrew. Boogie woogie band. Warner : Blossom. Unpriced UMJ (B79-51200)
Littell, Barbara. March for a celebration. Warner Blossom. Unpriced UMMGM (B79-50720)
Littell, Barbara. Strawberry rock. Warner : Blossom. Unpriced UMMJ (B79-50723)
Livingston, Jerry. Casper the friendly ghost. arr. Casper the friendly ghost. Warner : Blossom. Unpriced WMK/DW (B79-50379)
Supersounds series for young chorus. Lerner, Samuel. Popeye the sailor. I'm Popeye the sailorman. arr. I'm Popeye the sailor man : for two-part chorus and piano. Warner : Blossom. Unpriced FDW/JR (B79-50106)
Suppé, Franz von.
Fatinitza march. arr. Fatinitza march : based on themes from the operetta 'Fatinitza'. Bosworth & Co. £1.25 MK/AGM (B79-51012)
Das Pensionat. Vocal score. The finishing school : comic operetta in one act (two scenes). Weinberger. Unpriced CF (B79-50414)
Surge, illuminare. (Rorem, Ned). Boosey and Hawkes. Unpriced DK (B79-50439)
'Surge of the sea. arr. The song of the sea. An atairreachd ard = ('High surge of the sea'). (MacDonald, John). Bosworth and Co. Unpriced KDW (B79-50526)
Surinach, Carlos. Quartet, strings. arr. Concerto for string orchestra. Associated Music. £9.10 RXMK (B79-50666)
Survey of Christian hymnody. A joyful sound : Christian hymnody. (Reynolds, William Jensen). 2nd ed. Holt, Rinehart and Winston. £8.75 ADM(X) (B79-05497) ISBN 0-03-040831-8
Susanna's secret = Il segreto di Susanna = Susannens Geheimnis : overture. (Wolf-Ferrari, Ermanno). Weinberger. Unpriced MMJ (B79-50180)

Suter, Robert. Musik für Flöte und Gitarre. Eulenburg. £2.10 VRPLTS (B79-50757)
Sutermeister, Heinrich.
Consolatio philosophiae. Vocal score. Consolatio philosophiae : scène dramatique voix haute et orchestre in memoriam Ernest Ansermet (1977). Schott. £10.80 KFTDX (B79-50155)
Quadrifoglio : concerto per quattro fiati ed orchestra. Schott. £16.80 MPVNSF (B79-50586)
Suttner, Kurt. Das europäische Kunstlied : eine Auswahl von Klavierliedern aus vier Jahrhunderten für den Musikunterricht ... Schott. £6.00 KDW/AY (B79-50962)
Sutton, Richard. The Wagner companion. Faber. £12.50 : CIP rev. BWC (B78-40353) ISBN 0-571-10471-1
Swale, David. This endris night : S.A.T.B. Banks. Unpriced DP/LF (B79-50842)
Swann, Donald.
Round the piano with Donald Swann : a collection of songs with piano accompaniments. Bodley Head. Unpriced KDW/AY (B79-50961) ISBN 0-370-30173-0
Wacky and his fuddlejig : a children's Christmas musical

play. *Universal. Unpriced* CN/LF (B79-50017)
Swanwick, Keith. A bass for music education. *NFER.* Pbk. *£4.75* A(V) (B79-32714) ISBN 0-85633-180-5
Swarsenski, H.
Petite suite. (Debussy, Claude). 2nd ed. *Peters. Unpriced* QNVG (B79-50205)
Suite bergamasque. (Debussy, Claude). *Peters. Unpriced* QPG (B79-50211)
Swayne, Giles.
Canto for guitar. *Novello. £1.65* TSPMJ (B79-50309)
Suite, guitar. Suite for guitar. *Novello. £1.65* TSPMG (B79-50307)
Sweet and lowdown : America's popular song writers. (Craig, Warren). *Scarecrow Press : Distributed by Bailey and Swinfen. £18.75* AKDW/GB(YT/WT) (B79-11129) ISBN 0-8108-1089-1
Sweet Scottish isle. (Mullen, Brian). *(16 Mendip Rd) : Autumn Publications. Unpriced* KDW (B79-50959)
Sweet Scottish isle. *arr.* Sweet Scottish isle. (Mullen, Brian). *(16 Mendip Rd) : Autumn Publications. Unpriced* KDW (B79-50959)
Swift, Dave. Living in the city : a songbook. *59 Watney St., E.1 : Basement Writers.* Sd. *£0.15* KE/TSDW (B79-50545)
Swing und Beat, Schwarz auf weiss = Swing and beat. Black on white : Anregungen zum Musizieren auf Klavier und Elektronenorgel = Hints on playing the piano and the electronic organ. (Pieper, Manfred). *VEB Deutscher Verlag für Musik : Breitkopf und Härtel. £6.30* Q/AC (B79-50612)
Sycophantic fox and the gullible raven : S.A.T.B. & piano. (Tepper, Albert). *Boosey and Hawkes. £0.90* DW (B79-50861)
Symphonic music. (Huber, Paul). *R. Smith. Unpriced* WMJ (B79-51299)
Symphonie A-Dur, KV114. (Mozart, Wolfgang Amadeus). *Schott. £4.80* MRE (B79-51033)
Symphony. (Stedman, Preston). *Prentice-Hall. £9.70* AMME(X) (B79-32717) ISBN 0-13-880062-6
Symphony no.3, 'Espansioni'. Espansioni : Sinfonie III für grosses Orchester, Bariton und Tonband. 1974/1975. (Kelterborn, Rudolf). *Bärenreiter. £11.55* KGNE/MDX (B79-50156)
Symphony no.3, 'Kaddish'. Yit'ga dal. *arr.* Canon in five parts ... : for boys chorus with piano accompaniment. (Bernstein, Leonard). *Amberson : Schirmer (dist.). £0.35* DH (B79-50831)
Symphony no.24, op.273, 'Majnun'. Majnun symphony. (Symphony no.24). Op.273 : for tenor solo, four-part chorus of mixed voices, trumpet in C, solo violin and string orchestra. (Hovhaness, Alan). *Associated Music. £9.10* EMDX (B79-50869)
Take my life : tune, Charlton, words, Frances Ridley Havergal and Come, Holy Ghost : tune, Pentecost, words, Bishop J. Cosin, based on 'Veni creator spiritus'. (Wilson, Alan J). *Weinberger. Unpriced* DM (B79-50442)
'Talking machine review'. 'Blue Amberol' cylinders : a catalogue. (Carter, Sydney Horace). *19 Glendale Rd, Bournemouth BH6 4JA : 'Talking machine review'.* Sd. *£4.00* A/FE(QB/WT) (B79-05450) ISBN 0-902338-30-7
Tallis, Thomas.
Sancte Deus. *72 Brewery Rd, N.7 : Mapa mundi. Unpriced* EZDJ (B79-50066)
Videte miraculum : for 6 voices. *72 Brewery Rd, N.7 : Mapa Mundi. Unpriced* EZDJ (B79-50067)
Tanz-Suite ... für Blockflötenquartett (SATB ; ATTB) oder andere Melodieinstrumente (Violen oder Flöten), Schlagwerk ad lib. = Dance suite ... for recorder quartet (SATB ; ATTB) or other melodic instruments (viols or flutes), percussion instruments ad lib. (Gervaise, Claude). *Schott. Unpriced* VSNSK/AH/AYH (B79-51236)
Tanzlied. (Ritmo di joropo). (Poos, Heinrich). *Schott. £0.48* FEZDW (B79-50502)
Tarka the otter. (Fanshawe, David). *Chappell. Unpriced* QPK/JR (B79-51106)
Tarka the otter. Theme. *arr.* Tarka the otter. (Fanshawe, David). *Chappell. Unpriced* QPK/JR (B79-51106)
Tarr, Edward H. Chorale preludes, trumpet & organ. Die sechs Choralvorspiele für Trompete und Orgel = The six chorale preludes for trumpet and organ. (Krebs, Johann Ludwig). *Simrock. Unpriced* WSPLR (B79-50398)
Taschenpartituren. Klebe, Giselher. Symphony, no.3, op.52. Dritte Sinfonie für grosses Orchester, Op.52 = Third symphony for grand orchestra, op.52. *Bärenreiter. £13.20* MME (B79-50167)
Taste and see : for two-part chorus of women's voices with glockenspiel and triangle. (Wienhorst, Richard). *Associated Music. £0.35* FE/XTPLXTQWDK (B79-50499)
Tate, Joan. In my own key. (Söderström, Elisabeth). *H. Hamilton. £5.95 : CIP entry* AKFL/E(P) (B79-25330) ISBN 0-241-10318-5
Tate, Phyllis.
All the world's a stage. *Vocal score.* All the world's a stage : prologue, six variations, and epilogue for chorus and orchestra. *Oxford University Press. Unpriced* DX (B79-50864) ISBN 0-19-338344-6
Illustrations : for brass band. *Novello. Unpriced* WMJ (B79-50375)
Taubmann, Otto. Te Deum. Op.22. *Vocal score.* Te Deum. Op.22. (Berlioz, Hector). *Bärenreiter. £3.96* DGKHB (B79-50425)
Tausch, Franz. Duos, clarinet & bassoon, op.21. Three duos for clarinet and bassoon. Op.21. *Musica rara. Unpriced* VVPLVW (B79-51285)
Tausky, Margaret. Vilem Tausky tells his story : a two-part setting. (Tausky, Vilem). *Stainer and Bell. £6.00* A/EC(P) (B79-25860) ISBN 0-85249-478-5
Tausky, Vilem.
Das Pensionat. *Vocal score.* The finishing school : comic operetta in one act (two scenes). (Suppé, Franz von). *Weinberger. Unpriced* CF (B79-50414)
Vilem Tausky tells his story : a two-part setting. *Stainer and Bell. £6.00* A/EC(P) (B79-25860) ISBN 0-85249-478-5
Tavener, John. Thérèse. *Vocal score.* Thérèse ... *Chester Music. Unpriced* CC (B79-50817)
Taylor, Arthur Richard. Brass band. *Hart-Davis MacGibbon. £10.00* AWM(X) (B79-06709) ISBN 0-246-11082-1
Taylor, Cecil John. C. John Taylor's islands of beauty : ballad in English and Gaelic. *Isle of Seil, Oban, Argyll, Scotland : Highland Arts Studios. Unpriced* KDW (B79-50527)
Taylor, Dorothy. Singing rhymes. *Ladybird Books. £0.30* AJFDW/GR(VJ) (B79-06706) ISBN 0-7214-0537-1
Taylor, Jeremy James. Helen comes home, or, Achilles the heel. *French. £1.50 : CIP entry* BNEACN (B79-17762) ISBN 0-573-15004-4
Taylor, Ronald, *b.1924.* Richard Wagner : his life, art and thought. *Elek. £7.95* BWC(N) (B79-08130) ISBN 0-236-40071-1
Tchaikovsky, Peter.
Marche slave. Op.31. *arr.* Marche slave. *Oxford University Press. Unpriced* MK/AGM (B79-50162) ISBN 0-19-367910-8
Music from the ballet. *(7 Garrick St., W.C.2) : Middle Eight Music. Unpriced* UNSK/HM (B79-50733)
Sleeping beauty. Op.66. Panorama. *arr.* Panorama ... *R. Smith. Unpriced* WMK/HM (B79-50383)
Suite, orchestra, no.3, op.55, G major. Suite no.3 in G, op.55. *Eulenburg. Unpriced* MMG (B79-50170)
Tchaikovsky ballet music. (Warrack, John). *British Broadcasting Corporation.* Pbk. *£1.40* BTDAM/HM (B79-31929) ISBN 0-563-12860-7
Te Deum. Op.22. (Berlioz, Hector). *Bärenreiter. £3.96* DGKHB (B79-50425)
Teach yourself books. Chilton, John. Jazz. *Teach Yourself Books.* Pbk. *£1.95 : CIP rev.* AMT(X) (B79-15559) ISBN 0-340-23847-x
Teacher series of guitar publications. Nunn, Ruth. Moods for guitar. *Novello. £0.66* TSPMJ (B79-50308)
Teaching of Artur Schnabel. Schnabel's interpretation of piano music. (Wolff, Konrad). 2nd ed. *Faber.* Pbk. *£2.50* AQ/E(P) (B79-36916) ISBN 0-571-10029-5
Techniques and materials of tonal music : with an introduction to twentieth-century techniques. (Benjamin, Thomas). 2nd ed. *Houghton Mifflin. £9.75* A/R (B79-18563) ISBN 0-395-27066-9
Tedesco, Mario Castelnuovo-. *See* Castelnuovo-Tedesco, Mario.
Telemann, Georg Philipp.
Concerto, flute, violins (2) & continuo, G major. Concerto in G-dur für Flöte, 2 Violinen und Basso continuo = Concerto in G major for flute, 2 violins and basso continuo. *Amadeus : Bärenreiter. £3.25* NURNSF (B79-50597)
Concerto, oboe & string orchestra, D major. Concerto in D for oboe, violins and basso continuo. *Musica rara. Unpriced* RXMPVTF (B79-50260)
Concerto, oboe & string orchestra, D major. *arr.* Concerto in D for oboe, violins and basso continuo. *Musica rara. Unpriced* VTPK/LF (B79-50351)
Concerto, oboe & string orchestra, F major. Concerto in F for solo oboe, violin, strings and basso continuo. *Musica rara. Unpriced* RXMPVTF (B79-50261)
Concerto, oboe & string orchestra, F major. *arr.* Concerto in F for solo oboe, violin, strings and basso continuo. *Musica rara. Unpriced* VTPK/LF (B79-50352)
Der getreue Music Meister. Duet, flute & viola pomposa. *arr.* Dueto in G-dur für Flote und Violine = Duet in G major for flute and violin. *Amadeus : Bärenreiter. £1.85* VRPLS (B79-50755)
Der getreue Music Meister. *Selections.* 4 sonatas for treble recorder and basso continuo. *Musica rara. Unpriced* VSSPE (B79-50347)
Der getreue Music Meister. Sonata, bassoon & continuo, F minor. Sonate in f-moll für Fagott oder Violoncello und Basso continuo = Sonata in F minor for bassoon or cello and basso continuo. *Amadeus : Schott. Unpriced* VWPE (B79-50363)
Kleine Cammermusic. Die kleine Kammermusik : sechs Partiten für Blockflöte, Querflöte, Oboe oder Violine und Basso continuo = six partitas for recorder, flute, oboe or violin and basso continuo. *Amadeus : Eulenburg. £4.70* VSPG (B79-50764)
Sonata, recorder, violin & continuo, F major. 26 Triosonate in F-dur für Altblockflöte (Querflöte), Violine (Querflöte, Oboe) und Basso continuo. Sonata a tre in F major for treble recorder (flute), violin (flute, oboe) and basso continuo. *Amadeus : Breitkopf and Härtel. £2.80* NUSNTE (B79-51041)
Suite, trumpet & string orchestra, D major. Suite 1 for trumpet, strings and basso continuo. *Musica rara. Unpriced* RXMPWSG (B79-50262)
Suite, trumpet & string orchestra, D major. *arr.* Suite 1 for trumpet, strings and basso continuo. *Musica rara. Unpriced* WSPK/AG (B79-50396)
Tell me, dearest, what is love? : for mixed chorus a cappella. (Diemer, Emma Lou). *Broude : Breitkopf and Härtel. £0.42* EZDW (B79-50889)
Temperley, Nicholas. Musica Britannica : a national collection of music
Vol.43: English songs, 1800-1860. *Stainer and Bell. Unpriced* C/AYD (B79-50814) ISBN 0-85249-439-4
Ten CC. Bloody tourists. *arr.* Bloody tourists. *Chappell. Unpriced* KDW/GB (B79-50532)
Ten dance studies in jazz idiom : for trombone quintet. (Jahn, Thomas). *Schirmer. £8.50* WUNRHX (B79-50807)
Ten songs for high voice. (Boyce, William). *Stainer and Bell. Unpriced* KFTDW (B79-50554) ISBN 0-85249-493-9
Ten 'swingalong' songs. 10 'swingalong' songs : for the primaries. (Dainton, Marie Cleeve). *Regina Music. Unpriced* JFDW/GJ (B79-50129)
Ten traditional English carols. *Fenone Music, Breitkopf und Härtel. £0.95* TSPMK/DP/LF/AY (B79-50313)
Tenebrae factae sunt : for 4 voices. (Ammon, Blasius). *72 Brewery Rd, N.7 : Mapa mundi. Unpriced* EZDJ/LK (B79-50083)
Tennyson, Alfred, *Baron Tennyson.* Songs from 'The princess' : for unaccompanied equal voices (SSA-SSSAA). (Holst, Gustav). *Novello. £1.15* FEZDW (B79-50918)
Tepper, Albert.
4 American settings. Song of Thyrsis. Song of Thyrsis : S.A.T.B. & piano. *Boosey and Hawkes. £0.35* DW (B79-50860)
The sycophantic fox and the gullible raven : S.A.T.B. & piano. *Boosey and Hawkes. £0.90* DW (B79-50861)
Terpsichore. *Selections : arr.* Four dances ... guitar. (Praetorius, Michael). *Boosey and Hawkes. Unpriced* TSPMK/AH (B79-50710)
Terzakis, Dimitri. Quartet, strings, no.2. Streichquartett Nr.2. *Bärenreiter. £3.96* RXNS (B79-50270)
Terzett für Flöte (Piccolo), Klarinette und Fagott. (Vogel, Vladimir). *Eulenburg. £4.65* VNT (B79-50735)
Teske, Hermien.
Concerto, flute, violins (2) & continuo, G major. Concerto in G-dur für Flöte, 2 Violinen und Basso continuo = Concerto in G major for flute, 2 violins and basso continuo. (Telemann, Georg Philipp). *Amadeus Bärenreiter. £3.25* NURNSF (B79-50597)
Der getreue Music Meister. Duet, flute & viola pomposa. *arr.* Dueto in G-dur für Flote und Violine = Duet in G major for flute and violin. (Telemann, Georg Philipp). *Amadeus : Bärenreiter. £1.85* VRPLS (B79-50755)
Testimony. (Shostakovich, Dmitriĭ Dmitrievich). *H. Hamilton. £7.95 : CIP entry* BSGR(N) (B79-25857) ISBN 0-241-10321-5
Texas University at Austin. *See* University of Texas at Austin.
Thanksgiving to God, for his house. (Argento, Dominick). *Boosey and Hawkes. Unpriced* EZDH (B79-50875)
There shall a star from Jacob come forth : three excerpts from Christus. (Mendelssohn, Felix). *Addington Press. Unpriced* DH/LF (B79-50834)
There will always be ... (Coward, *Sir* Noël). *Chappell. Unpriced* KDW (B79-50525)
Thérèse. *Vocal score.* Thérèse ... (Tavener, John). *Chester Music. Unpriced* CC (B79-50817)
They call the wind Maria : S.A.C.(T.) B. with piano. (Loewe, Frederick). *Chappell. Unpriced* DW (B79-50850)
They that go down to the sea in ships : anthem for S.A.T.B. and organ. (Sumsion, Herbert). *Addington Press. Unpriced* DK (B79-50836)
They're playing our song. (Hamlisch, Marvin). *Chappell. Unpriced* KDW (B79-50956)
They're playing our song. *Selections : arr.* They're playing our song. (Hamlisch, Marvin). *Chappell. Unpriced* KDW (B79-50956)
Thin Lizzy.
Black rose : a rock legend. *Chappell. Unpriced* KDW/HKR (B79-50991)
Thin Lizzy : the best of ... *Chappell. Unpriced* KDW/GB (B79-50533)
Thin Lizzy : the best of ... (Thin Lizzy). *Chappell. Unpriced* KDW/GB (B79-50533)
Thirty easy classical duets : for unaccompanied clarinets. *Oxford University Press. Unpriced* VVNUK/AAY (B79-50356) ISBN 0-19-356566-8
This day to man. *Vocal score.* This day to man : six hymns for the Nativity for SATB and orchestra. (Hurd, Michael). *Novello. Unpriced* DE/LF (B79-50828)
This endris night : S.A.T.B. (Swale, David). *Banks. Unpriced* DP/LF (B79-50842)
Thomas, Brian Price-. *See* Price-Thomas, Brian.
Thomas, Ernst. Ferienkurse '78. (Internationale Ferienkurse für Neue Musik, *29, Darmstadt, 1978*). *Schott.* Pbk. *£9.60* A(XR9) (B79-14011)
Thomas, John, *b.1826.* Welsh melodies. Dafydd y garreg wen. Dafydd y garreg wen = David of the white rock. *Adlais. Unpriced* TQPM/T (B79-50294)
Thompson, Bradford. Christmas carols for young children : for piano, guitar and recorder. *East West : Breitkopf and Härtel. £1.50* JFE/NUSNTDP/LF/AY (B79-50943)
Thompson, Bradford G.
Frédéric François Chopin, 1810-1844. (Chopin, Frédéric). *East-West. Unpriced* QPJ (B79-50213) ISBN 0-904499-04-9
Johann Sebastian Bach 1685-1750. (Bach, Johann Sebastian). *East-West Publications. Unpriced* PWPJ (B79-50611)
Thompson, Diana. Pompaleerie jig. *E.J. Arnold.* Sd. *£1.30* A(VG/GR) (B79-04968) ISBN 0-560-00319-6
Thompson, Ed. Hauss-Musik, Tl.3. Danket dem Herren. *arr.* Give thanks to the Lord : for three-part chorus of women's voices a cappella. (Staden, Johann). *Schirmer. £0.35* FEZDH (B79-50500)

Thompson, Tierl.
Sisters in song : a collection of new songs from the women's liberation movement. *Onlywoman Press. Unpriced* KFE/TSDW/AY (B79-50996)
Sisters in song : a collection of new songs from the women's liberation movement. (Burgon, Geoffrey). *Onlywomen Press. Unpriced* KDGPR (B79-50951)
Thomson, John Mansfield. On music and musicians. (Falla, Manuel de). *Boyars : Distributed by Calder and Boyars. £5.95* A (B79-14910) ISBN 0-7145-2600-2
Thomson, Virgil. Man of iron : a portrait of Willy Eisenhart, for piano. *Schirmer. £1.20* QPJ (B79-50639)
Thorgerson, Storm. Wings tour USA. (Powell, Aubrey). *High St., Limpsfield, Surrey RH8 0DY : Paper Tiger.* Pbk. *£3.25* AKDW/GB/E(P/EM/XRF) (B79-05872) ISBN 0-905895-10-x
Thorne, Adrian. Classical harmony through figured bass. *Chappell. Unpriced* Q/RGD/AC (B79-51061)
Thou madest all things well : anthem for unison voices and organ. (Kidd, J Michael). *Weinberger. Unpriced* JFDH (B79-50935)
Though I am young. Gather your rosebuds. (Lawes, William). *Pro Cantione Antiqua : Breitkopf und Härtel. Unpriced* GEZDU (B79-50505)
Three. L'alphabet de la musique : Op.30. Sonatas 4, 7, 16. 3 Sonaten aus 'L'alphabet de la musique' = 3 sonatas from 'L'alphabet de la musique' : für Altblockflöte und Basso continuo = for alto recorder and basso continuo. (Schickhard, Johann Christian). *Pelikan : Bärenreiter. £9.10* VSSPE (B79-50769)
Three Addison anthems : for soprano, alto, tenor and bass. (Rose, Bernard). *Addington Press. Unpriced* EZDH (B79-50878)
Three authentic sonatas : oboe & basso continuo in F, opus 1, no.5, B flat, 'Fitzwilliam', C minor, opus 1, no.8. (Handel, George Frideric). *Nova Music. Unpriced* VTPE (B79-51259)
Three bears go on a picnic : a piano suite with narration. (Glover, David Carr). Revised ed. *Schroeder and Gunther. £1.35* QPG (B79-50626)
Three Choirs Festival Association. Two hundred and fifty years of the Three Choirs Festival : a commemoration in words and pictures. *c/o Arts Council of Great Britain, 105 Piccadilly, W1V 0AU : Three Choirs Festival Association.* Pbk. *£2.00* AD(YDGB/WE/X) (B79-07463)
Three Christmas carols. 3 Christmas carols : for unison voices and piano. (Berkeley, Michael). *Schirmer. Unpriced* JFDP/LF (B79-50126)
Three clarinets, cello and piano. (Feldman, Morton). *Universal. Unpriced* NUVNR (B79-50186)
Three duos for clarinet and bassoon. Op.21. (Tausch, Franz). *Musica rara. Unpriced* VVPLVW (B79-51285)
Three orchestral pieces from the incidental music to Sigurd Jorsalfar, op.56. (Grieg, Edvard). *Eulenburg. Unpriced* MM/JM (B79-50165)
Three organ voluntaries. (Davies, Peter Maxwell). *Chester Music. Unpriced* RJ (B79-51124)
Three pastiches. 3 pastiches : trumpet & piano. (Snell, Howard). *22 Woodcote Ave. : Dunster Music. Unpriced* WSPJ (B79-51317)
Three Renaissance quartets. *Oxford University Press. Unpriced* WNSK/AAY (B79-50389) ISBN 0-19-358490-5
Three short anthems. (Shephard, Richard). *Royal School of Church Music. Unpriced* DJ (B79-50835)
Three sketches for brass band. (Catelinet, Philip). *Paxton. Unpriced* WMJ (B79-51298)
Three sonatinas and a sonata : for piano solo. (Glover, David Carr). *Schroeder and Gunther. £1.75* QPEM (B79-50625)
Three ways to go : a suite for three guitars. *7 Garrick St., London W.C.2 : Middle Eight Music. Unpriced* TSNTK/AAY (B79-50301)
Threlfall, Robert. Hassan : the incidental music to the play by James Elroy Flecker. (Delius, Frederick). *Boosey and Hawkes. Unpriced* EM/JM (B79-50040)
Through music to the self : how to appreciate and experience music anew. (Hamel, Peter Michael). *Compton Press. £5.95* A/CC (B79-08926) ISBN 0-900193-53-0
Thurston, Frederick J. The clarinet : a comprehensive method for the Boehm clarinet. 3rd ed. (revised and enlarged). *Boosey and Hawkes. Unpriced* VV/AC (B79-51272)
Thymehaze : for alto recorder and piano. (Casken, John). *Schott. Unpriced* VSSPJ (B79-51254)
Tiertanzburlesken. *Vocal score.* Tiertanzburlesken. (Bresgen, Cesar). *Schott. Unpriced* FDW (B79-50103)
Tilmouth, Michael. Concerto, violin & string orchestra, R.761, C minor, 'Amato bene'. Concerto in C minor 'Amato bene', RV761, for violin and string orchestra. (Vivaldi, Antonio). *Oxford University Press. Unpriced* RXMPSF (B79-51138) ISBN 0-19-367972-8
Time of orchestral time. Jkesutora no toki no toki = Time of orchestral time. (Yūasa, Jōji). *Zen-on Music : Schott. £12.00* MMJ (B79-51026)
Time pieces : a collection of works for musical clocks by Handel and Haydn. *Fentone Music : Breitkopf und Härtel. Unpriced* TSPMK/B/FK (B79-50312)
Tin soldiers, and, Lords and ladies : two simple piano duets from the suite 'In the days of long ago'. (Furze, Jessie). *Roberton. £0.50* QNV (B79-50614)
Tircuit, Heuwell. Odoru katachi = Dance patterns : for percussion soloist and chamber orchestra. *Associated Music. £5.45* MPX (B79-50592)
Tiv song. (Keil, Charles). *University of Chicago Press. £7.00* BZMQTADW (B79-26553) ISBN 0-226-42962-8
To the limit. (Armatrading, Joan). *Chappell. Unpriced* KDW/HKR (B79-50539)
To the limit. *arr.* To the limit. (Armatrading, Joan). *Chappell. Unpriced* KDW/HKR (B79-50539)
Tobias, Fred. The children's crusade. The children's crusade : a morality play for the young, for four-part chorus of mixed voices, three soloists, narrator, piano and guitar accompaniment. (Lebowsky, Stanley). *Schirmer. £5.15* CN/L (B79-50416)
Tobin, Candida.
Christmas carols. *Helison Press. Unpriced* LK/DP/LF/AY (B79-50157) ISBN 0-905684-04-4
Folksong book 1. *Helicon Press. Unpriced* LK/DW/G/AY (B79-50158) ISBN 0-905684-01-x
Nursery rhymes. *Helicon Press. Unpriced* LK/DW/GK/AY (B79-50159) ISBN 0-905684-03-6
Wizard's way recorder colouring book. *Helicon Press. Unpriced* VS/AC (B79-50337) ISBN 0-905684-00-1
Tobin colour music system
Composition. Teacher's manual. *Southmill Rd, Bishop's Stortford, Herts. CM23 3DH : Helicon Press.* Sd. *£3.00* A(VC) (B79-14905) ISBN 0-905684-16-8
Tobin music system
Harmony. Teachers' manual. *Knight St., Sawbridgeworth, Herts. CM21 9AX : Helicon Press.* Sp. *£3.00* A(VC) (B79-14906) ISBN 0-905684-19-2
Rhythm and pitch. Teachers' manual. *Knight St., Sawbridgeworth, Herts. CM21 9AX : Helicon Press.* Sp. *£3.00* A(VC) (B79-14907) ISBN 0-905684-05-2
Scales and key signatures (the composer's palette). Teachers' manual. *Knight St., Sawbridgeworth, Herts. CM21 9AX : Helicon Press.* Sp. *£3.00* A(VC) (B79-14908) ISBN 0-905684-18-4
Toccata capricciosa : für Violoncello-Solo. Op.36. (Rózsa, Miklós). *Breitkopf and Härtel. £3.30* SRPMJ (B79-51160)
Toccata, organ. Variations on 'Amazing Grace'. Variations on 'Amazing grace' and Toccata : for organ. (Wills, Arthur). *Novello. £2.25* RJ (B79-51127)
Tom Jones. *Vocal score.* Tom Jones : comic opera in three acts based on the novel by Henry Fielding = opera comique en trois actes d'aprés le roman de Henry Fielding. (Philidor, François André Danican). *Boosey and Hawkes. £7.50* CC (B79-50013)
Tomkins, John. The King shall rejoice. *36 Ranelagh Gdns, W.6 : Cathedral Music. Unpriced* DK (B79-50028)
Tomlinson, Geoffrey. Marche slave. Op.31. *arr.* Marche slave. (Tchaikovsky, Peter). *Oxford University Press. Unpriced* MK/AGM (B79-50162) ISBN 0-19-367910-8
Tomus primus operis musici. Rorate coeli. Rorate coeli : motet for the Advent season, for 6 voices. (Handl, Jacob). *Mapa mundi. Unpriced* EZDJ/LEZ (B79-50072)
Tonal music : twelve analytic studies. (Kresky, Jeffrey). *Indiana University Press. £8.75* A/CB (B79-10475) ISBN 0-253-37011-6
Top Music an der Orgel : leicht verständlicher Einfuhrungskurs, für elektronische Heimorgel in 5 Bänden mit 40 Lektionen
Band 1: Lektion 1-8. (Enzberg, Hans). *Schott. £5.60* RPV/AC (B79-50243)
Band 2: Lektion 9-16. (Enzberg, Hans). *Schott. £5.60* RPV/AC (B79-50244)
Band 3: Lektion 17-24. (Enzberg, Hans). *Schott. £5.60* RPV/AC (B79-50245)
Band 4: Lektion 25-32. (Enzberg, Hans). *Schott. £5.60* RPV/AC (B79-50246)
Band 5: Lektion 33-40. (Enzberg, Hans). *Schott. £5.60* RPV/AC (B79-50247)
Torallo. Vivaldi themes : easy melodies transcribed for descant (tenor) recorder (or flute, oboe or violin) with symbols for accompaniment on the guitar (ad lib.). (Vivaldi, Antonio). *Ricordi. Unpriced* VSRPMK (B79-51243)
Tovim, Atarah Ben-. *See* Ben-Tovim, Atarah.
Townsend, Douglas. Sleeping innocence : a lullaby, for mixed chorus and piano. *Broude : Breitkopf and Härtel. £0.42* DW (B79-50451)
Townsend, Richard. Partsongs
Vol.1: for unaccompanied i.e. unaccompanied male voices (A(A)T(T)B(B)). *(Lyndhurst, Denton Rd, Ben Rhydding) : Pro Cantione Antiqua : Breitkopf and Härtel. £2.40* GEZDW (B79-50508)
Toyshop : a song/mime for all children. (Diamond, Eileen). *Chappell. Unpriced* JFDW/JN (B79-50520)
Tracey, Edmund. A waltz dream : operetta in three acts. (Dunn, Bernard). *10 Rathbone St., W1P 2BJ : Josef Weinberger.* Pbk. *£1.25* BSOTACF (B79-06705)
Traditional hornpipe suite : for brass band. (Cruft, Adrian). *(1 The Retreat, S.W.14) : Joad Press. Unpriced* WMHNG (B79-50372)
Transformations : for solo harp, op.141. (Rubbra, Edmund). *Lengnick. £1.00* TQPMJ (B79-50695)
Transposition à vue
1er recueil: Pièces ou fragments pour clarinette en si bémol à chanter, ou à jouer avec d'autres instruments-non transpositeurs-en lisant en clé d'ut 4e. *Chappell. Unpriced* VVK/AAY (B79-51274)
Trattenimenti per camera, op.5. Sonata, trumpets (2), strings & continuo, op.5, no.1, D major. Sonata, op.5, no.1, for 2 trombe (trumpets) strins and continuo. (Jacchini, Giuseppe Maria). *Musica rara. Unpriced* RXMPWSNUE (B79-50263)
Trattenimenti per camera, op.5. Sonata, trumpets (2), strings & continuo, op.5, no.1, D major. *arr.* Sonata, op.5, no.1, for 2 trombe (trumpets), strings and continuo. (Jacchini, Giuseppe Maria). *Musica rara. Unpriced* WSNTQK/LE (B79-50392)
Trattenimenti per camera. Sinfonia, trumpets (2) & string orchestra, op.5, no.8, D major. Sinfonia, op.5 no.8 for 2 trumpets, strings and basso continuo. (Jacchini, Giuseppe Maria). *Musica rara. Unpriced* RXMPWSNUE (B79-50671)
Trattenimenti per camera. Sinfonia, trumpets (2) & string orchestra, op.5, no.8, D major. *arr.* Sinfonia, op.5, no.8 for 2 trumpets, strings and basso continuo. (Jacchini, Giuseppe Maria). *Musica rara. Unpriced* WSNTQK/AE (B79-50799)
Traumgesicht : für Männerstimme allein (1971). (Huber, Klaus). *Ars viva : Schott. £3.00* GEZDW (B79-50506)
Travis, Roy. Concerto, piano. Piano concerto. *Oxford University Press. Unpriced* MPQF (B79-50581)
Treble clef choral series. Franz, Robert. Mutter, o sing 'mich zur Ruh', op.10, no.3. *arr.* Mother, O sing me to sleep = Mutter, O sing mich zur ruh' : for three-part chorus of female voices and piano. *Roberton. £0.24* FDW (B79-50910)
Tredici, David del. *See* Del Tredici, David.

Trenta melodie : per il corso preparatorio di chitarra classica. (Rossi, Abner). *Berben : Breitkopf und Härtel. £3.30* TS/AF (B79-50698)
Tres libros de música en cifra para vihuela. Fantasia no.9. *arr.* Fantasie no.9. (Mudarra, Alonso). *DeCamera : Schirmer. £1.50* TSPMK (B79-51189)
Trevor, Caleb Henry. A C.H. Trevor organ miscellany. *Elkin. £1.55* RK/AAY (B79-50655)
Triad Press bibliographical series.
Carpenter, Roger. Goodnight to Flamboro' : the life and music of William Baines. *22 Pheasants Way, Rickmansworth, Herts. : Triad Press.* Pbk. *£6.95 : CIP rev.* BBCN (B77-21345) ISBN 0-902070-22-3
Hold, Trevor. The walled-in garden : a study of the songs of Roger Quilter (1877-1953). *22 Pheasants Way, Rickmansworth, Herts. : Triad Press.* Pbk. *£4.95* BQI(N) (B79-05249)
Triban : telyn = harp. (Glyn, Gareth). *Adlais. Unpriced* TQPMJ (B79-50296)
Triebensee, Josef. Menuetto con variazioni in F, on a theme from Mozart's Don Giovanni : for 2 oboes, 2 clarinets, 2 bassoons and 2 horns. *Nova Music. Unpriced* UNN (B79-51208)
Trio sonata. (Hogwood, Christopher). *British Broadcasting Corporation.* Pbk. *£2.50* ANXNSE (B79-33556) ISBN 0-563-17095-6
Triptychon : für Orchester (1977). (Fortner, Wolfgang). *Schott. £20.00* MMJ (B79-50175)
Trois pièces facile : première position violon avec accompagnement de piano. (Deshaulle, Jacques). *Chappell. Unpriced* SPJ (B79-51149)
Trois trios concertants pour flûte, clarinette et basson. Ben.4705. 3 trios concertants pour flûte, clarinette et basson, Ben.4705. Trio no.2. Trio 2 for flute, clarinet and bassoon. (Pleyel, Ignaz Joseph). *Musica rara. Unpriced* VNTF (B79-50322)
Trojahn, Manfred.
Madrigal : für achtstimmigen Chor, 1975. *Bärenreiter. £3.96* EZDW (B79-50099)
Symphony, no.2. II. Sinfonie, 1978. *Bärenreiter. £12.54* MME (B79-50569)
Trompetenëtuden II = Trumpet studies II = Etudy pro trubku II. *Deutscher Verlag für Musik : Breitkopf und Härtel. Unpriced* WS/AC (B79-50797)
Troyens, part 2. Chasse royale et orage. Chase royale et orage. (Berlioz, Hector). *Bärenreiter. Unpriced* MMJ (B79-50173)
Trubitt, Allen R. Ear training and sight-singing : an integrated approach
Book 1. *Schirmer Books : Collier Macmillan.* Pbk. *£8.25* A/EF (B79-25327) ISBN 0-02-870810-5

Truscott, Harold. Havergal Brian's 'Gothic symphony' : two studies. *33 Coopers Rd, Little Heath, Potters Bar, Herts. EN6 1JQ : Havergal Brian Society.* Pbk. *£6.95(£4.75 to members of the Havergal Brian Society)* BBTNADX (B79-10481) ISBN 0-9505185-1-4
Tu es Petrus : for 8 voices. (Philips, Peter). *Mapa mundi. Unpriced* EZDJ (B79-50065)
Tučapský, Antonín. Our father. Otčenáš = Our Father : for full chorus of mixed voices, tenor or soprano solo, organ and harp. (Janáček, Leoš). *Roberton. £0.75 (Chorus score £0.28)* EJQPLRDTF (B79-50865)

Tucker, Norman, *b.1910.* Norman Tucker, musician : before and after two decades at Sadler's Wells : an autobiography. *74 Doneraile St., SW6 6EP : J.A. Ellison.* Pbk. *£4.95* AC(WB/P) (B79-17760) ISBN 0-904677-08-7
Tuckwell, Barry. Prélude, thème et variations pour cor. Prelude, theme and variations for French horn and piano. (Rossini, Gioacchino Antonio). *Schirmer. £3.65* WTP/T (B79-51322)
Tull, Fisher.
Concertino, oboe & string orchestra. Concertino for oboe and strings. *Boosey and Hawkes. Unpriced* RXMPVTFL (B79-51141)
Concertino, oboe & string orchestra. *arr.* Concertino for oboe and strings. *Boosey and Hawkes. Unpriced*

VTPK/LFL (B79-51265)
The final covenent : for symphonic band or wind ensemble. *Boosey and Hawkes. Unpriced* UMMJ (B79-50725)
An Indian prayer. *Boosey and Hawkes. Unpriced* DW (B79-50452)
Sarabande and gigue : E-flat alto saxophone and piano. *Boosey and Hawkes. Unpriced* VUSPH (B79-50777)
Tunley, David. Australian composition in the twentieth century. *Oxford University Press. £18.50* A/D(M/YX/XM76) (B79-33552) ISBN 0-19-550522-0
Turner, Bruno.
Liber magnificarum. Magnificat octavi toni. Magnificat octavi toni : for 8 voices. (Vivanco, Sebastian de). *Mapa mundi. Unpriced* EZDGKK (B79-50056)
Liber primus missarum. Ave maria. Ave Maria : for 8 voices. (Lobo, Alfonso). *72 Brewery Rd, N.7 : Mapa mundi. Unpriced* EZDJ (B79-50063)
Liber primus missarum. Ave regina coelorum. Ave regina coelorum : Compline and votive antiphon for the season from Christmas to the Purification. (Lobo, Alfonso). *72 Brewery Rd, N.7 : Mapa mundi. Unpriced* EZDGKR/LF (B79-50057)
Liber primus missarum. Credo quod redemptor mens vivit. Credo quod redemptor mens vivit : pro defunctis, for 4 voices. (Lobo, Alfonso). *Mapa mundi. Unpriced* EZDJ/KDN (B79-50068)
Liber primus missarum. O quam suavis est, Domine. O quam suavis est, Domine : motet for the Feast of Corpus Christi, for 6 voices. (Lobo, Alfonso). *72 Brewery Rd, N.7 : Mapa mundi. Unpriced* EZDJ/LNC (B79-50088)
Liber primus missarum. Quam pulchri sunt gressus tui. Quam pulchri sunt gressus tui. (Lobo, Alfonso). *Mapa mundi. Unpriced* EZDJ (B79-50064)
Liber primus missarum. Versa est in luctum. Versa est in luctum : ad exsequias Philip II, cathol. regis Hisp. = for the funeral of Philip II, Catholic King of Spain. (Lobo, Alfonso). *72 Brewery Rd, N.7 : Mapa mundi. Unpriced* EZDJ/KDN (B79-50069)
Liber primus missarum. Vivo ego, dicit Dominus. Vivo ego, dicit Dominus : motet for Lent for 4 voices. (Lobo, Alfonso). *72 Brewery Rd, N.7 : Mapa mundi. Unpriced* EZDJ/LG (B79-50080)
Magnificat praetur rerum seriem : upon the motet by Josquin, for 6 voices. (Lasso, Orlando di). *72 Brewery Rd, N.7 : Mapa mundi. Unpriced* EZDGKK (B79-50055)
Missa pro defunctis : for 2,3 and 4 voices. (Okeghem, Jean). *72 Brewery Rd, N.7 : Mapa mundi. Unpriced* EZDGKAV (B79-50052)
Motecta. Duo seraphim. Duo seraphim. (Guerrero, Francisco). *Mapa mundi. Unpriced* EZDJ (B79-50062)
Motecta festorum. Sancta Maria. Sancta Maria. (Esquivel, Juan). *72 Brewery Rd, N.7 : Mapa mundi. Unpriced* EZDJ (B79-50060)
Motectas festorum. Quem vidistis, pastores? Quem vidistis, pastores? (Victoria, Tomás Luis de). *72 Brewery Rd, N.7 : Mapa mundi. Unpriced* EZDJ/LF (B79-50079)
Quaeramus cum pastoribus : for 4 voices. (Cristo, Pedro de). *72 Brewery Rd, N.7 : Mapa mundi. Unpriced* EZDJ/LF (B79-50075)
Salvator mundi, Domine : Compline hymn for the Vigil of Christmas in the Sarum Use. (Shepherd, John). *72 Brewery Rd, N.7 : Mapa mundi. Unpriced* EZDJ/LF (B79-50078)
Veni Domine : motet for the Advent season for 5 voices. (Esquivel, Juan). *72 Brewery Rd, N.7 : Mapa mundi. Unpriced* EZDJ/LEZ (B79-50070)
Vox clamantis in deserto : motet for the Advent season for 4 voices. (Esquivel, Juan). *72 Brewery Rd, N.7 : Mapa mundi. Unpriced* EZDJ/LEZ (B79-50071)
Turok, Paul.
Songs, dances and studies : for band
Set 1. *Schirmer. £2.10* UMMJ (B79-50726)
Set 2. *Schirmer. £2.10* UMMJ (B79-50727)
Set 3. *Schirmer. £2.10* UMMJ (B79-50728)
T.V. detectives. *EMI. Unpriced* QPK/JS/AY (B79-50643)
'Twas the brass before Christmas : five garlands for brass quintet, for 2 trumpets, horn, trombone and tuba
Garland 1. *Schirmer. £2.50* WNRK/DP/LF/AY (B79-51310)
Garland 2. *Schirmer. £2.50* WNRK/DP/LF/AY (B79-51314)
Garland 3. *Schirmer. £2.50* WNRK/DP/LF/AY (B79-51311)
Garland 4. *Schirmer. £2.50* WNRK/DP/LF/AY (B79-51312)
Garland 5. *Schirmer. £2.50* WNRK/DP/LF/AY (B79-51313)
Twelve caprices. L'art de la flûte traversière. *Selections.* 12 caprices : for solo flute. (Lusse, Charles de). *Nova Music. Unpriced* VRPMJ (B79-51232)
Twelve days of Christmas : English traditional carol, S.A.T.B. unacc. (Carter, Andrew). *Banks. Unpriced* EZDW/LF (B79-50904)
Twelve new easy preludes for organ. (Albrechtsberger, Johann Georg). *Oxford University Press. Unpriced* RJ (B79-51121) ISBN 0-19-375207-7
Twelve O : twelve easy pieces for piano. (Walker, Robert E). *Novello. £1.95* QPJ (B79-51091)
Twenty piano selections by modern composers. 20 piano selections by modern composers. *EMI. Unpriced* QPK/AAY (B79-51094)
Twenty-two ct. gold.
22 ct. gold : for all organ. *EMI. Unpriced* RK/DW/GB/AY (B79-50656)
22ct. gold : for guitar. *EMI. Unpriced* TSPMK/DW/GB/AY (B79-50712)
22ct. gold : for piano solo. *EMI. Unpriced* QPK/DW/GB/AY (B79-50642)
Two at the piano : 50 duets for young pianists. (Gruber, Josef). *Faber Music. Unpriced* QNV (B79-50615)
Two Beethoven sketchbooks : a description with musical extracts. (Nottebohm, Gustav). *Gollancz. £4.95* BBJ(QVB) (B79-14912) ISBN 0-575-02583-2
Two concerto movements. (Vivaldi, Antonio). *Banks. Unpriced* TSNUK (B79-50302)
Two elegiac melodies. Op.34. (Grieg, Edvard). *Eulenburg. Unpriced* MMJ (B79-50177)
Two fanfares for a festival : for brass, timpani, and percussion. (Hodkinson, Sydney). *Associated Music. £7.25* WMGN (B79-50791)
Two fiddlers = Die beiden Musikanten : opera in two acts = Oper in zwei Akten. (Davies, Peter Maxwell). *Boosey and Hawkes. Unpriced* CN (B79-50016)
Two fiddlers. *Vocal score.* The two fiddlers = Die beiden Musikanten : opera in two acts = Oper in zwei Akten. (Davies, Peter Maxwell). *Boosey and Hawkes. Unpriced* CN (B79-50016)
Two flourishes : for organ. *Banks. Unpriced* RGN (B79-50233)
Two hands-twelve notes
Book 1: A picture-book for young pianists. (Runze, Klaus). *Schott. £3.00* Q/AC (B79-51052)
Book 2: Playing with music. (Runze, Klaus). *Schott. £2.50* Q/AC (B79-51053)
Two hundred and fifty years of the Three Choirs Festival : a commemoration in words and pictures. *c/o Arts Council of Great Britain, 105 Piccadilly, W1V 0AU : Three Choirs Festival Association.* Pbk. *£2.00* AD(YDGB/WE/X) (B79-07463)
Two likes for contrabass, 1976. (Antoniou, Theodore). *Bärenreiter. £5.94* SSPMJ (B79-50693)
Two masonic pieces for organ. (Naumann, Johann Gottlieb). *Oxford University Press. Unpriced* RJ (B79-50650)
Two nativity songs. (Cary, Tristram). *Oxford University Press. Unpriced* EZDP/LF (B79-50885) ISBN 0-19-343536-5
Two pieces from España. (Albéniz, Isaac). *Oxford University Press. Unpriced* VVNTQK (B79-50782) ISBN 0-19-355137-3
Two quartets : for four guitars. (Hunt, Oliver). *Schott. Unpriced* TSNS (B79-50700)
Two ragtime trios : for 2 clarinets and tenor saxophone (or bass clarinet). *7 Garrick St., W.C.2 : Middle Eight Music. Unpriced* VNTK/AHXJ (B79-50323)
Two Salieri canons. (Salieri, Antonio). *Boosey and Hawkes. Unpriced* GE/XTBDW/X (B79-50108)
Two Singers. *See*
Patterson, John.
Patterson, Minna.
Two songs of the nativity : for two-part choir and piano. (Price, Beryl). *Roberton. £0.24* FDP/LF (B79-50491)
Tye, Christopher. The Mass Euge bone : for 6 voices. *72 Brewery Rd, N.7 : Mapa mundi. Unpriced* EZDG (B79-50051)
Über allen strahlt die Sonne : Variationen für Klavier über allerlei Themen. (Schwaen, Kurt). *Verlag Neue Musik Breitkopf und Härtel. Unpriced* QP/T (B79-50619)
Ulvaens, Björn. Chiquitita. *arr.* Chiquitita. (Andersson, Benny). *Chappell. Unpriced* KDW/GB (B79-50530)
Under the double eagle = Unter dem Doppeladler : march, (op.159). (Wagner, Josef Franz). *Bosworth & Co. Unpriced* MK/AGM (B79-50163)
Understanding music. (Hopkins, Antony). *Dent. £6.95 : CIP rev.* A/C (B79-15552) ISBN 0-460-04376-5
Underwood, John, *b.1934.* How to succeed in the music business. (Dann, Allan). *Wise Publications; 78 Newman St., W1P 3LA : Distributed by Music Sales Limited.* Pbk. *£2.50* A/GB (B79-10119) ISBN 0-86001-454-1
Unfinished journey. (Menuhin, Yehudi). *Futura Publications.* Pbk. *£1.60* AS/E(P) (B79-11136) ISBN 0-7088-1329-1
Ungaretti, Giuseppe. Symphony no.3, 'Espansioni'. Espansioni : Sinfonie III für grosses Orchester, Bariton und Tonband, 1974/1975. (Kelterborn, Rudolf). *Bärenreiter. £11.55* KGNE/MDX (B79-50156)
Unicorn : for violin and piano. (Dalby, Martin). *Novello. £2.00* SPJ (B79-50275)
Union of Soviet Socialist Republics. *Akademiía nauk. See* Akademiía nauk SSSR.
University of Cambridge. *Guild of Change Ringers. See* Cambridge University Guild of Change Ringers.
University of East Anglia. *Centre of East Anglian Studies.* Music in eighteenth-century Norwich and Norfolk. (Fawcett, Trevor). *Norwich NR4 7TJ : Centre of East Anglian Studies, University of East Anglia.* Sd. *£1.75* A(YDDS/XF101) (B79-33550)
University of Glasgow. *Library.* Musicke of sundrie kindes : handlist to the exhibition held in the Glasgow University Library, Exhibition Room, 11th January-18th February 1978. *Glasgow G12 8QG : The Library.* Sd. *£0.50* A(U/YDLJ/WM) (B79-14348) ISBN 0-85261-148-x
University of London. *Warburg Institute. See* Warburg Institute.
University of Oxford. *Bodleian Library. See* Bodleian Library.
University of Texas at Austin. *Humanities Research Center.* The Gostling manuscript. *University of Texas Press. £24.50* ADK(XEYK37) (B79-04542) ISBN 0-292-72713-5
Unpublished religious song-book of mid-eighteenth century Russia. (Akademiía nauk SSSR. *Biblioteka. MSS.* (33.3.5)). *c/o C.L. Drage, 94 Inverness Terrace, W.2 : The editors.* Pbk. *£2.00* AKDH/LSC(YM/XFX31) (B79-37420)
Uns ist ein Kind geboren. BWV142. Overture. *arr.* Overture to cantata 'For us a Child is born' (Uns ist ein Kind geborn sic) : for organ and piano. (Bach, Johann Sebastian). *Sycamore : Schirmer (dist.). £1.50* QPLRK (B79-51110)
Unter dem Doppeladler. Op.159. *arr.* Under the double eagle = Unter dem Doppeladler : march, (op.159). (Wagner, Josef Franz). *Bosworth & Co. Unpriced* MK/AGM (B79-50163)
Upton, Stuart. Sir Dan Godfrey & the Bournemouth Municipal Orchestra : a biographical discography, copiously illustrated with pictures and facsimile reproductions covering countless famous personalities and related material. New enlarged ed. *4 Harvest Bank Rd, West Wickham, Kent : Vintage Light Music Society.* Sd. *Unpriced* A/EC/FD(P/WT) (B79-11941)
Urman, David. On music and musicians. (Falla, Manuel de). *Boyars : Distributed by Calder and Boyars. £5.95* A (B79-14910) ISBN 0-7145-2600-2
Valenti, Fernando. Essercizi (1738) : 30 sonatas for keyboard. (Scarlatti, Domenico). *Schirmer. £7.55* QRPE (B79-51112)
Valenti, Michael. Snow White and the seven dwarfs. *Vocal score.* Snow White and the seven dwarfs. *Associated Music. Unpriced* CM (B79-50819)
Van, Jeffrey. Das wohltemperierte Clavier. Fugue 14. BWV859. *arr.* Fugue 14 ... for three guitars. (Bach, Johann Sebastian). *Associated Music. £2.75* TSNTK/Y (B79-50701)
Van Appledorn, Mary Jeanne. Set of five : for piano. *Oxford University Press. Unpriced* QPJ (B79-50219)
Van Beethoven, Ludwig. *See* Beethoven, Ludwig van.
Van Horn, James. The community orchestra : a handbook for conductors, managers and boards. *Greenwood Press. £11.75* AM/E(QB) (B79-33555) ISBN 0-313-20562-0
Vance, Joel. Fats Waller : his life and times. *Robson. £5.50 : CIP rev.* AMT(P) (B79-16104) ISBN 0-86051-077-8
Vance, Margaret. I will give thanks : for four-part chorus of mixed voices with piano accompaniment. *Schirmer. £0.45* EZDK (B79-50883)
Variations for small orchestra. (Boatwright, Howard). *Oxford University Press. Unpriced* MRJ (B79-51036)
Variations on 'Amazing Grace'. Variations on 'Amazing grace' and Toccata : for organ. (Wills, Arthur). *Novello. £2.25* RJ (B79-51127)
Variations on 'Amazing grace' and Toccata : for organ. (Wills, Arthur). *Novello. £2.25* RJ (B79-51127)
Variations on La folia, op.6, no.6 : for 2 treble recorders and basso continuo. (Schickhardt, Johann Christian). *Nova Music. Unpriced* VSSNTPW/T (B79-51244)
Varii capricci. (Walton, *Sir* William). *Oxford University Press. Unpriced* MM/Y (B79-50166) ISBN 0-19-368453-5
Vaughan Williams, Ralph. Concerto, Tuba. Concerto for bass tuba and orchestra. *Oxford University Press. Unpriced* MPWVF (B79-50591) ISBN 0-19-369454-9
Vaughan Williams in Dorking : a collection of personal reminiscences of the composer Dr Ralph Vaughan Williams, O.M. (Dorking and Leith Hill District Preservation Society. *Local History Group*). *c/o C. Newbery, 'Wrencot', Partridge La., Newdigate, Dorking, Surrey : The Group.* Sd. *£0.80* BVD(YDCHD/P (B79-21875)
Veal, Arthur. Prelude, interlude and carillon : (for organ). *Cramer. Unpriced* RJ (B79-50236)
Vecchi, Horatio. Canzonetti ... libro quarto a quattro voci. Partiro si. Partirò sì = Parting is pain : for four-part chorus of mixed voices a cappella. *Schirmer. £0.35* EZDU (B79-50475)
Vejvanovský, Pavel Josef.
Balletti pro tabula. *Selections : arr.* Suite in B-Dur für Trompete und Orgel, 1670. *Merseburger : Bärenreiter. Unpriced* WSPLRK/AE (B79-50806)
Sonata la posta : für drei Posaunen und Orgel, 1667. *Merseburger : Bärenreiter. £2.97* WUNTRE (B79-50808)
Veni Domine : motet for the Advent season for 5 voices. (Esquivel, Juan). *72 Brewery Rd, N.7 : Mapa mundi. Unpriced* EZDJ/LEZ (B79-50070)
Veni spiritus : for soprano and baritone soloists, chorus and orchestra. (Burgon, Geoffrey). *Chester Music. Unpriced* EMDGKADD/LN (B79-50042)
Veni spiritus. *Vocal score.* Veni spiritus : for soprano and baritone soloists, chorus and orchestra. (Burgon, Geoffrey). *Chester Music. Unpriced* EMDGKADD/LN (B79-50042)
Ventiquattro momenti musicali. 24 momenti musicali : per flauto e pianoforte nelle 24 tunalità del sistema temperato 1° volume: 1-12. (Montanari, Nunzio). *Bèrben. Unpriced* VRPJ (B79-51224)
Verdi, Giuseppe.
Messa di requiem. Requiem. *Dover Publications Constable. Unpriced* EMDGKAV (B79-50043) ISBN 0-486-23682-x
Quattro pezzi sacri. Laudi alla vergine Maria. Laudi alla vergine Maria = Prayer to the Virgin Mary : for four-part chorus of female voices. *Roberton. £0.32* FEZDH (B79-50916)
Versa est in luctum : ad exsequias Philip II, cathol. regis Hisp. = for the funeral of Philip II, Catholic King of Spain. (Lobo, Alfonso). *72 Brewery Rd, N.7 : Mapa mundi. Unpriced* EZDJ/KDN (B79-50069)
Versicles and responses (including the Sovereign's Accession) : S.A.(T.)T.B. (Jackson, Francis). *Banks. Unpriced* EZDGMM (B79-50459)
Verzeichnis der Schubert-Handschriften in der Musiksammlung der Wiener Stadt- und Landesbibliothek. (Wiener Stadt- und Landesbibliothek). *17 Bucklersbury, Hutchin, Herts. SG5 1BB : Bärenreiter for the International Association of Music Libraries and the International Musicological Society.* Pbk. *£28.05* BSF(TE) (B79-10755)
Verzeichnis der Schubert-Handschriften in der

Musiksammlung der Wiener Stadt- und Landesbibliothek. (Wiener Stadt- und Landesbibliothek). *17 Bucklersbury, Hutchin, Herts. SG5 1BB : Bärenreiter for the International Association of Music Libraries and the International Musicological Society.* Pbk. *£28.05* BMS(TC) (B79-10755)

Victoria, Tomás Luis de.

Motecta. O quam gloriosum est regnum. Motet and mass, O quam gloriosum est regnum. *Eulenburg. Unpriced* EZDJ/LQ (B79-50091)

Motecta, Sancta Maria. Sancta Maria, and, Ecce sacerdos magnus : for four part chorus of mixed voices unaccompanied. *Roberton. £0.28* EZDJ (B79-50469)

Motectas festorum. Quem vidistis, pastores? Quem vidistis, pastores? *72 Brewery Rd, N.7 : Mapa mundi. Unpriced* EZDJ/LF (B79-50079)

Officium defunctorum. Missa pro defunctis. Requiem à 6 (1605). *Oxenford Imprint. Unpriced* EZDGKAV (B79-50053)

Videte miraculum : for 6 voices. (Tallis, Thomas). *72 Brewery Rd, N.7 : Mapa Mundi. Unpriced* EZDJ (B79-50067)

Vidi turbam magnam : motet for All Saints' Day, for 4 voices. (Porta, Constanzo). *72 Brewery Rd, N.7 : Mapa mundi. Unpriced* EZDJ/LQ (B79-50090)

Vieira, Luiz. Prelúdio pra Ninar Gente Grande. *arr.* Prelúdio pra Ninar Gente Grande. *Rio Musical : Essex Music. Unpriced* QPK (B79-51093)

Vier Winde = Four-winds : suite ; für Orgel, for organ, 1975. (Křenek, Ernst). *Bärenreiter. £6.60* RG (B79-50232)

Viereck, Peter. The day's no rounder than its angles are. *arr.* The day's no rounder than its angles are : three songs for medium voice and string quartet. (Beeson, Jack). *Boosey and Hawkes. Unpriced* KFVDW (B79-50558)

Vierundzwanzig Caprices-Études, opus 26. 24 Caprices-Études, opus 26 : für Flöte solo = for solo flute = pour flûte seule. (Boehm, Theobald). Reprint der Schott-Originalausgabe von 1852. *Schott. £4.00* VR/AF (B79-51213)

Vierzig freym Aurerlieder. Anhang. 40 freym Anrerlieder. Anhang. Two masonic pieces for organ. (Naumann, Johann Gottlieb). *Oxford University Press. Unpriced* RJ (B79-50650)

Vintage Alice : fantascene on a mad tea-party. (Del Tredici, David). *Boosey and Hawkes. Unpriced* KFLE/MDX (B79-51000)

Vintage Light Music Society. Sir Dan Godfrey & the Bournemouth Municipal Orchestra : a biographical discography, copiously illustrated with pictures and facsimile reproductions covering countless famous personalities and related material. (Upton, Stuart). New enlarged ed. *4 Harvest Bank Rd, West Wickham, Kent : Vintage Light Music Society.* Sd. *Unpriced* A/EC/FD(P/WT) (B79-11941)

Vintage years. (Stewart, Rod). *Chappell. Unpriced* KDW/HKR (B79-50990)

Viola

1: Stücke für Viola und Klavier. *Neue Musik : Breitkopf and Härtel. £2.10* SQP/AY (B79-51156)

Viola d'amore. (Danks, Harry). 2nd ed. *7 Summit Gardens, Halesowen, West Midlands B63 4SP : Stephen Bonner. Unpriced* ASQQ/B (B79-09707)

Violin fancies. *Chappell. Unpriced* SPK/AAY (B79-51152)

Viozzi, Giulio. Suite variata : per chitarra. *Bèrben Breitkopf and Härtel. £2.35* TSPMG (B79-51179)

V.I.P. piano solos

Book 2. *Chappell. Unpriced* QPK/DW/GB/AY (B79-51102)

Book 3. *Chappell. Unpriced* QPK/DW/GB/AY (B79-51103)

Book 4. *Chappell. Unpriced* QPK/DW/GB/AY (B79-51104)

Vivaldi, Antonio.

Il cimento dell'armonia e dell'inventione. Op.8, Concerto, oboe & string orchestra, P.259, D minor. Concerto in d minor, RV454 (F.VII/1), P.259, for oboe, strings and basso continuo. *Musica rara. Unpriced* RXMPVTF (B79-50668)

Il cimento dell'armonia e dell'inventione. Op.8 Concerto, oboe & string orchestra, P.259, D minor. *arr.* Concerto in d minor, RV454, (F.VII/1), P.259 for oboe, strings and basso continuo. *Musica rara. Unpriced* VTPK/LF (B79-50774)

Il cimento dell'armonia e dell'inventione. Op.8. Le quattro stagione. Autunno.. *arr.* Four seasons, op.8 (Concerto for violin and orchestra)

Autumn : for violin and piano. *Schirmer. £2.40* SPK/LF (B79-50682)

Il cimento dell'armonia e dell'inventione. Op.8, nos 1-4. *arr.* Four seasons, op.8. (Concerto for violin and orchestra

Op.8, no.4: Winter : for violin and piano. *Schirmer. £2.40* SPK/LF (B79-51154)

Concerto, oboe & string orchestra, R.455, F major. Concerto in F, RV.455, (P.306) for oboe, strings and basso continuo. *Musica rara. Unpriced* RXMPVTF (B79-50669)

Concerto, oboe & string orchestra, R.455, F major. *arr.* Concerto in F, RV.455, (P.306) for oboe, strings and basso continuo. *Musica rara. Unpriced* VTPK/LF (B79-50775)

Concerto, oboe & string orchestra, R.461, A minor. Concerto in A minor for oboe, strings and continuo, RV461 (F.VII,no.5) (P.42). *Musica rara. Unpriced* RXMPVTF (B79-51139)

Concerto, oboe & string orchestra, R.461, A minor. *arr.* Concerto in A minor for oboe, strings and continuo, RV461 (F.VII,no.5) (P.42). *Musica Rara. Unpriced* VTPK/LF (B79-51263)

Concerto, oboe & string orchestra, R.463, A minor. Concerto in A minor for oboe, strings and continuo, RV463 (F.VII,no.13). *Musica rara. Unpriced* RXMPVTF (B79-51140)

Concerto, oboe & string orchestra, R.463, A minor. *arr.* Concerto in A minor for oboe, strings and continuo, RV463 (F.VII,no.13). *Musica rara. Unpriced* VTPK/LF (B79-51264)

Concerto, violin & string orchestra, R.761, C minor, 'Amato bene'. Concerto in C minor 'Amato bene', RV761, for violin and string orchestra. *Oxford University Press. Unpriced* RXMPSF (B79-51138) ISBN 0-19-367972-8

L'estro armonico. Op.3. *Selections : arr.* Two concerto movements. *Banks. Unpriced* TSNUK (B79-50302)

Vivaldi themes : easy melodies transcribed for descant (tenor) recorder (or flute, oboe or violin) with symbols for accompaniment on the guitar (ad lib.). *Ricordi. Unpriced* VSRPMK (B79-51243)

Vivaldi themes : easy melodies transcribed for descant (tenor) recorder (or flute, oboe or violin) with symbols for accompaniment on the guitar (ad lib.). (Vivaldi, Antonio). *Ricordi. Unpriced* VSRPMK (B79-51243)

Vivanco, Sebastian de. Liber magnificarum. Magnificat octavi toni. Magnificat octavi toni : for 8 voices. *Mapa mundi. Unpriced* EZDGKK (B79-50056)

Vivo ego, dicit Dominus : motet for Lent for 4 voices. (Lobo, Alfonso). *72 Brewery Rd, N.7 : Mapa mundi. Unpriced* EZDJ/LG (B79-50080)

Vlad, Roman. Stravinsky. 3rd ed. *Oxford University Press. £5.95* BSV(N) (B79-11126) ISBN 0-19-315444-7

Vocal trios.

Benger, Richard. Fare well. *Edwin Ashdown. £0.20* FDW (B79-50101)

Benger, Richard. Music : for S.S.C. *Edwin Ashdown. £0.25* FDW (B79-50102)

Vogel, Vladimir.

Musette. *arr.* Musette : für Gitarre solo = for guitar solo. *Schott. £2.00* TSPMK/AHS (B79-50311)

Terzett für Flöte (Piccolo), Klarinette und Fagott. *Eulenburg. £4.65* VNT (B79-50735)

Voigt, Erna. Peter and the wolf. *Blackie. £3.75* BPPAMBN (B79-35567) ISBN 0-216-90875-2

Von Dittersdorf, Carl Ditters. *See* Dittersdorf, Carl Ditters von.

Von Eybler, Joseph. *See* Eybler, Joseph von.

Von Fallersleben, Hoffmann. *See* Fallersleben, Hoffmann von.

Von Goethe, Johann Wolfgang. *See* Goethe, Johann Wolfgang von.

Von Knorr, Ernst Lothar. *See* Knorr, Ernst Lothar von.

Von Lannoy, Eduard. *See* Lannoy, Eduard von.

Von Liliencron, Detlev. *See* Liliencron, Detlev von.

Von Salis-Seewis, Johann Gaudenz. *See* Salis-Seewis, Johann Gaudenz von.

Von Suppé, Franz. *See* Suppé, Franz von.

Von Weber, Carl Maria, *Freiherr. See* Weber, Carl Maria von. Freiherr.

Von Westernhagen, Curt. *See* Westernhagen, Curt von.

Vox clamantis in deserto : motet for the Advent season for 4 voices. (Esquivel, Juan). *72 Brewery Rd, N.7 : Mapa mundi. Unpriced* EZDJ/LEZ (B79-50071)

Voxman, Himie.

3 trios concertants pour flûte, clarinette et basson, Ben.4705. Trio no.2. Trio 2 for flute, clarinet and bassoon. (Pleyel, Ignaz Joseph). *Musica rara. Unpriced* VNTF (B79-50322)

Duos, clarinet & bassoon, op.21. Three duos for clarinet and bassoon. Op.21. (Tausch, Franz). *Musica rara. Unpriced* VVPLVW (B79-51285)

Trio, bassoons & continuo, G major. Trio in G for 2 bassoons and basso continuo. (Schiffelholz, Johann Paul). *Musica rara. Unpriced* VWNTPW (B79-50362)

Voyage : for string orchestra. (Corigliano, John). *Schirmer. Unpriced* RXMJ (B79-50664)

Voyage of Edgar Allan Poe : opera in two acts. (Argento, Dominick). *Boosey and Hawkes. Unpriced* CC (B79-50413)

Voyage of Edgar Allan Poe. *Vocal score.* The voyage of Edgar Allan Poe : opera in two acts. (Argento, Dominick). *Boosey and Hawkes. Unpriced* CC (B79-50413)

Wachhaus, Gustav. Fundamental classroom music skills : theory and performing techniques. *Holt, Rinehart and Winston.* Sp. *£7.75* A(VG) (B79-12529) ISBN 0-03-041775-9

Wachst, Liebchen, Du. *arr.* Serenade : for four-part chorus of mixed voices with piano accompaniment. (Albert, *Prince Consort of Victoria, Queen of Great Britain*). *Roberton. £0.24* DW (B79-50449)

Wacky and his fuddlejig : a chidren's Christmas musical play. (Swann, Donald). *Universal. Unpriced* CN/LF (B79-50017)

Wade, Annette. Musical instruments. (Ardley, Neil). *Macmillan.* Pbk. *£0.50* AL/B (B79-22637) ISBN 0-333-26156-9

Wagner, Josef Franz. Unter dem Doppeladler. Op.159. *arr.* Under the double eagle = Unter dem Doppeladler : march, (op.159). *Bosworth & Co. Unpriced* MK/AGM (B79-50163)

Wagner, Richard. Wesendonk-Lieder : for soprano voice and orchestra. *Eulenburg. £2.15* KFLE/MDW (B79-50999)

Wagner companion. *Faber. £12.50 : CIP rev.* BWC (B78-40353) ISBN 0-571-10471-1

Waldman, Robert. A rag bag : for piano. *Schirmer. £1.75* QPJ (B79-50640)

Walker, Daniel Pickering. Studies in musical science in the late Renaissance. *Warburg Institute etc.. £15.00* A/AM(XDYAK181) (B79-17759) ISBN 0-85481-056-0

Walker, Robert E. Twelve O : twelve easy pieces for piano. *Novello. £1.95* QPJ (B79-51091)

Walker, Sue. The day the animals sang : a musical for children. *Mayhew-McCrimmon. Unpriced* CN/LF (B79-50821) ISBN 0-85597-202-5

Walled-in garden : a study of the songs of Roger Quilter (1877-1953). (Hold, Trevor). *22 Pheasants Way, Rickmansworth, Herts. : Triad Press.* Pbk. *£4.95* BQI(N) (B79-05249)

Waller, Thomas. Fats Waller. *EMI. Unpriced* KDW/GB (B79-50138)

Walsh, Diane. Appello : for piano. (Kolb, Barbara). *Boosey and Hawkes. Unpriced* QPJ (B79-50218)

Walter, Heinz. Eine Auswahl aus 'Sechs Kinderstücke'. Op.72 und 'Lieder ohne Worte'. (Mendelssohn, Felix). *Breitkopf und Härtel. £2.10* QPJ (B79-51085)

Walters, Harold L. Scenes from the west : flute sextet or choir. *Rubank : Novello. Unpriced* VRNQ (B79-50740)

Walton, *Sir* William.

Belshazzar's feast : for baritone solo, mixed choir, and orchestra. Limited ed. *Oxford University Press. £60.00* EMDD (B79-50041) ISBN 0-19-338463-9

Façade 2 : a further entertainment. *Oxford University Press. Unpriced* KHYE/NYENQ (B79-51010) ISBN 0-19-359406-4

Orb and sceptre. *arr.* Orb and sceptre. *Oxford University Press. Unpriced* WMK/AGM (B79-51303) ISBN 0-19-368537-x

Varii capricci. *Oxford University Press. Unpriced* MM/Y (B79-50166) ISBN 0-19-368453-5

Waltz dream : operetta in three acts. (Dunn, Bernard). *10 Rathbone St., W1P 2BJ : Josef Weinberger.* Pbk. *£1.25* BSOTACF (B79-06705)

Waltz-rondo for piano. (Ives, Charles). *Schirmer. £3.65* QPHW/W (B79-50629)

Warburg Institute. Studies. Walker, Daniel Pickering. Studies in musical science in the late Renaissance. *Warburg Institute etc.. £15.00* A/AM(XDYAK181) (B79-17759) ISBN 0-85481-056-0

Warburton, Annie Osborne. Harmony : a textbook for class use on aural foundations. New ed. *Longman.* Pbk. *£1.95* A/R (B79-35972) ISBN 0-582-33071-8

Wardian, Jeanne Foster. Introduction to music fundamentals : a programmed textbook for the elementary classroom teacher. (Andrews, J Austin). 4th ed. *Prentice-Hall.* Sp. *£8.00* A/M(VG) (B79-00564) ISBN 0-13-489575-4

Warfield, Gerald. Layer analysis : a primer of elementary tonal structures. *Longman.* Sp. *£6.35* A/PF (B79-50004) ISBN 0-582-28069-9

Warrack, John.

The concise Oxford dictionary of opera. (Rosenthal, Harold). 2nd ed. *Oxford University Press. £6.95* AC(C) (B79-23401) ISBN 0-19-311318-x

Tchaikovsky ballet music. *British Broadcasting Corporation.* Pbk. *£1.40* BTDAM/HM (B79-31929) ISBN 0-563-12860-7

Warren, Harry. The works of Harry Warren. *EMI. Unpriced* KDW/JR (B79-50145)

Wasn't that a mighty day! : Christmas spiritual for mixed voices, accompanied (S.A.T.B.). (Ehret, Walter). *Broude : Breitkopf and Härtel. £0.42* DW/LC/LF (B79-50863)

Wastall, Peter.

Baroque music for trumpet : including music by Albinoni, Charpentier, Keller, Molter, Telemann, Torelli. *Boosey and Hawkes. £1.65* WSP/AY (B79-50393)

Learn as you play clarinet. *Boosey and Hawkes. Unpriced* VV/AC (B79-51273)

Learn as you play flute. *Boosey and Hawkes. £0.85* VR/AC (B79-51212)

Learn as you play trumpet & cornet. *Boosey and Hawkes. Unpriced* WS/AC (B79-51316)

Water babies. *Selections: arr.* The water babies. (Coulter, Phil). *Chappell. Unpriced* QPK/JR (B79-51105)

Waterman, Fanny.

Piano playtime : very first solos and duets

Book 2. *faber Music. Unpriced* QP/AY (B79-50207)

Waterman, Ivan. Keith Moon : the life and death of a rock legend. *Arrow Books.* Pbk. *£1.00* AKDW/HKR/E(P) (B79-31933) ISBN 0-09-920930-6

Waterman/Harewood piano series.

Gruber, Josef. ABC. Two at the piano : 50 duets for young pianists. *Faber Music. Unpriced* QNV (B79-50615)

Piano playtime : very first solos and duets

Book 2. *faber Music. Unpriced* QP/AY (B79-50207)

Watkins, Maurine Dallas. Chicago. *Adaptations.* Chicago : a musical vaudeville. (Ebb, Fred). *French.* Sd. *£1.65* BKDEACM (B79-06704) ISBN 0-573-68081-7

Watson, Derek. Richard Wagner : a biography. *Dent. £15.00 : CIP rev.* BWC(N) (B79-21149) ISBN 0-460-03166-x

Watts, Isaac.

Hush! My dear. (Nettleton carol) : for mixed chorus and piano. (Ehret, Walter). *Broude : Breitkopf and Härtel. £0.42* DP/LF (B79-50839)

Let all on earth their voices raise : for four-part chorus of mixed voices with piano accompaniment. (Kirk, Theron). *Schirmer. Unpriced* DH (B79-50832)

Ways with music.

See-saw sacaradown : fourteen childrens sic songs with simple accompaniments for classroom instruments. *Chappell. Unpriced* JFE/XDW/GJ/AY (B79-50947)

Winch, Richard. The pedlar of Swaffham : a children's cantata with simple accompaniments for piano and classroom instruments. *Chappell. Unpriced* JFE/NYDSDX (B79-50944)
Weaver, Blue. (Our love). Don't throw it all away. *arr.* (Our love). Don't throw it all away. (Gibb, Barry). *Stigwood Music. Unpriced* UMK/DW (B79-51203)
Webb, Andrea.
Sisters in song : a collection of new songs from the women's liberation movement. *Onlywoman Press. Unpriced* KFE/TSDW/AY (B79-50996)
Sisters in song : a collection of new songs from the women's liberation movement. (Burgon, Geoffrey). *Onlywomen Press. Unpriced* KDGPR (B79-50951)
Webber, Julian Lloyd. The romantic cello. *Chappell. Unpriced* SRPK/AAY (B79-50288)
Weber, Carl Maria von, *Freiherr.*
6 petites pièces faciles. Op.3. Marcia. *arr.* March. Op.3, no.5. *Roberton. Unpriced* SPK/AGM (B79-50280)
12 allemandes pour le piano forte. Op.4. *Selections : arr.* Five German dances. *Oxford University Press. Unpriced* UMK/AH (B79-50316) ISBN 0-19-368668-6
Fughettas, piano, op.1. *arr.* Six fughettas. Op.1. *Schott. Unpriced* VVNSK (B79-51275)
Trio, flute, cello & piano, op.63. Trio, op.63, for flute, cello (or viola) and piano. *Schirmer. £6.10* NURNT (B79-51039)
Waltzes, piano. *Selections : arr.* Five waltzes. *Oxford University Press. Unpriced* UMK/AHW (B79-50317) ISBN 0-19-368704-6
Webster, Michael. Sonata, piano duet, op.6, D major. *arr.* Sonata in D major, op.6, for clarinet and piano. (Beethoven, Ludwig van). *Schirmer. £3.05* VVPK/AE (B79-50784)
Wedding album. *Edwin Ashdown. Unpriced* RK/KDD/AY (B79-50242)
Wedding bouquet : organ music for the marriage ceremony. *Novello. Unpriced* RK/KDD/AY (B79-51130)

Weep no more : for women's chorus a cappella. (Diemer, Emma Lou). *Broude : Breitkopf and Härtel. £0.42* FEZDW (B79-50917)
Weepin' Mary : negro spiritual, S.A.T.B. unaccompanied. (Clements, John). *EMI. Unpriced* EZDW/LC (B79-50487)
Wehrle, Heinz. Choral-Toccata, 'O Heiland, reiss die Himmel auf' : Melodie Augsburg 1666. *Eulenburg. £1.85* RJ (B79-50651)
Weidlich, Joseph.
Fantasie, lute, C minor. *arr.* Fantasie (in C minor). (Weiss, Sylvius Leopold). *DeCamera : Schirmer. £1.50* TSPMK (B79-51191)
Four pieces. (Dlugoraj, Wojciech). *DeCamera : Schirmer. £1.50* TSPMK (B79-51188)
Greensleeves. *arr.* Greensleeves. (Cutting, Francis). *DeCamera : Schirmer. £1.50* TSPMK/T (B79-51198)
Intabulatura de lauto. *Selections : arr.* Two pieces. (Dalza, Joan Ambrosio). *DeCamera : Schirmer. £1.50* TSPMK (B79-51187)
Lute music. *Selections : arr.* Four pieces. (Newsidler, Hans). *DeCamera : Schirmer. £1.50* TSPMK (B79-51190)

Tres libros de música en cifra para vihuela. Fantasia no.9. *arr.* Fantasie no.9. (Mudarra, Alonso). *DeCamera : Schirmer. £1.50* TSPMK (B79-51189)
Weihnachts-Orgel : Top Music an der Orgel, die schönsten Weihnachtslieder für elektrönische Heimorgel im Schwierigkeitsgrad 1-5 der Hans Enzberg-Schule. *Schott. £4.80* RPVK/DP/LF/AY (B79-51134)
'Weihnachtskonzert' : Zyklus zu Advent bis Epiphanians, für Blechbläser und Orgel. (Wenzel, Eberhard). *Bärenreiter. £2.31* NWXPF (B79-50603)
Weiland, Frits C. Internationale Diskographie elektronischer Musik = International electronic music discography = Discographie internationale de la musique electronique. (Kondracki, Miroslaw). *Schott.* Pbk. *£11.20* APV/FD(WT) (B79-35641)
Wein, Weib und Gesang. Op.333. *arr.* Wine, women and song. (Strauss, Johann, *b.1825*). New revised ed. *Schott. £0.90* VSNRQK/AHW (B79-50762)
Weinmann, Alexander. Divertimento, violas (2) & double bass. Divertimento in D-dur für zwei Violen und Kontrabass = Divertimento in D major for two violas and double bass. (Albrechtsberger, Johann Georg). *Amadeus : Bärenreiter. Unpriced* RXNT (B79-50675)
Weiss, Günther. Sonatas, viola d'amore & continuo, 'Stockholm'. 'Stockholmer Sonaten' für Viola d'amore (Viola) und Basso continuo = 'Stockholm sonatas' for viola d'amore (viola) and basso continuo
2: Sonatas in ... B flat major ... G minor ... A minor. (Ariosti, Attilio). *Bärenreiter. £5.28* SQQPE (B79-50287)

Weiss, Sylvius Leopold.
Fantasie, lute, C minor. *arr.* Fantasie (in C minor). *DeCamera : Schirmer. £1.50* TSPMK (B79-51191)
Suite, lute, A major. *arr.* Suite in A. *Schott. £3.20* TSPMK/AG (B79-51194)
Suite, lute, D major. *arr.* Suite in D. *Schott. £2.60* TSPMK/AG (B79-51195)
Welsh Arts Council. David Wynne. (Jones, Richard Elfyn). *University of Wales Press for the Welsh Arts Council.* Pbk. *£1.50 : CIP rev.* BWY (B79-09705) ISBN 0-7083-0714-0
Welsh melodies. Dafydd y garreg wen. Dafydd y garreg wen = David of the white rock. (Thomas, John, *b.1826*). *Adlais. Unpriced* TQPM/T (B79-50294)
Welsh popular songs : a collection of some of the most popular Welsh songs and hymns ... *(82 Princess St.) : Music Exchange. Unpriced* EZDW/AYDK (B79-50480)

Wenzel, Eberhard. 'Weihnachtskonzert' : Zyklus zu Advent bis Epiphanians, für Blechbläser und Orgel. *Bärenreiter. £2.31* NWXPF (B79-50603)
Werkreihe für Bläser und Sänger. Praetorius, Michael. Musae Sioniae Tl.3. Allein Gott in der Höh sei Ehr. Allein Gott in der Höh sei Ehr : Choralbearbeitung für zwei vierstimmige Chöre. *Bärenreiter. £1.16* EZDH (B79-50462)
Werner, Martin. Music. (Politoske, Daniel Theodore). 2nd ed. *Prentice-Hall. £9.05* A(X) (B79-34988) ISBN 0-13-607556-8
Wesendonk-Lieder : for soprano voice and orchestra. (Wagner, Richard). *Eulenburg. £2.15* KFLE/MDW (B79-50999)
Wesley-Smith, Martin. Machine : a music mime, for choir, percussion and tape. *Universal. Unpriced* FE/XMDW/JN (B79-50915)
Westcott, Graham C. Someone's singing, Lord. Melody part. Someone's singing, Lord : hymns and songs for children. *A & C Black. Unpriced* JFADM/AY (B79-50125) ISBN 0-7136-1847-7
Westernhagen, Curt von. Wagner : a biography
Vol.2: 1864-83. *Cambridge University Press. £12.50* BWC(N) (B79-17761) ISBN 0-521-21932-9
Weston, Pamela.
17 classical solos : for unaccompanied clarinet. *Fentone Music : Breitkopf and Härtel. £1.85* VVPMK/AAY (B79-51290)

Duo, clarinets, op.2, no.1, C major. Grand duo, op.2, no.1 : for two clarinets. (Boufil, Jacques Jules). *Fentone Music. £1.80* VVNU (B79-50783)
Wetzlar, Horst.
Balletti pro tabula. *Selections : arr.* Suite in B-Dur für Trompete und Orgel, 1670. (Vejvanovský, Pavel Josef). *Merseburger : Bärenreiter. Unpriced* WSPLRK/AE (B79-50806)
Bläsermusik alter Meister : für zwei Trompeten und drei Posaunen. *Merseburger : Bärenreiter. £1.32* WNQ (B79-50793)
Fünf Choralvorspiele : für Trompete und Orgel, 1975. (Zipp, Friedrich). *Merseburger : Bärenreiter. £4.46* WSPLR (B79-50805)
Sonata la posta : für drei Posaunen und Orgel, 1667. (Vejvanovský, Pavel Josef). *Merseburger : Bärenreiter. £2.97* WUNTRE (B79-50808)
What a day : Dobry den : a choral cycle, for two-part chorus of young voices with piano accompaniment or a cappella. (Laburda, Jiří). *Schirmer. £2.10* FDW (B79-50495)
What Child is this? S.A.T.B. (acc. or unacc.), English traditional melody. (Willcocks, *Sir* David). *Oxford University Press. Unpriced* DP/LF (B79-50447) ISBN 0-19-343071-1
Which one's Cliff? The illustrated 'Which one's Cliff?'. (Richard, Cliff). *Hodder and Stoughton.* Pbk. *£2.95 : CIP entry* AKDW/GB/E(P) (B78-29837) ISBN 0-340-23413-x
White, Eric Walter. Stravinsky. 2nd ed. *Faber. £13.50 : CIP entry* BSV (B79-25328) ISBN 0-571-04923-0
White, Estelle. Good morning, Jesus : twenty-four songs for children. *(55 Leigh Rd) : Kevin Mayhew. Unpriced* JFDW/GJ (B79-50940)
White, Ian.
Concerto, viola d'amore, oboe d'amore & continuo, F major. Concerto for viola d'amore or viola, oboe d'amore or viola and basso continuo with cello. (Böhm, I C F). *(Little Margaret, Penmans Green, Chipperfield) : E.L. White. Unpriced* NUPNTF (B79-50596)
Divertimento for violin, viola d'amore and gamba. (Haydn, Joseph). *(Little Margaret, Penmans Green, Chipperfield) : E.L. White. Unpriced* RXNTK (B79-50678)
Harmonia artificiosa Partia, violas d'amore (2) & continuo, no.7 C minor. *Viola d'amore parts.* Harmonia artificiosa, partita no. VIII in fact, 7 : for two violas d'amore and cello, with optional organ or harpsichord. (Biber, Heinrich). *(Little Margaret, Penmans Green, Chipperfield) : E.L. White. Unpriced* SQQ (B79-50688)
Lamento. (Eymwag, Joachim). *(Little Margaret, Penmans Green, Chipperfield) : E.L. White. Unpriced* KE/NXNRDW (B79-50544)
Quintet, strings, D major. Quintet, vln., viola, viola d'amore, cello, bass. (Eybler, Joseph von). *(Little Margaret, Penmans Green, Chipperfield) : E.L. White. Unpriced* RXNR (B79-50672)
Sinfonia, viola d'amore, violin & continuo, D major. Sinfonia for viola d'amore, violin and basso. (Schmidt). *(Little Margaret, Penmans Green, Chipperfield) : E.L. White. Unpriced* NXNTE (B79-50606)
Whiteley, Faith. A first violin book. *Oxford University Press. Unpriced* S/AF (B79-51145) ISBN 0-19-359511-7
Whitman, Walt. By the roadside : six songs to poems by Walt Whitman, for soprano and piano. (Schonthal, Ruth). *Oxford University Press. Unpriced* KFLDW (B79-50150)
Whittall, Mary.
Richard Wagner's music dramas. (Dahlhaus, Carl). *Cambridge University Press. £7.50* BWCAC (B79-33553) ISBN 0-521-22397-0
Wagner : a biography
Vol.2: 1864-83. (Westernhagen, Curt von). *Cambridge University Press. £12.50* BWC(N) (B79-17761) ISBN 0-521-21932-9
Whitter, Mark. Stardance carol : S.A.T.B. *Banks. Unpriced* EXRVDP/LF (B79-50871)
Whitworth, John. More guitar pieces : folktunes and Elizabethan pieces. *Holley Music. Unpriced* TSPMK/AAY (B79-50310)
Who wants to sing? : (what it's all about). 2nd and enlarged ed.. *9 Kinnaird Terrace, Antrim Rd, Belfast BT14 6BN : John Patterson.* Pbk. *£3.80* AB/E (B79-06707)
Why are Covent Garden seat prices so high? (Blaug, Mark). *Royal Opera House Covent Garden, WC2 7QA : Royal Opera House Covent Garden Ltd.* Sd. *Unpriced* AC/E(YC/QB/K) (B79-04908)
Wichmann, Russell G. Once in royal David's city : carol for two-part mixed chorus and organ with optional chimes. *Oxford University Press. Unpriced* DP/LF (B79-50030)
Wicklund, Anders.
Concerto, oboe & string orchestra, D major. *arr.* Concerto in D for oboe, violins and basso continuo. (Telemann, Georg Philipp). *Musica rara. Unpriced* VTPK/LF (B79-50351)
Concerto, oboe & string orchestra, F major. Concerto in F for solo oboe, violin, strings and basso continuo. (Telemann, Georg Philipp). *Musica rara. Unpriced* RXMPVTF (B79-50261)
Concerto, oboe & string orchestra, F major. *arr.* Concerto in F for solo oboe, violin, strings and basso continuo. (Telemann, Georg Philipp). *Musica rara. Unpriced* VTPK/LF (B79-50352)
Wie die Wolke. Op.6, no.5. *arr.* As the clouds with longing wander : Wie die Wolke : for three-part chorus of women's voices with piano accompaniment. (Brahms, Johannes). *Schirmer. £0.35* FDW (B79-50493)
Wie schön leuchtet der Morgenstern. *Vocal score.* Wie schon leuchtet der Morgenstern = How fair the morning star doth glow : Kantate Dom. II. p. Epiph. (Bach, Wilhelm Friedemann). *Belwin-Mills. £2.25* DE/LFP (B79-50422)
Wiegold, Mary. Catalogue of music broadcast on Radio 3
1975. (British Broadcasting Corporation). *B.B.C.* Pbk. *£4.50* A/JT(XQQ) (B79-29149) ISBN 0-563-17372-6
Wiener Stadt- und Landesbibliothek.
Verzeichnis der Schubert-Handschriften in der Musiksammlung der Wiener Stadt- und Landesbibliothek. *17 Bucklersbury, Hutchin, Herts. SG5 1BB : Bärenreite for the International Association of Music Libraries and the International Musicological Society.* Pbk. *£28.05* BMS(TC) (B79-10755)
Verzeichnis der Schubert-Handschriften in der Musiksammlung der Wiener Stadt- und Landesbibliothek. *17 Bucklersbury, Hutchin, Herts. SG5 1BB : Bärenreite for the International Association of Music Libraries and the International Musicological Society.* Pbk. *£28.05* BSF(TE) (B79-10755)
Wienhorst, Richard.
Bless the Lord, O my soul : for two-part chorus of women's voices with glockenspiel and triangle accompaniment. *Associated Music. £0.30* FE/XTPLXTQWDK (B79-50498)
Taste and see : for two-part chorus of women's voices with glockenspiel and triangle. *Associated Music. £0.35* FE/XTPLXTQWDK (B79-50499)
Wiggins, Bram.
12 allemandes pour le piano forte. Op.4. *Selections : arr.* Five German dances. (Weber, Carl Maria von, *Freiherr*). *Oxford University Press. Unpriced* UMK/AH (B79-50316) ISBN 0-19-368668-6
A second wind band book. *Oxford University Press. Unpriced* UM/AY (B79-50718) ISBN 0-19-369831-5
Waltzes, piano. *Selections : arr.* Five waltzes. (Weber, Carl Maria von, *Freiherr*). *Oxford University Press. Unpriced* UMK/AHW (B79-50317) ISBN 0-19-368704-6
Wiklund, Anders. Concerto, oboe & string orchestra, D major. Concerto in D for oboe, violins and basso continuo. (Telemann, Georg Philipp). *Musica rara. Unpriced* RXMPVTF (B79-50260)
Wilde, David. Consolations. G.172. Consolations. (Liszt, Franz). *Stainer and Bell. Unpriced* QPJ (B79-50632) ISBN 0-85249-526-9
Wilde, Oscar. Requiescat : S.S. and piano. (Benger, Richard). *Edwin Ashdown. £0.20* FLDW (B79-50919)
Wilker, Elisabeth. Bibliographie des Musikschriftums 1972. *Schott. £30.00* A(T) (B79-30467)
Wilkins, Eithne. Selected letters of Gustav Mahler. (Mahler, Gustav). *Faber. £15.00 : CIP rev.* BME(N) (B79-14911) ISBN 0-571-08643-8
Wilkinson, Caroline. Catalogue of music broadcast on Radio 3
1975. (British Broadcasting Corporation). *B.B.C.* Pbk. *£4.50* A/JT(XQQ) (B79-29149) ISBN 0-563-17372-6
Wilkinson, Keith. Béatrice et Bénédict. Overture. *arr.* Overture Beatrice and Benedict. (Berlioz, Hector). *R. Smith. Unpriced* WMK (B79-51301)
Will you be my partner? : a quodlibet. (Hudson, Hazel). *Edwin Ashdown. £0.25* FDW (B79-50911)
Willcocks, *Sir* David.
Carols for choirs
3: Fifty carols ; edited and arranged by David Willcocks and John Rutter. *Oxford University Press. Unpriced* DP/LF/AY (B79-50031) ISBN 0-19-353570-x
What Child is this? S.A.T.B. (acc. or unacc.), English traditional melody. *Oxford University Press. Unpriced* DP/LF (B79-50447) ISBN 0-19-343071-1
Williams, A. I love thy church, O God : for four-part chorus of mixed voices with optional piano accompaniment. (Snyder, Wesley). *Schirmer. Unpriced* EZDH (B79-50880)
Williams, Aaron. Geistliche Chormusik. Die mit Thränen säen. *arr.* Fantasia a 5. (Schütz, Heinrich). *Ricordi.*

Unpriced VSNRK/DJ (B79-50338)
Williams, Don. Don Williams : piano/vocal. *Chappell. Unpriced* KDW/GC/AY (B79-50979)
Williams, Huw. Canu'r bobol. *Gwasg Gee. £4.00* ADW(YDK) (B79-04543)
Williams, John.
Caprice, violin, op.1, no.24, A minor. *arr.* Caprice no.24. (Paganini, Nicolò). *Boosey and Hawkes. Unpriced* TSPMK/T (B79-50715)
Sextet, string instruments, op.18, B flat major. Andante. *arr.* Theme and variations. (Brahms, Johannes). *Boosey and Hawkes. Unpriced* TSNUK (B79-50702)
Superman. Theme. *arr.* Theme from 'Superman'. *Warner. Unpriced* QPK/JR (B79-50225)
Terpsichore. *Selections : arr.* Four dances ... guitar. (Praetorius, Michael). *Boosey and Hawkes. Unpriced* TSPMK/AH (B79-50710)
Williams, Patrick. The shepherd's lottery. Symphony. *arr.* Gavot, from symphony no.4. (Boyce, William). *Edwin Ashdown. £0.40* RK/AHM (B79-50237)
Williamson, Malcolm.
Concerto, pianos (2) & string orchestra. Concerto for two pianos and string orchestra. *Weinberger. Unpriced* RXMPQNUF (B79-50667)
The lion of Suffolk : for organ. *Weinberger. Unpriced* RJ (B79-50652)
Willis, Allee. Boogie wonderland. *Rondor : Chappell. Unpriced* KDW/GB (B79-50534)
Willison, David. Pocket musical history : with biographical list of famous composers and landmarks in the history of musical development. Revised ed.. *421a Brighton Rd, Croydon, Surrey CR2 6YR : Alfred Lengnick and Co.* Sd. *£0.10* A(X) (B79-07464)
Wills, Arthur.
Missa in memoriam Benjamin Britten : Holy Communion series 3 for S.A.T.B. and organ. *Addington Press. Unpriced* DGS (B79-50830)
Resurrection : for organ. *Weinberger. Unpriced* RJ (B79-51126)
Variations on 'Amazing Grace'. Variations on 'Amazing grace' and Toccata : for organ. *Novello. £2.25* RJ (B79-51127)
Wilmer, Valerie. Jazz at Ronnie Scott's. *Hale. £5.80* AMT(M) (B79-16103) ISBN 0-7091-6907-8
Wilson, Alan J. Charlton. Take my life : tune, Charlton, words, Frances Ridley Havergal and Come, Holy Ghost : tune, Pentecost, words, Bishop J. Cosin, based on 'Veni creator spiritus'. *Weinberger. Unpriced* DM (B79-50442)

Wilson, Brian. Pet sound plus : 24 greatest hits ... (Beach Boys). *Chappell. Unpriced* KDW/HKR (B79-50540)
Wilson, Thomas. Soliloquy : for guitar. *Bèrben : Breitkopf and Härtel. £1.90* TSPMJ (B79-51186)
Wilson, Thomas Brendan. Canción : for solo guitar. *Scotus : Schirmer. Unpriced* TSPMJ (B79-50707)
Wiltshire service : Holy Communion series 3, for congregation and choir (SATB) with organ or piano. (Shephard, Richard). *Royal School of Church Music. Unpriced* DGS (B79-50430)
Wimberger, Gerhard. Motus : für grosses Orchester. *Bärenreiter. £8.91* MMJ (B79-50579)
Winch, Richard. The pedlar of Swaffham : a children's cantata with simple accompaniments for piano and classroom instruments. *Chappell. Unpriced* JFE/NYDSDX (B79-50944)
Windscore. Meyerbeer, Giacomo. Le prophète. March. *arr.* Coronation march. (Le prophète). *Novello. £2.00* UMK/AGM (B79-50315)
Wine, women and song. (Strauss, Johann, *b.1825*). New revised ed. *Schott. £0.90* VSNRQK/AHW (B79-50762)
Wings greatest. (McCartney, Paul). *MPL : Music Sales. Unpriced* KDW/GB (B79-50136)
Wings tour USA. (Powell, Aubrey). *High St., Limpsfield, Surrey RH8 0DY : Paper Tiger.* Pbk. *£3.25* AKDW/GB/E(P/EM/XRF) (B79-05872) ISBN 0-905895-10-x
Winold, Allen. Introduction to music theory. 2nd ed. *Prentice-Hall.* Pbk. *£8.40* A/AM (B79-30253) ISBN 0-13-489666-1
Wir sind die Musikanten : eine kleine Instrumentenschau für Orchester, Chor ad lib. (2 gl. Stimmen) und Sprecher ad lib. (Maasz, Gerhard). *Schott. £6.00* MJ (B79-50161)
With one voice · a hymn book for all the churches. 2nd ed. *Collins. Unpriced* JDADM/AY (B79-50116) ISBN 0-00-599581-7
With one voice : a hymn book for all the churches with Catholic supplement. *Collins. Unpriced* DM/AY (B79-50443)
With one voice : a hymn book for all the churches, with Catholic supplements. *Collins. Unpriced* JADM (B79-50929) ISBN 0-00-599636-8
With one voice. *Congregation part.* With one voice : a hymn book for all the churches. 2nd ed. *Collins. Unpriced* JDADM/AY (B79-50116) ISBN 0-00-599581-7
Withams, Eric. The gorgon's head. *Universal. Unpriced* CQN (B79-50824)
Within easy reach : 10 easy pieces for guitarists with small hands = 10 pezzi facili por chitarristi con le mani piccole = 10 leichte Stücke für Gitarrenspieler mit kleinen Händen. (Duarte, John William). *Ricordi. Unpriced* TSPMJ (B79-51184)
Wizard's way recorder colouring book. (Tobin, Candida). *Helicon Press. Unpriced* VS/AC (B79-50337) ISBN 0-905684-00-1
Wohltemperierte Clavier. Fugue 14. BWV859. *arr.* Fugue 14 ... for three guitars. (Bach, Johann Sebastian). *Associated Music. £2.75* TSNTK/Y (B79-50701)
Wolf-Ferrari, Ermanno. Il segreto di Susanna. Overture. Susanna's secret = Il segreto di Susanna = Susannens Geheimnis : overture. *Weinberger. Unpriced* MMJ (B79-50180)
Wolfe, Daniel. Sacrae symphoniae, bk.2. O quam suavis. O quam suavis : for eight-part chorus of mixed voices with organ accompaniment. (Gabrieli, Giovanni). *Schirmer. £0.75* DGKJ/LNC (B79-50427)
Wolff, Konrad. Schnabel's interpretation of piano music. 2nd ed. *Faber.* Pbk. *£2.50* AQ/E(P) (B79-36916) ISBN 0-571-10029-5
Wolff, Konrad. Teaching of Artur Schnabel. *For later edition see* Wolff, Konrad. Schnabel's interpretation of piano music.
Woll, Allen L. Songs from Hollywood musical comedies, 1927 to the present : a dictionary. *Garland. £15.00* ACM/JR(WT) (B79-50406) ISBN 0-8240-9958-3
Women composers : a handbook. (Stern, Susan). *Scarecrow Press : Distributed by Bailey and Swinfen. £6.00* A/D(M/C) (B79-02985) ISBN 0-8108-1138-3
Women's voices : eleven songs for soprano and piano. (Rorem, Ned). *Boosey and Hawkes. Unpriced* KFLDW (B79-50549)
Wonder why book of XYZ of musical instruments. (Goffe, Toni). *Transworld.* Sd. *£0.75* AL/B (B79-16838) ISBN 0-552-57030-3
Wood, Gareth. Concertino, horn (tenor) & brass band. Concertino for tenor horn and brass band. *R. Smith. Unpriced* WMPWTTFL (B79-51306)
Woodford, Peggy. Mozart. *Midas Books. £6.50 : CIP entry* BMS(N) (B78-05401) ISBN 0-85936-050-4
Woodham, Ronald. Quintet, strings, no.1, K.174, B flat major. Quintet, B flat major for 2 violins, 2 violas and cello K.174. (Mozart, Wolfgang Amadeus). *Eulenburg. £1.55* RXNR (B79-51142)
Wooding, Dan. Rick Wakeman : the caped crusader. *Panther.* Pbk. *£0.95* AKDW/HKR/E(P) (B79-19446) ISBN 0-586-04853-7
Woods, Fred. Folk revival : the rediscovery of a national music. *Blandford Press. £3.95 : CIP rev.* A/G (B79-14913) ISBN 0-7137-0970-7
Woods, Stanley. Little blue boy : for tenor horn and brass band. *Chester Music. Unpriced* WMPWTT (B79-51305)
Works of Harry Warren. (Warren, Harry). *EMI. Unpriced* KDW/JR (B79-50145)
Works of Henry Purcell
Vol.3: Dido and Aeneas. (Purcell, Henry). *Novello. £10.00* C/AZ (B79-50815)
Workshop. Hoch, Peter. Ensemble/séparé : fur 1-4 Instrumentalspieler = for 1 to 4 players. *Schott. £6.00* LN (B79-50563)
World of baroque & classical musical instruments. (Montagu, Jeremy). *David and Charles. £8.95 : CIP rev.* AL/B(XEG194) (B79-07466) ISBN 0-7153-7593-8
World's favorite masterworks for flute
Book 1. *Ashley : Phoenix. Unpriced* VR/AY (B79-50739)

Book 2. *Ashley : Phoenix. Unpriced* VR/AY (B79-50737)

Book 3. *Ashley : Phoenix. Unpriced* VR/AY (B79-50738)

World's favorite series.
World's favorite masterworks for flute
Book 1. *Ashley : Phoenix. Unpriced* VR/AY (B79-50739)
World's favorite masterworks for flute
Book 2. *Ashley : Phoenix. Unpriced* VR/AY (B79-50737)

World's favorite masterworks for flute
Book 3. *Ashley : Phoenix. Unpriced* VR/AY (B79-50738)

Wright, Benedict. A plainsong mass book. *Catholic Truth Society. Unpriced* JEZDG/AY (B79-50512)
Writers and their background. Matthew Arnold. *Bell. £7.50* A(C) (B76-09358) ISBN 0-7135-1818-9
Wulstan, David.
Officium defunctorum. Missa pro defunctis. Requiem à 6 (1605). (Victoria, Tomás Luis de). *Oxenford Imprint. Unpriced* EZDGKAV (B79-50053)
Orlando Gibbons II : full anthems, hymns and fragmentary verse anthems. (Gibbons, Orlando). *Stainer and Bell. Unpriced* DK (B79-50026) ISBN 0-85249-517-x
Wye, Trevor.
Capriccios, flute. Twenty-four capriccios for solo flute. (Boehm, Theobald). *Chester Music. Unpriced* VR/AF (B79-50736)
Flute encores
Vol.1. *Chester Music. Unpriced* VRPK/AAY (B79-50750)

Flute trios
Vol.1. *Chester Music. Unpriced* VRNT/AY (B79-51216)
Vol.2. *Chester Music. Unpriced* VRNT/AY (B79-51217)
XYZ of musical instruments. Wonder why book of XYZ of musical instruments. (Goffe, Toni). *Transworld.* Sd. *£0.75* AL/B (B79-16838) ISBN 0-552-57030-3
Yakeley, June. Spanish masters : 19 original easy pieces. *Ricordi. Unpriced* TSPM/AYK (B79-50305)
Yancy, Marvin.
Our love. *arr.* Our love. *Chappell. Unpriced* DW (B79-50036)
Our love. *arr.* Our love. *Chappell. Unpriced* DW (B79-50037)
Our love. *arr.* Our love. *Chappell. Unpriced* FDW (B79-50105)
Year book
1978-1979. (Royal College of Organists). *Kensington Gore, SW7 2QS : The College.* Sd. *£1.15* AR(YC/VP/Q/BC)
1979. (British Federation of Music Festivals). *106 Gloucester Place, W1H 3DB : The Federation.* Sd. *£1.50* A(YC/WE/Q/BC) (B79-18561)
Yearbook
1979. (British Country Music Association). *PO Box 2, Newton Abbot, Devon TQ12 4HT : The Association.* Pbk. *Unpriced* AKDW/GC(BC) (B79-34987)
Yeomen of the guard, or, The merryman and his maid. (Gilbert, *Sir* William Schwenck). *42 Bloomsbury St., W.C.1 : Godfrey Cave Associates Ltd. £5.50* BSWACF (B79-16840) ISBN 0-906223-06-7
Yes. Yes. Tormato. *Warner : Music Sales. Unpriced* KDW/HKR (B79-50141)
Yes. Tormato. (Yes). *Warner : Music Sales. Unpriced* KDW/HKR (B79-50141)
Yesterday when I was young. (Aznavour, Charles). *W.H. Allen. £5.95* AKDW/GB/E(P) (B79-36914) ISBN 0-491-02446-0
Yip-i-addy-i-ay yip-i-addy-i-ay. *Melody part.* Yip-i-addy-i-ay yip-i-addy-i-ay : songs for junior and middle school with optional parts for recorder and percussion. *Chappell. Unpriced* JFDADW/AY (B79-50934)
Yost, Michel. Duets, clarinets, op.5, nos.1-3. Six duos. Op.5, nos.1-3 for 2 clarinets. *Musica rara. Unpriced* VVNU (B79-51276)
You needed me. (Goodrum, Randy). *Chappell. Unpriced* UMK/DW (B79-51204)
You needed me. *arr.* You needed me : S.A.B. with piano and optional drums. (Goodrum, Randy). *Chappell. Unpriced* DW/GBB (B79-50862)
You needed me. *arr.* You needed me : S.S.A. with piano and optional drums. (Goodrum, Randy). *Chappell. Unpriced* FDW/GBB (B79-50912)
Young, Donald J. Sermon on the mount. *Vocal score.* Sermon on the mount : for four-part chorus of mixed voices with piano accompaniment. *Schirmer. £0.45* DH (B79-50433)
Young, Neil. After the gold rush. *arr.* After the gold rush. *Warner : Music Sales. Unpriced* KDW/HKR (B79-50142)
Young, Phyllis. Playing the string game : strategies for teaching cello and strings. *University of Texas Press. £10.50* ARW/E(VC) (B79-20274) ISBN 0-292-73814-5
Young reader's guides to music. Hosier, John. The sorcerer's apprentice, and other stories. *Oxford University Press.* Pbk. *£1.50* ABN (B79-50005) ISBN 0-19-314922-2
Your baby needs music. (Cass-Beggs, Barbara). *Ward Lock. £4.95* A(Z) (B79-50405) ISBN 0-7063-5900-3
Youth songs : a collection for soloists and groups. *Salvationist Publishing & Supplies. £2.95* DM/AY (B79-50837)
Yüasa, Jōji. Time of orchestral time. Jkesutora no toki no toki = Time of orchestral time. *Zen-on Music : Schott. £12.00* MMJ (B79-51026)
Yule : for two speakers, children's voices, games players, piano, with occasional recorders : melodicas, tuned and untuned percussion. (Leaper, Kenneth). *Chappell. Unpriced* FE/NYHSDE/LF (B79-50913)
Yun, Isang. Muak : tänzerische Fantasie für grosses Orchester, 1978. *Bote und Bock. £9.60* MMH (B79-51019)
Zabrack, Harold. Scherzo, piano. *arr.* Scherzo : hommage à Prokofieff. *Boosey and Hawkes. Unpriced* QNVK (B79-51063) ISBN 0-934286-14-0
Zamoyski, Adam. Chopin : a biography. *Collins. £7.95* BCE(N) (B79-32719) ISBN 0-00-216089-7
Zbinden, Julien François. Prelude & fugue, organ, op.58. Prélude et fugue pour grand orgue, op.58 (1978). *Eulenburg. £2.10* R/Y (B79-50648)
Zehm, Friedrich. Alla danza : lateinamerikanische Tänze (Cha-Cha, Tango argentino, Bossa nova) zu vier Stimmen, Stabspiele, Schlagzeug und Klavier, für Orchester, Streichorchester oder Instrumentalenensemble. *Schott. £8.00* MK/AH/AYU (B79-50566)
Zempléni, Kurnél. Klavierwerke = Piano works
Heft 12: Einzelne Charakterstücke 2 = Individual character pieces. (Liszt, Franz). *Bärenreiter. £5.94* QP/AZ (B79-50618)
Zettler, Richard.
Beliebte Volkslieder : für Posaune mit 2. Stimme ad lib. *Schott. £2.40* WUPMJ (B79-50401)
Bläsersätze nach europäischen Volksliedern = Wind pieces from European folksongs : für vier Blechbläser, 2 Trompeten, (Flügelhörner, Horn ad lib., 2 Stimme), 2 Posaunen (Tenorhorn, Bariton, ad lib Tuba) = for four brass instruments, 2 trumpets, (flugelhorns, horn ad lib. 2nd part) 2 trombones (baritone euphonium, ad lib. tuba). *Schott. £3.40* WNSK/DW/G/AYB (B79-50390)
Zguta, Russell. Russian minstrels : a history of the skomorokhi. *Clarendon Press. £8.95* AKDW/G(YM/XCE751) (B79-24590) ISBN 0-19-815652-9
Ziegenrücker, Wieland. Swing und Beat, Schwarz auf weiss = Swing and beat. Black on white : Anregungen zum Musizieren auf Klavier und Elektronenorgel = Hints on playing the piano and the electronic organ. (Pieper, Manfred). *VEB Deutscher Verlag für Musik : Breitkopf und Härtel. £6.30* Q/AC (B79-50612)
Ziele des Musik-Lernens
T.1: Beitrag zur Entwicklung ihrer Theorie. (Abel-Struth, Sigrid). *Schott.* Pbk. *£8.00* A(VC/YE) (B79-14009)
Zigeunerliebe. *Selections: arr.* Zigeunerliebe : Melodienfolge. (Lehár, Franz). Neue Ausgabe. *Glocken. Unpriced* UMK/DW (B79-50319)
Zimmer, Ulrich W. Sechs englische Psalmen. Hob. XXIII Anhang, Nachtrag. Sechs Psalmen = Six psalms : für dreistimmigen gemischten Chor = for three-part mixed chorus, Hob. XXIII Anhang, Nachtrag. (Haydn, Joseph). *Bärenreiter. £2.31* EZDR (B79-50471)
Zimmermann, Heinz Werner. Drei Nestroy-Collagen : für gemischten Chor und zwei Klaviere. *Bärenreiter. £13.20*

DW (B79-50038)

Zimmermann, Ildo. Sinfonia come un grade lamento (1977). Dem Andenken Frederico sic García Lorca. *VEB Deutscher Verlag für Musik*. *£3.30* MME (B79-51015)

Zimmermann, Udo. Psaslm der Nacht : für sechzehnstimmigen Frauenchor, Männerstimmen, Schlagwerk und Orgel. *Bärenreiter*. *£7.92* ERPLXDH/KDN (B79-50046)

Zipp, Friedrich. Fünf Choralvorspiele : für Trompete und Orgel, 1975. *Merseburger : Bärenreiter*. *£4.46* WSPLR (B79-50805)

Zukerman, George. Quintet, bassoon & string quartet, no.4, D major. Quintet no.4 for bassoon and strings. (Brunetti, Gaetano). *Musica rara*. *Unpriced* NVWNR (B79-50192)

Zwei Hände-zwölf Tasten. *English*. Two hands-twelve notes Book 1: A picture-book for young pianists. (Runze, Klaus). *Schott*. *£3.00* Q/AC (B79-51052)

Zwei Hände-zwölf Tasten. *English*. Two hands-twelve notes Book 2: Playing with music. (Runze, Klaus). *Schott*. *£2.50* Q/AC (B79-51053)

Zwei Suiten für zwei Altblockflöten und Basso continuo Suite 1: C-Dur = C major. (Pez, Johann Christoph). *Schott*. *£4.00* VSSNTPWG (B79-51247)

Zweite Violinkonzert : in Form einer Ballade. Concerto, violin, no.2. 2 Violinkonzert : in Form einer Ballade, für Violine und Orchester, (1978). (Baur, Jürg). *Breitkopf und Härtel*. *£8.40* MPSF (B79-51028)

Zweiter Sinfonie, 1978. Symphony, no.2. II. Sinfonie, 1978. (Trojahn, Manfred). *Bärenreiter*. *£12.54* MME (B79-50569)

Zwölf neue leichte Präludien. Op.2. 12 neue leichte Präludien. Op.2. Twelve new easy preludes for organ. (Albrechtsberger, Johann Georg). *Oxford University Press. Unpriced* RJ (B79-51121)   ISBN 0-19-375207-7

Zwota-Sonate, 1974 : Blockflöte und Klavier. (Krug, Reinhold). *Neue Musik : Breitkopf and Härtel*. *£3.90* VSPE (B79-51237)

Subject Index

Cantatas, Secular: Female voices, Children's voices
    FDX
Cantatas, Secular: Female voices, Children's voices:
    Unison: Accompanied by recorders, keyboard &
    percussion   JFE/NYFSDX
Cantatas, Secular: High voice   KFTDX
Cantatas, Secular: Middle voice   KFVDX
Cantatas, Secular: Soprano voice: Accompanied by
    orchestra   KFLE/MDX
Cantatas, Secular: Soprano voice: Accompanied by string
    quartet   KFLE/RXNSDX
Cantatas, Secular: Unaccompanied works   EZDX
Canticles: Evening Prayer: Anglican liturgy: Female
    voices, Children's voices   FDGPP
Canticles: Evening Prayer: Anglican liturgy: Treble voices
    FLDGPP
Canticles: Evening Prayer: Anglican liturgy:
    Unaccompanied works   EZDGPP
Canticles: Morning Prayer: Anglican liturgy   DGNP
Carols   DP
Carols: Accompanied by tambourine   EXRVDP
Carols: Arrangements for accordion solo
    RSPMK/DP
Carols: Arrangements for brass quintet   WNRK/DP
Carols: Arrangements for chrod organ   RPVCK/DP
Carols: Arrangements for clarinet, unaccompanied
    VVPMK/DP
Carols: Arrangements for electronic organ
    RPVK/DP
Carols: Arrangements for guitar solo   TSPMK/DP
Carols: Arrangements for instrument(s)   LK/DP
Carols: Arrangements for orchestra   MK/DP
Carols: Arrangements for piano duet, 4 hands
    QNVK/DP
Carols: Arrangements for piano solo   QPK/DP
Carols: Arrangements for recorder quartet
    VSNSK/DP
Carols: Arrangements for trumpets unaccompanied
    WSPMK/DP
Carols: Female voices, Children's voices   FDP
Carols: Female voices, Children's voices: Unison
    JFDP
Carols: Female voices, Children's voices: Unison:
    Accompanied by keyboard & percussion
    JFE/NYLDP
Carols: Female voices, Children's voices: Unison:
    Accompanied by recorder, strings & keyboard
    trio   JFE/NUSNTDP
Carols: Female voices, Children's voices: Unison:
    Accompanied by various instruments
    JFE/LDP
Carols: Solo voice   KDP
Carols: Unaccompanied male voices   GEZDP
Carols: Unaccompanied works   EZDP
Carols: Unison: Accompanied by guitar   JE/TSDP
Cantatas, Secular: Female voices, Children's voices:
    Unison: Accompanied by recorder, strings,
    keyboard & percussion   JFE/NYDSDX
Cello   SR
Cello & orchestra   MPSR
Cello & viola   SQPLSR
Celtic music: Collections: Arrangements for harp
    TQPMK/AYCC
Chaconnes: String orchestra   RXMHJN
Chamber music   N
Chamber music: Books   AN
Chamber music: Brass   WN
Chamber music: Clarinets   VVN
Chamber music: Descant recorders   VSRN
Chamber music: Flutes   VRN
Chamber music: Guitars   TSN
Chamber music: Horns   WTN
Chamber music: Oboes   VTN
Chamber music: Percussion   XN
Chamber music: Pianos   QN
Chamber music: Recorders   VSN
Chamber music: Saxophones   VUN
Chamber music: Strings   RXN
Chamber music: Strings, bowed & unbowed   RWN
Chamber music: Treble recorders   VSSN
Chamber music: Trombones   WUN
Chamber music: Trumpets   WSN
Chamber music: Violins   SN
Chamber music: Wind   UN
Chamber orchestra   MR
Chamber orchestra: Accompanying vocal quintet
    JNBE/MR
Change ringing: Church bells: Books   AXSR/E
Chansons: Unaccompanied works   EZDU
Charles, Ray: Books   AMT(P)
Children's hymns: Female voices, Children's voices:
    Unison   JFDM/GJ
Children's hymns: Female voices, Children's voices:
    Unison: Accompanied by instruments
    JFE/LDM/GJ
Children's musical plays: Full scores   CQN
Children's musical plays: Nield, D.: Books
    BNEACN
Children's songs: Arrangements for descant recorder,
    keyboard & percussion   NYFSRK/DW/GJ
Children's songs: Female voices, Children's voices: Unison
    JFDW/GJ
Children's songs: Female voices, Children's voices:
    Unison: Accompanied by percussion band
    JFE/XMDW/GJ
Children's songs: Female voices, Children's voices:
    Unison: Accompanied by various instruments
    JFE/LDW/GJ

Children's songs: Female voices, Children's voices:
    Unison: Voice parts   JFADW/GJ
Children's voices: Choral works   F
Children's voices: Unison   JF
Child's voice   KF
Choirs: Music   D
Choirs: Music: Bach, J.S.: Books   BBCAD
Choirs: Music   AD
Chopin, Frédéric: Books   BCE
Choral music   D
Choral music: Bach, J.S.: Books   BBCAD
Choral music: Books   AD
Chord organ   RPVC
Christmas: Carols   DP/LF
Christmas: Carols: Accompanied by tambourine
    EXRVDP/LF
Christmas: Carols: Arrangements for accordion solo
    RSPMK/DP/LF
Christmas: Carols: Arrangements for brass quintet
    WNRK/DP/LF
Christmas: Carols: Arrangements for chord organ
    RPVCK/DP/LF
Christmas: Carols: Arrangements for clarinet,
    unaccompanied   VVPMK/DP/LF
Christmas: Carols: Arrangements for electronic organ
    RPVK/DP/LF
Christmas: Carols: Arrangements for guitar solo
    TSPMK/DP/LF
Christmas: Carols: Arrangements for instrument(s)
    LK/DP/LF
Christmas: Carols: Arrangements for orchestra
    MK/DP/LF
Christmas: Carols: Arrangements for piano duet, 4 hands
    QNVK/DP/LF
Christmas: Carols: Arrangements for piano solo
    QPK/DP/LF
Christmas: Carols: Arrangements for recorder quartet
    VSNSK/DP/LF
Christmas: Carols: Arrangements for trumpet,
    unaccompanied   WSPMK/DP/LF
Christmas: Carols: Female voices, Children's voices
    FDP/LF
Christmas: Carols: Female voices, Children's voices:
    Unison   JFDP/LF
Christmas: Carols: Female voices, Children's voices:
    Unison: Accompanied by keyboard & percussion
    JFE/NYLDP/LF
Christmas: Carols: Female voices, Children's voices:
    Unison: Accompanied by recorder, strings and
    keyboard trio   JFE/NUSNTDP/LF
Christmas: Carols: Solo voice   KDP/LF
Christmas: Carols: Unaccompanied male voices
    GEZDP/LF
Christmas: Carols: Unaccompanied works
    EZDP/LF
Christmas: Carols: Unison: Accompanied by guitar
    JE/TSDP/LF
Christmas: Compline: Divine Office: Unaccompanied
    works   EZDGKR/LF
Christmas: Motets   DJ/LF
Christmas: Motets: Unaccompanied works
    EZDJ/LF
Christmas: Motets, Anthems, Hymns, Carols, etc.
    DH/LF
Christmas: Motets, Anthems, Hymns, etc.: Female voices,
    Children's voices   FDH/LF
Christmas: Musical plays: Vocal scores   CM/LF
Christmas: Organ   R/LF
Christmas: Religious cantatas   DE/LF
Christmas: Religious cantatas: Female voices, Children's
    voices: Accompanied by recorders & percussion
    FE/NYHSDE/LF
Christmas: Songs: Unaccompanied works
    EZDW/LF
Christmas: Spirituals: Choral music   DW/LC/LF
Church choral music: Books   AD/LD
Cinema: Music Arrangements for piano solo
    QPK/JR
Cinema: Rock: Arrangements for organ
    RK/DW/HKR/JR
Cinema: Rock songs: Arrangements for guitar
    TSPMK/DW/HKR/JR
Cinema: Songs: Female voices, Children's voices
    FDW/JR
Cinema: Songs: Solo voice   KDW/JR
Clarinet (B flat)   VV
Clarinet: Accompanying soprano voice   KFLE/VV
Clarinet & basson   VVPLVW
Clarinet & oboe   VTPLVV
Clarinet & orchestra   MPVV
Clarinet & strings: Chamber music   NVV
Clarinet, strings & keyboard: Chamber music   NUV
Clarinets (2) & piano   VVNTQ
Clocks, musical: Arrangements for guitar, unaccompanied
    TSPMK/B/FK
Collected works of individual composers   QP/AZ
Collected works of individual composers   C/AZ
Collected works of individual composers: Recorder
    (treble) & piano   VSSPE/AZ
Collected works of individual composers: Sonatas: Piano
    solo   QPE/AZ
Coltrane, John: Bools   AMT(P)
Communion: Anglican liturgy   DGS
Communion: Anglican liturgy: Unison   JDGS
Compline: Unaccompanied works   EZDGKR
Composers: Encyclopaedias   A(M/C)
Composers, Individual: Books   A(P)
Composition: School: Books   A/D(VF)

Concertinos: Arrangements for clarinet & piano
    VVPK/LFL
Concertinos: Arrangements for flute & piano
    VRPK/LFL
Concertinos: Arrangements for oboe & piano
    VTPK/LFL
Concertinos: Brass band   WMFL
Concertinos: Clarinet & orchestra   MPVVFL
Concertinos: Oboe & string orchestra   RXMPVTFL
Concertos: Alto saxophone & wind band
    UMPVUSF
Concertos: Arrangements for alto saxophone & piano
    VUSPK/LF
Concertos: Arrangements for double bass & piano
    SSPK/LF
Concertos: Arrangements for flute & piano
    VRPK/LF
Concertos: Arrangements for oboe & piano
    VTPK/LF
Concertos: Arrangements for recorders, string & keyboard
    quartet   NUSNSK/LF
Concertos: Arrangements for recorders (treble) (2) &
    keyboard   VSSNTPWK/LF
Concertos: Arrangements for violin & piano
    SPK/LF
Concertos: Brass & keyboard   NWXPF
Concertos: Cello & orchestra   MPSRF
Concertos: Flute & orchestra   MPVRF
Concertos: Flute, strings & keyboard quartet
    NURNSF
Concertos: Flutes (2) & string orchestra
    RXMPVRNUF
Concertos: Guitar quartet   TSNSF
Concertos: Keyboard & string orchestra
    RXMPPWF
Concertos: Oboe & string orchestra   RXMPVTF
Concertos: Piano & orchestra   MPQF
Concertos: Pianos (2) & string orchestra
    RXMPQNUF
Concertos: Symphony orchestra   MMF
Concertos: Trumpet & orchestra   MPWSF
Concertos: Tuba & orchestra   MPWVF
Concertos: Tuba & percussion   WVPLXF
Concertos: Viola & orchestra   MPSQF
Concertos: Violin & orchestra   MPSF
Concertos: Violin & string orchestra   RXMPSF
Concertos: Wind trio   VNTF
Concertos: Woodwind instruments (4) & orchestra
    MPVNSF
Concertos: Woodwind, string & keyboard trio
    NUPNTF
Concertos: Woodwind, strings, keyboard & percussion
    septet   NYDPNPF
Conducting: Books   A/EC
Cork: Collections: Folk songs: Unaccompanied unison
    voices   JEZDW/G/AYDQC
Corpus Christi: Motets: Unaccompanied works
    EZDJ/LNC
Corpus Christi: Vespers: Divine Office   DGKJ/LNC
Cotton, Reynell: Books   BCMT
Counterpoint: Books   A/RM
Country: Songs: Vocal solo   KDW(GC
Country music: Books   A/GC
Country music: Books   AKDW/GC
Country music: Singers: Books   AKDW/GC/E(M)
Criticism: Opera   AC/CC

Dance suites: Guitar, unaccompanied   TSPMHG
Dance suites: Symphony orchestra   MMHG
Dances: Alto saxophone & piano   VUSPH
Dances: Arrangements for brass band   WMK/AH
Dances: Arrangements for clarinet & piano
    VVPK/AH
Dances: Arrangements for descant recorder duet
    VSRNUK/AH
Dances: Arrangements for guitar solo   TSPMK/AH
Dances: Arrangements for guitars (2)   TSNUK/AH
Dances: Arrangements for orchestra   MK/AH
Dances: Arrangements for piano solo   QPK/AH
Dances: Arrangements for recorder quartet
    VSNSK/AH
Dances: Arrangements for recorder trio
    VSNTK/AH
Dances: Arrangements for recorders (4) & piano
    VSNRQK/AH
Dances: Arrangements for violin solo   SPMK/AH
Dances: Arrangements for violin, unaccompanied
    SPMK/AH
Dances: Arrangements for wind band   UMK/AH
Dances: Arrangements for woodwind, strings & percussion
    sextet   NYEPNQK/AH
Dances: Brass band   WMH
Dances: Brass ensemble   WNH
Dances: Chamber orchestra   MRH
Dances: Descant recorder duet   VSRNUH
Dances: Harpsichord solos   QRPH
Dances: Light orchestra   MSH
Dances: Piano solos   QPH
Dances: String orchestra   RXMH
Dances: Symphony orchestra   MMH
Dances: Violin solo   SPMH
Dances for dancing: Piano solo   QPH/H
Debussy, Claude - related to Wagner, R.   BBVT(Z)
Debussy, Claude: Books   BDJ

136

Parton, Dolly: Books AKDW/GC/E(P)
Passacaglias: Harpsichord solo QRPHT
Passions: Bach, J.C.: Books BBCADD/LK
Pavanes: Arrangements for guitar, unaccompanied TSPMK/AHVG
Percussion & electronic instrument XPLPV
Percussion band XM
Percussion band: Accompanying female voices, children's voices FE/XM
Percussion instruments X
Percussion instruments: Accompanying female voices, children's voices FE/X
Percussion instruments: Accompanying female voices, children's voices: Unison JFE/X
Percussion instruments: Accompanying male voices GE/X
Percussion instruments: Accompanying unison choral works JE/Z
Percussion instruments: Books AX
Percussion & flute: Accompanying choral music EVRPLX
Percussion & keyboard: Ensembles: Accompanying choral works ENYL
Percussion & keyboard: Ensembles: Accompanying female voices, children's voices: Unison JFE/NYL
Percussion & keyboard: Ensembles: Chamber music NYL
Percussion & orchestra MPX
Percussion & organ: Accompanying choral works ERPLX
Percussion & piano: Concertos QPLX
Percussion & recorders: Ensembles: Accompanying female voices, children's voices FE/NYHS
Percussion & strings: Ensembles: Chamber music NYJ
Percussion & viola SQPLX
Percussion, wind & keyboard: Ensembles: Chamber music NYF
Percussion, wind & strings: Ensembles: Accompanying soprano voice KFLE/NYE
Peter and the wolf: Prokofiev, S. BPPAM
Phrynis Records: Books A/FD
Physics: Music: Books A/B
Piano Q
Piano: Books AQ
Piano: Mozart, W. A.: Books BMSAQ
Piano & orchestra MPQ
Piano & organ QPLR
Piano & percussion: Concerts QPLX
Pianolas: Books A/FP
Pianos (2) & string orchestra: Concertos RXMPQNU
Pipes, Bamboo VSY
Plainchant: Unaccompanied unison voices JEZDT
Plays: Music: Symphony orchestra MM/JM
Plays, Musical: Books ACM
Plays, Musical: Full scores CQM
Plays, Musical: Kander, J.: Books BKDEACM
Plays, Musical: Nield, D.: Books BNEACM
Plays, Musical: Parr, A. BPDRACM
Plays, Musical: Sharky, J. BSGNHACM
Plays, Musical: Vocal scores CM
Plucked string instruments T
Plucked string instruments: Accompanying female voice, child's voice KFE/T
Plucked string instruments: Accompanying solo voice KE/T
Plucked string instruments: Books AT
Polkas: Arrangements for electronic organ RPVK/AHVH
Polylingual terminology A(QTF)
Popular music: Books A/GB
Popular songs: Arrangements for accordion RSPMK/DW/GB
Popular songs: arrangements for chord organ RPVCK/DW/GB
Popular songs: Arrangements for clarinet & piano VVPK/DW/GB
Popular songs: Arrangements for flute & piano VRPK/DW/GB
Popular songs: Arrangements for guitar TSPMK/DW/GB
Popular songs: Arrangements for instrument(s) LK/DW/GB
Popular songs: Arrangements for organ RK/DW/GB
Popular songs: Arrangements for piano solo QPK/DW/GB
Popular songs: Arrangements for violin & piano SPK/DW/GB
Popular songs: Books ADW/GB
Popular songs: Choral music DW/GB
Popular songs: Female voices, Children's voices FDW/GB
Popular songs: Solo voice KDW/GB
Popular songs: Solo voice: Books AKDW/GB
Postage stamps - music expounded through A(ZE)
Poulenc, Francis: Books BPO
Preces & responses: Anglican liturgy: Unaccompanied works EZDGMM
Presbyterian Church: Books ADM/LSF
Presley, Elvis: Books AKDW/HK/E(P)
Primary schools: Activities: Books A/GR(VG)
Primary schools: Education: Books A(VG)
Primary schools: Rudiments: Books A/M(VG)
Prokofiev, Sergei: Books BPP
Proper of the Mass: Accompanied by orchestra EMDGK

Protestant church music: Books ADGTCW
Psalms DR
Psalms: Accompanied by trumpets (2) & organ EWSNTPLRDR
Psalms: Female voices, Children's voices FDR
Psalms: Female voices, Children's voices: Accompanied by viola & organ FE/SQPLRDR
Psalms: Solo voice KDR
Psalms: Unaccompanied works EZDR
Psaltery TWT

Quartets: Brass ensemble WNS
Quartets: Clarinet VVNS
Quartets: Double bass SSNS
Quartets: Flute, strings & keyboard NURNS
Quartets: Guitar TSNS
Quartets: Percussion instruments XNS
Quartets: Recorder VSNS
Quartets: Recorder, strings & keyboard NUSNS
Quartets: Saxophone VUNS
Quartets: String ensemble RXNS
Quartets: String ensemble: Accompanying soprano voice KFLE/RXNS
Quartets: Strings & keyboard NXNS
Quartets: Strings & keyboard: Books ANXNS
Quartets: Trumpet, strings & keyboard NUXSNS
Quartets: Tuba WVNS
Quartets: Woodwind & keyboard quartet: Accompanying high voice KFTE/NWPNS
Questions & answers: Books A(DE)
Questions & answers: Popular singers: Books AKDW/GB/E(M/DE)
Quilter, Roger: Books BQI
Quintets: Bassoon & strings NVWNR
Quintets: Brass ensemble WNR
Quintets: Clarinet & strings NVVNR
Quintets: Clarinet, strings & keyboard NUVNR
Quintets: Recorder VSNR
Quintets: String ensembles RXNR
Quintets: String instruments (bowed & unbowed) RWNR
Quintets: Strings & keyboard: Accompanying vocal solos KE/NXNR
Quintets: Trumpet, string & keyboard NUXSNR
Quintets: Vocal ensembles JNB
Quintets: Wind ensemble UNR
Quintets: Wind & keyboard NWNR
Quintets: Woodwind, strings & percussion NYEPNR

Radio: Books A/JT
Ragtime: Arrangements for flute & piano VRPK/AHXJ
Ragtime: Arrangements for guitar TSPMK/AHXJ
Ragtime: Arrangements for string quartet RXSNK/AHXJ
Ragtime: Arrangements for woodwind trio VNTK/AHXJ
Ragtime: Piano: Books AQPHXJ
Ragtime: Piano solos QPHXJ
Recorded jazz: Books AMT/FD
Recorded music: Composers: Books A/D(M/FD)
Recorded music: Electronic music APV/FD
Recorded music: Godfrey, Sir D. A/EC/FD(P)
Recorded music: Music hall: Books AKDW/JV/FD
Recorded music: Popular music: Books A/GB/FD
Recorded music: Rock A/HKR/FD
Recorded music: Rock: Books AKDW/HKR/FD
Recorded popular songs: Solo voice: Books AKDW/GB/FD
Recorder VS
Recorder: Accompanying unison choral works JE/VS
Recorder: Solos VSPM
Recorder & guitar VSPLTS
Recorder, keyboard & percussion: Chamber music NYFS
Recorder, keyboard & percussion: Ensembles: Accompanying female voices, children's voices: Unison JFE/NYFS
Recorder, strings & keyboard: Chamber music NUS
Recorder, strings, keyboard & percussion: Ensembles: Accompanying female voices, children's voices: Unison JFE/NYDS
Recorder (descant) VSR
Recorder (descant), percussion & keyboard NYFSR
Recorder (treble) VSS
Recorders & percussion: Ensembles: Accompanying female voices, children's voices FE/NYHS
Recorders, strings & keyboard: Accompanying female voices, children's voices: Unison JFE/NUS
Recorders (4) & piano VSNRQ
Reggae: Books AKDW/GBSR
Regimental marches: Military band UMMGM/KH
Religious cantatas DE
Religious cantatas: Accompanied by keyboard & percussion ENYLDE
Religious cantatas: Accompanied by orchestra EMDE

Religious cantatas: Female voices, Children's voices FDE
Religious cantatas: Female voices, Children's voices: Accompanied by recorders & percussion FE/NYHSDE
Religious choral music: Bach, J.S.: Books BBCADC
Religious music: Motets, Anthems, Hymns, etc. DH
Accompanied by organ & percussion ERPLXDH
Accompanied by tambourines EXRVDH
Accompanied by trumpets (2) & organ EWSNTPLRDH
Accompanied by various instruments ELDH
Arrangements for accordion solo RSPMK/DH
Arrangements for brass quintet WNRK/DH
Arrangements for chord organ RPVCK/DH
Arrangements for clarinet, unaccompanied VVPMK/DH
Arrangements for electronic organ RPVK/DH
Arrangements for guitar solo TSPMK/DH
Arrangements for instrument(s) LK/DH
Arrangements for orchestra MK/DH
Arrangements for piano duet, 4 hands QNVK/DH
Arrangements for piano solo QPK/DH
Arrangements for recorder quartet VSNSK/DH
Arrangements for recorder quintet VSNRK/DH
Arrangements for trumpet, unaccompanied WSPMK/DH
Books ADH
Choral scores DADH
Female voices, Children's voices FDH
Female voices, Children's voices: Accompanied by glockenspiel & triangle FE/XTPLXTQWDH
Female voices, Children's voices: Accompanied by viola & organ FE/SQPLRDH
Female voices, Children's voices: Unison JFDH
Female voices, Children's voices: Unison: Accompanied by keyboard & percussion JFE/NYLDH
Female voices, Children's voices: Unison: Accompanied by recorder, strings & keyboard trio JFE/NUSNTDH
Female voices, Children's voices: Unison: Accompanied by various instruments JFE/LDH
Female voices, children's voices: Unison: Choral scores JFADH
Solo voice KDH
Solo voice: Books AKDH
Soprano duets: Accompanied by violins (2) & keyboard JNFLEE/SNTPWDH
Soprano voice KFLDH
Soprano voice: Accompanied by clarinet & piano KFLE/VVPDH
Unaccompanied female voices, children's voices FEZDH
Unaccompanied male voices GEZDH
Unaccompanied works EZDH
Unaccompanied works: Unison JEZDH
Unison JDH
Unison: Accompanied by guitar JE/TSDH
Unison: Accompanied by handbells JE/XSQDH
Voice parts JDADH
Religious Oratorios, Cantatas, Masses, Music: DC
Accompanied by keyboard & percussion ENYLDC
Accompanied by orchestra EMDC
Female voices, Children's voices FDC
Female voices, Children's voices: Accompanied by recorders & percussion FE/NYHSDC
Unaccompanied works EZDC
Religious musical plays: Full scores CQM/L
Religious musical plays: Vocal scores CM/L
Requiem masses: Accompanied by orchestra EMDGKAV
Requiem masses: Unaccompanied choral works EZDGKAV
Revues: Aman, D. BAPACP
Rhodesia: Books BZNM
Richard, Cliff: Books AKDW/GB/E(P)
Ringing: Church bells: Books AXSR/E
Rock: Books A/HKR
Rock: Songs: Arrangements for organ RK/DW/HKR
Rock: Songs: Books AKDW/HKR
Rock: Songs: Vocal solo KDW/HKR
Rock 'n' roll: Songs: Solo voice: Books AKDW/HK
Rock 'n' roll singers: Books AKDW/HK/E(M)
Rock songs: Arrangements for guitar TSPMK/DW/HKR
Roman liturgy: Accompanied by orchestra EMDFF
Roman liturgy: Beethoven, L. van: Books BBJADFF
Roman liturgy: Books ADFF
Roman liturgy: Choral works DFF

138

Songs: Arrangements for recorder & guitar
VSPLTSK/DW
Songs: Arrangements for trumpet, unaccompanied
WSPK/DW
Songs: Arrangements for trumpets (2) & piano
WSNTQK/DW
Songs: Arrangements for violin & piano   SPK/DW
Songs: Arrangements for wind band   UMK/DW
Songs: Arrangements for woodwind trio   VNTK/DW
Songs: Baritone voice   KGNDW
Songs: Bawd: Books   AKDW/K/G/KDX
Songs: Books   ADW
Songs: Choral music   DW
Songs: Choral music: Accompanied by harp
ETQDW
Songs: Choral music: Unaccompanied works
EZDW
Songs: Cotton, R.: Books   BCMTADW
Songs: Female voice: Accompanied by woodwind, strings,
keyboard & percussion septet
KFE/NYDPNPDW
Songs: Female voice: Child's voice: Solos: Accompanied
by guitar   KFE/TSDW
Songs: Female voices, Children's voices   FDW
Songs: Female voices, Children's voices: Accompanied by
percussion band   FE/XMDW
Songs: Female voices, Children's voices: Choral scores
FADW
Songs: Female voices, Children's voices: Unison
JFDW
Songs: Female voices, Children's voices: Unison:
Accompanied by percussion band
JFE/XMDW
Songs: Female voices, Childrens voices: Unison:
Accompanied by various instruments
JFE/LDW
Songs: Female voices, Children's voices: Unison: Books
AJFDW
Songs: High voice   KFTDW
Songs: High voice: Accompanied by woodwind &
keyboard quartet   KFTE/NWPNSDW
Songs: Male voices   GDW
Songs: Male voices: Accompanied by bell lyra
GE/XTBDW
Songs: Middle voice   KFVDW
Songs: Solo voice   KDW
Songs: Solo voice: Accompanied by guitar
KE/TSDW
Songs: Solo voice: Accompanied by strings & keyboard
trio   KE/NXNTDW
Songs: Soprano voice   KFLDW
Songs: Soprano voice: Accompanied by oboe
KFLE/VTDW
Songs: Soprano voice: Accompanied by orchestra
KFLE/MDW
Songs: Soprano voice: Accompanied by wind, strings &
percussion septet   KFLE/NYENPDW
Songs: Soprano voice, unaccompanied   KFLEZDW
Songs: Soprano voices   FLDW
Songs: Tenor voice   KGHDW
Songs: Tiv tribe: Nigeria: Books   BZMQTADW
Songs: Unaccompanied female voices, children's voices
FEZDW
Songs: Unaccompanied male voices   GEZDW
Songs: Unaccompanied solo voice   KEZDW
Songs: Unaccompanied works: Unison   JEZDW
Songs: Unison: Accompanied by guitar   JE/TSDW
Songs: Unison: Accompanied by recorder sextet
JE/VSNQDW
Songs: Unison female voices, children's voices: Choral
scores   JFADW
Songs: Vocal quintet: Accompanied by chamber orchestra
JNBE/MRDW
Songs: Vocal solos: Accompanied by strings & keyboard
quintet   KE/NXNRDW
Soprano voice   KFL
Soprano voice: Books   AKFL
Soprano voices: Choral works   FL
Soprano voices: Unison   JFL
Spain: Collections: Female voices, Children's voices:
Unison: Accompanied by instruments
JFE/LDW/G/AYK
Spain: Collections: Guitar, unaccompanied
TSPM/AYK
Speaker   KHY
Spirituals: Choral music   DW/LC
Spirituals: Unaccompanied voices   EZDW/LC
Stabat mater: Proper of the Mass: Unaccompanied works
EZDGKADD/LK
Stories: Books   ABN
Stories: Peter and the wolf: Prokofiev, S.
BPPAMBN
Straus, Oscar: Books   BSOT
Stravinsky, Igor: Books   BSV
String bass   SS
String ensembles   RW
String ensembles: Accompanying soprano voice
KFLE/RW
Strings & keyboard: Books   ANX
Strings & keyboard: Ensembles: Accompanying solo voice
KE/NX
Strings & percussion: Ensembles: Accompanying wind,
strings & percussion   KHYE/NYE
Strings & keyboard: Ensembles: Chamber music
NX
Strings & percussion: Ensembles: Chamber music
NYJ
Strings & wind: Ensembles: Chamber music   NV

Strings & woodwind: Ensembles: Chamber music
NVP
Strings, wind & keyboard: Ensembles: Chamber music
NU
Strings, wind & percussion: Ensembles: Accompanying
soprano voice   KFLE/NYE
Strings, wind & percussion: Ensembles: Chamber music
NYE
Suites: Arrangements for guitar duet   TSNUK/AG
Suites: Arrangements for guitar solo   TSPMK/AG
Suites: Arrangements for symphony orchestra
MRK/AG
Suites: Arrangements for trumpet & piano
WSPK/AG
Suites: Arrangements for pianos (2), 4 hands
QNUK/AG
Suites: Brass band   WMG
Suites: Cello solo   SRPMG
Suites: Clarinet solo   VVPMG
Suites: Double bass quartet   SSNSG
Suites: Guitar duet   TSNUG
Suites: Guitar solo   TSPMG
Suites: Harpsichord solos   QRPG
Suites: Horn solo   WTPMG
Suites: Hornpipes: Brass band   WMHNG
Suites: Military band   UMMG
Suites: Oboe & piano   VTPG
Suites: Organ   RG
Suites: Piano duets, 4 hands   QNVG
Suites: Piano solo   QPG
Suites: Recorder & piano   VSPG
Suites: String orchestra   RXMG
Suites: Symphony orchestra   MMG
Suites: Treble recorder & piano   VSSPG
Suites: Treble recorders (2) & keyboard
VSSNTPWG
Suites: Trumpet & string orchestra   RXMPWSG
Sullivan, Sir Arthur Seymour: Books   BSW
Sullivan, Sir Arthur Seymour. The Mikado: Books
BSWACF
Sullivan, Sir Arthur Seymour. The yeomen of the guard:
Books   BSWACF
Symphonies: Arrangements for cello & viola
SQPLSSK/LE
Symphonies: Arrangments for violins (3) & piano
SNSQK/LE
Symphonies: Beethoven, L. van: Books   BBJAMME
Symphonies: Books   AMME
Symphonies: Chamber orchestra   MRE
Symphonies: Symphony orchestra   MME
Symphony orchestra   MM
Symphony orchestra: Beethoven, L. van: Books
BBJAMM
Symphony orchestra: Books   AMM

Tambourine: Accompanying choral works   EXRV
Tape: Recorder   VS/FT
Tape: Songs: Vocal quintet: Accompanied by chamber
orchestra   JNBE/MRDW/FJ
Tape recordings: Books   A/FG
Tape with woodwind, keyboard & percussion septet
NYDPNP/FT
Tarantellas: Organ   RHVS
Tausky, Vilem: Books   A/EC(P)
Tchaikovsky, Peter: Books   BTD
Te Deum: Matins: Divine Office   DGKHB
Te Deum: Morning Prayer: Anglican Liturgy
DGNQ
Teaching – related to composers   A(VC/Z)
Teaching: Performance: Bowed string instruments
ARW/E(VC)
Teaching: Piano: Books   AQ/E(VC)
Teaching: Singing   AK/E(VC)
Teaching methods: Education: Books   A(VC)
Television music: Arrngements for piano solo
QPK/JS
Tenor horn & brass band   WMPWTT
Tenor saxophone   VUT
Tenor voice   KGH
Terminology: Books   A(QT)
Teyte, Dame Maggie: Books   AKFL/E(P)
Thalben-Ball, George: Books   AR/E(P)
Theatre: Music: Symphony orchestra   MM/JM
Theatre: Symphony orchestra   MM/JM
Theatre music: Wind, strings & percussion   NYE/J
Theory: Books   A/AM
Thoroughbass: Piano   Q/RGD
Three Choirs Festival: Books   AD(YDGB/WE/X)
Tiv tribe: Nigeria: Books   BZMQT
Tonality: Books   A/PF
Treble recorder   VSS
Treble voice   KFL
Treble voice: Books   AKFL
Treble voices: Choral works   FL
Treble voices: Unison   JFL
Triangle & glockenspiel: Accompanying female voices,
Children's voices   FE/XTPLXTQW
Trios: Flute   VRNT
Trios: Flute & strings   NVRNT
Trios: Flute, strings & keyboard   NURNT
Trios: Guitar   TSNT
Trios: Oboe   VTNT
Trios: Percussion ensemble   XNT
Trios: Recorders   VSNT

Trios: Recorder, strings & keyboard   NUSNT
Trios: Recorders, strings & keybpard: Accompanying
female voices, children's voices: Unison
JFE/NUSNT
Trios: String ensembles   RXNT
Trios: Strings & keyboard   NXNT
Trios: Strings & keyboard: Accompanying solo voice
KE/NXNT
Trios: String & percussion   NYJNT
Trios: Treble recorder   VSSNT
Trios: Trombone, strings & keyboard   NUXUNT
Trios: Trumpet, strings & keyboard   NUXSNT
Trios: Wind & keyboard   NWNT
Trios: Woodwind instruments   VNT
Trios: Woodwind & keyboard   NWPNT
Trios: Woodwind & strings   NVPNT
Trios: Woodwind, strings & keyboard   NUPNT
Trombone   WU
Trombone, strings & keyboard: Chamber music
NUXU
Trombones (2) & organ   WUNTR
Trumpet   WS
Trumpet & orchestra   MPWS
Trumpet & organ   WSPLR
Trumpet & string orchestra   RXMPWS
Trumpets (2) & organ: Accompanying choral music
EWSNTPLR
Trumpets (2) & piano   WSNTQ
Trumpets (2) & string orchestra   RXMPWSNU
Tuba   WV
Tuba & orchestra   MPWV
Tuba & percussion   WVPLX
Tucker, Norman: Books   AC(WB/P)
Tutors: Accordion   RS/AC
Tutors: Brass instruments   W/AC
Tutors: Cello   SR/AC
Tutors: Electronic organ   RPV/AC
Tutors: Flute   VR/AC
Tutors: Guitar   TS/AC
Tutors: Piano   Q/AC
Tutors: Recorder   VS/AC
Tutors: Thorough bass: Piano   Q/RGD/AC
Tutors: Trumpet   WS/AC
Tutors: Violin   S/AC

Unaccompanied alto saxophone solos   VUSPM
Unaccompanied cello solos   SRPM
Unaccompanied choral works   EZ
Unaccompanied clarinet solos   VVPM
Unaccompanied descant recorder solos   VSRPM
Unaccompanied double bass solos   SSPM
Unaccompanied female voices, children's voices: Choral
works   FEZ
Unaccompanied guitar solos   TSPM
Unaccompanied harp solos   TQPM
Unaccompanied horn   WTPM
Unaccompanied male voices: Choral music   GEZ
Unaccompanied recorder solos   VSPM
Unaccompanied saxophone solos   VUPM
Unaccompanied treble recorder   VSSPM
Unaccompanied trombone solos   WUPM
Unaccompanied trumpet solos   WSPM
Unaccompanied unison choral works   JEZ
Unaccompanied viola solos   SQPM
Unaccompanied violin solos   SPM
Unison choral music: Books   AJ
Unison choral works   J
United States: Books   A(YT)
United States: Collections: Folk dances: Arrangements for
violin, unaccompanied   SPMK/AH/G/AYT
United States: Collections: Popular songs: Vocal solo
KDW/GB/AYT
United States: Jazz: Books   AMT(YT)
United States: Popular songs: Solo voice: Books
AKDW/GB(YT)
United States: Teaching: Books   A(VC/YT)

Variations: Arrangements for guitar, unaccompanied
TSPMK/T
Variations: Arrangements for wind band   UMK/T
Variations: Brass quintet   WNR/T
Variations: Clarinet & strings quintet   NVUNR/T
Variations: Concertos: Guitar quartet   TSNSF/T
Variations: Dances: Chamber orchestra   MRH/T
Variations: Flute & piano   VRP/T
Variations: Guitar solo   TSPM/T
Variations: Harp, unaccompanied   TQPM/T
Variations: Horn & piano   WTP/T
Variations: Oboe & piano   VRP/T
Variations: Piano solos   QP/T
Variations: Piano & orchestra: Arrangements for pianos
(2), 4 hands   QNUK/L/T
Variations: Recorders (treble) (2) & keyboard
VSSNTPW/T
Variations: String orchestra   RXM/T
Variations: Symphony orchestra   MM/T
Variations: Treble recorder solo   VSSPM/T
Vaughan Williams, Ralph: Books   BVD
Veni sancte spiritus: Accompanied by orchestra
EMDGKADD/LN

List of Music Publishers

While every effort has been made to check the information given in this list with the publishers concerned, the British Library cannot hold itself responsible for any errors or omissions.

ACUFF-ROSE, Music Publishers, 14 St. George St., London W.1. *Tel:* 01–629–0392
Grams: Acufrose London.

ARS VIVA, 48 Great Marlborough St., London W1V 2BN.

ASHDOWN, Edwin Ashdown Ltd, 275–281 Cricklewood Broadway, London NW2 6QR. *Tel:* 01–450–5237.

ASSOCIATED BOARD OF THE ROYAL SCHOOLS OF MUSIC (Publications Dept). 14 Bedford Square, London WC1B 3JG. *Tel:* 01–636–6919.
Grams: Musexam London WC1.

ASSOCIATED MUSIC Publishers, Inc. c/o G. Schirmer Ltd. 140 Strand, London WC2R 1HH *Tel:* 01–836–4011

BANKS, Music Publications. 139 Holgate Road, York YO2 4DF

BÄRENREITER Ltd. 17–18 Bucklersbury, Hitchin, Herts SG5 1BB *Tel:* 0462–57535

B.B.C. *See* British Broadcasting Corporation.

BELWIN-MILLS Music Ltd. 250 Purley Way, Croydon CR9 4QD *Tel:* 01–681–0855
Grams: Belmilmus Croydon.

BLACK. A & C. Black Ltd. 35 Bedford Row, London WC1R 4JH. *Tel:* 01–242–0946.
Grams: Biblios London WC1. *Telex:* 21792/Ref 2546.

BOOSEY AND HAWKES Music Publishers Ltd. 295 Regent St., London W1R 8JH *Tel:* 01–580–2060
Grams: Sonorous London W1.
Trade: The Hyde, Edgware Rd, London NW9 6JN *Tel:* 01–305–3861
Grams: Sonorous London NW9.

BOSWORTH and Co. Ltd. 14–18 Heddon St., London W1R 8DP. *Tel:* 01–734–0475.
Grams: Bosedition London W1.

BREITKOPF AND HÄRTEL (London) Ltd. 20 Earlham St., London WC2H 9LN *Tel:* 01–836–3066.

BRITISH BROADCASTING CORPORATION. BBC Publications, 35 Marylebone High St., London W1M 4AA. *Tel:* 01–580–5577.
Grams: Broadcasts London. *Telex:* 265781.

CALDER AND BOYARS, Ltd. 18 Brewer St., London W1R 4AS. *Tel:* 01–734–6900.
Grams: Bookdom London W1.

CAMBRIDGE UNIVERSITY PRESS. (Publishing Division). P.O. Box 110, Cambridge CB2 3RL.
Trade: University Printing House, Shaftesbury Road, Cambridge. *Tel:* 0223–312393. *Telex:* 817342.
Editorial: The Pitt Building, Trumpington St., Cambridge. *Tel:* 0223–64122. *Telex:* 817256.

CAMPBELL CONNELLY and Co. Ltd. 10 Denmark St., London WC2. *Tel:* 01–863–1653.

CATHEDRAL MUSIC, 36 Ranelagh Gardens, London W6.

CATHOLIC TRUTH SOCIETY. 38 Eccleston Sq., London SW1V 1PD *Tel:* 01–834–4392.
Grams: Apostolic London SW1.

CHAPPELL and Co. Ltd. 50 New Bond St., London W1A 2BR *Tel:* 01–629–7600
Grams: Symphony London. *Telex:* 268403.

CHESTER. J. and W. Chester/Edition Wilhelm Hansen London Ltd. 7 Eagle Court, London EC1M 5QD. *Tel:* 01–253–6947.
Grams: Guarnerius London EC1.

CLARENDON PRESS *See* Oxford University Press.

CLIFFORD ESSEX Music Co. Ltd. 20 Earlham St., London WC2 *Tel:* 01–836–2810.
Grams: Triomphe London WC2.

COLLIER MACMILLAN Publishers. 35 Red Lion Square, London WC1 *Tel:* 01–831–6100.

COLLINS. William Collins, Sons and Co. Ltd. 14 St. James's Place, London SW1. *Tel:* 01–493–7070.
Grams: Herakles London SW1.

CRAMER. J.B. Cramer and Co. Ltd. 99 St. Martin's Lane, London WC2N 4AZ. *Tel:* 01–240–1612.

DALTON, Gilbert Dalton, 25 Shenick Rd, Skerries.

DONEMUS *See* Lengrick.

ELKIN and Co. Ltd. Borough Green, Sevenoaks, Kent. *Tel:* 0732–88–3261.
Grams: Novellos Sevenoaks.

E.M.I. Music Publishing Ltd. 138 Charing Cross Road, London WC2 *Tel:* 01–836–6699.

ESSEX MUSIC Ltd. 19 Poland St., London W1. *Tel:* 01–734–8121.
Grams: Sexmus London.

EULENBERG. Ernst Eulenberg Ltd. 48 Great Marlborough St., London W1V 2BN *Tel:* 01–437–1246.

EVANS BROS. Ltd. Montague House, Russell Sq., London WC1B 5BX. *Tel:* 01–637–1466.
Grams: Byronitic London WC1.

FABER MUSIC Ltd. 3 Queen Sq., London WC1N 3AU. *Tel:* 01–278–6881.
Grams: Fabbaf London WC1.

GALLIARD *See* Stainer and Bell.

HODDER AND STOUGHTON, Ltd. P.O. Box 700, Mill Road, Dunton Green, Sevenoaks, Kent TN13 2YA. *Tel:* 0732–50111.
Grams: Hodderbooks, Sevenoaks. *Telex:* 95122.

JOAD PRESS. 1 The Retreat, London, SW1.

LENGNICK. Alfred Lengnick and Co. Ltd. Purley Oaks Studios, 421a Brighton Road, South Croydon, Surrey CR2 6YR. *Tel:* 01–660–7646.

LEONARD, GOULD AND BOLTTLER, 99 St. Martin's Lane, London WC2N 4AZ *Tel:* 01–240–1612

MUSICA RARA, 2 Great Marlborough St., London W1. *Tel:* 01–437–1576.

MACMILLAN Publishers Ltd. 4 Little Essex St., London WC2R 3LF. *Tel:* 01–836–6633.
Grams: Publish London WC2. *Telex:* 262024.

MAPA MUNDI. 72 Brewery Road, London N.7.

MERCIER PRESS Ltd. 4 Bridge St., Cork, Eire.
Dublin Office: 25 Lower Abbey St., Dublin 1.

MIDDLE EIGHT MUSIC. 7 Garrick St., London W.C.2.

MOORLEY'S BIBLE AND BOOKSHOP, Ltd. 8 Nottingham Road, Ilkeston, Derbyshire, DE7 5RE *Tel:* 0602–320643.

MUSIC SALES Ltd. 78 Newman St., London W1. *Tel:* 01–636–9033.

NOVELLO and Co. Ltd. Borough Green, Sevenoaks, Kent TN15 8DT *Tel:* 0732–88–3261.
Grams: Novellos Sevenoaks.

OLIVER AND BOYD, (A division of Longman Group, Ltd). 23 Ravelston Terrace, Edinburgh, EH4 3TJ. *Tel:* 031–343–1991.
Grams: Almanac Edinburgh. *Telex:* 727511.

OPEN UNIVERSITY PRESS. c/o Open University Educational Enterprises Ltd. 12 Cofferidge Close, Stony Stratford, Milton Keynes, MK11 1BY

OXFORD UNIVERSITY PRESS, Walton St., Oxford OX2 6DP. *Tel:* 0865–56767.
Grams: Clarendon Press Oxford. *Telex:* 837330.

OXFORD UNIVERSITY PRESS (Music Department) 37 Dover St., London W1X 4AH. *Tel:* 01–629–8494.

PAXTON. Borough Green, Sevenoaks, Kent TN15 9DT.

PETERS Edition. 119 Wardour St., London W1. *Tel:* 01–437–1456.
Trade: 10 Baches St., London N1 6DN. *Tel:* 01–253–1638.

PRENTICE-HALL International Inc. Attn. Donald Deeks, 66 Wood Lane End, Hemel Hempstead, Herts HP2 4RD. *Tel:* Hemel Hempstead 58531.

RICORDI. G. Ricordi and Co. (London), Ltd. The Bury, Church St., Chesham, Bucks HP5 1JG. *Tel:* Chesham 3311.
Grams: Ricordi Chesham.

ROBERTON Publications. The Windmill, Wendover, Aylesbury, Bucks HP22 6JJ *Tel:* Wendover (0296) 623107.

ROYAL SCHOOL OF CHURCH MUSIC. Addington Place, Croydon CR9 5AD. *Tel:* 01–654–7676.
Grams: Cantons Croydon.

SALVATIONIST PUBLISHING AND SUPPLIES Ltd. 117 Judd St., London WC1H 9NN. *Tel:* 01–387–1656.
Grams: Savingly London WC1.

SCHIRMER. G. Schirmer Ltd (Music Publishers). 140 Strand, London WC2R 1HH. *Tel:* 01–836–4011.

SCHOTT and Co. Ltd. 48 Great Marlborough St., London W1V 2BN *Tel:* 01–437–1246.
Grams: Shotanco London.

SCHROEDER. A. Schroeder Music Co. Ltd. 15 Berkeley St., London W1. *Tel:* 01–493–2506/9532.

SIMROCK. N. Simrock. Lyra House, 67 Belsize Lane, London NW3 5AX *Tel:* 01–749–8038.

STAINER AND BELL Ltd. 82, High Road, London N2 9PW *Tel:* 01–444–9135.

STUDIO MUSIC Co. 77–79 Dudden Hill La.. London NW10 2UA.

UNITED MUSIC PUBLISHERS Ltd. 1 Montague St., London WC1B 5BS. *Tel:* 01–636–5171.

UNIVERSAL Edition (London) Ltd. 2 Fareham St., London W1V 4DU. *Tel:* 01–437–5203. *Grams:* Alkamus London W1.

VERLAG NEUE MUSIK *See* Breitkopf und Härtel.

WEINBERGER, Josef Weinberger Ltd. 10 Rathbone St., London W1P 2BJ *Tel:* 01–580–2827. *Grams:* Operetta London W1

YOSELOFF. Thomas Yoseloff, Ltd. Magdalen House, 136–148 Tooley St., London SE1 2TT. *Tel:* 01–407–7566.